The
Industrial Minerals
HandyBook
second edition

A Guide to Markets, Specifications, & Prices

by

Peter W. Harben

Dedicated to

the US Bureau of Mines, an unappreciated and undervalued national resource that is becoming an endangered species. May it long continue to dispel the ignorance of others.

Part I

Silica

Sulphur

Industrial Minerals

Iron Oxide

Nitrogen Compounds

Potash

Diatomite

Feldspar

Market Profiles

Sodium Sulfate

Soda Ash

Zeolites

Carbonate Rocks

Nepheline Syenite

Phosphate Rock

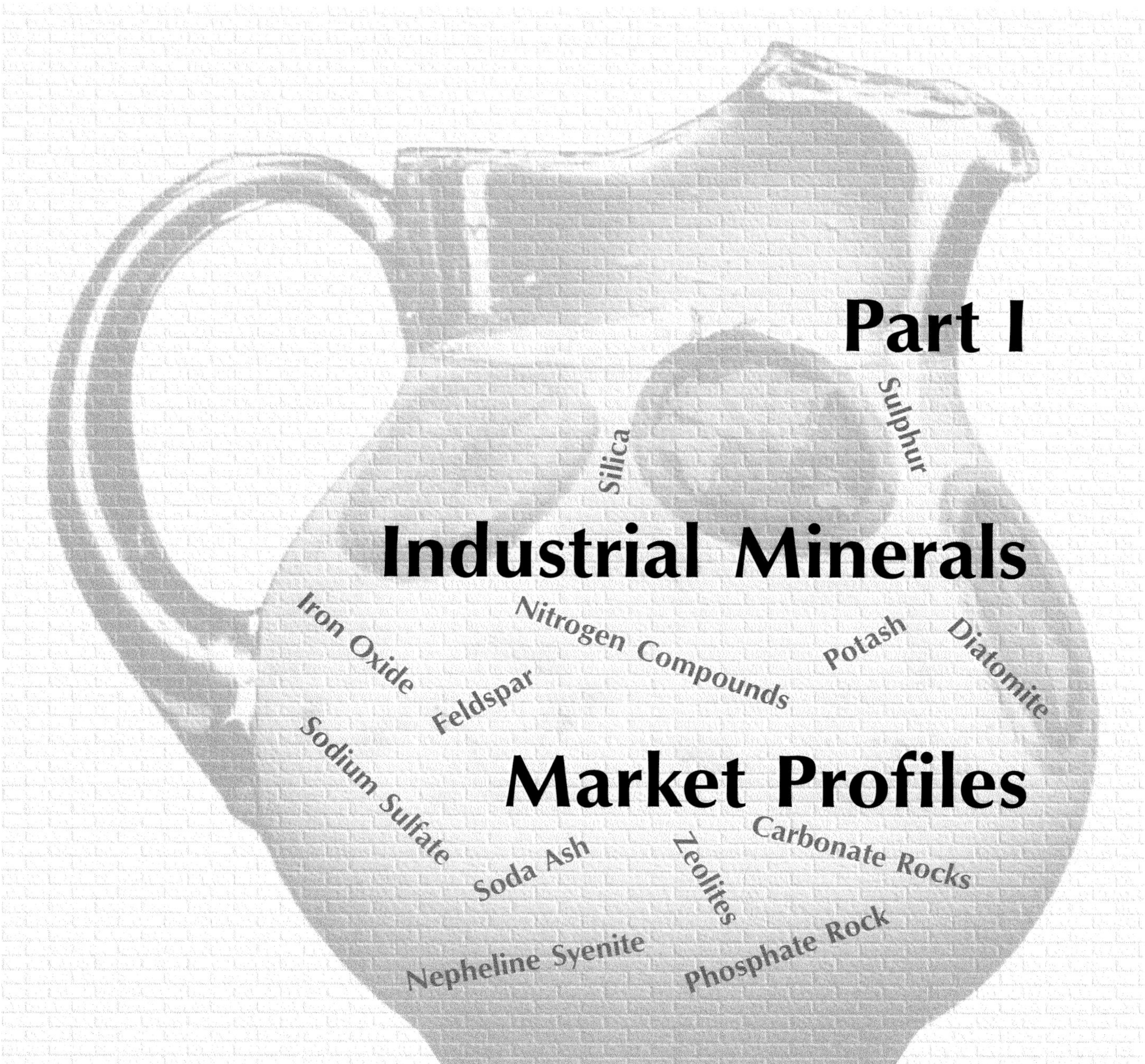

Published by
Industrial Minerals Division
Metal Bulletin PLC
London, United Kingdom

Data conversion & design:

    computer deZines, Mount Vision, NY, USA.

Film output:

    American Graphics & Printing, Inc., Utica, NY

Printed by:

    Warwick Printing Company Limited., Warwick, England

ISBN: 0 947671 90 0

PREFACE

This second edition of *The Industrial Minerals HandyBook* follows a similar pattern as the first but is intended to go further and deeper. The challenge has been to keep the publication a reasonable length for the sake of the reader and publisher alike, an onerous task given the breadth and complexity of the subject. As with many writing projects, the hardest decisions involve what to leave out rather than what to include. Silicon in the form of modern computerization has helped by converting large laborious spreadsheets of data into neat visual charts.

Each chapter is intended to be a mini-profile of a mineral and its main downstream products or derivatives. Wherever possible, data includes:

- ➤ Properties and main uses
- ➤ Approximate capacity utilization
- ➤ Heath, safety, and environmental concerns
- ➤ Substitutes and alternatives
- ➤ Production history from 1980 to 1993
- ➤ Harmonized Tariff Schedule (HTS)
- ➤ The derivation of the names of the important industrial minerals (etymology).

- ➤ Capacity of the major producing countries
- ➤ Relevant market conditions and marketing factors
- ➤ Recycling opportunities
- ➤ Leading producing, importing, and exporting countries
- ➤ Listing of countries with the highest apparent consumption
- ➤ Current and historical prices (1980-1993)

International data and examples are provided wherever possible, although there is a bias toward North American and to a lesser extent European standards. A great deal of detailed information on consumption and prices is derived from the United States, more specifically from the publications of the US Bureau of Mines. In fact, without its invaluable data, this would be a very thin book indeed. Hence the dedication. No apology is needed for this politically incorrect bias since the USBM provides the most detailed and consistent data on the world of minerals and the United States is the largest market in the world for most products.

In order to save repetition, a limited number of symbols are employed in the text with ➔ meaning "used to manufacture or in the manufacture of" and [   ] meaning "consumed or used in or as". For example,

Salt (via electrolysis in diaphragm, mercury, or membrane cell) ➔ caustic soda (NaOH a.k.a. lye) + chlorine (1.75 t of salt yields 1.0 t chlorine + 1.1 t caustic soda). NaOH is an extremely versatile source of Na_2O (77.5%) [pulp & paper; soap & detergents; alumina processing; water treatment; pesticides; petroleum refining; food preparation; textiles & dyes] and a feedstock or intermediate chemical. NaOH + phosphoric acid ➔ sodium orthophosphate ➔ sodium tripolyphosphates (STPP) [detergents; food].

TRANSLATES TO

Salt through the process of electrolysis in either a diaphragm, mercury, or membrane cell is used to manufacture caustic soda (NaOH) also known as lye together with chlorine. The consumption of 1.75 tonnes of salt yields 1.0 tonnes of chlorine and 1.1 tonnes of caustic soda. Caustic soda is an extremely versatile source of soda and contains 77.5% Na_2O. The soda is used in the manufacture of pulp & paper and soap & detergents; in alumina processing and water treatment; as well as in pesticides, petroleum refining, food preparation, textiles & dyes, and as a feedstock or intermediate chemical. For example, caustic soda when added to phosphoric acid produces sodium orthophosphate and then sodium tripolyphosphates (STPP) used in detergents and food.

Metric tonnes (t), kilograms (kg), and US dollars ($) are used throughout unless otherwise stated. Prices are current as of the fourth quarter of 1994.

Industrial minerals remain indispensable to modern life and just as complex. It is hoped that this second attempt to produce a concise guide to such a diversified group of minerals will help both the novice and experienced mineral hand.

Peter Harben
Morris, New York
March 1995

GEOGRAPHIC DISTRIBUTION USED

For convenience, some data has been divided into regions. The following is the arbitrary divisions used.

NORTH AMERICA	EUROPEAN UNION	NON-EU EUROPE	AUSTRALASIA	AFRICA
Canada	Belgium	Albania	Afghanistan	Algeria
Mexico	Denmark	Armenia	Australia	Angola
United States	France	Austrial	Bangladesh	Benin
SOUTH AMERICA	Germany	Azerbaijan	Burma (Myanmar)	Botswana
Argentina	Greece	Belarus	Bhutan	Burkina Faso
Bolivia	Ireland	Bosnia	Caledonia	Burundi
Brazil	Italy	Bulgaria	China	Cameroons
Chile	Luxembourg	Croatia	Hong Kong	Central African Rep.
Colombia	Netherlands	Czech Republic	India	Chad
Ecuador	Portugal	Czechoslovakia*	Indonesia	Congo
French Guyana	Spain	Estonia	Japan	Cote d'Ivoire
Guyana	United Kingdom	Finland	Kampuchea	Egypt
Paraguay		Georgia	Kazakhstan	Ethiopia
Peru		Hercegovina	Kyrgyzstan	Gabon
Suriname		Hungary	North Korea	Gambia
Uruguay		Iceland	South Korea	Ghana
Venezuela		Latvia	Laos	Guinea
C. AMERICA/CARIB.		Lithuania	Malaysia	Guinea Bissau
Bahamas		Macedonia	Mongolia	Kenya
Barbados		Moldavia	Nepal	Lesotho
Belize		Montenegro	New Zealand	Liberia
Bermuda		Norway	Pakistan	Libya
Costa Rica		Poland	Papua New Guinea	Madagascar
Cuba		Romania	Philippines	Malawi
Dominica		Russia	Singapore	Mali
Dominican Rep.		Serbia	Sri Lanka	Martinique
El Salvador		Slovakia	Taiwan	Mauritania
Guadaloupe		Slovenia	Tajikistan	Mauritius
Guatemala		Sweden	Thailand	Morocco
Haiti		Switzerland	Turkmenistan	Mozambique
Honduras		Turkey	Uzbekistan	Namibia
Jamaica		Ukraine	Vietnam	Niger
Martinique		USSR**	**MIDDLE EAST**	Nigeria
Nicaragua		Yugoslavia***	Bahrain	Rwanda
Panama			Cyprus	Senegal
Trinidad & Tobago			Iran	Sierra Leone
			Iraq	Somalia
			Jordan	South Africa
			Kuwait	Sudan
			Lebanon	Swaziland
			Oman	Tanzania
			Qatar	Togo
			Saudi Arabia	Tunisia
			Syria	Uganda
			United Arab Emirates	Zaire
			Yeman, PDR	Zambia
			Yeman, Arab Rep.	Zimbabwe

* *Now the Czech Republic and Slovakia;*

** *Includes Russia, Ukraine, Belarus, Lithuania, Georgia, Azerbaijan, Latvia, Moldavia, Estonia, and Armenia;*

*** *Includes Croatia, Bosnia, Hercegovina, Serbia, Montenegro, Macedonia, Slovenia*

AFS	American Foundryman's Association		mL	milliliter
ag.	agriculture or agricultural		mm	millimeter
agg.	aggregate		µg	micrograms
a.k.a.	also known as		µm	micrometer (micron) one millionth of a meter
ANSI	American National Standards Institute			
API	American Petroleum Institute		MSHA	(US) Mines Safety & Health Agency
APS	average particle size		NA	not available
ASTM	American Society for Testing and Materials		NF	nonferrous
avdp	avoirdupois		N.F.	National Formulary
AWWA	American Water Works Association		ng	nanograms
bbl	barrel		nm	nanometer
BD	bulk density		OCMA	Oil Companies Materials Association
cal.	calories		ODP	Ozone Depletion Potential
calc.	calcined		OSHA	Occupational Safety & Health Administration
cm	centimeter			
conc.	concentrate		PCC	precipitated calcium carbonate
cp	centipoise		PCE	Pyrometric cone equivalent
e.g.	for example		ppm	parts per million
EPA	(US) Environmental Protection Agency		ppb	parts per billion
f	foot or feet		ppt.	precipitated
FDA	Food and Drug Administration		PS	particle size
FG	fiberglass		PSD	particle size distribution
FGD	flue gas desulfurization		psi	pounds per square inch
g	gram		sec	second
GCC	ground (natural) calcium carbonate		SG	specific gravity
H	Mohs hardness		stu	short ton unit (amount of material that contains 20 lb. say BeO)
ha	hectares			
HAR	high aspect ratio		t	metric tonne
HTS	Harmonized Tariff Schedule		tech.	technical (grade)
IARC	International Agency for Research on Cancer		UC	uniformity coefficient
i.e.	that is		USP	US Pharmacopeia
Imp.	Imperial (gallon)		USSR	the union of fifteen republics prior to 1991
in	inch			
ISO	International Standards Organization			
kg	kilogram			
Kw	kilowatt			
L	liter			
LAR	Low aspect ratio			
lbs	pounds			
LOI	loss on ignition			
lst.	limestone			
m	meter			
M.	million			
Mcf	million cubic feet			
mg	milligram			
min	minute			
min.	minimum			

NOTES

All prices are in US dollars per metric tonne or per kilogram

Exchange rates used include:

£1.00 = US$1.50
DM1.55 = US$1.00
¥100.00 = US$1.00
C$1.00 = US$0.75

Contents

Minerals	Formula	% Sb	Color	SG	H
Native antimony	Sb	100.0	tin white	6.7-6.8	3-3.5
Stibnite	Sb_2S_3	71.1	lead gray	4.52-4.62	2

Stibnite is the prominent commercial antimony mineral, and may be weathered to various oxides including kermesite ($2Sb_2S_3 \cdot Sb_2O_3$); senarmonite (isometric Sb_2O_3); stibiconite ($H_2Sb_2O_5$); and valentinite (orthorhombic Sb_2O_3). Secondary antimony is produced from the smelting and refining of lead and silver ores and from recycled scrap.

PROPERTIES & USES: Smelting antimony ore (5-25% S ores roasted to antimony oxide; 25-40% S ore and mixed sulfide and oxide ore smelted in a blast furnace; 45-60% S ore melted and solidified under a reducing atmosphere; rich oxide ore direct reduced with iron scrap; complex ore leaching and electrolysis) → antimony metal and antimony oxide (Sb_2O_3) which are refined to antimony starred regulus (>99.6% or >99.99% Sb) and purified Sb_2O_3. Energy requirements per tonne of antimony metal and antimony oxide from stibnite ore are 163 and 186 BTUs respectively.

Antimony is used as the metal [power transmission equipment; solder] or as an alloying compound where it increases hardness, strength, and resistance to chemical corrosion. Antimony (often recycled) + lead → antimonial lead [lead-acid storage batteries; ammunition and shot; tank linings; type metal; roofing sheets; cable sheaths]. High-purity grades of antimony oxide (>99.8%) are used as a catalyst [electronics; thermoplastics]. Antimony oxide aids in the removal of bubbles in optical glass [cameras, photocopiers, binoculars, spectacles]. Some grades of antimony oxide contain additives (ethylene glycol, liquid chlorinated paraffin, mineral oil, or a liquid vinyl plasticizer) to control mechanical properties and viscosities (and control dusting).

Antimony oxide (Sb_2O_3) alone or more commonly + halogens such as chlorine and bromine (the synergistic agent) → halogenated compounds with excellent fire-proofing properties [fire retardants in thermoplastics (ABS, PET, high-impact polystyrene, PBT, and nylon); textiles; adhesives; paper; rubber; paint]. The

Primary antimony consumption in the United States

tonnes antimony content

Metal products | Nonmetal products | Flame-retardants

Metal products include ammunition, antimonial lead, bearing metal and bearings, cable coverings, collapsible tubes and foil, sheet and pipe, solder, type metal. Nonmetal products are used in ammunition primers, ceramics and glass, fireworks, pigments, and rubber. Flame-retardants are used in adhesives, paper, pigments, plastics, rubber, and textiles.

tinting strength of antimony oxide determines the whitening effect on the final product; in general, the tinting strength decreases when the APS is large (>2 μm) or very small (<0.1 μm). Most commercial grades have an APS of about 1 μm.

Antimony oxide is an important starting point in the manufacture of many antimony chemicals. Antimony oxide + nitrates or peroxide → antimony pentoxide (Sb_2O_5) with a low opacity [textile fire retardant]; + base → sodium antimonate ($NaSbO_3$) with high opacity [dark colored textile fire retardant; specialty glass decolorizer & fining agent]. Antimony oxide → antimony pentasulfide (Sb_2S_5) [vulcanizing agent in rubber; pigment], antimony trisulfide (Sb_2S_3) [primer in ammunition; smoke maker; UV reflecting pigment in camouflage paints], antimony trichloride ($SbCl_2$) [medicine; catalyst].

QUALITY & SPECIFICATIONS: *Chemical-grade ore:* - ore sufficiently pure to produce the oxide, chloride, or other compounds directly requires <0.25% As & Pb, with no single metallic impurity >0.1%.

Crude antimony oxide:- <98% Sb_2O_3; *Commercial antimony oxide:-* 99.2% to 99.5% Sb_2O_3 with impurities such as As, Fe, & Ti. Tinting strength, related to the APS (0.3-6 μm), is critical. Main grades include high-tint (APS 1.0-1.8 μm); low tint (APS 2.5-5.0 μm); ultra-fine (APS 0.2-0.4 μm).

Antimony metal:- Grade A min. 99.8% antimony, max. 0.05% As, 0.10% S, 0.15% Pb, & 0.05% others; Grade B min. 99.5% antimony, max. 0.1% As, 0.1% S, 0.2% Pb, & 0.1% each other element.

CAPACITY: (antimony content) 102,000 t (mine); 110,000 t (smelter).

WORLD CAPACITY UTILIZATION: NA.

MARKET CONDITIONS: Stable but with volatile prices due to uncontrolled output.

MARKETING FACTORS: Manufacturing level and fire legislation.

HEALTH & SAFETY: Environmental concerns include the control of emissions and effluent during the treatment of antimony ores and metal; antimony metal and antimonial lead from slags, drosses, flue dusts, and residues at the smelter are recovered. The metal used, for example, in storage batteries is recycled. Largely based on health & safety concerns, antimony oxide is replacing lead and arsenic in optical glass manufacture.

SUBSTITUTES & ALTERNATIVES: Batteries:- graphite, lead-calcium storage batteries, lithium, manganese, rare earths. **Fire retardant:-** ATH, asbestos, borates, bromine, chromite, diatomite, magnesite & magnesia, perlite, phosphates, pumice, vermiculite. **Hardening agent:-** Sn, Ca, Cd, Se, Sr, S. **Opacifier:-** Ti, Zr, Pb, Zn, Cr, Sn. **Pigments:-** compounds of Ti, Zn, Cr, Sn, and Zr.

RECYCLING: Secondary antimony, mainly as antimonial lead, is extracted from the lead battery plates contained in lead-acid storage batteries. New scrap comes from dross and residues from the manufacturing process.

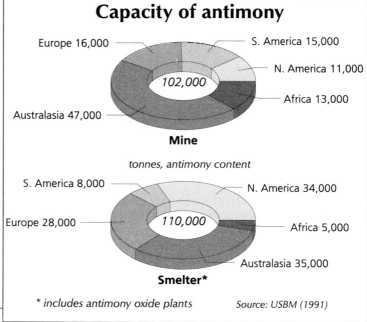

Capacity of antimony

Europe 16,000 — S. America 15,000
— N. America 11,000
102,000
— Africa 13,000
Australasia 47,000

Mine

tonnes, antimony content

S. America 8,000 — N. America 34,000
Europe 28,000 — 110,000 — Africa 5,000
— Australasia 35,000

Smelter*

* includes antimony oxide plants   *Source: USBM (1991)*

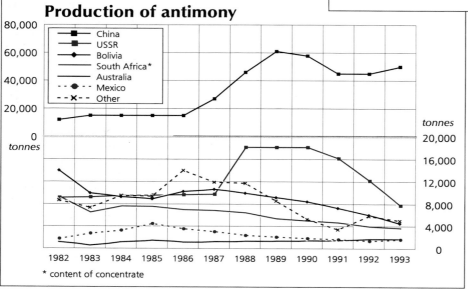

Production of antimony

Legend:
- China
- USSR
- Bolivia
- South Africa*
- Australia
- Mexico
- Other

1982 1983 1984 1985 1986 1987 1988 1989 1990 1991 1992 1993

* content of concentrate

PRODUCERS & WORLD TRADE: Production of antimony is totally dominated by China together with several moderately large suppliers. All the producers are large exporters of either antimony ore, oxide, or metal. Additional trade is generated by the re-export of processed antimony products based on imported ore. For the most part, imports and consumption are confined to developed economies.

ANTIMONY COMPOUND	SYNONYMS	FORMULAS	SB CONTENT
Metallic antimony	Antimony regulus	Sb	99.5 - 99.5
Antimony oxychloride	Basic antimony chloride, Powder of Al garoth, Mercurius vitae	$SbOCl$	70.3
Antimony pentoxide	Antimonic oxide, Antimony (V) oxide, Stibic anhydride, Antimonic acid	Sb_2O_5	37.6
Antimony trichloride	Butter of antimony, Antimony (III) chloride, Antimonous chloride, Antimony chloride	$SbCl_3$	53.4
Antimony trioxide	Antimony oxide, Antimony (III) oxide, Diantimony trioxide, Antimony bloom, Flowers of antimony	Sb_2O_3	41.8
Antimony trisulfide	Stibnite, Native antimony sulfide, Antimony glance, Needle antimony, Liquated antimony, Antimony gray, Antimony sesquisulfide	Sb_2S_3	35.9
Sodium antimonate	Sodium meta-antimonate	$NaSbO_3$	63.2
Stibine	Antimony hydride	SbH_3	97.6

ANTIMONY LEADERS IN PRODUCTION AND TRADE

Producers (metal content)	Ore importers	Metal importers	Oxide importers	Ore exporters	Metal exporters	Oxide exporters
China	France	United States	United States	China	China	China
Russia	Thailand	Japan	Japan	Bolivia	Former USSR	United States
Bolivia	Japan	Germany	Germany	Mexico	United States	France
South Africa	United States	France	Italy	Australia	Bolivia	United Kingdom
USSR	Belgium	Belgium	United Kingdom	Canada	Turkey	South Africa
Kyrgyzstan	South Korea	South Korea	Netherlands	Morocco	United Kingdom	Belgium
Mexico	United Kingdom	Taiwan	Belgium	Thailand	Germany	Bolivia
Australia	Argentina	India	Canada	South Africa	France	Germany
Czechoslovakia	Brazil	Italy	France	Peru	Mexico	Netherlands
Guatemala	Spain	Spain	Taiwan	Austria	Italy	Former USSR
Serbia & Mont.	Germany	United Kingdom	Sweden	France	Peru	Italy
Tajikistan		Brazil	Spain			
Peru		Malaysia	South Korea			
Canada		Canada	Australia			
Turkey		Venezuela	Thailand			

PRICES: United States antimony fluoborate $6.65/kg (liquid concentrate, drums). Antimony metal $1.82-1.92/kg (bulk). Antimony oxide $3.30-5.50/kg (high tint, bags, freight equalized, E. of Rockies). Antimony trichloride $7.90/kg (anhydrous, solid, drum). Europe lump sulfide ore $14.50-15.50/t unit (60% Sb, CIF Europe). Antimony oxide (typical 99.5% Sb_2O_3, FOB Antwerp) $1,800/t (Chinese); $2,250/t (European). Metal Bulletin (MB) Free Market $3,000-3,250/t (Regulus, min. 99.6%, in warehouse). Hong Kong $2,950-3,050/t (Regulus 99.65% CIF Hong Kong). Japan ¥280,000 ($2,800)/t (ex-warehouse, Tokyo, Market).

HTS CODES: 2617.10.0000 (ore & concentrates); 2825.80.0000 (antimony oxide); 8118.00.0000 (antimony and articles thereof, including waste and scrap).

ETYMOLOGY: Antimony is from the Greek *anti* = *against* plus *monos* = *a metal seldom found alone*. **Stibnite** from the Greek *stimmi* and Latin *stibium* = old names for antimony. **Kermesite** from *kermes*, a name given in old chemistry to red amorphous antimony trisulfide often mixed with antimony trioxide. **Senarmonite** for Henri Hureau de Sénarmont (1808-1862), French physicist and mineralogist, School of Mines, Paris, who first described the species. **Stibiconite** from the Greek *stimmi* and Latin *stibium* = *antimony* and Greek for *powder* or *dust*, because it often occurs as a powder. **Valentinite** for Basilius Valentinus (pseudonym for Johannes Thölde), German alchemist working on the properties of antimony in the late 17th and early 18th century.

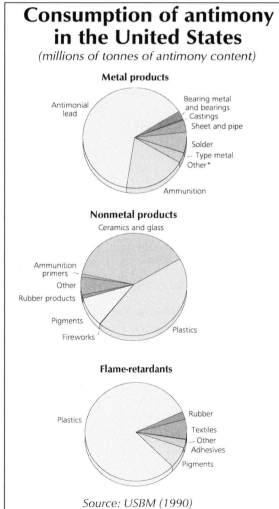

Consumption of antimony in the United States
(millions of tonnes of antimony content)

Source: USBM (1990)

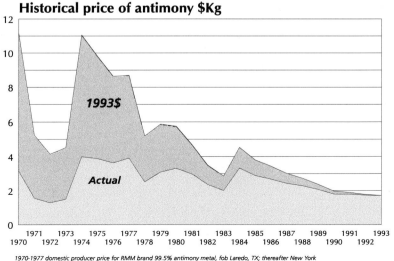

Historical price of antimony $Kg

1970-1977 domestic producer price for RMM brand 99.5% antimony metal, fob Laredo, TX; thereafter New York Dealer price for 99.5% to 99.6% imported metal cif US ports

ASBESTOS

Minerals	Formula	Color	SG	H
Amosite	$MgFe_6[(OH)Si_4O_{11}]_2$	brown	3.45	5-6
Chrysotile	$Mg_6[(OH)_4Si_2O_5]_2$	white	2.4-2.6	2.5-4
Crocidolite	$Na_2Fe_5[(OH)]Si_4O_{11}]_2$	blue	3.2-3.3	5-6

PROPERTIES & USES: The three main asbestos minerals form flexible fibers [woven into textiles] that are chemically inert [filters], resistant to heat & chemical attack, incombustible, and have low thermal conductivity [fire-proofing insulation; specialty paints; brake & clutch friction materials]; they resist wear and rot, and have high electrical resistance [packing & seals, papers & felts, linoleum underlay], and provide structural strength and excellent insulation characteristics [asbestos/cement pipe, sheet, panel; filler in flooring and tiles]. Some specific properties are outlined in the table.

QUALITY & SPECIFICATIONS: In Canada, chrysotile asbestos fibers are classified into seven groups based on fiber length, from the longest in group 1 to the shortest in group 7, each with sub-categories. Major producers classify asbestos into grades based on the type of asbestos, fiber length, and/or surface area. Grades produced in Canada and Africa are summarized in the tables over the page.

PROPERTIES OF ASBESTOS

	Amosite	Chrysotile	Crocidolite
Structure	Lamellar. Coarse to fine fibrous and asbestiform	Usually high fibrous fibers fine and easily separable	Fibrous in ironstones
Crystal system	Monoclinic	Monoclinic	Monoclinic
Luster	Vitreous, pearly	Silky	Silky to dull
Texture	Coarse but pliable	Soft to harsh	Soft to harsh
Max. length of fiber	70mm	40mm	70mm
Diameter of fibril	0.100µm	0.020µm	0.080µm
Diameter of industrial fiber	1-2µm	0.1-1.0µm	1-2µm
Surface area BFT m²/g	8.9	17-60	9-10.5
Tensile strength, (Mpa)	98-588	490-1,961	706-2,206
Specific heat (J/g°C)	816	1,110	842
Specific heat (J/Kg°K)	449	619	468
Deterioration temp. (°C)	600-800	450-700	400-600
Melting point of residue (°C)	1,100	1,500	1,000
Electric charge	Negative	Positive	Negative
Refractive index	1.64±	1.51-1.55	1.7
Filtration properties	Fast	Slow	Fast
Resistance to acids/alkalis	Good	Poor	Good
Resistance to heat	Good; brittle at high temperatures	Good; brittle at high temperatures	Poor; fuses
Modulus of elasticity, kPa	163M.	160M.	187M.
Spinnability	Fair	Very good	Fair
Flexibility/pliability	Low	Excellent	Good
Mineral impurities	Iron	Iron	Iron

Source: Badollet, 1951; Harben, 1992; Virta and Mann, 1994

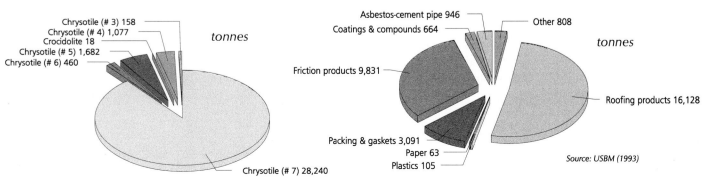

Consumption of asbestos in the United States by grade and type

tonnes

Chrysotile (# 3) 158
Chrysotile (# 4) 1,077
Crocidolite 18
Chrysotile (# 5) 1,682
Chrysotile (# 6) 460
Chrysotile (# 7) 28,240

Consumption of asbestos in the United States by industry

tonnes

Asbestos-cement pipe 946
Coatings & compounds 664
Other 808
Friction products 9,831
Roofing products 16,128
Packing & gaskets 3,091
Paper 63
Plastics 105

Source: USBM (1993)

CLASSIFICATION OF QUEBEC ASBESTOS

LONG FIBER

Group No. 1 (Textile or spinning fiber)
No. 1 Crude. Crosss fiber veins having ¾-inch (19 mm) staple and longer.

Group No. 2 (Textile or spinning fiber)
No. 2 Crude. Cross fiber veins having 3/8-inch (9.5 mm) staple up to ¾-inch (19 mm). Run-of-mine crude consists of unsorted crudes. Sundry crudes consist of crudes other than above specified.

Group No. 3 (Textile or spinning fiber)

	Guaranteed Minimum Shipping Test			
	½ inch,oz	4 Mesh,oz	10 Mesh,oz	Pan,oz
3F	10.5	3.9	1.3	0.3
3K	7	7	1.5	0.5
3R	4	7	4	1
3T	2	8	4	2
3Z	1	9	4	2

MEDIUM FIBER

Group No. 4 (Asbestos cement fiber)

4A	0	8	6	2
4D	0	7	6	3
4H	0	5	8	3
4H	0	5	7	4
4K	0	4	9	3
4M	0	4	8	4
4R	0	3	9	4
4T	0	2	10	4
4Z	0	1.5	9.5	5

Group No. 5 (Paper stock grades)

5D	0	0.5	10.5	5
5K	0	0	12	4
5M	0	0	11	5
5R	0	0	10	6
5Z	0	0	8.6	7.4

Group No. 6 (Paper and shingle fibers)

6D	0	0	7	9
6F	0	0	6	10

SHORT FIBER

Grade No. 7 (Shorts and floats)

7D	0	0	5	11
7F	0	0	4	12
7H	0	0	3	13
7K	0	0	2	14
7M	0	0	1	15
7R	0	0	0	16
7T	0	0	0	16
7RF & 7TG floats	0	0	0	16
7W	0	0	0	16

Group No. 8 & 9 (Sands and gravels)

8S	0	0	0	16
	Minimum 50 lb/cubic foot			
8T	0	0	0	16
	Minimum 75 lb/cubic foot			
9T	0	0	0	16
	More than 75 lb/cubic foot			

CLASSIFICATION OF AFRICAN CHRYSOTILE

Grade	Description
SHABANI DISTRICT OF ZIMBABWE	
C&G1	Long crudy textile fiber
C&G2	Textile fiber
C&G3	Long shingle fiber
C&G4	Shingle fiber
C&G5	Short shingle fiber/paper stock
MASHABA DISTRICT OF ZIMBABWE	
VRA-2	Textile fiber
VRA-3	Long shingle fiber
VRA-4	Shingle fiber
HAVELOCK MINES, S. AFRICA	
HVL2	Textile fiber
HVL3	Long shingle fiber
HVL4	Shingle fiber
HVL5	Short shingle/paper stock
MSAULI MINE, TRANSVAAL, S. AFRICA	
Msauli	Grade 4
Msauli	Grade 5
BARBERTON DISTRICT, TRANSVAAL, S. AFRICA	
Amianthus 1 & 2	Textile fiber
Amianthus F	Long shingle fiber
Amianthus AA	Shingle fiber
BARBERTON DISTRICT, NEAR NELSPRUIT, TRANSVAAL, S. AFRICA	
Munnik-Myburgh M1	Textile fiber
Munnik-Myburgh M3	Long shingle fiber
Munnik-Myburgh M4	Shingle fiber

CLASSIFICATION OF CAPE BLUE (CROCIDOLITE)

Grade	Average fiber length inches	Surface area (Rigden), cm²/g
C	1¼ - 1¾	1,500
S	¼ - ¾	5,500
S 80	¼ - ¾	9,500
P 25	¼ - ¾	8,300
H	⅛ - ½	7,500
H 80	⅛ - ½	10,000
713	⅛ - ½	13,000
WDS	⅛ - ⅜	9,000

CLASSIFICATION OF AFRICAN AMOSITE

Grade	Average fiber length inches	
S 11	1 -	1½
W 3	½ -	1½
K3	½ -	1½
SK	3/16 -	¾
S 33	⅛ -	½
S33/35	⅛ -	½
GW	⅛ -	¼
GK	⅛ -	¼
S 44	⅛ -	¼
RK	⅛ -	¼
6605	1/16 -	¼

Penge, Weltevreden, and Kromellenboog mines

WORLD CAPACITY: Chrysotile 4.8M. t; crocidolite 0.2 M. t; amosite 0.1M. t.

WORLD CAPACITY UTILIZATION: 68%.

MARKET CONDITIONS: Declining rapidly and irreversibly.

MARKETING FACTORS: Construction activity has been the traditional indicator of asbestos demand. Asbestos has been under strong environmental attack for many years and despite some reassessment, the market is unlikely to be revived and the main emphasis is on substitutes (see below).

HEALTH & SAFETY: Asbestos has been under strong environmental attack for many

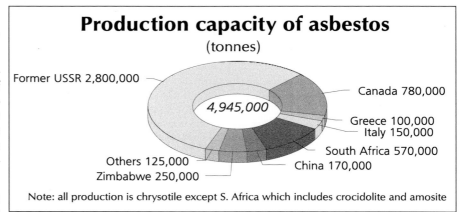

Production capacity of asbestos
(tonnes)

Former USSR 2,800,000

4,945,000

Canada 780,000
Greece 100,000
Italy 150,000
South Africa 570,000
China 170,000

Others 125,000
Zimbabwe 250,000

Note: all production is chrysotile except S. Africa which includes crocidolite and amosite

years and the US EPA instigated a phase out of asbestos in the 1990s, which was overturned by an Appeals Court in 1991. This was clarified in 1993 as authorizing the use in the United States of asbestos-cement sheets (corrugated or flat), asbestos-cement shingles, asbestos clothing roofing felt, millboard, pipeline wrap, and vinyl asbestos tile. However, the use of corrugated paper, commercial paper, flooring felt, rollboard and specialty paper was prohibited (see table). In addition, all new uses of asbestos (i.e. commercial uses that were not manufactured, processed or imported on July 12, 1989) were prohibited.

In 1992 OSHA issued a final rule which removed the nonasbestiform varieties of anthophyllite $(Mg,Fe)_7[(OH)Si_4O_{11}]_2$, tremolite $Ca_2(Mg, Fe)_5[(OH)Si_4O_{11}]_2$, and actinolite $Ca_2(Mg, Fe)_5[(OH)Si_4O_{11}]_2$ from the scope of its asbestos standard. The nonasbestiform varieties will be regulated according to limits set for "particulates not otherwise regulated."

In 1994 a federal judge accepted the Center for Claims Resolution's plan to settle future asbestos damage claims out of court under an agreed formula. Also in 1994 OSHA revised the standards for air quality lowing the permissible exposure levels of asbestos from 2.0 to 0.2 fibers per cubic centimeter (the regulation is being challenged in the courts). MSHA is planning to bring its standards in line with the OSHA level.

Crystalline silica has been classified as a probable carcinogen by the IARC (see silica for further details). Therefore, because of its crystalline silica content, unless processing has the capability to reduce the crystalline silica content to less than 0.1%, asbestos comes under the OSHA Hazard Communication Standards, 29 CFR Section 1900.1200 which require labeling and other forms of warning, material safety data sheets, and employee training for products containing identified carcinogens with concentrations greater than 0.1%.

SUBSTITUTES & ALTERNATIVES: The list of asbestos substitutes is long. However, few if any can substitute alone and "fiber cocktails" are required which tend to be more expensive and less effective than asbestos. **Fire retardant:-** ATH, antimony oxide, borates, bromine, chromite, diatomite, magnesite & magnesia, perlite, phosphates, pumice, vermiculite. **Filter media:-** activated carbon/anthracite, cellulose, diatomite, garnet, iron oxide (magnetite), perlite, pumice, silica sand, ilmenite. **Friction material:-** barite, bauxite & alumina, clays (attapulgite, kaolin, sepiolite), garnet, graphite, gypsum, mica, pumice, pyrophyllite, silica, slate, vermiculite, wollastonite, zircon. **Insulation:-** diatomite, foamed glass, metals, or cement, perlite, pumice, vermiculite, wollastonite, zeolites.

RECYCLING: Virtually none.

ASBESTOS SUBSTITUTES AND ALTERNATIVE PRODUCTS

A/C pipe	Ductile iron, PVC pipe, prestressed concrete, reinforced concrete pipe
A/C sheet	Fibrillated PP, Ca silicate, cement, cellulose fibers, fiberglass, wood, ceramic fiber, corrugated fiber board reinforced plastic, corrugated PVC, fiberglass reinforced cement, vinyl siding, aluminum siding
Coatings	Cellulose, PE films, ceramic fiber, clay, talc, limestone, wollastonite, fiberglass, carbon fiber, PP fiber, aramid, PE fiber
Flooring	Fiberglass, vinyl compositions, clay, PE pulp, talc, ceramic fiber
Friction	Semi-metallic brakes, fiberglass, aramid fibers, mineral fibers, steel fibers, cellulose (A/T), Franklin Fiber
Insulation	Fiberglass, ceramic fiber, calcium silicate, cement
Packings	Fiberglass, carbon fiber, graphite, aramid fiber, cellulose, ceramic fiber, PTFE, mica
Paper	Fiberglass, ceramic fiber, cellulose
Paper board	Non-fibrous minerals, wollastonite, ceramic fibers
Pipe wrap	Non-fibrous minerals, urethane coatings, plastic coatings
Plastics	Fiberglass, PTFE, mica, wollastonite, porcelain, fumed silica powder, Franklin Fiber
Tape	Cellulose, urethane tape, carbon-based tape
Textile	Fiberglass, ceramic fiber, carbon fiber, aramid fiber, PBI

Source: Virta, 1994.

PRODUCERS & WORLD TRADE: In line with the declining market for asbestos and the concern over health & safety, the number of asbestos producers has been reduced through closures and rationalization. Production and exports are dominated by the Former USSR, Canada, and South Africa.

PRODUCTION AND TRADE IN ASBESTOS (TONNES)

	Production	Imports	Exports	Apparent Consumption	Net Supplier	Net Consumer
North America	724,000	82,434	678,360	128,074	595,926	
South America	392,232	45,287	53,142	384,377	7,855	
Central America & Carib.		4,711		4,711		(4,711)
European Union	85,993	293,315	63,531	315,777		(229,784)
Non-EU Europe	2,307,525	213,371	210,232	2,310,664		(3,139)
Australasia	236,284	664,410	4,211	896,483		(660,199)
Middle East	18,086	8,398	1,586	24,898		(6,812)
Africa	358,299					

NOTE: Numbers are approximate and rounded for 1990 or thereabouts; data for Africa incomplete

Source: British Geological Survey

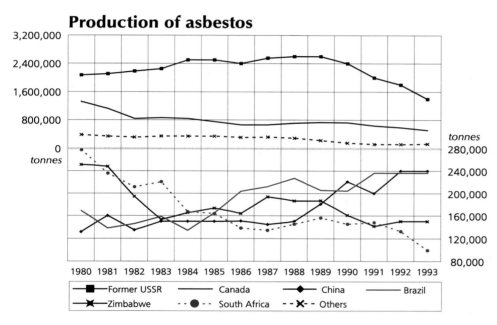

Production of asbestos

ASBESTOS LEADERS

Producers	Exporters
Former USSR	Canada
Canada	Former USSR
Brazil	Greece
China	Brazil
South Africa	United States
Zimbabwe	Others
Colombia	Hungary
Greece	Italy
India	Singapore
Swaziland	China
Italy	Austria
United States	Germany

Importers	
Japan	Poland
India	United States
South Korea	Mexico
France	Spain
Italy	Hungary
Germany	Czeckoslovakia

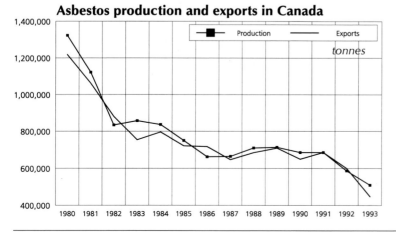

Asbestos production and exports in Canada

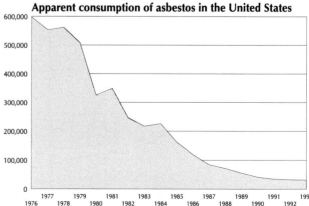

Apparent consumption of asbestos in the United States

HTS CODES: Unmanufactured:- 2524.00.0010 (amosite); 2524.00.0020 (crocidolite); 2524.00.0030 (crude chrysotile); 2524.00.0040 (spinning fiber chrysotile); 2524.00.0050 (chrysotile, other); 2524.00.0060 (asbestos, other).

Manufactured:- 6811.10 (corrugated sheets of asbestos-cement, of cellulose fiber-cement or the like); 6811.20 (sheets n.e.s., panels, tiles etc. of asbestos-cement, cellulose fiber-cement, etc.); 6811.30 (tubes, pipes, and tube or pipe fittings of asbestos-cement, of cellulose fiber-cement, etc.); 6811.90 (articles n.e.s. of asbestos-cement, of cellulose fiber-cement, or the like); 6812.10 (fabricated asbestos fibers; mixtures with a basis of asbestos or with a basis of asbestos and magnesium carbonate); 6812.20 (asbestos yarn and thread); 6812.30 (asbestos cord and string, whether or not plaited); 6812.40 (asbestos woven or knitted fabric); 6812.50 (asbestos clothing, clothing accessories, footwear and headgear); 6812.60 (asbestos paper, millboard and felt); 6812.70 (compressed asbestos fiber jointing, in sheets or rolls); 6812.90.10 (asbestos belting); 6812.90.20 (asbestos gaskets); 6812.90.90 (other asbestos fabricated products n.e.s.); 6813.10.10 (asbestos brake linings and pads for motor vehicles of heading Nos. 87.02, 87.03, 87.04, or 87.05); 6813.10.90 (other asbestos brake linings and pads); 6813.90.10 (asbestos clutch facings for motor vehicles of heading Nos. 87.02, 87.03, 87.04, or 87.05); 6813.90.90 (other asbestos friction material and articles n.e.s.).

PRICES: FOB mine Chrysotile (Canada) $1,100-1,300/t (#3); $810-1,050/t (#4); $458-675/t (#5); $320-440/t (#6); $150-300/t (#7).

Chrysotile (S. Africa) $360-440/t (#5); $300-350/t (#6); $200-290/t (#7). Crocidolite (S. Africa) $760-920/t (long); $680-750/t (medium); $640-720/t (short).

Canadian prices converted from C$ at US$0.75 = C$1.00.

ETYMOLOGY: Actinolite after the Greek *actino = ray* and *lithos = stone* in reference to its occurrence in bundles of radiating needles. **Amosite** is an acronym of Asbestos Mines of South Africa. **Anthophyllite** after the neo-Latin *anthophyllum = clove* for its brown color, Greek *lithos = stone*. **Asbestos** after the Latin and Greek *asbestos = inextinguishable* alluding to its early uses as a wick. **Chrysotile** from the Greek *chrysotos = gilded* in reference to its color and nature. **Crocidolite** from the Greek *krokis* or *krokidos = the nap on cloth* and *lithos = stone*. **Tremolite** for the Tremola Valley, near St. Gotthard, Switzerland, and Greek *lithos = stone*.

APPARENT CONSUMPTION OF ASBESTOS (TONNES)

	Apparent Consumption
Former USSR	2,096,300
Japan	292,701
Brazil	190,563
China	190,411
Colombia	173,970
South Africa	161,494
Zimbabwe	160,500
India	130,165
Italy	78,545
South Korea	76,849
France	63,571
Germany	56,284
Poland	56,026
Canada	55,394
Mexico	40,224
Spain	39,482
Swaziland	35,938
Iran	35,738
Yugoslavia	34,828
Czechoslovakia	32,923
United States	32,456
Indonesia	28,599
Malaysia	28,276
Hungary	27,591
Turkey	26,759
Belgium	26,204
Bulgaria	24,706
United Kingdom	15,731
Portugal	12,284
Greece	11,329
Chile	7,749
Sri Lanka	7,002
Argentina	6,947
Netherlands	6,014

NOTE: Numbers are approximate and rounded for 1990 or thereabouts; absence of a country does not necessarily indicate no production or trade; absence of a number does not necessarily mean zero

Source: British Geological Survey

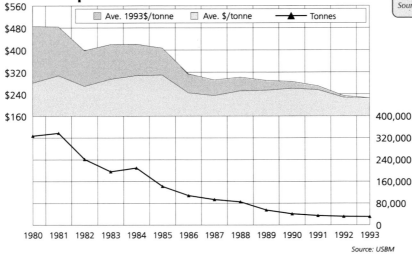

US Imports of unmanufactured asbestos

Legend: Ave. 1993$/tonne — Ave. $/tonne — Tonnes

Source: USBM

Minerals	Formula	Color
Attapulgite	$(OH_2)_4(OH)_2Mg_5Si_8O_{20}\cdot 4H_2O$ (ideal)	cream/gray
Sepiolite	$Si_{12}Mg_9O_{30}(OH)_6(OH_2)_4\cdot 6H_2O$ (ideal)	gray

Attapulgite-sepiolite clay mineral group is known as the hormite group. Palygorskite is the mineralogical name for the more commercial name attapulgite which is also known as fuller's earth in the United States. In the southeastern United States, the name attapulgite is applied to palygorskite with an aspect ratio of less than 10:1. Less common names include "mountain cork" and "mountain leather".

PROPERTIES & USES: Attapulgite & sepiolite are clays (magnesium aluminum silicates) with a chain-type structure (forming needle-shaped crystals) rather than flake-like (bentonite) or plate-like (kaolin). When dispersed, the needle-shaped crystals (1 μm long, 0.01 μm wide) are inert and nonswelling, but form a random lattice entrapping liquid and providing thickening, suspending, and thixotropic (gelling) properties [adhesives; cosmetics; caulks & sealants; liquid detergents & shampoos; flexographic inks; latex paints; polishes; ready mix tape compound]. Unlike Na bentonite, attapulgite & sepiolite do not flocculate with electrolytes (a.k.a. salt-water clay) and are stable at high temperatures [salt-water drilling muds; drilling geothermal wells]. Drilling muds containing attapulgite and sepiolite show minimal variation in viscosity and gel strength with large changes in electrolyte content (US attapulgite yield value is about 100 bbl/t).

Attapulgite & sepiolite have excellent sorptive properties largely because the extremely porous structure translates to a BET surface area of about 150 m^2/g for attapulgite and 300 m^2/g for sepiolite. In addition, substitution of magnesium and iron for aluminum generates an excess negative charge and a cation exchange world capacity of 20 to 50 milliequivalents per 100 g (less than smectite but higher than kaolin) [animal feed additive; floor absorbent; carrier/dilutant for pesticides; excipient in pharmaceuticals; oil spill clean-up material; pet litter; potting mixes]. Lightweight clays (400-700kg/m^3) used for pet litter include attapulgite and sepiolite (heavyweight clays, 800-980kg/m^3, include bentonite). In animal feed, attapulgite and sepiolite are used as binders for pelletized feeds, carriers of supplement (minerals, vitamins, antibiotics), free-flowing additives for feeds in flour, and lubricants to reduce die friction and improve the yield in pelletization process. They are also reported to increase feed efficiency and improve digestive hygiene. In addition to a high liquid absorbing world capacity, clays used as floor absorbents need to have good mechanical strength, be chemically inert (not react with the absorbed liquid), and non-flamable.

The numerous channels or holes (6Å diameter) are filled with water molecules or hydrated cations which may be driven off by heating to 500°C. Since rehydration is slow, these low volatile material (LVM) clays have enhanced sorptive properties. Clays dried at 200°C are known as regular volatile material (RVM). The approximate order of sorptivity is water > alcohols > acid > aldehydes > ketones > n-olifins > neutral esters > aromatics > cycloparaffins > paraffins [decolorizing oils].

Block sepiolite (meerschaum) may be carved.

QUALITY & SPECIFICATIONS: As mined, the ore is a mixture of attapulgite (70-80%), montmorillonite, sepiolite, other clays, quartz, calcite. After processing, divided into gellent or colloidal (some with chemical additives) and sorptive grades.

Drilling muds:- gellent grades for drilling muds covered under API Specification 13A, Specifications for Drilling-Fluid Materials, 1993 (see table).

Sorptive: depending on temperature of drying, sorptive grades may be divided into regular, LVM, and RVM grades. Absorbents are covered under Federal Specifications P-A-1056A, Absorbent Material, Oil and Water (for floors and decks).

Pet litter:- acceptance as a pet litter depends on absorbency, bulk density, granule size, formation of dust, and odor.

Pesticide carriers:- 1 - 5 mm as a regular carrier and <150 μm for application as a dust.

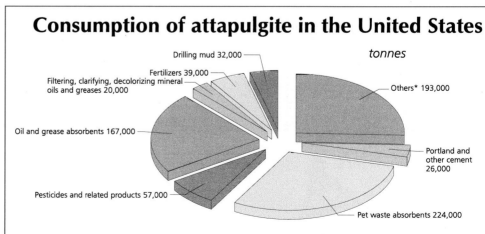

Consumption of attapulgite in the United States

tonnes

- Drilling mud 32,000
- Fertilizers 39,000
- Filtering, clarifying, decolorizing mineral oils and greases 20,000
- Oil and grease absorbents 167,000
- Pesticides and related products 57,000
- Others* 193,000
- Portland and other cement 26,000
- Pet waste absorbents 224,000

* includes animal feed, animal oil, gypsum products, absorbents, fillers, extenders, binders, filtering, clarifying, mortar and cement refractories, plastics, roofing tiles, water treatment and filtering, waterproofing and sealing.

Source: USBM (1993)

WORLD CAPACITY: 3.85M. t.

CAPACITY UTILIZATION: 80%.

MARKET CONDITIONS: Growing.

MARKETING FACTORS: Oil/gas drilling activity which is influenced by the price of oil, the state of the world economy, and politics. Success in capturing market share in the growing pet litter market. The development of new uses is critical.

HEALTH & SAFETY: Crystalline silica has been classified as a probable carcinogen by the IARC (see silica for further details). Therefore, because of its crystalline silica content, unless processing has the capability to reduce the crystalline silica content to less than 0.1%, attapulgite and sepiolite come under the OSHA Hazard Communication Standards, 29 CFR Section 1900.1200 which require labeling and other forms of warning, material safety data sheets, and employee training for products containing identified carcinogens with concentrations greater than 0.1%.

The acicular nature of these clays ("microfibrous morphology") has generated some health & safety concerns. The German Consumer Council identified "microscopic needle-shaped fibers" in cat litter containing attapulgite and sepiolite, although subsequent studies have found them to be harmless. Still the perception remains.

SUBSTITUTES & ALTERNATIVES:
Animal feed and supplement:- bentonite, perlite, talc, vermiculite, zeolites. **Absorbent/pet litter:**- bentonite, diatomite, gypsum, zeolites. **Carrier:**- bentonite, diatomite, kaolin, peat, pumice, pyrophyllite, talc, vermiculite, zeolites. **Thickener & gelling agent**: bentonite, various polymers, cellulosic thickeners.

RECYCLING: Virtually none.

PRODUCERS & WORLD TRADE:
Attapulgite and sepiolite supply is restricted to a handful of countries with the United States and Spain dominating. Both of these producers are major exporters.

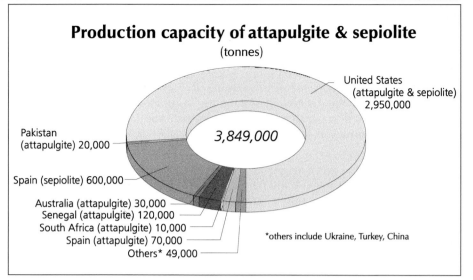

Production capacity of attapulgite & sepiolite
(tonnes)

3,849,000

United States (attapulgite & sepiolite) 2,950,000

Pakistan (attapulgite) 20,000

Spain (sepiolite) 600,000

Australia (attapulgite) 30,000
Senegal (attapulgite) 120,000
South Africa (attapulgite) 10,000
Spain (attapulgite) 70,000
Others* 49,000

*others include Ukraine, Turkey, China

SEPIOLITE FOR ANIMAL FEED

	Binder	Anti-caking agent & carrier
Particle size (mesh ASTM)	<100	50-120
Bulk density (g/l)	545±40	615±30
Moisture (%)	8±2	8±2
Westinghouse oil absorption (%)	-	92±7
Linseed oil absorption (%)	93±5	-
Water retention (%)	150	147
Mohs' hardness	2.0-2.5	2.0-2.5
Cation exchange capacity (meq/100g)	15±5	15±5

Source: Tolsa SA, Spain

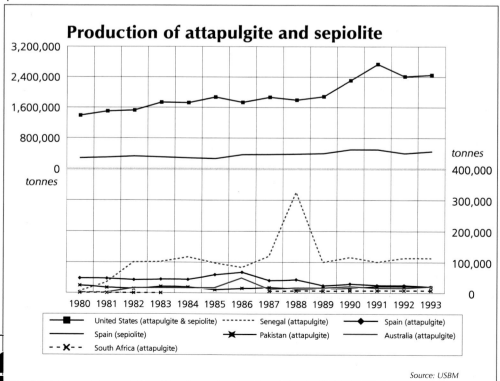

Production of attapulgite and sepiolite

United States (attapulgite & sepiolite)	Senegal (attapulgite)	Spain (attapulgite)
Spain (sepiolite)	Pakistan (attapulgite)	Australia (attapulgite)
South Africa (attapulgite)		

Source: USBM

SPECIFICATIONS FOR COMMERCIAL ATTAPULGITE

GRADES

Mineralogy(%)		0416G	1630G	2560G	050F	080F
Attapulgite	80-90	4.75mm-1.18mm	1.18mm-0.60mm	0.71mm-0.25mm	85-95%-250µm	85-95%-160µm
Quartz	5 - 10	MPS 2.36 mm	MPS 0.85 mm	MPS 0.425 mm	MPS 160 µm	MPS 35 µm
Dolomite	0 - 10	+4.75 mm 3.0% max.	+ 1.18 mm 3.0% max.	+ 0.71 mm 3.0% 'max.		
Kaolin	0 - 10	-1.18 mm 7.0% max.	- 0.60 mm 7.0% max	- 0.25 mm 7.0% max.		

Chemical Analysis (typical %)		Physical properties	
SiO_2	58.5	Color	white to light buff/gray
Al_2O_3	11.8	Moisture (as packed)	3.0 - 8.0 per cent w/w
MgO	5.3	Loose bulk density	0.45 - 0.65 g/cm^3 (450-650 kg/m^3)
Fe_2O_3	4	Water absorption	80 - 120 per cent w/w
CaO	1.6	Oil absorption	70 - 110 per cent w/w
K_2O	1.8	Surface area (BET)	135 - 140 m^2/g
Other oxides	1.5	Cation exchange capacity	30 - 40 m eq./100g
LOI	15.5	pH (5% suspension)	7.5 - 9.5

Source: Mallina Holdings, Australia

LEADERS IN ATTAPULGITE AND SEPIOLITE

Producers	Exporters	Importers
United States*	United States	Canada
Spain*	Spain	Netherlands
Spain**	Senegal	S. Africa
Senegal***	Australia	Saudi Arabia
Pakistan***		Japan
Australia***		Germany
South Africa***		United Kingdom

* attapulgite & sepiolite; ** sepiolite; *** attapulgite

ATTAPULGITE & SEPIOLITE IN DRILLING MUDS

Suspension properties, viscometer dial reading @ 600rpm

	30 min.
Residue >75µm	8.0 wt. % max.
Moisture	16.0 wt. % max.

API Specification 13A, Specifications for
Drilling-Fluid Materials, 1993

COMPARISON OF ATTAPULGITE, BENTONITE, AND KAOLIN AS THICKENERS

	Attapulgite	Bentonite	Kaolin
Principal mineral	Attapulgite	Montmorillonite	Kaolinite
Crystal structure	Chain	3-layer sheet	2-layer sheet
Particle shape	Lath-like	Flake	Plate
Particle size	Extremely fine (<0.5µm)	Extremely fine (<0.5 µm)	Very fine to medium (.5-10µm)
Color	Light cream	Variable, grey to white	White
Thickening power	High	High	Medium to low
Effects of salts	Little or none	Flocculates	Flocculates
Method of thickening	Colloidal interaction network	Particle interaction network with swelling	Flocculation at low pH gives medium thickening. At neutral or basic pH its slurries are generally thin and non-thickening.

Source: Engelhard Corporation

PRICES: United States attapulgite, FOB plant, Georgia, truckload, bags $130-220/t (granular, 6/30 mesh); $190-550/t (granular, processed, 40/100 - 4/8 mesh); $220-550/t (powder, 40-100% -325 mesh); $220-550/t (specialty gel grades).

HTS CODES: 2508.02.0000 (Fuller's and decolorizing earths); 3802.90.2000 (activated earths).

ETYMOLOGY: Attapulgite for Attapulgus, Georgia, USA (?). **Fuller's earth** clay used by the fuller to degrease cloth in a process known as fulling. **Meerschaum** from the Greek *meer = sea* and *schaum = froth* for its light weight and color. **Palygorskite** for the location "in der Paligorischen Distanz" of the second mine on the Popovka River, Urals, former USSR, where it was observed. **Sepiolite** from the Greek *sepion = the bone of the cuttle-fish* and *lithos = stone* since the bone of the cuttle-fish is light and porous like the mineral.

Mineral	Formula	%BaO	Color	SG	H
Barite	$BaSO_4$	65.7	white-brown	up to 4.5	3-3
Witherite	$BaCO_3$	77.7	White-gray, yellowish	4.2	3-3.5

Barite is virtually the exclusive commercial source of barium. Witherite is a very minor source, although significant deposits have been reported in China.

PROPERTIES & USES: Barite is a clean, relatively soft, virtually inert, and quite inexpensive mineral with a high SG [weighting agent in drilling mud]. Drilling muds account for more than 90% of the worldwide market for barite.

The properties noted for drilling muds plus its light color and high brightness (up to 90+%), low oil absorption, and wetability by oils allow barite to be used as a filler and weighting agent [acoustical compounds; adhesives; athletic goods (bowling balls, golf balls, tennis balls); carpet backing; friction materials; linoleum; mold release agents; paints including primer (automotive and appliance), topcoats (automotive), gloss enamels, powder coatings, semi-gloss and gloss latexes, and industrial and architectural coatings; paper (bristolboard, heavy printing paper, playing cards); radiation shielding; rope finishes; rubber (floor mats, white-walled tires, tires for heavy construction vehicles); urethane foams]. Brightness may be increased through bleaching with sulfuric acid. Other relevant properties include thermal stability (1,580°C), thermal conductivity (6×10^{-3} cal/cm), specific heat (0.11 cal/g°C), dielectric constant (7.3), and coefficient of thermal expansion (10×10^{-6}).

For higher purity and brightness, synthetic barium fillers are used: BaS + zinc sulfate → lithopone, a mixture of 70% $BaSO_4$ and 30% ZnS [white pigment in paint and artist's colors]; and BaS + Na_2SO_4 → precipitated $BaSO_4$ (blanc fixe) with a brightness of 95-99%, APS 0.5-4 µm, SG 4-4.2, and H3-4 is used as a filler [paint, rubber, inks, photographic paper] and in medicine [barium meal in X-rays; pharmaceuticals].

Barite is used as a source of BaO in glassmaking where it acts as a flux, oxidizer, and decolorizer giving greater brilliance and clarity to the finished glass.

The high SG is used in the construction industry to weigh down underwater pipelines. Barite absorbs gamma radiation and can replace lead in nuclear shields.

High-purity barite is a feedstock for the chemical industry. Lump barite + finely powdered coal heated to 1,250-1,350°C in a rotary kiln reduces to form 80-85% barium sulfide (BaS or black ash which is soluble in water) which is washed, leached, and filtered to a pure BaS used as a precursor for a range of barium chemicals. The barite feedstock requires low iron, silica, and alumina.

$$BaSO_4 + 4C \rightarrow BaS + 4CO$$

BaS + CO_2 or Na_2CO_3 → barium carbonate (98.5% $BaCO_3$) [TV and optical glass; ceramic glazes; porcelain enamels; ferrites; scum control in brickmaking].

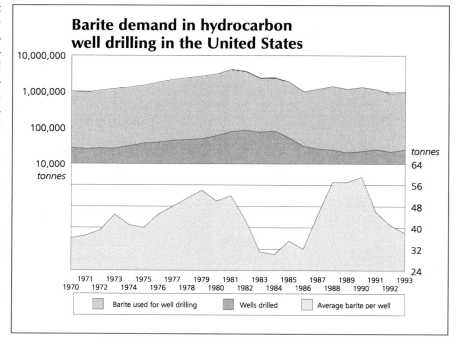

Barite demand in hydrocarbon well drilling in the United States

Legend: Barite used for well drilling | Wells drilled | Average barite per well

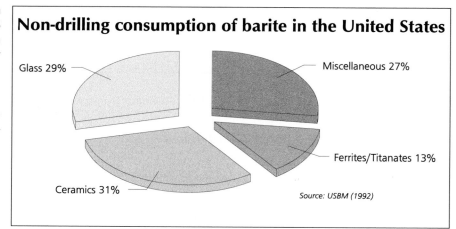

Non-drilling consumption of barite in the United States

Glass 29%
Miscellaneous 27%
Ferrites/Titanates 13%
Ceramics 31%

Source: USBM (1992)

BaS (or $BaCO_3$) + HCl → barium chloride, either anhydrous $BaCl_2$ [steel hardening salts; welding flux compound; magnesium production; water treatment] or crystal $BaCl_2 \cdot 2H_2O$ [sulfate removal, manufacture of molecular sieves]; + C and heat → barium oxide/hydroxide [dehydration/deacidification of fats, oils, and waxes; metallurgy; manufacture of oil and grease additives; feed for organic barium salts]; $+HNO_3$ → barium nitrate [green signal flares, tracer bullets, primers & detonators; enamels]; + TiO_2 → barium titanate [ceramics for electronics]; $BaCl_2$ (electrolyzed in a fused state) or BaO (reduced by metallic Al or Si @ 1,200°C) → barium metal [electronic alloys; "getter" to remove gas].

QUALITY & SPECIFICATIONS: *API drilling mud grade barite:-* 4.2 SG min.; 250 ppm Ca max., 95% -45 μm (325 mesh). This is covered in API Specification 13A, *Specifications for Drilling-Fluid Materials, 1993* - see table. Minerals commonly associated with barite that should be minimized include gypsum (Ca), siderite and dolomite carbonate released at high temperature, and pyrrhotite (sulfide ions released in high pH conditions).

Paint filler-grade barite:- min. 95% $BaSO_4$; max. 0.05% Fe_2O_3, 2.0% foreign matter; 0.5% moisture (ASTM D-280); 0.2% water soluble compounds (ASTM D-1208); PS 99.98% -37 μm (400 mesh) or Hegman 6.5 (ASTM D-1366); brightness 80%+, oil absorption 5kg/45kg (ASTM D-281), and pH 6.4 (ASTM D-1208).

Chemical-, X-Ray-, and glass-grade barium sulfate:- see table.

Barium carbonate:- see table.

WORLD CAPACITY: 8.2M. t.

CAPACITY UTILIZATION: 65%.

MARKET CONDITIONS: Stable.

MARKETING FACTORS: Oil/gas drilling activity and mud supply companies dominate the barite market which is influenced by the price of oil, the state of the world economy, and politics.

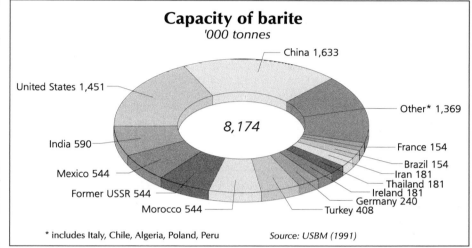

Capacity of barite
'000 tonnes

8,174

China 1,633
United States 1,451
Other* 1,369
France 154
Brazil 154
Iran 181
Thailand 181
Ireland 181
Germany 240
Turkey 408
Morocco 544
Former USSR 544
Mexico 544
India 590

* includes Italy, Chile, Algeria, Poland, Peru   Source: USBM (1991)

HEALTH & SAFETY: Crystalline silica has been classified as a probable carcinogen by the IARC (see silica for further details). Therefore, because of its crystalline silica content, unless processing has the capability to reduce the crystalline silica content to less than 0.1%, barite comes under the OSHA Hazard Communication Standards, 29 CFR Section 1900.1200 which require labeling and other forms of warning, material safety data sheets, and employee training for products containing identified carcinogens with concentrations greater than 0.1%.

Alaska requires that barite used in drilling mud contain <3ppm Cd and <1ppm Hg; this limit may be applied to California and Gulf Coast states. This may preclude the use of barite associated with metal sulfides. Other proposed rules include the banning of any discharge from drilling platforms within 6.4 km of the shore; discharge within this limit would be required to contain <3ppm Cd and <1ppm Hg.

Although barite is virtually inert, the water-soluble barium compounds are toxic if ingested.

SUBSTITUTES & ALTERNATIVES: Filler:- ATH, calcium carbonate, diatomite, feldspar, kaolin, mica, nepheline syenite, perlite, talc, microcrystalline silica, ground silica flour and synthetic silica, wollastonite. **Glass:-** strontium carbonate. **Weighting agent:-** celestite, hematite, ilmenite, iron ore.

RECYCLING: Virtually none as barite is discarded on completion of the drilling.

PRODUCTION AND TRADE IN BARITE (TONNES)

	Production	Imports	Exports	Apparent Consumption	Net Supplier	Net Consumer
North America	809,000	1,052,296	63,611	1,797,685		(988,685)
South America	213,730	100,397	94,739	219,388		(5,658)
European Union	587,369	716,466	379,033	924,802		(337,433)
Non-EU Europe	1,252,005	373,359	338,863	1,286,501		(34,496)
Australasia	2,216,817	306,636	1,882,664	640,789	1,576,028	
Middle East	54,000	7,753		61,753		(7,753)
Africa	460,593	5,833	393,577	72,849	387,744	

NOTE: Numbers are approximate and rounded for 1990 or thereabouts.   *Source: British Geological Survey*

ANALYSIS OF BARIUM CARBONATE GRADES (%)

		Germany Grade A	Germany Grade B	Germany Grade C	Germany Grade D
$BaCO_3/SrCO_3$	min.	99	99	99	99
SrO	max.	1.4	1.4	1.4	1.4
CaO	max.	0.17	0.17	0.17	0.17
Na_2O	max.	0.02	0.02	0.20	0.20
Fe_2O_3	max.	0.007	0.007	0.007	0.007
Total S as SO_3	max.	0.40	0.36	0.40	0.40
Insoluble in HCl	max.	0.40	0.40	1.20	1.20
Moisture	max.	0.05	0.08	0.04	0.04
BD loose (kg/l)		0.55-0.75	0.40-0.55	1.40-1.80	1.60-2.00
BD tapped (kg/l)		1.00-1.40	0.70-1.00	1.60-2.10	2.10-2.50
Sieve residue >45µ	max.	1%	1%		
Screen analysis					
>0.200mm	max.			2%	
<0.15mm	max.			5%	
>1.00mm	max.				0%
>0.85mm	max.				5%
<0.15mm	max.				15%

Source: Solvay Barium Strontium GmbH

REQUIREMENTS FOR WEIGHTING AGENTS

	Barite	Hematite
Density, g/cm³ min.	4.2	5.05
Water soluble alkaline earth metals as calcium, mg/kg max.	250	100
Residue >75µ	3% wt. % max.	1.5% wt. % max.
Residue >45µ	n.s.	1.5% wt. % max.
Particles >6µ in equivalent spherical diameter	30% wt. % max.	15% wt. % max.

API Specification 13A, Specifications for Drilling-Fluid Materials, 1993

SPECIFICATIONS FOR BARITE

	Glass grade	For $BaCO_3$
$BaSO_4$	min. 95	92-96 (lump) 96-98
SiO_2	max. 1.5	
Fe_2O_3	max. 0.15	max. 1
Al_2O_3	max. 0.15	
$SrSO_4$		max. 1
CaF_2		max. 0.5
Size		
<850µ	100%	
<150µ	max. 5%	

SPECIFICATIONS OF A COMMERCIAL FILLER-GRADE BARITE

	United States Industrial grade BARA-200C	United States Industrial grade BARA-325N	United States Plastics Cimbar 1025P	United States Plastics Barimite 4009P	United States Powder coatings CIMBAR CF	United States Paints, plastics CIMBAR UF
$BaSO_4$	94	92	97 - 98	94 - 96	98	98
SiO_2	2.5	6.0				
Total silicates			0.2	2.5	0.82	0.82
$SrSO_4$	1.5	0.4				
Fe_2O_3	0.50	0.2	0.015	0.4	0.04	0.04
MgO	0.03	0.05				
CaO	0.03	0.2				
Al_2O_3	0.05	0.3	0.01	0.05	0.01	0.01
Total heavy metals					0.05	0.05
Moisture	<0.1	<0.1			0.15	0.15
LOI			0.25	0.75	0.75	0.75
Oil absorption	8 - 9	9 - 10	11.0 - 12.0	7.0 - 9.0	10	11
Dry brightness			89.0 - 92.0	65.0 - 75.0	90+	90+
Surface area, m²/g			2.0	0.8		
Mean particle size, µm			2.0 - 3.0	8.5 - 9.5	4.8	2.5
% passing 200 mesh	97.0	99.8				
% passing 325 mesh	85.0	98.0				

Source: CIMBAR Performance Minerals

PRODUCERS & WORLD TRADE: Barite is a fairly common, low priced mineral that is available in many countries. Nevertheless, there is extensive international trade designed to deliver large quantities to the drilling region. In many cases, barite is shipped in a crude form and ground to specification close to the point of consumption.

PRICES: Barite Europe $67.50-78/t (OCMA, bulk, del. Aberdeen);$78-90/t (OCMA, bulk, del. Great Yarmouth); $292-330/t (white, paint grade, 96-98% BaSO$_4$, 99% 350 mesh, del. UK); $210-225/t (micronized, off white, min. 99% <20 μm, del. UK). Morocco $37-40/t (unground, OCMA/API, bulk, SG 4.22, FOB); $85 (ground, bags, FOB). Turkey $51-53/t (ground, OCMA/APA, big bags (1.5 t), FOB S. Turkey). United States (API, lump, CIF Gulf Coast) $40-45/t (Chinese); $35-40/t (Indian); 70-85/t (ground API grade); extra-fine pigment grade $160/t.

BARITE LEADERS

Producers	Exporters	Importers
China	China	United States
India	Morocco	Germany
Former USSR	India	United Kingdom
United States	Turkey	Norway
Turkey	Bulgaria	Japan
Morocco	Thailand	Netherlands
Mexico	Ireland	Venezuela
Germany	France	Indonesia
Bulgaria	Netherlands	Former USSR
Thailand	Peru	Italy
Ireland	Belgium	Romania
Brazil	Mexico	South Korea
France	Germany	France
United Kingdom	Chile	Singapore
Romania	United Kingdom	Abu Dhabi

APPARENT CONSUMPTION OF BARITE (TONNES)

United States	1,476,790
Former USSR	581,900
Germany	428,249
Mexico	268,845
United Kingdom	259,613
India	245,850
Turkey	189,978
Norway	177,902
Romania	129,500
Italy	107,614
Brazil	87,502
Venezuela	84,105
Indonesia	77,148
Czechoslovakia	57,200
France	56,626
Bulgaria	54,693
Iran	54,000
Canada	52,050
South Korea	51,639
Argentina	50,212
Poland	39,353
Former Yugoslavia	36,215
Algeria	35,578
Tunisia	32,787
Australia	30,972
Spain	27,359
Abu Dhabi	25,986
Pakistan	23,329
Netherlands	21,641
Colombia	21,409
Malaysia	19,432
China	19,123
Denmark	16,917
Singapore	12,268
Taiwan	11,960

NOTE: Numbers are approximate for 1990

Source: British Geological Survey

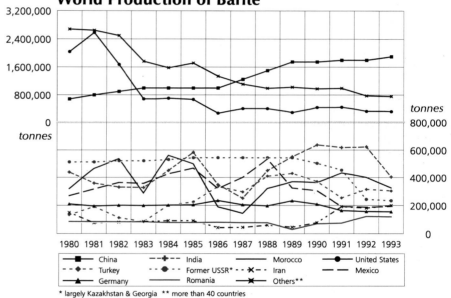

World Production of Barite

Legend: China, India, Morocco, United States, Turkey, Former USSR*, Iran, Mexico, Germany, Romania, Others**

* largely Kazakhstan & Georgia ** more than 40 countries

Barium carbonate (FOB works) $639/t (precipitated, bulk); $650/t (precipitated, bags); $695/t (photo-grade, bags). Barium chloride (ex-works) $627/t (tech. crystals, bags); $821/t (tech., anhydrous, drums); $8/kg (reagent grade, crystals, drums). Barium monohydrate $1,276-1,320/t (bags, FOB works). Barium octahydrate $770/t (bags, FOB works). Barium nitrate $715/t (bags, ex-works). Barium peroxide $11.55-12.10/kg (drums, ex-works). Barium stearate $2.86/kg (bulk, FOB destination). Barium sulfate $1.54-1.76/kg (USP, X-ray diagnosis grade, powder). Barium sulfide (black ash) $706/t (drums, ex-works). Blanc fixe $0.45/kg.

HTS CODES: 2511.10.50 (crude barite); 2511.10.10 (ground barite); 2511.20.00 (witherite); 2816.30.00 (barium oxide, hydroxide, peroxide); 2827.38.00 (barium chloride); 2833.27.00 (barium sulfate); 2834.29.50 (barium nitrate); 2836.60.00 (barium carbonate).

ETYMOLOGY: Barite from the Greek *barys* = *heavy* or *dense*. **Barylite** from the Greek *barys* = *heavy* or *dense*, *lithos* = *stone*. **Blanc fixe** from the French *blanc* = *white* and *fixe* = *settled* referring to the precipitate of barium sulfate. **Witherite** for William Withering (1741-1799), English physician & mineralogist.

Bauxite is an impure mixture of the three minerals listed below; proportions vary from deposit to deposit.

Minerals	Formula	%Al₂O₃	Color	SG	H
Gibbsite	$Al_2O_3 \cdot 3H_2O$	65.4	gray	2.3-2.4	2.3-3.5
Boehmite	$Al_2O_3 \cdot H_2O$	85.0	gray	3.01-3.06	4-5
Diaspore	$Al_2O_3 \cdot H_2O$	85.0	gray	3.3-3.5	6.5-7

PROPERTIES & USES: Bauxite ore (>45% Al_2O_3) is the dominant commercial source of alumina (Al_2O_3). Bauxite via the Bayer process → Bayer alumina + cryolite (Na_3AlF_6) + CaF_2 + coke + recycled aluminum → aluminum metal (99.7%) with low density, high electrical & thermal conductivity, corrosion resistance, and good malleability, is nonmagnetic and nonsparking [containers & packaging; electrical goods; structural materials including construction, aerospace, automobiles - see below]. Aluminum may be alloyed and treated to produce products with a high strength-to-weight ratio.

$$Al_2O_3 \cdot 3H_2O + 2NaOH \rightarrow Na_2O \cdot Al_2O_3 + 4H_2O + \text{red mud}$$
bauxite   caustic soda   sodium aluminate   filtered

$$Na_2O \cdot Al_2O_3 + 4H_2O \rightarrow Al_2O_3 \cdot 3H_2O + 2NaOH$$

$$Al_2O_3 \cdot 3H_2O \rightarrow Al_2O_3 + 3H_2O$$
calcined

Aluminum metal → aluminum bromide [catalyst]; → aluminum formacetate [textile water repellent]; → aluminum isopropylate [dehydrating agent; waterproofing textiles; catalyst]; → aluminum nitrate [catalyst in petroleum refining; incandescent filaments; leather tanning; printing mordent].

AVERAGE ALUMINA CONTENTS

	% Al₂O₃
Fused white alumina	100
Tabular alumina	100
Fused brown alumina	96
Calcined bauxite, Guyana (gibbsite)	75-90
Calcined bauxite, China (diaspore)	75-90
Mullite, fused or sintered	72
Bauxitic kaolins	60-70
Dumortierite	64.5
Andalusite, kyanite, sillimanite	62.9
Kaolin	44-48
Flint clay	40-45
Alunite	37
Pyrophyllite, calcined	25-29
Pyrophyllite	20-25

Bauxite → sodium aluminate solution [cleaning compounds; mordant; paper sizing; sewage & water treatment] → aluminum (tri)hydrate ($Al(OH)_3$ or ATH), a white, bright, fine and platy [filler/pigment in adhesives, cosmetics; paper, rubber, sealants], chemically pure and consistent (99.7% equivalent to 64.5% Al_2O_3) raw material [catalysts; ceramics; dentifrice formulas; glass; synthetic zeolite production], mildly abrasive (H2.5-3.5) [toothpaste] powder that evolves combined water at 200-400°C and thus acts as a fire retardant, smoke suppressant, & white filler [carpet backing; plastics; rubber; synthetic marble].

ATH → alumina [see below]; → activated alumina [acid neutralizer in transformer oil; catalyst support; chromatographic absorption; desiccant; leather tanning]; → aluminum acetate [feed for aluminum stearate; waterproofing]; → aluminum borate [glass and ceramics]; → aluminum carbide [methane generation; drying agent; metallurgy]; → aluminum chlorhydrate [drying agent in antiperspirants]; → aluminum chloride [see below]; → aluminum fluoride [ceramics; feedstock for high-purity Al metal; feedstock for synthetic cryolite]; → aluminum nitrate [catalyst in petroleum refining; incandescent filaments; leather tanning; printing mordent]; → aluminum oleate [food additive; lube oil thickener; paint drier; plastics lubricant; waterproofing]; → low-iron aluminum sulfate (alum) [catalyst; cosmetics; water treatment; sizing agent in paper; pharmaceuticals; pigments]; → sodium aluminate [feed for alumina gel; clarification in sugar refining; soaps & cleaning compounds; water softening; welding rod flux].

ATH (or bauxite or aluminum metal) + HCl → aluminum chloride [catalyst for aviation gas isomerization and the manufacture of ethylbenzene, ethyl chloride, butyl rubber, etc.] → lithium or sodium aluminum hydride [feedstock for Al, Ge, Si, Sn hydride; H_2 source; rocket propellant]; → aluminum borohydride [jet fuel additive]; → aluminum chloride solution [antiseptic/antiperspirant; pectin; photofixing bath; wood preservative].

Consumption of bauxite in the United States
'000 tonnes, dry equivalent

Alumina 11,002
Abrasive* 203
Chemical 225
Refractory 429
Other 58

* includes consumption by Canadian abrasive industry

ATH + H_2SO_4 ➔ aluminum sulfate or alum [antiperspirant; clarifier for fats and oils; deodorizer & decolorizer in petroleum processing; fireproofing; leather tanning; water clarifier in papermaking; water treatment].

$$2Al(OH)_3 + 3H_2SO_4 + 8H_2O \rightarrow Al_2(SO_4)_3 + 14H_2O$$
ATH   sulfuric acid   alum

Alum ➔ ultra-pure alumina (99.98-99.995%) [advanced ceramics and bioceramics; filler; polishing compound; chemicals]; ➔ aluminum hydroxide [feed for alumina acetate]; ➔ aluminum phosphate [catalyst; ceramics; dental cement; glass; refractory bonding agent]; ➔ aluminum ammonium sulfate [baking powder; dye mordant; medicine; water & sewage treatment]; ➔ aluminum potassium or sodium sulfate [baking powder; ceramics; medicine; leather tanning; paper size precipitant; sugar refining; textile mordent; waterproofing].

Alumina ➔ aluminum metal [see above & below]; ➔ aluminum chloride [see below]; ➔ refined, calcined (alpha) alumina containing >99% Al_2O_3, with H9 and a melting point of 3,700°C, resistance to corrosion and chemical attack, good thermal conductivity and electrical insulation [abrasive & polishing compounds; catalytic support; refractories; ceramics]; (or ATH) ➔ tabular or sintered alumina with a melting point of 2,040°C, H9, low-consistent shrinkage, high density and low porosity, high electrical resistivity, resistance to thermal shock, abrasion, and chemical attack [catalyst carriers; cutting tools; dehydrating agent; filler in epoxy resin; glass tank blocks; electrical insulators (high-voltage equipment, spark plugs); high-temperature refractories; spherical proppants].

Abrasive-grade bauxite ➔ fused brown alumina (94-97% Al_2O_3) with H9, SG of 3.94-3.98, an uneven fracture, inertness, and heat resistance (melting point 2,050°C) [bonded and coated abrasives; optical powders; non-slip flooring; refractories]. Alumina ➔ white fused alumina (99.5-99.9% Al_2O_3) with H9+ and good friability [abrasive for grinding, lapping, and polishing; refractories]. Fused alumina + Cr_2O_3 ➔ pink (0.5%) or red (2%) fused alumina [tough abrasive]; + fused magnesia ➔ fused synthetic spinels with excellent refractory properties [Al & Mg metal smelting; cement kilns; induction furnaces] (see magnesia for details). Fused alumina, a.k.a. synthetic or artificial corundum.

Refractory-grade bauxite calcined @ 925-1,040°C ➔ calcined alumina {high-alumina refractories for iron and steel; cement; glass}. 2 tonnes of crude ore yields 1 tonne of calcined bauxite. Calcined bauxite + silica ➔ synthetic mullite (sintered, fused, or fused zirconia) [refractories for glass and steel; ceramic kiln furniture; tubes in electrical furnaces and thermocouples]; + zirconia ➔ AZ abrasives; + limestone ➔ calcium aluminate cement (CAC) [refractory binder].

QUALITY & SPECIFICATIONS: Crude bauxite contains 5-30% moisture and <1% when dried. Chemical specifications vary according to end use.

Abrasive-grade calcined bauxite:- max. 0.1% CaO and calcined product should contain minimal fines, low free moisture.

Aluminum oxide powder (typical):- 95.23% Al_2O_3, 1.44% SiO_2, 2.64% TiO_2, 0.22% Fe_2O_3, 0.07% Na_2O, 0.26% MgO, 0.02% Cr_2O_3, 0.12% CaO.

High alumina cement-grade bauxite:- moderately high alumina (pref. diaspore); Al_2O_3:SiO_2 ratio >10:1; Al_2O_3:Fe_2O_3 = 2-2.5:1.

Chemical grade bauxite:- Al_2O_3:Fe_2O_3 of 100:1 is the ideal, although in practice for potable water treatment it is >23:1 with no toxic compounds; for waste water it is 4:1. For the production of aluminum sulfate, the AWWA permits a higher iron content (if the iron content of the treated water is not increased) plus up to 10% silica. Gibbsite preferred as it is the most soluble bauxite.

Metallurgical-grade bauxite:- high Al_2O_3:SiO_2 ratio. Gibbsite or boehmite.

Proppant-grade bauxite:- high alumina, low silica and clays, iron content is not critical.

Refractory-grade calcined bauxite:- see table plus, low alkalis, min. SG 3.1. Gibbsite in Guyana and Brazil, diaspore in China.

Steel flux grade bauxite:- max. 7% SiO_2 and trace P_2O_5 and S.

There are numerous grades of aluminas and their fused products based on a combination of chemical purity.

WORLD CAPACITY: 42M. t alumina.   **CAPACITY UTILIZATION:** 92%.

MARKET CONDITIONS: Stable.   **MARKETING FACTORS:** Manufacturing and economy.

HEALTH & SAFETY: Crystalline silica has been classified as a probable carcinogen by the IARC (see silica for further details). Therefore, because of its crystalline silica content, unless processing has the capability to reduce the crystalline silica content to less than 0.1%, bauxite comes under the OSHA Hazard Communication Standards, 29 CFR Section 1900.1200 which require labeling and other forms of warning, material safety data sheets, and employee training for products containing identified carcinogens with concentrations greater than 0.1%.

SPECIFICATIONS FOR RAW BAUXITE BY END USE (%)

	Metallurgical	Chemical	Cement (calcined)	Refractory (calcined)	Abrasive
Al_2O_3	50-55	min. 55	45-55	min. 84.5	80-88
SiO_2	0-15	5-18	max. 6	max. 7.5	4-8
Fe_2O_3	5-30	max. 2	20-30	max. 2.5	2-5
TiO_2	0-6	0-6	3	max. 4	2-5

CHEMICAL COMPOSITION OF COMMERCIAL CALCINED BAUXITE (%)

	Guyana Refractory (RASC)	China Refractory	China Refractory 85	China Refractory 80	China Refractory 75	Brazil Refractory	Australia Abrasive	Guinea Abrasive
Al_2O_3 min.	86.50	86.0				85.0	80.0	88.0
typical	88.30	89.0	87.50	84.50	78.60	85-87	82-84	90.0
SiO_2 max.	7.50	7.0				10.5	7.0	3.0
typical	6.50	6.0	6.00	6.50	14.50	8.5-10.0	4.7-5.5	1.2
Fe_2O_3 max.	2.50	2.0	1.50	1.50	1.20	2.3	7.5	8.0
typical	1.75	1.2	1.6-2.2	6.0	1.2			
TiO_2 max.	—	3.30				2.4	—	5.0
typical	3.20	3.30	3.75	4.00	3.50	1.9-2.3	3.5-3.8	4.0
LOI max.	0.50	0.50				0.5	1.0	2.0
typical	0.25	0.05	0.20	0.20	0.20	0.0-0.5	0.5	0.8
BD	3.10		3.10	2.80	2.70			
PCE	40+		38	38	37			

RASC - Refractory A-Grade Super-Calcined

CHEMICAL COMPOSITIONS OF FUSED SYNTHETIC MULLITE (%)

	Germany Hüls	UK Kieth Ceramics	Brazil Elfusa	USA Washington Mills	Hungary Hungalu	Japan Showa Denko
Al_2O_3	75.2	76.3	72.3	77.7	76.0	76.8
SiO_2	24.5	23.3	28.5	21.8	23.0	22.8
TiO_2	0.01	0.02	0.0	0.05	0.05	-
Fe_2O_3	0.05	0.10	0.13	0.12	0.08	0.05
CaO	0.04	-	0.15	-	0.15	-
MgO	0.03	-	0.05	-	0.10	-
Na_2O	0.20	0.30	0.38	0.35	0.25	0.19
K_2O	0.01	0.02	0.04	-	-	-

See kaolin for additional data on mullite.

ALUMINUM TRIHYDRATE (ATH) SPECIFICATIONS

	Hydral 705 Fine	Hydral 710 Fine	Hydral 710B Fine	Lubral 710 Fine	C-31 Coarse	C-31 coarse Coarse	C-37 Coarse
Al_2O_3	64.1	64.1	64.7	64.0	65.0	65.0	64.2
SiO_2	0.04	0.04	0.07	0.04	0.01	0.01	0.07
Fe_2O_3	0.01	0.01	0.02	0.01	0.004	0.004	0.004
Na_2O (total)	0.60	0.45	0.45	0.45	0.15	0.2	0.5
Na_2O (soluble)	0.22	0.10	0.10	0.10			
Moisture @ 110°C	0.3-1.0	0.3-1.0	0.3-1.0	0.3-1.0	0.04	0.04	0.2
Bulk density, loose (g/m^3)	0.08-0.14	0.13-0.22	0.13-0.22	0.13-0.2	1.0-1.1	1.1-1.3	0.8-1.0
Bulk density, packed (g/m^3)	0.09-0.20	0.26-0.45	0.26-0.45	0.23-0.4	1.2-1.4	1.4-1.6	1.0-1.1
Surface area (m^2/g)	12-15	6-8	6-8	6-8	0.15	0.1	0.2
Color	white	white	near white	near white	white	white	off-white
GE brightness	94+	94+	90+	90+			

Source: Alcoa

CHEMICAL COMPOSITIONS OF ALUMINAS AND FUSED DERIVATIVES

	Refined calcined alpha aluminas				Reactive	Tabular alumina	Fused alumina	Fused mullite	Fused AZS
	Normal Na_2O	Inter. Na_2O	Low Na_2O	Extra high purity					
Al_2O_3	98.9-99.7	99.2-99.8	99.5-99.8	>99.93	99.5+	99+	77.7	47.00	
SiO_2	0.02-0.05	0.02-0.07	0.07-0.12	0.015	0.04-0.08	0.06-0.2	0.05	22.0	16.5
Fe_2O_3	0.04-0.05	0.04-0.06	0.04-0.06	0.009	0.01-0.02	0.06-0.3	0.15	0.12	<0.20
Na_2O	0.3-0.6	0.15-0.25	<0.13	<0.02	0.08	0.02-0.10	0.50	0.35	0.30
ZrO_2	-	-	-	-	-	-	-	-	36.00
TiO_2	-	-	-	-	-	-	0.02	0.05	0.20

Although some experiments on animals have indicated that certain aluminas may cause lung damage, the danger is mainly one of perception.

SUBSTITUTES & ALTERNATIVES: Abrasives:- corundum/emery, diamonds, diatomite, feldspar, garnet, iron oxide (magnetite), nepheline syenite, olivine, perlite, pumice, silica sand, staurolite, tripoli, and silicon carbide, ilmenite. **Al_2O_3 source** (all currently uneconomical):- clay, alunite, anorthosite, oil shale. **Filler (ATH)**:- barite, calcium carbonate, diatomite, feldspar, kaolin, mica, nepheline syenite, perlite, talc, microcrystalline silica, ground silica flour and synthetic silica, wollastonite. **Fire retardant (ATH)**:- antimony oxide, asbestos, borates, bromine, chromite, diatomite, magnesite & magnesia, perlite, phosphates, pumice, vermiculite. **Friction material**:- asbestos, barite, clays (attapulgite, kaolin, sepiolite), garnet, graphite, gypsum, mica, pumice, pyrophyllite, silica, slate, vermiculite, wollastonite, zircon. **Metal**:- beryllium, magnesium, steel, titanium (metal); PET, glass, & paper (containers). **Refractories**:- andalusite, chromite, kyanite, dolomite, graphite, magnesite, olivine, pyrophyllite, refractory clays, silica, sillimanite, zircon.

FUSED ALUMINA ABRASIVES

	Calcined alumina White	Calcined alumina-chrome ore Pink	Calcined alumina chromium oxide Ruby	Bauxite Black	Bauxite,iron borings, sodium carbonate Monoxline	Calcined alumina, baddeleyite or zircon 10% ZrO_2	Bauxite,coke, iron borings, baddeleyite or zircon 25% ZrO_2	Bauxite, zircon sand, coke, and iron borings 40% ZrO_2
Al_2O_3	99.53	98.79	96.77	71.7	99.27	86.15	70.84	53.80
TiO_2		0.28	0.25	4.25	0.57	2.25	0.91	1.50
SiO_2	0.04	0.18	0.11	12.0	0.03	1.25	0.94	1.50
Fe_2O_3	0.10	0.33	0.18	8.30	0.08	0.23	0.27	0.27
Na_2O	0.33	0.23	0.61		0.05			
Cr_2O_3		0.07	2.03					
MgO			0.04				27.04	43.00
CaO		0.12	0.01	1.20		10.10	0.06	0.05
C	0.03	0.02		2.60				
Color	White	Bluish pink	Ruby	Black	Gray	Dark gray	Gray	Light-gray
Fired color	White	Pink			Pink-beige			
APS, µm	2500		1000			100	20	
Std. friability 14 grit(%)	69-54	65-46	35.4		37.7	12	8	15
Std. friability 20 grit(%)	65-62				48-46	25		
BD 14 grit (%)	1.62-1.76	1.75-1.95	1.92		1.90	2.14	2.18	2.30
BD 20 grit (%)	1.75-1.83				1.91-2.03	2.10		
Hardness K 100	1965	2000	2200		2000	2200		1140
Shape	Sharp-edged, blocky	Blocky, sharp-edged			Blocky	Blocky	Blocky	Blocky

Source: Cichy, 1990

FUSED ALUMINA AND ALUMINA COMPOSITIONS FOR REFRACTORY GRAIN

	White fused alumina	Brown High TiO_2	Brown Low TiO_2	Mullite Black	Mullite Black	Mullite White	Mullite White	Zirconia-mullite	Magnesia-spinel
Al_2O_3	99.5	96.00	98.41	98.17	76.0	77.70	75.60	45.8	70.63
Fe_2O_3	0.08	0.10	0.25	0.15	0.90	0.12	0.10	0.15	0.10
SiO_2	0.02	0.80	0.4	0.50	20.00	21.8	23.1	17.5	0.07
TiO_2	0.01	2.50	0.6	0.90	2.50	0.05	0.03	0.17	0.01
ZrO_2		0.20						36	
CaO	0.02	0.08	0.14	0.12					0.28
MgO	0.01	0.22				0.35	0.10		28.83
Na_2O	0.30	0.02	0.08	0.03	0.10		0.31	0.25	0.08
T.C.	0.05	0.1							0.06
S		0.01							
Melting pt. (°C)	2,050	2,000+				1,850	1,850	1,750	2,135
Density (g/cm³)	3.97	3.92	3.94			3.08	3.05	3.58	3.56

Source: Cichy, 1990

RECYCLING: In developed countries, often more than 60% of aluminum metal is recycled including used beverage cans or UBCs. This practice combines environmental awareness with commercial good sense since much of the cost of production (the energy required to smelt the aluminum) remains in the recycled material. Refractory linings from iron and steel or glass furnaces have been recycled for some time. However, material is consumed during use, separation and purification are difficult, and degradation of some chemical and physical properties generally means that the recycled material is used for a lower grade of product (termed "down-cycling"). The overall effect of refractory recycling on raw material consumption appears to be limited for the near term.

PRODUCERS & WORLD TRADE: World production is dominated by metallurgical-grade bauxite. Guyana, China, and Brazil are noted for the production and export of refractory-grade bauxite, and Guinea and Australia for abrasive grade. Since the manufacture of alumina-bases products often requires large quantities of energy, particularly fused grades, these producers generally have access to low-cost (HEP) electricity.

PRICES: Dried bauxite:- Australia $15/t; Guyana & Jamaica $30-35/t; Surinam $35/t.

Calcined bauxite (refractory):- Guyana $175/t (FOB railcar Baltimore, MD or FOB Burnside, LA); Chinese (min. 87% Al_2O_3, typical BD 3.15, FOBT) $47-50/t (Shanxi, shaft, lump); $65-70/t (Shanxi, rotary, lump); $55-60/t (Guizhou, round, lump); $80-90/t (metric graded sizes).

Calcined alumina $390/t (United States, bulk, ex-works); $418/t (United States, bags, ex-works); $375-4655/t (98.5-99.5% Al_2O_3); $425-500/t (med. soda content, del. UK) . Fused alumina (94% Al_2O_3, brown, CIF N. Europe) $550-750/t (FEPA 8-220, European/US); $550-650/t (FEPA 8-220, Chinese); $480-500 (refractory, Chinese). Sintered (tabular) alumina $900-1,000/t. Activated alumina $905/t (granular, ex-works). Aluminum:- metal $1.65-1.90/kg (>99.5%); paste $4.82-2.47/kg (leafing grade, standard lining, delivered); powder $3.56/kg (leafing grade, standard lining, delivered); powder $5.59/kg (leafing grade, extra-fine lining, delivered).

Alum, $165/t (technical); $290/t (iron-free). Alum, ammonium $770/t (tech., gran., bags). Alum, potassium $770/t (tech., gran., bags). ATH $280/t (white, bulk, ex-works). Alumi-

World production of bauxite

'000 tonnes

Australia — Guinea — Jamaica — Brazil — India — Former USSR — Suriname — Venezuela — China — Guyana — Others

num acetate $7.46/kg (basic, drums, ex-works). Aluminum chloride $1.58/kg (anhydrous, freight equalized). Aluminum formate $1.21/kg (dibasic, liquid, 8% Al_2O_3). Aluminum sulfate $270 (commercial grade, 17% Al_2O_3, E. and Gulf Coasts); $358-380/t (iron-free, 17% Al_2O_3, dry, bags).

HTS CODES: 2606.00.00 (aluminum ores and conc.); 2606.00.0030.8 (calcined bauxite, refractory grade); 2606.00.0060.1 (calcined bauxite, other); 2818.10.10.004 (artificial corundum, crude); 2818.10.20.002 (artificial corundum, in grains, ground, pulverized, or refined); 2508.60 (mullite); 2818.30.00.002 (aluminum hydroxide); 7601.10.30 (unwrought metal in coils); 7601.10.60 (unwrought other than Si-Al alloys); 7602.00.00 (waste and scrap).

ETYMOLOGY: Aluminum from the Latin *alumen* = *alum*, original name for natural aluminum sulfate. **Alunite** Latin *alumen* = alum (see above) and French *alun* = alum. **Boehmite** for Johannes Böhm (1857-1938), German geologist and first observer. **Bauxite** for Les Baux, near Arles, France where it was discovered by P. Berthierin. **Diaspore** from the Greek *dia* = *through* and *speirein* = *to scatter* in reference to its characteristic decrepitation on heating. **Gibbsite** for George Gibbs (1776-1833), owner of the mineral collection acquired by Yale early in the 19th century. **Mullite** for the island of Mull, Scotland and the Greek *lithos* = stone.

BAUXITE LEADERS			
Producers (bauxite)	**Producers (alumina)**	**Exporters (bauxite)**	**Importers (bauxite)**
Australia	Australia	Australia	United States
Guinea	Former USSR	Guinea	Former USSR
Jamaica	United States	Jamaica	Japan
Brazil*	Jamaica	Brazil*	Canada
India	China	Surinam	Brazil
Former USSR	Brazil	Venezuela	Venezuela
Surinam	India	China*	Germany
Venezuela	Surinam	Guyana*	France
China*	Venezuela	Sierra Leone	Ireland
Guyana*	Canada	Greece	Italy
Greece	Spain	Hungary	Spain
* includes refractory grade			

Montmorillonite group	Formula
Montmorillonite	$5Al_2O_3 \cdot 2MgO \cdot 24SiO_2 \cdot 6H_2O(Na_2O, CaO)$
Hectorite	$16MgO \cdot Li_2O \cdot 24SiO_2 \cdot 6(F, H_2O)(Na_2O)$
Saponite	$18MgO \cdot Al_2O_3 \cdot 22SiO_2 \cdot 6H_2O)(Na_2O, CaO)$
Beidellite	$13Al_2O_3 \cdot 5Al_2O_3 \cdot 38SiO_2 \cdot 12H_2O(CaO, Na_2O)$
Nontronite	$6Fe2O_3 \cdot Al_2O_3 \cdot 22SiO_2 \cdot 6H_2O)(Na_2O, CaO)$

Bentonite is a clay consisting essentially of smectite minerals, in particular montmorillonite which is by far the most common of the group. Related products include sub-bentonite (low or moderately swelling varieties) and metabentonite (illite-smectite mixed layer minerals, altered volcanic ash with later potassium addition). Hectorite is a magnesium, lithium smectite clay containing >1% LiO_2 and >4% F. Saponite is a swelling clay with low cation-exchange capacity.

PROPERTIES & USES: Bentonite comprises loosely tied silica/alumina sheets which can be easily subdivided in aqueous solutions into unit-celled particles about 0.003 µm thick and less than 0.1 µm long. This ease of separation together with the unbalanced negative electric charges which repel each other in polar media such as water (i.e. flocculation) promote excellent dispersion in water. Bentonite has exchangeable Na^+, Ca^{++}, or Mg^{++} cations and exhibits far greater ion-exchange world capacity than any other mineral except for zeolites. These exchangeable cations influence the properties of clay (and therefore its commercial utilization) and provide a basis for a broad classification into Na-bentonite (a.k.a. swelling, Wyoming or Western type bentonite) with a high swelling capacity and Ca-bentonite (a.k.a. nonswelling, Fuller's Earth in the UK, and southern bentonite when describing occurrences in some US Gulf Coast states) with a low swelling capacity. Another critical difference is that Na-bentonite remains stable above 400°C whereas Ca-bentonite does not. Ca bentonite can be treated with soda ash (Na_2CO_3) to form a sodium-exchanged bentonite with improved swelling properties.

In water, relatively large flakes of Na- bentonite disperse into colloidal particles (APS 1-100 µm) activating dormant electrochemical energy carried in the crystal lattice and imparting dilatancy (swelling up to about 15 and even 30 times its original dry bulk volume without agitation), viscosity (resistance to flow), and thixotropy (gelling strength). These properties are utilized in drilling to provide suspending power, form an impervious coating on the drill-hole walls, and supply lubrication [oil and gas exploration and production drilling; water drilling; exploration drilling]. Bentonite constitutes up to 5% by weight of drilling muds. Bentonite acts as an emulsifying agent for oil-water mixtures in drilling fluids whereby it collects many types of inorganic and organic compounds through adsorption, absorption, and chemical activity. During drilling the viscosity removes drill cuttings and floats them to the surface; when still the thixotropic gel strength prevents settling. Hectorite has similar properties.

In addition to gelling & thixotropic properties, Na-bentonite has good plasticity and lubricity, high shear & compression strength, impermeability, and low compressibility and consolidation and therefore is used in civil engineering [landfill caps; slurry trench cutoff walls; diaphragm wall construction; pond linings]. Na-bentonite has excellent plasticity, dry-bonding strength, and strength at high temperatures, and 6-8 kg are added to one tonne of dry iron ore to form pellets [iron-ore pelletization]. Good bonding characteristics with fast green strength, superior hot strength, high durability & rebound, and low permeability mean it constitutes 4-6% and up to 10% of foundry molding sands [iron and steel foundries]. Ca-bentonite may be used in lower temperature foundry sands. Na-bentonite is used to provide a bond in brake linings and as a plasticizer in refractory, abrasive, and ceramic mixes.

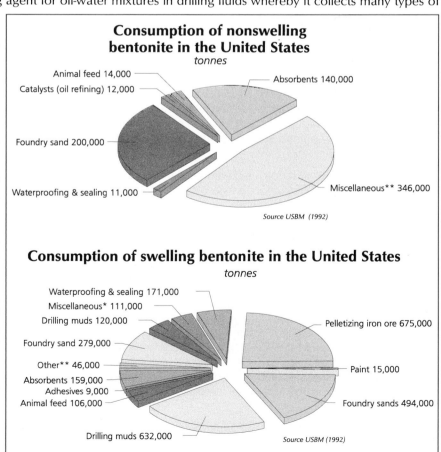

Consumption of nonswelling bentonite in the United States
tonnes

Animal feed 14,000
Catalysts (oil refining) 12,000
Absorbents 140,000
Foundry sand 200,000
Waterproofing & sealing 11,000
Miscellaneous** 346,000

Source USBM (1992)

Consumption of swelling bentonite in the United States
tonnes

Waterproofing & sealing 171,000
Miscellaneous* 111,000
Drilling muds 120,000
Foundry sand 279,000
Other** 46,000
Absorbents 159,000
Adhesives 9,000
Animal feed 106,000
Drilling muds 632,000
Pelletizing iron ore 675,000
Paint 15,000
Foundry sands 494,000

Source USBM (1992)

Consumption of swelling bentonite in the United States

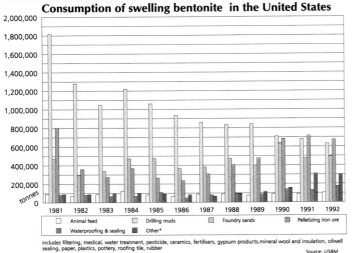

includes filtering, medical, water treatment, pesticide, ceramics, fertilisers, gypsum products, mineral wool and insulation, oilwell sealing, paper, plastics, pottery, roofing tile, rubber

Source: USBM

Consumption of non-swelling bentonite in the United States

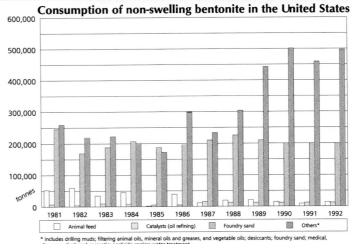

* includes drilling muds; filtering animal oils, mineral oils and greases, and vegetable oils; desiccants; foundry sand; medical, pharmaceutical, and cosmetic; pesticide carrier; water treatment

Source: USBM

Consumption of Fuller's earth (montmorillonite) in the United States

Oil and grease absorbents — Pesticides and related products — Pet waste absorbents — Others*

* includes animal feed; drilling mud; gypsum products, absorbents; fillers, extenders, binders; filtering & clarifying,; mortar and cement refractories; plastics, roofing tiles; water treatment; waterproofing and sealing. Source: USBM.

Na-bentonite may be treated with chemicals to produce organophilic compounds (organoclays) which when added to liquid organic systems, alter the rheological characteristics including viscosity, solid suspension, and thixotropy [carbonless copy paper; cosmetics; drilling muds; gelling greases; paints; printing inks; refining oils, fats, and solvents].

Bentonite exhibits good adsorption (the ability to attract and hold ions or molecules of gas or liquid) and absorption (the ability to assimilate or incorporate material). Ca-bentonite adsorbs moisture more rapidly, but Na-bentonite has a greater capacity. Ca-bentonite can be treated with inorganic acid (acid-activated montmorillonite) in order to dissolve impurities like calcite, replace exchangeable divalent calcium with monovalent hydrogen ions, and leach ferric, ferrous, aluminum, and magnesium ions thus altering the crystal structure and increasing the specific surface area and porosity. Bentonite is used to adsorb impurities such as wax, tar, and foreign matter and therefore clarify, decolorize, deodorize, dehydrate, and/or neutralize the liquid [refining animal and vegetable oils such as linseed, cottonseed, rapeseed, palm, peanut, olive, and sunflower; tallow; lard; turpentine; cleaning fluids, vinegar; wine; beer; syrups]. It adsorbs impurities and coagulates bacteria, and softens water by removing calcium and magnesium salts [water and sewage treatment].

Bentonite is highly hygroscopic, and when crushed and dried to 5% moisture, will adsorb moisture rapidly [pet litter; pesticide carrier; animal feed pelletization; waste disposal; soil stabilization]. It has the advantage of adsorbing up to 5 times its own weight in liquid, and tends to clump together when wetted allowing easy separation.

Some calcium bentonites are extremely white (white bentonite) and are used for emulsion stabilization and as a gelling agent [cosmetics, toiletries, and household products], as a plasticizer [electrical ceramics], and as softening agent [detergents].

Si/Al catalysts may be produced from clays such as bentonite by acid treatment and calcining in order to remove alkalis, alkaline earths, Fe, and some of the Mg & Al [petroleum refining].

Hectorite's small crystal size, large surface area, and high cation exchange capacity give viscosities and swelling properties higher than that of montmorillonite [drilling muds]. Hectorite or hectorite blended with montmorillonite (i.e. magnesium aluminum silicates or MAS) is utilized to provide physical properties including suspension [pharmaceuticals such as antacids; abrasive cleaners; liquid detergents], gelling [cosmetic face masks, gel baths, shaving gels, acne creams], bodying and flow characteristics through thixotropy [cosmetics and personal care products, toothpaste, shampoos], rheological control [organic thickening agents such as xanthan gum, cellulosics, and acrylic polymers], binding [eye shadow, deodorant sticks, lipstick], emulsion stabilization [oil and water emulsions in body lotions, shampoos], and disintegration time and debittering [tablet coating].

QUALITY & SPECIFICATIONS: *Drilling mud grade:-* Specifications are covered by the API based in the United States and OCMA in Europe, and both have come together to produce the specifications listed below.

Particularly important criteria for drilling includes mud yield, i.e. barrels of mud with an apparent viscosity of 15 centipoise produced from 1 ton of clay; gel strength, i.e. the difference in yield value immediately after agitation and after standing 10 minutes; and by the wall building properties as measured by the water loss through a filter paper when a 15-centipoise clay is subjected to a pressure of 100 psi (by measuring the thickness and character of the filter cake in the water-loss test). Some typical results are given in the table.

BENTONITE IN DRILLING MUDS

Requirement	API Bentonite	OCMA Bentonite
Suspension properties		
Viscometer dial		
reading @ 600 rpm	30 minutes	30 minutes
Yield point/plastic		
viscosity ratio, max.	3	6
Filtrate volume, cm^3, max.	15.0	16.0
Residue >75 μm max.	4.0 wt. %	2.5 wt. %
Moisture, max.	10.0 wt. %	13.0 wt. %

Source: API Specification 13A, Specification for Drilling-Fluid Material, 1993

API TEST RESULTS ON CLAY

	Yield bbl. 15 cp mud/ton in fresh water	Solids in filter cake (wt./%)	API water loss @ 15 cp	Filter cake permeability (microdarcys)	pH
Hectorite	160	6.5	7	0.85	8.6
Na-bentonite	125	10	11	1.8	8.2
Ca-bentonite	15-75	15-50	10-15	1.5-2.1	7.5-8.7
Attapulgite	105	23	105	68	7.1

ANALYSIS OF COMMERCIAL BENTONITE

	W. US (Na) Standard foundry	W. US (Na) Pure bentonite	S. US (Ca) Foundry	United Kingdom Calcium
SiO_2	63.59	61.3-64	62.12	55.2
Al_2O_3	21.43	19.8	17.33	13.7
Fe_2O_3	3.78	3.9	5.30	8.1
CaO	0.66	0.6	3.68	6.3
MgO	2.03	1.3	3.30	3.3
Na_2O	2.70	2.2	0.50	trace
K_2O	0.31	0.4	0.55	0.6
TiO_2	NA	0.1	NA	0.7
Trace elements	NA	3.2	NA	NA
Bound water	5.50	7.2	7.22	9.9

CHEMICAL ANALYSIS OF HECTORITE

	Disaster Peak, NV	Hector, CA	Kirkland, AZ
SiO_2	58.7	55.1	59.8
Al_2O_3	0.58	0.33	0.45
TiO_2	0.05	0.01	trace
Fe_2O_3	0.38	0.12	0.09
MgO	25.10	24.51	26.30
MnO	nd	trace	trace
CaO	1.70	0.90	1.10
Na_2O	0.21	2.20	0.05
K_2O	0.06	0.08	0.11
P_2O_5	nd	0.21	trace
Li_2O	1.50	1.14	1.10
CO_2	nd	0.60	nd
F	5.00	4.75	3.60
H_2O+	10.20	2.84	9.50
H_2O-		8.93	
Cl	nd	0.21	nd

Source: Odom, 1992

PRODUCTION AND TRADE IN BENTONITE* (TONNES)

	Production	Imports	Exports	Apparent Consumption	Net Supplier	Net Consumer
North America	6,422,184	281,709	691,674	6,012,219	409,965	
South America	313,978	71,191	14,325	370,844		(56,866)
C. America & Carib.	14,300			14,300		
European Union	2,151,086	754,519	412,077	2,493,528		(342,442)
Non-EU Europe	2,828,004	85,938	41,181	2,872,761		(44,757)
Australasia	982,614	465,764	159,045	1,289,333		(306,719)
Middle East	102,352	21,895	12,088	112,159		(9,807)
Africa	158,614	4,127	106,700	56,041	102,573	

*includes bentonite (mainly sodium bentonite) and fuller's earth (mainly calcium bentonite)

NOTE: Numbers are approximate and rounded for 1991 or thereabouts.

Source: British Geological Survey

Wet-screen analysis or grit test requires <2.5% residue (grit) on a 200 mesh US Series sieve.

Foundry-grade:- generally 92% montmorillonite, 3% quartz, and 5% feldspars; 6-12% moisture; pH >8.3; <0.70% CaO; 600-850 liquid limit (the ability to hold water without flowing); green compressive strength (58.7 kPa), green deformation (2.5%), green shear strength (17.3 kPa), green tensile strength (10.3 kPa), & dry compressive strength (656 kPa), methylene blue world capacity (100 Meg/100 g). PS ranges from 65 to 95% -75 µm with 90 to 95% the most common. Specifications covered by Steel Founders Society of America SFSA Designation 13T-65.

Iron-ore pelletizing:- No standardized specifications, but guidelines are 70 to 90% -44 µm, 10% moisture.

Absorbent granules:- require a uniform mixture of minerals of the silicate type; must be clean, uniform, free of lumps or foreign matter.

Catalyst grade:- extremely pure smectite with a very low iron content.

WORLD CAPACITY: 11.25M. t.

CAPACITY UTILIZATION: 70%.

MARKET CONDITIONS: Steady to declining.

MARKETING FACTORS: Oil/gas drilling activity which is influenced by the price of oil, the state of the world economy, and politics; iron ore and steel industry which are influenced by the state of the economy; civil engineering depends on construction activity which is influenced by the state of the economy; new uses.

HEALTH & SAFETY: Crystalline silica has been classified as a probable carcinogen by the IARC (see silica for further details). Therefore, because of its crystalline silica content, unless processing has the capability to reduce the crystalline silica content to less than 0.1%, bentonite comes under the OSHA Hazard Communication Standards, 29 CFR Section 1900.1200 which require labeling and other forms of warning, material safety data sheets, and employee training for products containing identified carcinogens with concentrations greater than 0.1%.

SUBSTITUTES & ALTERNATIVES: Absorbent/pet litter:- attapulgite/sepiolite, diatomite, gypsum, zeolites. **Carrier:-** attapulgite, bentonite, diatomite, kaolin, peat, pumice, pyrophyllite, sepiolite, talc, vermiculite, zeolites. **Drilling muds:-** various polymers & attapulgite. **Iron-ore pelletization:-** polymers. **Refining mineral oils:-** activated bauxite, magnesium silicates. **Thickener & gelling agent:-** attapulgite/sepiolite, various polymers, cellulosic thickeners.

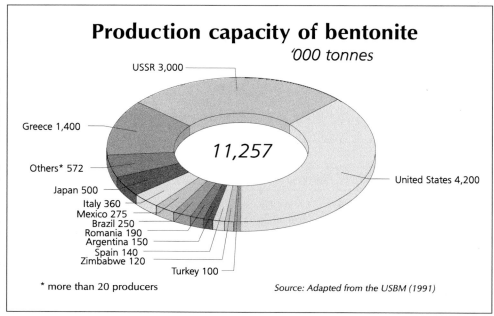

Production capacity of bentonite

'000 tonnes

11,257

USSR 3,000
Greece 1,400
Others* 572
Japan 500
Italy 360
Mexico 275
Brazil 250
Romania 190
Argentina 150
Spain 140
Zimbabwe 120
Turkey 100
United States 4,200

* more than 20 producers

Source: Adapted from the USBM (1991)

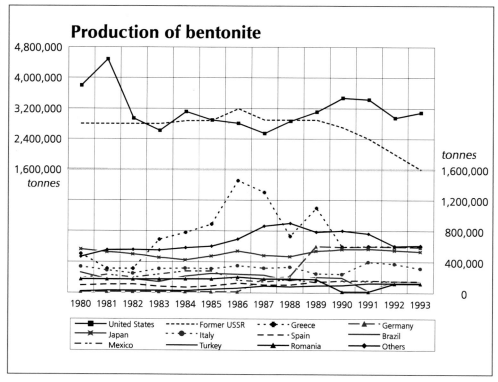

Production of bentonite

tonnes / tonnes

United States	Former USSR	Greece	Germany
Japan	Italy	Spain	Brazil
Mexico	Turkey	Romania	Others

RECYCLING: Bentonite may be recovered from foundry molds. In the clarification process, after filtering the bentonite may be recovered, repurified by calcination, and reused. Some recovery is possible from drilling muds, although the cost of separating the various components of the mud is high compared with the price of the individual constituents.

PRODUCERS & WORLD TRADE: Bentonite production is dominated by the United States, the former USSR, and to a lesser extent Greece. Many of the world's bentonite specifications are based on material from Wyoming which may be regarded as the market leader for many end uses including drilling muds.

APPARENT CONSUMPTION OF BENTONITE* (TONNES)

	Apparent Consumption
United States	5,484,880
Former USSR	2,400,000
Germany	1,112,430
Japan	799,294
Greece	499,663
Canada	361,611
Italy	320,697
United Kingdom	249,736
Brazil	201,526
India	174,786
Mexico	165,728
Spain	126,715
Romania	120,000
France	106,012
Argentina	82,600
Czechoslovakia	75,818
Former Yugoslavia	74,771
South Africa	72,709
Australia	69,739
Turkey	65,616
Malaysia	60,785
Peru	55,383
Philippines	50,566
Cyprus	46,312
South Korea	44,542
Netherlands	41,435
Poland	41,062
Iran	40,452
Algeria	34,355
Taiwan	34,227
Pakistan	30,052
Thailand	22,407
Kuwait	21,395
Austria	20,157
Indonesia	18,727
Sweden	17,293
Norway	17,174
Hungary	17,088
Denmark	16,283
Switzerland	16,199

*includes bentonite (mainly sodium bentonite) and fuller's earth (mainly calcium bentonite)

NOTE: Numbers are approximate for 1990

Source: British Geological Survey

PRICES: Bentonite:- United States (Wyoming, FOB plant, rail cars) $27.50-44/t (crude, bulk); $33-44/t (foundry-grade, bags); $33044/t (API grade, bags). Europe (del. UK) Wyoming, foundry grade 85% -200 mesh $195-210/t (bags); civil engineering grade $120-135/t (bulk); OCMA grade $120-127.50/t (bulk). Fuller's Earth, soda ash treated, foundry grade $147-180/t (bags, del. UK).

HTS CODES: 2508.10.0000 (bentonite); 2508.20.0000 (US fuller's earth & decolorizing earths).

ETYMOLOGY: Beidellite for a locality at Beidell, Colorado. **Bentonite** for the Benton Shale named for Fort Benton, Montana, United States (originally named Taylorite for the Taylor Ranch, the site of the first mine near Rock River, Wyoming, which opened in 1888). **Fuller's earth** is the clay used by the fuller to degrease cloth in a process known as fulling. **Hectorite** for Hector, California, United States. **Montmorillonite** for Montmorillon, Vienne, France. **Nontronite** for the locality in Arrondissement of Nontron, near the village of Saint Pardoux, France. **Saponite** from the Latin *sapo (-idos)* = *soap* for its soaplike appearance. Loosely-used synonyms for bentonite include volcanic clay, soap clay, mineral soap, bleaching and absorbent clays and earths.

BENTONITE LEADERS

Producers	Importers	Exporters
United States	Canada	United States
Former USSR	Japan	Greece
Germany	Germany	United Kingdom
Greece	United Kingdom	India
Japan	France	Germany
Italy	Italy	Spain
India	Netherlands	Italy
United Kingdom	Malaysia	Netherlands
Mexico	Brazil	Turkey
Brazil	Spain	France
Spain	Taiwan	Indonesia
Romania	Australia	Argentina
Argentina	Thailand	Cyprus
Turkey	Kuwait	Czechoslovakia
Canada	Austria	Australia
Czechoslovakia	Sweden	South Korea
Former Yugoslavia	Norway	Canada
South Africa	Denmark	Austria
Cyprus	Switzerland	Mexico
Peru	South Korea	Hungary
Australia	Indonesia	Former Yugoslavia

*includes bentonite (mainly sodium bentonite) and fuller's earth (mainly calcium bentonite)

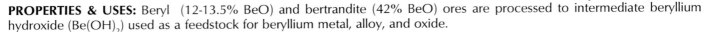

Minerals	Formula	%BeO	Color	SG	H
Beryl	$Be_3Al_2Si_6O_{18}$	14.0	white/blue/green	2.6-2.9	7.5
Bertrandite	$Be_4Si_2O_7(OH)_2$	42.4	white	2.6	6

Other beryllium minerals include barylite ($BaBe_2Si_2O_7$ – 15.4 - 15.8% BeO); chrysoberyl ($BeAlO_4$ – 16.9 - 19.7% BeO); and phenacite (Be_2SiO_4 – 44.0 - 45.6% BeO).

PROPERTIES & USES: Beryl (12-13.5% BeO) and bertrandite (42% BeO) ores are processed to intermediate beryllium hydroxide ($Be(OH)_2$) used as a feedstock for beryllium metal, alloy, and oxide.

Beryllium hydroxide dissolved in ammonium bifluoride, smelted in an induction furnace with magnesium, and vacuum melted → beryllium, a white, low density metal. Beryllium metal, available as a powder, rod, sheet, foil, billet, or ingot, is transparent to X-rays [X-ray windows]; dissipates heat, and reflects neutrons [canning material, neutron moderator, control rods, and reflector in nuclear reactors and nuclear-powered space systems]; and exhibits high stiffness, light weight (SG 1.93 i.e. two-thirds that of aluminum), and dimensional stability over a wide temperature range [aerospace vehicles; audio components; high-speed computer components; inertial guidance systems; military aircraft brakes; mirrors; space optical system components].

Beryllium hydroxide + electrolytic copper + carbon in an electric arc furnace → beryllium-copper master alloy (4% beryllium). Re-melting + copper → various beryllium-copper alloys cast into slabs or billets. The alloys are nonmagnetic with high electrical and thermal conductivity, fatigue and corrosion resistance, and considerable strength and hardness [specialized engineering]. Formed into strips [springs, connectors, and switches for automobiles, aerospace, computers, home appliances, various instrumentation]; large-diameter tubing [drilling equipment; bushings and bearings in heavy equipment]; rods [connectors in fiber optic communication systems]; wire [printed circuit boards]; bar and plate [resistance-welding parts; machinery components; molds for glass, metal, and plastic forming].

Beryllium hydroxide + sulfuric acid and calcining the beryllium sulfate tetrahydrate @ 1,430°C → beryllium oxide or beryllia. This is a good heat conductor and electrical insulator, has high hardness and strength [automotive ignition systems; ceramics for computers; electrical insulators; power transistors; electronic circuitry substrate; lasers] and is transparent to microwaves [microwave communication systems, microwave ovens].

Gem quality beryl includes aquamarine (blue), emerald (green), golden beryl (canary to gold yellow), heliodor (yellow-green), morganite (pink), red beryl (red).

QUALITY & SPECIFICATIONS: Beryl ore averages 10-12% BeO and the average bertrandite ore grade in Utah is 0.69% BeO. Specifications of commercial beryllium-copper alloy, beryllium, beryllia are summarized in the tables.

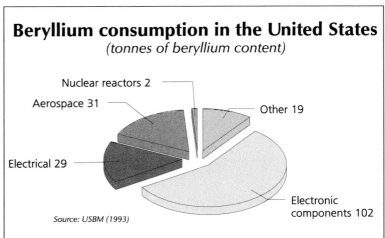

Beryllium consumption in the United States
(tonnes of beryllium content)

Nuclear reactors 2
Aerospace 31
Electrical 29
Other 19
Electronic components 102

Source: USBM (1993)

BERYLLIUM LEADERS

Producers	Exporter	Importers*
United States	Brazil	United States
China	United States	Singapore
Russia	China	Japan
Brazil	Russia	United Kingdom
Kazakhstan	Kazakhstan	Germany
Madagascar	Madagascar	France
Zimbabwe	Zimbabwe	Korea
Argentina	Argentina	Netherlands
Portugal	Portugal	Canada
Mozambique	Mozambique	
Rwanda	Rwanda	
South Africa	South Africa	

*including alloys

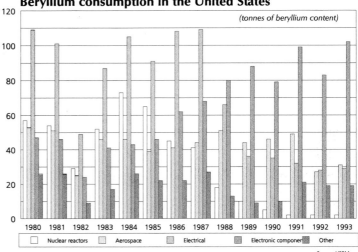

Beryllium consumption in the United States
(tonnes of beryllium content)

Legend: Nuclear reactors, Aerospace, Electrical, Electronic components, Other

Source: USBM

WORLD CAPACITY: Beryl 600 t. **CAPACITY UTILIZATION:** NA.

MARKET CONDITIONS: Steady/declining.

MARKETING FACTORS: Hi-tech manufacturing/nuclear industry/R&D.

HEALTH & SAFETY: Beryllium dust and fumes have been recognized as the cause of beryllosis, a serious chronic lung disease. In the EPA standards, beryllium processing plant airborne emissions are limited to 10g of beryllium over a 24-hour period (The Clean Air Act) and a concentration level of 130 µg/l of beryllium to protect aquatic organisms from acute health effects and 5.3 µg/l for protection of chronic health effects (The Clean Water Act). For human health, EPA established a concentration of 3.7 ng/l during the ingestion of water and fish, and a concentration of 64.1 ng/l during the ingestion of fish only. OSHA and MSHA standards limit the 8-hour exposure level to an average of 2 µg/m^3 with a peak of 25 µg/m^3 not to exceed 30 minutes, and a ceiling concentration of 5 µg/m^3.

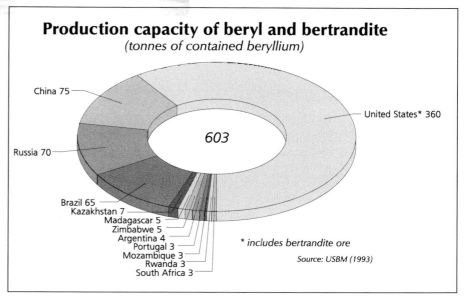

Production capacity of beryl and bertrandite
(tonnes of contained beryllium)

603

- China 75
- Russia 70
- Brazil 65
- Kazakhstan 7
- Madagascar 5
- Zimbabwe 5
- Argentina 4
- Portugal 3
- Mozambique 3
- Rwanda 3
- South Africa 3
- United States* 360

* includes bertrandite ore

Source: USBM (1993)

SUBSTITUTES & ALTERNATIVES: Metal:- aluminum, steel, titanium, graphite composites. **Alloys:**- phosphor bronze (alloys).

RECYCLING: Virtually no old scrap is recovered from finished products because of the low beryllium content in most products and the difficulty in separation. Home scrap and new scrap is generated by fabricators from their machining and stamping operations; an estimated 80% is returned to the manufacturer for reprocessing.

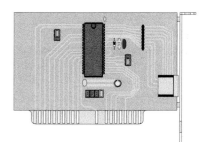

SPECIFICATIONS FOR BERYLLIUM-COPPER ALLOY (WEIGHT %)

Brush Alloy No.	25	165	10	50
Be	1.80 - 2.00	1.60 - 1.79	0.40 - 0.7	0.25 - 0.50
Co	-	-	2.4 - 2.7	1.4 - 1.7
Minimum Co + Ni	0.20	0.20	-	-
Maximum Co + Ni + Fe	0.60	0.60	-	-
Ag	-	-	-	0.90 - 1
Cu	Balance	Balance	Balance	Balance
Density, g/cm^3	8.36	8.41	8.82	8.82

Source: Brush Wellman Inc.

SPECIFICATIONS FOR BERYLLIUM (WEIGHT %)

	Commercial beryllium powder SP-2—F	National Defense Stockpile hot pressed powder billet		
		Grade A	Grade B	Grade C
Min. Be	98.5	98.0	98.0	94.0
Max. BeO	1.5	1.5	2.2	9.0
Max. Al	0.10	0.07	0.10	0.16
Max. C	0.15	0.10	0.15	0.25
Max. Fe	0.13	0.12	0.15	0.25
Max. Mg	0.08	0.80	0.08	0.08
Max. Si	0.06	0.80	0.08	0.08
Max. each other	0.04	0.04	0.04	0.10

Source: Brush Wellman Inc., National Stockpile Purchase Specifications P-110a-R1, March 25, 1983 and P-110B, October 18, 1985.

ANALYSIS OF A 99.5% BeO CERAMIC THERMALOX 995

Impurity (ppm)	
Al	46
Fe	32
Cr	8
Mn	<2
Ni	9
B	2
Ca	31
Co	<1
Cu	3
Si	1,861
Mg	992
Li	2
Zn	<20
Ti	5
Cd	nd
Na	173
Ag	<1
Mo	<3
Pb	2

Source: Brush Wellman Inc.

PRODUCERS & WORLD TRADE: The number of suppliers is extremely limited with the United States the sole producer of bertrandite. Although the overall market is small, a large proportion enters international trade.

Production of beryl

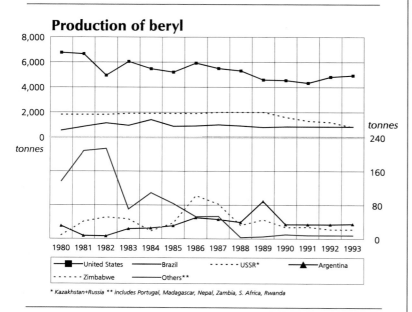

United States — **Brazil** — **- - - - - USSR*** — **▲ Argentina** — **- - - - - Zimbabwe** — **Others****

** Kazakhstan+Russia ** includes Portugal, Madagascar, Nepal, Zambia, S. Africa, Rwanda*

PRICES: Beryl ore $78-85/stu (short ton unit or the amount of material that contains 20 lb. BeO). Beryllium:- vacuum cast ingot $678/kg (98.5% pure); metal powder $650/kg (98.5% pure). Beryllium oxide powder $160/kg. Beryllium-copper master alloy $352/kg contained Be. Beryllium-copper alloy:- $12.14-13.86/kg (casting alloy); $22.53/kg (rod, bar, wire); $20.35/kg (strip). Beryllium-aluminum alloy $572/kg.

HTS CODES: 2617.90.0030 (ore & conc.); 2825.90.1000 (beryllium oxide or hydroxide); 7405.00.6030 (beryllium-copper master alloy); 8112.11.6000 (unwrought beryllium); 8112.19.0000 (wrought beryllium); 8112.11.30000 (beryllium waste and scrap).

ETYMOLOGY: Aquamarine from the Latin *aqua marina = seawater* alluding to its pale bluish-green color. **Barylite** from the Greek *barys = heavy* or *dense, lithos = stone*. **Bertrandite** for Marcel Alexandre Bertrand (1847-1907), French mineralogist. **Beryl** from the Greek *beryllos of* uncertain etymology applied to beryl and green gems. **Chrysoberyl** from the Greek *chrysos = golden* or *yellow* plus *beryllos = beryl*. **Heliodor** from the Greek *helios = sun* — "gift of the sun". **Morganite** for John Pierpont Morgan, American banker and gem enthusiast. **Phenacite** from the Greek *phenax = to cheat* since it was often mistaken for quartz.

POSTSCRIPT: The American Bicycle Manufacturing Co., of St. Cloud, Minnesota, made a bicycle frame from beryllium that weighed less than 5 kg compared with 11 kg for steel and almost 9 kg for aluminum. The bad news is that it cost $25,000.

Beryllium price history

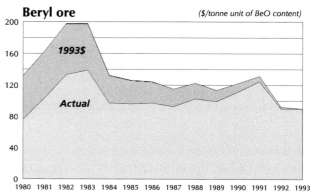

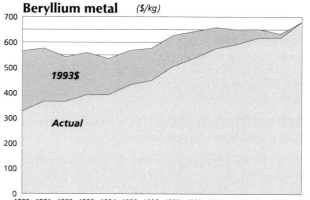

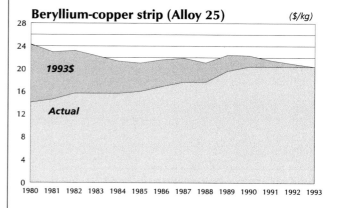

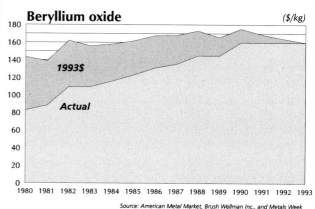

Source: American Metal Market, Brush Wellman Inc., and Metals Week

Minerals	Formula	%B$_2$O$_3$	Color	SG	H
Borax (tincal)	Na$_2$B$_4$O$_7$·10H$_2$O	36.5	white (blue/green)	1.7	2.0-2.5
Kernite	Na$_2$B$_4$O$_7$·4H$_2$O	51.0	white	1.95	3
Ulexite	NaCaB$_5$O$_9$·8H$_2$O	43.0	white	1.95	3
Probertite	NaCaB$_5$O$_9$·5H$_2$O	49.6	white	2.14	3.5
Colemanite	Ca$_2$B$_6$O$_{11}$·5H$_2$O	50.8	colorless/white	2.4	4.0-4.5
Priceite (Pandermite)	Ca$_4$B$_{10}$O$_{19}$·7H$_2$O	49.8	white	2.42	3-3.5
Hydroboracite	CaMgBO$_8$(OH)$_6$·3H$_2$O	50.5	white	2.16	2-3
Datolite	CaBSiO$_4$(OH)	21.8	colorless/pale green, yellow	2.8-3.0	5-5.5
Szaibelyite	MgBO$_3$(OH)	41.4	white/straw yellow	2.6	3-3.5

Commercial products	Formula	%B$_2$O$_3$
Borax decahydrate	Na$_2$B$_4$O$_7$·10H$_2$O	36.5
Borax pentahydrate	Na$_2$B$_4$O$_7$·5H$_2$O	47.8
Boric acid	H$_3$BO$_3$	56.3
Anhydrous borax	Na$_2$B$_4$O$_7$	69.2
Sodium octaborate	Na$_2$B$_8$O$_{13}$	82.0
Anhydrous boric acid	B$_2$O$_3$	100.0
Elemental boron	B	321.8

Less common or alternative names include rasorite for kernite, pandermite for priceite, kramerite for probertite, ascharite for szaibelite, mohavite for tincalconite, and boronatrocalcite for ulexite.

PROPERTIES & USES: Source of chemical B$_2$O$_3$ either in the form of borax (sodium) concentrates, decahydrate, pentahydrate, or anhydrous borax; colemanite (calcium) concentrate; datolite (calcium) concentrate; ulexite (sodium-calcium) concentrate; or boric acid (hydrous or anhydrous) or numerous boron chemicals manufactured from the ores. Kernite (sodium) concentrate is used in California as a feedstock for boric acid.

The largest consumer of boron is the glass industry where it alters thermal expansion, durability, melting rate (flux), devitrification, and optical properties (increases the refractive index). Na-borate or boric acid (no or low Ca) for borosilicate glass or PYREX, a specialty glass with high chemical resistance and a low expansion coefficient [chemical process plant; cookware; glass fiber; laboratory glassware; pharmacy glass; vacuum flasks]. Na-, Ca-borates, or boric acid may be used in insulation fiberglass [thermal insulation] and Ca-borate or boric acid (low or no Na) in textile-grade fiberglass [glass-reinforced plastics]. B$_2$O$_3$ content of common glass types is shown in the table. Boron has similar effects in the ceramics field [porcelain enamels, frits, glazes].

Tincal concentrate feedstock → anhydrous borax [borosilicate glass; fertilizers; fiberglass (insulation); metallurgical fluxing, brazing and soldering; porcelain enamels, frits and glazes]; → borax decahydrate/pentahydrate [high-grade cement; detergent, soaps, and cleansers; electrical insulation; fertilizer; fiberglass (insulation); fire retardants; glazes; herbicide; leather tanning; paper; pharmaceuticals/cosmetics; textile dyes; toilet preparations; water softener wood preservative]; → boric acid (see below); → disodium octaborate [fire retardant; wood preservative; fertilizer]; sodium metaborate [photography; textile finishing; herbicide]; → sodium pentaborate [fertilizer; fire retardant]; → sodium perborate [dentifrices; disinfectant; mouthwash; soaps/detergents; textile bleach and dyes].

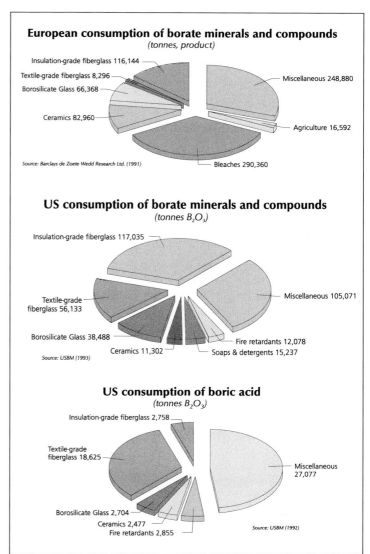

European consumption of borate minerals and compounds
(tonnes, product)

Insulation-grade fiberglass 116,144
Textile-grade fiberglass 8,296
Borosilicate Glass 66,368
Ceramics 82,960
Miscellaneous 248,880
Agriculture 16,592
Bleaches 290,360

Source: Barclays de Zoete Wedd Research Ltd. (1991)

US consumption of borate minerals and compounds
(tonnes B$_2$O$_3$)

Insulation-grade fiberglass 117,035
Textile-grade fiberglass 56,133
Borosilicate Glass 38,488
Ceramics 11,302
Miscellaneous 105,071
Fire retardants 12,078
Soaps & detergents 15,237

Source: USBM (1993)

US consumption of boric acid
(tonnes B$_2$O$_3$)

Insulation-grade fiberglass 2,758
Textile-grade fiberglass 18,625
Borosilicate Glass 2,704
Ceramics 2,477
Fire retardants 2,855
Miscellaneous 27,077

Source: USBM (1992)

BORATE LEADERS

Producers Minerals	Exporters Minerals	Importers Minerals	Producers Boric acid	Exporters Boric acid	Importers Boric acid
United States	Turkey	Netherlands	United States	United States	Japan
Turkey	United States	France	France	Chile	Germany
Chile	Chile	Italy	Italy	Former USSR	France
Former USSR	Former USSR	Japan	Chile	France	Belgium
Argentina	Argentina	Spain	Former USSR	Italy	United Kingdom
Bolivia	Bolivia	United States	China	Turkey	Italy
Peru	Peru	Mexico	Turkey	Argentina	Spain
China	China	Canada	Argentina	Bolivia	Netherlands
		Brazil	Japan	Peru	Taiwan
		Korea	India		Korea
		Taiwan	Bolivia		Canada
		Australia	Peru		Mexico

Colemanite concentrate [fiberglass (textile-grade); metallurgy] → sodium perborate [see above]; → boric acid [see below].

Ulexite [fertilizer; glass; fiberglass (insulation); metallurgical flux; wood preservative]; → synthetic colemanite [fiberglass (textile-grade); metallurgy]; → boric acid [see below].

Datolite [frits; glass]; → boric acid [see below] → synthetic colemanite [fiberglass (textile-grade); metallurgy]; → disodium octaborate [fire retardant; wood preservative; fertilizer].

Tincal, colemanite, ulexite, kernite → boric acid [antiseptics; borosilicate glass; catalyst (air oxidation of hydrocarbons); fiberglass (insulation and textile-grade); nuclear applications; pharmaceuticals & cosmetics; photography; porcelain enamels, frits, glazes; liquid SO_3 stabilizer; textile treating] → ammonium pentaborate & tetraborate [fireproofing]; zinc borate [flame retardants; fungicide].

Boric acid as an intermediate or feedstock → ammonium tetraborate [fireproofing; neutralizing agent]; → boron metal [abrasives; delay fuses; aluminum refining; nuclear shielding; solar batteries; semiconductors; feedstock for boron phosphide; hexaboron silicide, tetraboron silicide]; → boron carbide (B_4C) [loose-grain lapping abrasive; nuclear control rods; wear-resistant parts (e.g. nozzles)]; → boron fiber [sporting goods]; → boron nitride [boron fibers; high-temp. lubricant; refractory; thermionic devices]; boron phsophate [ultra low loss dielectric]; → boron tribromide/diborane [high-energy fuels; higher boron hydrides; polymerization catalyst for ethylene]; → boron trichloride [feedstock for boron trifluoride, diborane, organoboron compounds; flux; polymerization agent for driers; liquid SO_3 stabilizer]; → boron trifluoride [catalyst; neutron analysis]; → cubic boron nitride (CBN) [superabrasive]; → cupric metaborate [fireproofing; fungicide; pigment]; → ferroboron [transformers]; → lead borate [lead glass; paint]; → lithium tetraborate [ceramics]; → fluoboric acid [feedstock for various fluoborates]; potassium borates [casein solvent; feedstock for boron compounds; metallurgical welding & brazing; photography]; → zinc borate [ceramics; fire retardant; fungicide; pharmaceuticals].

QUALITY & SPECIFICATIONS: Ore is purchased and priced based on the B_2O_3 content. Calcined colemanite conc. contains approx. 42% B_2O_3 with As (penalty element) ranging from 30 to 2,000 ppm; technical grade boric acid contains 56.3% B_2O_3. Glass use requires a low content of coloring metals such as Fe, Co, Ni, Cu, & Ti. Typical analyses are given in the tables.

WORLD CAPACITY: 1.4M. t B_2O_3.

CAPACITY UTILIZATION: Approx. 60%.

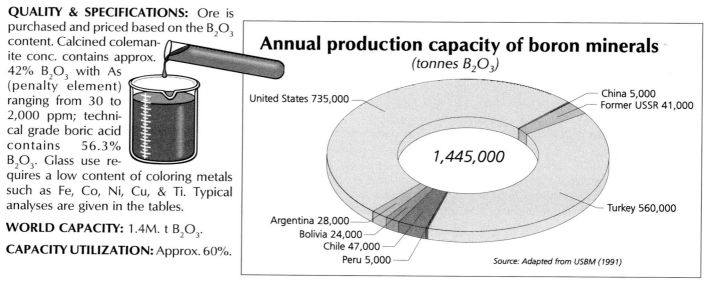

Annual production capacity of boron minerals
(tonnes B_2O_3)

1,445,000

United States 735,000

China 5,000
Former USSR 41,000

Turkey 560,000

Argentina 28,000
Bolivia 24,000
Chile 47,000
Peru 5,000

Source: Adapted from USBM (1991)

TYPICAL BORON CONTENT BY GLASS TYPE (% BY WEIGHT)

Container glass - white	—
Container glass - green	—
Flat glass	—
Pressed ware	—
Boro-silicate glass	12.9
Lead-crystal glass	0.025
CRT faceplate	—
Fiber optics	22.0
Glass ceramics	—
Textile fiberglass	
A-Glass $(Al_2O_3+Fe_2O_3)$	—
C-Glass $(Al_2O_3+Fe_2O_3)$	5.0
D-Glass	22.5
E-Glass	7.5
R-Glass	—
S-Glass	—
AR-Glass	—

TYPICAL CHEMISTRY OF GLASS TYPES CONTAINING BORON (% BY WEIGHT)

	Container glass	Fiber-glass E	Boro-silicate glass	Lead-crystal glass	Fiber optics
SiO_2	72.0	54.5	80.2	60.0	61.0
Al_2O_3	2.0	14.5	2.4	0.02	3.0
Na_2O	14.0	{0.8	4.2	1.0	14.0
K_2O	—	—	—	14.9	—
CaO	10.0	17.0	0.1	0.2	—
MgO	—	4.5	—	—	—
B_2O_3	7.0	7.5	12.9	0.025	22.0
Fe_2O_3	—	0.5	—	—	—
PbO	—	—	—	31.4	—
TiO_2	—	0.1	—	—	—
SO_3	1.0	—	—	—	—

Source: Adapted from various & Bourne, 1994

COMPOSITION OF GLASS AND CERAMIC FIBERS CONTAINING BORON (% BY WEIGHT)

	C-Glass	D-Glass	E-Glass	Ceramic fibers
SiO_2	65.0	74.0	54.5	52.9
Al_2O_3	{ 4.0	—	14.5	45.1
Fe_2O_3	{	0.2	0.5	<0.1
B_2O_3	5.0	22.5	7.5	0.08
CaO	14.0	0.5	17.0	—
MgO	3.0	0.2	4.5	—
Na_2O	0.5	1.0	{0.8	<0.2
K_2O	8.0	1.5	{—	—
BaO	1.0	NA	NA	—
TiO_2	NA	NA	0.1	1.7

MARKETING FACTORS: Influenced by the economy generally and the construction industry specifically. Supply dominated by limited number of large producers with extensive deep-sea trade, although South America and former USSR increasing influence in the market. Consumption dominated by industrialized regions and growing elsewhere.

SUBSTITUTES & ALTERNATIVES: Chemically the only source of B_2O_3. Major competition in the form supplied, i.e. borax, colemanite, synthetic colemanite, ulexite, or boric acid. **Cleansers & detergents**: phosphates, silica (sodium silicate), soda ash, sodium sulfate, zeolites. **Fire Retardant:**- ATH, antimony oxide, asbestos, bromine, chromite, diatomite, magnesite & magnesia, perlite, phosphates, pumice, vermiculite. **Insulation (replacing fiberglass):**- asbestos, diatomite, foamed glass, metals, or cement, perlite, pumice, vermiculite, wollastonite, zeolites.

RECYCLING: Virtually none except for recycled glass (cullet). Extracting the B_2O_3 value is difficult and uneconomical because of the need to segregate borosilicate glass from other glass types, separate the fiberglass from the resin, and the relatively small boron content involved.

PRODUCERS & WORLD TRADE: Turkey based on borax, colemanite, & ulexite ore, the United States on borax, South America on ulexite, and Russia on datolite dominate world supply. Because of the limited number of suppliers, considerable tonnages of borate concentrates, chemicals, or boric acid enter world trade.

PRICES: Anhydrous borax $720/t (99-99.5% B_2O_3, bulk, ex-works); $765/t (99-99.5% B_2O_3, bags, ex-works); $1,275-1,360/t (bags, del. UK).

Borax decahydrate $257/t (99.5% B_2O_3, bulk, ex-works); $302/t (99% B_2O_3, bags, ex-works); $680-765/t (granular, technical, del. UK). Borax pentahydrate $294/t (99.5% B_2O_3, bulk, ex-works); $339/t (99.5% B_2O_3, bags, ex-works); $600-690/t (granular, technical, del. UK).

Boric acid (granular, technical, 99.9% B_2O_3, ex-works) $708/t (bulk) $753/t (bags).

Colemanite (Turkey, 40-42% B_2O_3, lump) $270/t (CIF USA).

Synthetic colemanite (Chile, 40-42% B_2O_3, ground, bags) $360-400/t (FOB Arica, Chile). Ulexite (Turkey, 37% B_2O_3) $230/t (CIF USA).

PRODUCTION AND TRADE IN BORATE MINERALS (TONNES, GROSS WEIGHT)

	Production	Imports	Exports	Apparent Consumption	Net Supplier	Net Consumer
North America	1,250,000	260,000	300,000	1,210,000	40,000	
South America	229,000		90,000	139,000	90,000	
European Union		1,280,000	450,400	829,600		(829,600)
Non-EU Europe	1,310,000		911,000	399,000	911,000	
Australasia	27,000	215,000	1,600	240,400		(213,400)

Numbers are approximate and rounded for 1991 or thereabouts

PRODUCTION AND TRADE IN BORIC ACID (TONNES, GROSS WEIGHT)

	Production	Imports	Exports	Apparent Consumption	Net Supplier	Net Consumer
North America	138,000	14,500	47,000	105,500	32,500	
South America	36,000		32,000	4,000	32,000	
European Union	77,000	65,000	43,000	99,000		(22,000)
Non-EU Europe	58,000		12,000	46,000	12,000	
Australasia	28,600	36,700	3,600	61,700		(33,100)

Numbers are approximate and rounded for 1991 or thereabouts

Ammonium pentaborate $2,090/t (granular, bags, ex-works). Potassium tetraborate (ex-works) $3.08/kg (granular, bags); $3.19/kg (granular, drums); $3.41/kg (powder, bags); $3.52/kg (powder, drums). Boron trichloride (FOB works, cylinders) $16.68/kg. Boron trifluoride (FOB works) $11.55-14.63/kg (cylinders); $10/t (bulk). Fluoboric acid (drums, ex-works, freight equalized) $2.25/kg. Lead fluoborate (liquid conc., drums, ex-works, freight equalized) $2.20/kg. Potassium bromohydride (powder, drums, ex-works) $59.60-65.00/kg. Sodium borate $1.14/kg (NF, granular or powder, bags, ex-works). Sodium borohydride (ex-works) $51/15.kg (powder, drums); $42/kg (stabilized water solution, 12% $NaBH_4$, tankwagon). Sodium metaborate (granular, bags, ex-works) $1.00/kg (octahydrate); $1.40 (tetrahydrate). Sodium perborate tetrahydrate $0.80/kg (bags, ex-works). Zinc borate (technical, drums, ex-works) $2.40/kg.

HTS CODES: 2440.11.0000 (anhydrous refined borax); 2840.19.0000 (other refined borax); 2840.30.0010 (sodium perborate); 2840.30.0050 (other perborates); 2810.00.00 (boric acid); 2528.90.0010 (natural Ca borates); 2528.10.0010 (natural Na borates); 2528.90.0050 (other natural borates);

ETYMOLOGY: Boracite is derived from *borax*. **Borax** from the Persian *burah* and Arabic *buraq*, both old names for the mineral. **Colemanite** for William Tell Coleman (1824-1893), a borate developer in California. **Kernite** for Kern County, California. **Meyerhofferite** for Wilhelm Meyerhoffer (1864-1906), German chemist. **Priceite** for Thomas Price (b. 1837?), Welsh-American mineralogist. **Probertite** for Frank Holman Probert (1876-1940), Dean of the Mining College, University of California. **Sassolite** for Sasso, Tuscany, Italy where first observed, Greek *lithos = stone*. **Szaibelyite** for Stephan Szaibely (1777-1855), Hungarian mine surveyor of Rézbánya.

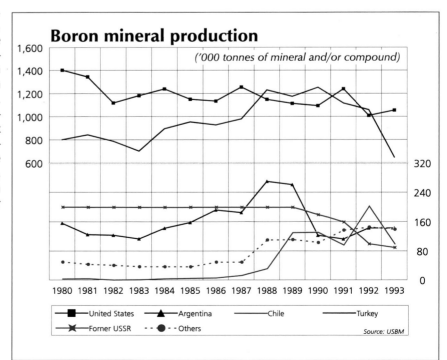

Boron mineral production
('000 tonnes of mineral and/or compound)

Legend: United States, Argentina, Chile, Turkey, Former USSR, Others

Source: USBM

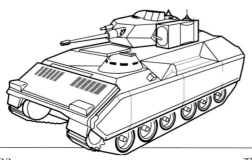

BORATE PRICE HISTORY

Borax pentahydrate
(granular, 99.9%, bulk, ex-work, USA)

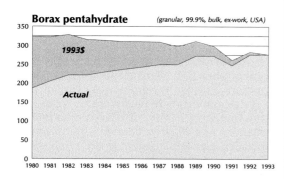

Borax decahydrate
(granular, 99.5%, bulk, ex-work, USA)

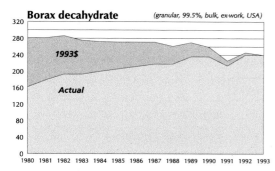

Anhydrous borax
(granular, 99.5%, bulk, ex-work, USA)

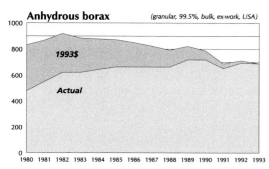

Colemanite
(FOB E. USA)

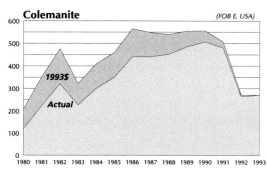

Boric acid
(granular, 99.9% bulk, ex-works, USA)

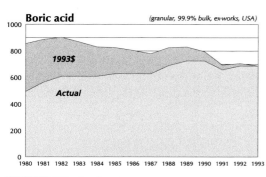

SODIUM BORATES

	Turkey	USA	USA	USA
		Borax	Borax	
		decahydrate	pentahydrate	Borax
		standard	technical	anhydrous
	Tincal			
	Etibank	NACC	US Borax	NACC
B_2O_3	32-34	38.6	48.8	68.8
Na_2O	15.0	16.7	21.7	30.6
Water of X'tion	NA	45.6	29.5	NA
Cl	NA	0.04	3.2	NA
SO_4	NA	NA	<0.05	0.03
Fe_2O_3	NA	NA	0.30	0.0005

Colemanite	Turkey	Turkey	Turkey	Chile
	Bigadiç	Espey	Hisarçik	Arica
	Etibank	Etibank	Etibank	Quiborax
B_2O_3	40-42	40-42	40-42	42
CaO	NA	24-26	24-26	33
Na_2O-K_2O	NA	NA	NA	0.4 max
SiO_2	NA	NA	NA	3.0 max
As_2O_3 (ppm)	100	1,200	3,500	150 max
Fe_2O_3	0.03-0.07	0.3-0.4	NA	0.10 max

Washed ulexite	Chile
	Quiborax
	Typical
B_2O_3	39.82
H_3BO_3	69.99
Na_2O	7.14
CaO	12.44
SO_4	1.97
Cl	0.72
Fe_2O_3	0.18
Al_2O_3	0.81
As	<0.01

Boric acid	USA	Chile	Chile	USA
	Technical	Technical	Tech Glass	Anhydrous HP
	NACC	Quiborax	Quiborax	US Borax
H_3BO_3	100	99.5	99.9	99.0
SO_4	0.08	NA	NA	
SO_3 (ppm)	NA	600	150	
Cl (ppm)	65	250	50	
Fe_2O_3 (ppm)	NA	10	10	
Na				0.1 max
CaO	NA	NA	NA	0.03 max
SiO_2				0.3 max
MgO	NA	NA	NA	0.03 max
Al_2O_3	NA	NA	NA	0.2 max

Source: Company literature

No commercial bromine minerals are known, and supplies are from natural sodium bromide in seawater (average 60-65 ppm bromine) and brines (e.g. 5,000 ppm in Arkansas and 14,000 ppm in waste brines in Israel).

PROPERTIES & USES: Along with fluorine, chlorine, iodine, and astatine, bromine is part of the halogen family. Elemental bromine is a dark red liquid with bleaching and disinfectant properties [analytical reagent; clear brine drilling fluids; sanitary preparations for water treatment & swimming pools; manufacture of dyes, inks, resins, & rubber products; high-intensity light bulbs]. The starting point for a number of commercial chemicals ➔ tetrabromobisphenol-A, decabromodiphenyl oxide, bromotrifluoromethane, bromochlorodifluoromethane, vinyl chloride, ammonium bromide [all fire retardants used in polymer systems including epoxies, high-impact polystyrenes, ABS, and polyurethanes]; ➔ calcium bromide [high-density, solids-free completion, packer, and workover drilling fluids; sedative in pharmaceuticals; photography; intermediate in production of organic calcium compounds]; ➔ ethyl bromide [intermediate synthesis in the manufacture of dyes, fragrances, vitamins, & pharmaceuticals]; ➔ ethylene dibromide (EDB) [additive as a lead scavenger in leaded gasoline; reagent in the synthesis of dyes & pharmaceuticals; anesthetic, sedative, and antispasmodic agent]; ➔ methyl bromide [agriculture fumigant; herbicide, insecticide, rodenticide; soil sterilant; space fumigant]; ➔ potassium bromate [photographic development; sedative; bread additive]; ➔ potassium or sodium bromide ➔ silver bromide [emulsions for photographic film, plates, and papers]; ➔ sodium bromate [neutralizer in permanent wave preparations; cellulose bleach; sedative; malting beer]; ➔ zinc bromide [high-density, solids-free completion, packer, and workover drilling fluids; sink-float separation; gamma radiation shield].

QUALITY & SPECIFICATIONS: *Purified grade elemental bromine:-* >99.7% bromine, no iodine, <0.1% chlorine, and an SG of not less than 3.1 at 10° - 20°C.

Technical bromine:- 99.5% pure with low chlorine, moisture, and organic matter.

USP and analytical grade:- 0.3% chlorine, 0.05% iodine, 0.002% sulfur (0.006% SO_4), and no more organic matter in 1ml than will saturate 50 ml of 5% NaOH solution.

WORLD CAPACITY: 520,000 t. **CAPACITY UTILIZATION:** 80%.

MARKET CONDITIONS: Declining slightly, especially as a fuel additive.

MARKETING FACTORS: level of no-lead gasoline production/ fire regulations/health & safety.

HEALTH & SAFETY: Liquid bromine attacks the skin and relatively low concentrations of bromine vapor irritate the eyes and respiratory system. Vapor concentrations of 500 to 1,000 ppm by volume are fatal on short exposure and 40 - 60 ppm is dangerous on exposure for 30 minutes to 1 hour. The maximum safe exposure for 8 hours is less than 1 ppm at which level bromine can be detected by odor. Gaseous bromine is neutralized with controlled amounts of gaseous ammonia, bromine spills by a solution of sodium thiosulfate. Methyl bromine has been assigned an ozone depletion potential (ODP) of 0.44 - 0.69; The Clean Air Act of 1990 requires a production phaseout by the year 2000 of any substance with an ODP of 0.2 or greater. In 1993 the EPA ordered a phaseout by the year 2000 of the pesticide methyl bromide. The health effects of several brominated substances including bromoform, methyl bromide, and vinyl bromide are under investigation by regulatory authorities. The EPA granted an exemption to several states for the use of bromoxynil to control weeds in rice. Halons, CFCs that contain bromine, have been caught up with the CFC phaseout (see fluorspar).

BROMINE LEADERS

Producers	Exporters	Importers
United States	Israel	Netherlands
Israel	United Kingdom	France
Former USSR	United States	United Kingdom
United Kingdom	Germany	Germany
France	Netherlands	Belgium
Japan	Belgium	Canada
China	Italy	Italy
India	Canada	United States
Germany	Mexico	Hungary
Italy	Argentina	South Korea
Spain	Brazil	Mexico
	Colombia	India
	Peru	Israel
	Venezuela	Spain

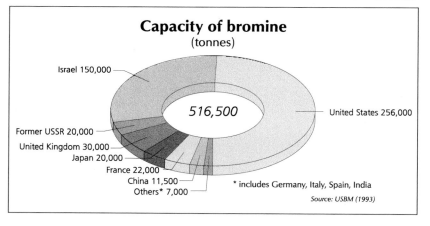

Capacity of bromine
(tonnes)

516,500

Israel 150,000
United States 256,000
Former USSR 20,000
United Kingdom 30,000
Japan 20,000
France 22,000
China 11,500
Others* 7,000

* includes Germany, Italy, Spain, India

Source: USBM (1993)

SUBSTITUTES & ALTERNATIVES: Chemical & sanitation:- chlorine and iodine. **Fire retardant:-** ATH, antimony oxide, asbestos, borates, chromite, diatomite, magnesite & magnesia, perlite, phosphates, pumice, vermiculite. **Gasoline additive:-** aniline and several alcohols. **Halon 1301:-** perfluorobutane, perfluoropropane as fire retardants.

RECYCLING: Bromine contained in the waste from various processes may be reprocessed through absorption towers to yield elemental bromine. Hydrogen bromide derived from elemental bromination may be cleaned up and recovered.

PRODUCERS & WORLD TRADE: Production is confined to about a dozen countries which generate international trade.

PRICES: Ammonium bromide (N.F., granular, drums, carlots or truckloads, FOB works) $2.42-2.88/kg. Sodium bromide $1.54/kg (tech., bags, ex-works). Bromine (ex-works) $1.23-1.50/kg (bulk tank cars); 2.70/kg (drums, truckloads). Bromochloromethane $2.80 (bulk, FOB Magnolia, AR). Ethyl bromide $2.80/kg tech., 98%, drums, truckloads). Ethylene dibromide $2.09/kg (drums, carlots); $1.25/kg (tank deliveries). Hydrobromic acid $0.92/kg (48%, drums, carlots, truckloads, FOB). Hydrogen bromide $10.45/kg (anhydrous, cylinders, truckloads). Lithium bromide $15.30-16.68/kg (anhydrous, drums, delivered). Magnesium bromide hexahydrate $5.50/kg (drums). Methyl bromide $1.70/kg (tank cars). Potassium bromohydride $59.60-65.00/kg (powder, drums, ex-works). Sodium bromide $1.54/kg (bags, ex-works). Potassium bromate $3.94/kg (granular, powder, ex-works). Potassium bromide $$2.42-2.46/kk (NF, granular, powder, drums, FOB works).

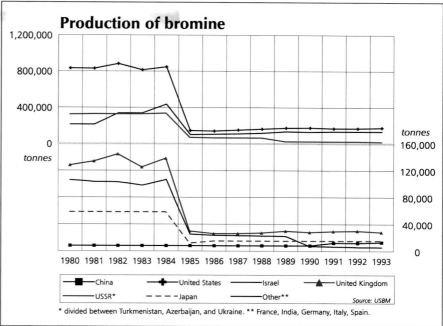

Production of bromine

China — United States — Israel — United Kingdom — USSR* — Japan — Other**

Source: USBM

* divided between Turkmenistan, Azerbaijan, and Ukraine. ** France, India, Germany, Italy, Spain.

HTS CODES: 2801.30.20 (bromine); 2811.19.50.50 (hydrobromic acid); 2827.51.20 (potassium bromide); 2827.59.05 (ammonium bromide); 2827.59.20 (calcium bromide); 2829.90.10.00 (potassium bromate); 2829.90.50 (sodium bromate); 2827.51.10 (sodium bromide); 2903.30.05 (ethylene dibromide); 2903.30.15.20 (methyl bromide); 2903.40.0020 (chlorobromodifluormethane); 2903.59.05 (dibromoethyldibromocycloxethane);2905.50.50 (dibromo-meopentyl glycol); 2908.10.25 (tetrabromobisphenol); 290930.07 (decabromdiphenyl oxide and octabromdiphenyl oxide).

ETYMOLOGY: Bromine from the Greek *bromos* = *stench* in reference to its characteristic odor. **Bromargyrite** from the Greek *bromos* = *stench* and *argyros* = *silver* alluding to composition.

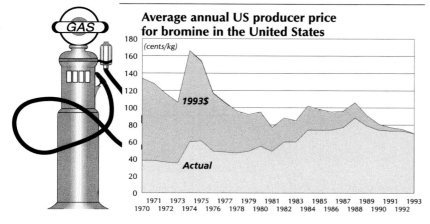

Average annual US producer price for bromine in the United States

(cents/kg)

1993$

Actual

APPARENT CONSUMPTION OF BROMINE (TONNES)

	Apparent Consumption
United States	174,812
Israel	95,214
Former USSR	60,000
United Kingdom	30,836
France	25,514
Japan	15,000
Netherlands	10,054
Germany	5,750

NOTE: Numbers are approximate and rounded; absence of a country does not necessarily indicate no production or trade; absence of a number does not necessarily mean zero

Source: British Geological Survey

PRODUCTION AND TRADE IN BROMINE (TONNES)

	Production	Imports	Exports	Apparent Consumption	Net Supplier	Net Consumer
North America	177,000	2,441	2,943	176,497	503	
South America		35		35		(35)
European Union	47,000	34,187	5,062	76,126		(29,126)
Non-EU Europe	60,000	527		60,527		(527)
Australasia	16,505	351		16,856		(351)
Middle East	127,000	99	31,885	95,214	31,786	
Africa		21		21		(21)

NOTE: Numbers are approximate and rounded for 1990 or thereabout; data for Africa incomplete   Source: British Geological Survey

CARBONATE ROCKS including cement & lime

Carbonate rocks including limestone, chalk, marble, carbonatite, vein calcite, travertine, shells, aragonite sand, and dolomite, contain calcium carbonate, aragonite, and/or dolomite; magnesite and iron carbonates are covered separately.

Minerals	Formula	Color	%CaO	%CO$_2$	%MgO	SG	H
Calcite	CaCO$_3$	white-gray	56	44	-	2.7	3.0
Aragonite	CaCO$_3$	white	56	44	-	2.9	3.5-4.0
Dolomite	CaMg(CO$_3$)$_2$	white-gray	30.4	47.7	21.9	2.8-2.9	3.5-4.0

PROPERTIES & USES: Most carbonate rocks have widespread availability at relatively low cost.

PHYSICAL: Limestone and dolomite (and very rarely marble) may be crushed for use as an aggregate, concrete ingredient, ballast, fill, etc. based on strength/hardness (related to density, porosity, and homogeneity), particle shape (after crushing should be as cubic as possible with no laminations or incipient cracks), chemical soundness (minimum soluble minerals like sulfates), and a lack of dusts and fines such as clay, silt, and soil. In general, limestone is not used in high-wear sites or for major highways because of its inferior hardness factors (average values for the aggregates are given in the table).

Dimension stone has color/aesthetics, compressive & flexural strength, resistance to abrasion, staining, & weathering (marble and some limestones). In commercial terms, marble can include such things as onyx, travertine, and verde antique as well as recrystallized limestone and dolomite.

All the carbonates may be ground and used as inert pigments or fillers (ground calcium carbonate or "whiting") in numerous manufactured products. Characteristics of natural CaCO$_3$ are given in the table. Specifications range from relatively crude & cheap fillers contributing bulk & weight [asphalt; carpet backing; joint cement] through intermediate grades also contributing whiteness & brightness (80%+) with a medium particle size [putty, caulks, and sealants] to fine and ultrafine grades that are truly "functional fillers" with specific requirements in terms of purity, brightness (>90%), opacity, particle shape, APS & PSD, surface area, rheological properties & viscosity, water & oil absorption, bulk density [paper; paint; plastics; rubber]. Details are provided under quality & specifications. Calcium carbonate reduces the quantity of pigment material required in paint, and reduces the demand for the polymer and elastomer in plastics and rubber.

Still finer and purer grades are from precipitated calcium carbonate (PCC) made by recarbonizing calcined limestone to precipitate out CaCO$_3$ (see below) [paper; plastics]. Surface coated calcium carbonate is used in some industries, for example in plastics it encourages dispersion in polymers and in paint it reduces sedimentation, prevents the flotation of color pigments, and contributes to the full tinting power of the paint.

CHEMICAL: Carbonate rocks are used as a source of chemical lime (CaO) and magnesia (MgO) for a number of chemical process industries that require neutralization, coagulation, causticization, dehydration, and/or absorption. Alternatively, calcining carbonate rocks at 1,000-1,1000°C yield lime including quicklime (CaO), hydrated or slaked (Ca(OH)$_2$), dolomitic quicklime (CaO·MgO), type N dolomitic hydrate (Ca(OH)$_2$·MgO), type S dolomitic hydrate (Ca(OH)$_2$·Mg(OH)$_2$), and dead-burned dolomite or "refractory lime". This is also the basic chemical procedure to produce precipitated calcium carbonate (PCC).

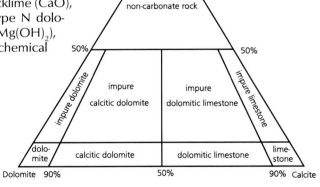

Other Minerals (mostly insolubles)

non-carbonate rock

impure dolomite / impure limestone

impure calcitic dolomite | impure dolomitic limestone

dolomite | calcitic dolomite | dolomitic limestone | limestone

Dolomite 90% — 50% — 90% Calcite

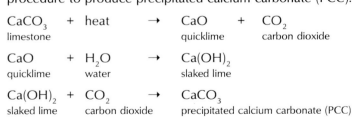

CaCO$_3$ + heat → CaO + CO$_2$
limestone _ _ quicklime _ carbon dioxide

CaO + H$_2$O → Ca(OH)$_2$
quicklime _ water _ slaked lime

Ca(OH)$_2$ + CO$_2$ → CaCO$_3$
slaked lime _ carbon dioxide _ precipitated calcium carbonate (PCC)

In many industries, either the carbonate rock or lime (the more reactive of the two materials) may be used as the source of CaO (and MgO). Lime or limestone acts as a flux and scavenger removing P, Si, Al, and S in the reduction of iron ores (60-65kg lime/t steel in BOF and 30kg/t in electric furnace and mini-mill) [ferrous smelting]; controls pH in flotation and reduces cyanide loss in leaching [nonferrous metallurgy]; causticizes sodium carbonate solutions to regenerate NaOH and remove silica in the Bayer process [aluminum refining]; used in the manufacture of magnesia [Dow seawater and natural brine process; seawater magnesia process]; reacts with SO$_2$ to form calcium bisulfite in the sulfite pulp (Kraft) process [pulp & paper]; acts as a flux & filler in glazes & enamels [ceramics]; acts as a causticizer with brine and ammonia in the Solvay process (635kg quicklime/t soda ash) [soda ash manufacture]; acts as flux, stabilizer & strengthener in lime-soda glass [flat & container glass production]; removes sulfur in gas-stack scrubbing systems [flue-gas desulfurization or FGD plants]; provides acid neutralization and alkylation, and precipitates various waste products in water systems [environmental applications; agriculture; municipal and industrial water treatment; sewage treatment]; and flocculates and precipitates colloidal impurities [sugar refining].

Hydrated lime, limestone, and dolomite are a source of CaO (and MgO) in agriculture [composting; soil liming; plant nutrient; poultry & animal feed additive] and construction [soil stabilization; masonry mortar; plaster & stucco; sand-lime bricks; bituminous paving; whitewash].

PHYSICAL PROPERTIES OF AGGREGATES BY ROCK TYPE

| | Bulk Specific Gravity | Absorption (%) | Loss of Abrasion | | |
			Deval Test (%)	LA Test (%)	Tough-ness*
Basalt	2.86	0.5	3.1	14	19
Chert	2.50	1.6	8.5	26	12
Diabase	2.96	0.3	2.6	18	20
Dolomite	2.70	1.1	5.5	25	9
Gneiss	2.74	0.3	5.9	45	9
Granite	2.65	0.3	4.3	38	9
Limestone	2.66	0.9	5.7	26	8
Marble	2.63	0.2	6.3	47	6
Quartzite	2.69	0.3	3.3	28	16
Sandstone	2.54	1.8	7.0	38	11
Schist	2.85	0.4	5.5	38	12

* height in cm for a 2 kg steel plunger to cause a rock core about 2.5 cm diameter and 2.5 cm high to fail

Source: Woolf, 1953

PHYSICAL PROPERTIES OF CALCIUM CARBONATE FILLERS

	Rhombo-hedral Calcite PCC	Scaleno-hedral Calcite PCC	Orth-rhombic Aragonite PCC	Fine-ground limestone	Ultrafine-ground limestone
Refractive index	1.58	1.58	1.63	1.58	1.58
Specific gravity	2.71	2.71	2.92	2.71	2.71
TAPPI brightness (%)	99	99	99	95	95
Surface area, m^2/g	6-8	9-15	9-13	5-7	10-12
Einlehner Abrasion (mg)	3	3-5	4-8	8	4
Particle size, SediGraph					
+5 µm (%)	-	2	3	20	3
-2 µm (%)	99	45	75	70	90
Mean, µm	0.7	1.0-3.0	0.5-1.0	2.0	0.8

Source: Trivedi and Hagemeyer, 1994

PHYSICAL PROPERTIES OF CALCIUM CARBONATE PIGMENTS

| | Natural | | Precipitated | |
	Fine-ground limestone	Ultrafine-ground limestone	Calcite	Aragonite
Specific gravity	2.71	8.71	2.71	2.93
Index of refraction, mean	1.58	1.58	1.58	1.63
Hardness, (Mohs scale)	3	3	3.0	3.5
Decomposition temp, °C	800-900	800-900	800-900	800-900
Valley Abrasion, mg	25	10	5	8
Brightness, % (GE)	95	96	98	99
Oil absorption, cc/100 g	13	23	30	55
Surface area, m²/g	3.2	9.6	6.8	8.5

Source: Trivedi and Hagemeyer, 1994

Quicklime → calcium carbide [acetylene production; calcium metal; graphite manufacture; iron & steel purification]; → calcium citrate [citric acid]; → calcium chlorate [disinfectant; feedstock for chlorine dioxide, potassium chlorate; photography; pyrotechnics]; → calcium cyclamate/calcium saccharin [sweetening agent]; → calcium cyanimide [N fertilizer].

Limestone plus the proper proportion of silica, alumina, and iron heated to 1,480°C form calcium aluminosilicate clinker; the addition of 3-5% gypsum (sulfate retards setting) and grinding produce portland cement [general construction; concrete]. Variations include white cement (high, low-iron raw materials) [decorative concrete such as terrazo, highway lane markets; architectural concrete]; masonary cement (cement with interground hydrated lime, limestone, chalk, etc.) [mortars for masonry construction]; oil-well cement remains fluid for more than 4 hours [seals on oil and gas wells]; aluminous cement or calcium aluminate cement (CAS) [refractories].

MgO as dolomite, magnesite, or MgO itself is refractory [magnesia refractories]. Dolomite is a concentrated source of chemical MgO → magnesium metal [structural uses like alloys, die casting, and wrought products; chemical desulfurization of iron & steel; reducing agent in the production of Be, Ti, Zr, Hf, and U]; → magnesium oxide [refractories; pharmaceuticals; glass; magnesium chemical feedstock; fertilizers].

COMMERCIAL OYSTER SHELLS

$CaCO_3$	93.0
Ca	37.0
CO_3	56.0
Mg	0.2
Na	0.8
Cl	0.6
Mn	85 ppm
K	131 ppm
Fe	0.15 ppm
Cu	6 ppm
Organic matter	2.8
Density (g/cm^3)	2.8
Bulk density (g/cm^3)	0.4
Oil absorption (g oil/100 g Oyta-laminar)	51.0

Source: Oytaco Ltd, Denmark

CHEMICAL COMPOSITION OF COMMERCIAL DOLOMITE & DOLOMITE PRODUCTS (%)

	Spain Stone	USA Quicklime	USA Normal hydrate	UK Dead-burned*	Norway Stone	UK Stone	Germany Stone
	glass	glass	glass	refractory	filler	roadstone	dolime
CaO	31.1	56.61	47.95	56.90	30.6	32.5	31.5
MgO	21.7	40.29	34.13	40.7	22.0	18.0	20.2
Fe_2O_3	0.10	0.13	0.11	0.9	0.03	0.8	0.4
Al_2O_3	0.02	0.29	0.25	0.5	0.05	0.6	0.4
SiO_2	0.05	0.57	0.47	1.0	0.6	2.0	0.5
LOI	47.0	-	-	-	47.0	45.1	47.0
BD	-	-	-	3.25	-	2.68	2.7

* pelletized, double-burnt (United Kingdom)

CHEMICAL COMPOSITION OF CALCIUM CARBONATE ROCKS (%)

	USA Lst filler	USA Marble filler	Italy Marble filler	USA PCC filler	USA Lst glass	USA Lst agric.	UK Calcite* terrazzo	USA Oyster shells	UK Chalk filler	UK Met. lst./ aggregate
$CaCO_3$	96	95 min.	98.05	98.4	98.0	97.1	98.64	96-98	97.18	0.5
$MgCO_3$	1.5	3.0 max.	2.34	0.7	1.3	2.0	0.44	1.0	0.46	3.8
SiO_2	1.2		0.11	0.05	0.15	NA	0.69	0.5-1.5	1.82	18.2
Al_2O_3	0.3		0.05	-	0.08	NA	0.01	0.1-0.25	0.17	5.4
Fe_2O_3	0.08	-	0.02	0.10	0.12	NA	0.03	0.1-0.15	0.10	2.1
H_2O	0.25			0.3	0	1-2.5				
Brightness	96	92-95		98	-		-	-	-	86-93

* byproduct of fluorspar & barite extraction

COMPOSITION OF ARAGONITE (%)

	Chemical analysis	US sieve #	Screen analysis retained wt%	Cumulative retained wt%
$CaCO_3$	97	20	3	3
SiO_2	0.04	30	3	6
Fe_2O_3	0.02	40	23	29
Al_2O_3	0.02	50	25	54
MgO	0.23	70	22	76
Mn	0.0005-0.005	100	12	88
Sr	0.1-1.0	140	10	98
S organic	0.13	200	2	100
S inorganic	0.01	-200	trace	
Chlorides as NaCl	0.25			
Other organics	0.41			
LOI	44.3			

SPECIFICATION OF COMMERCIAL LIME

	Lump/ granular quicklime	Hydrated lime
Dry state	CaO	$Ca(OH)_2$
CaO	94.57	96.6
$CaCO_3$	4.18	0.86
SiO_2	0.83	0.67
MgO	0.25	0.2
Al_2O_3	0.2	0.14
Fe_2O_3	0.05	0.05
Trace elements	0.1	0.08
Moisture (free)	-	0.6
As dispatched		
$Ca(OH)_2$	5.14	-
LOI	2.84	-
Neutralizing value	95.5	-
Bulk density (Kg/m³)	1,040 - 1,200	-
Loose	-	480
Compacted	-	590

Source: RMC Industrial Minerals Ltd. (UK)

PARTICLE SIZES FOR FILLER APPLICATIONS (µM)

	Mean	Top	Use
Bulk			
Coarse	22-40	420	joint cement, carpet backing, asphalt roofing
Medium	12-22	100	caulk, putty, sealants, rubber
Fine			
Fine	3-10	44	paper, paint, plastics, rubber
Ultrafine	0.7-2	10	paper, paint, plastics

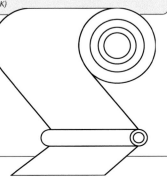

QUALITY & SPECIFICATIONS: Diverse uses have diverse quality requirements. For many uses, price, availability, and consistency are paramount.

LIMESTONE & DOLOMITE: Size requirements are: >1 meter (dimension stone), >30 cm (building stone, riprap, and armor stone), 1-20 cm (aggregate for concrete, roadstone, railway ballast, roofing granules, terrazzo, stucco), 0.2-5 cm (chemicals and glass), 3-8 cm (filter-bed stone, poultry grit), <4 cm (aglime), <3 cm (foundry and fluxstone), <0.2 mm. (filler, mild abrasive, glazes and enamels, mine dust, fungicide and insecticide carrier), <0.1 mm (FGD reagent).

Aggregate in concrete:- free from clay, mica, shale, or other platy or laminated particles, soluble sulfide or organic matter; low amorphous silica content ; 0.04-0.06% chloride.

Cement:- as low as 65% $CaCO_3$ but with low alkalis, <4% MgO, <1.5% acid insol. residue, < 0.1% F, <0.5% phosphates, zinc, and lead, <3% LOI.

Coal dust fire dampener:- <4% SiO_2, 100% -840 μm and 70% -75 μm.

Crushed stone (aggregate):- details vary by end use and region; common tests include aggregate abrasion value (AAV), aggregate crushing value (ACV); 10% fines value; aggregate impact value (AIV); polished stone value (PSV); flakiness index; specific gravity tests (bulk SG & apparent SG).

Dimension stone:- important characteristics covered by ASTM standards include water absorption/bulk specific gravity (ASTM C 97), modulus of rupture (ASTM C 99), compressive strength (ASTM C 170), abrasion resistance (ASTM C 241), flexural strength (ASTM C 880).

Environmental uses:- 85-95% $CaCO_3$ with max 5% MgO and insolubles and 100% -2mm; -200 μm for acid rain neutralization.

Fillers (typical):- dry brightness of 80%+ (putty) to 96% (paper coating); oil absorption 18-21; surface area 1.5-4 m^2/g; bulk density 0.6-0.8 g/cc (10-30 lbs/ft^3); pH 9-9.5. In plastics, additional chemical requirements include low Cu, Pb, and Mn content since these elements inhibit vulcanization and aging, and <0.005% CuO, <0.02% MnO (for children's toys).

TYPICAL CaO AND MgO CONTENT BY GLASS TYPE (% BY WEIGHT)

	CaO	MgO
Container glass - white	11.3	0.1
Container glass - green	11.4	0.1
Flat glass	8.2	4.0
Pressed ware	6.2	4.4
Borosilicate glass	0.1	—
Lead-crystal glass	0.2	—
CRT faceplate	3.5	3.5
Fiber optics	—	—
Glass ceramics	2.7	—
Textile fiberglass		
A-Glass	9.0	3.5
C-Glass	14.0	3.0
D-Glass	0.5	0.2
E-Glass	17.0	4.5
R-Glass	9.0	6.0
S-Glass	—	10.0
AR-Glass	—	—

SPECIFICATIONS FOR LIMESTONE & DOLOMITE USED IN GLASS (%)

Chemical	Flat glass Limestone	Flat glass Dolomite	Container glass Limestone	Container glass Dolomite
CaO min.	54.85	29.5	-	-
MgO	0.80 max.	21.40 min.	±0.3	±0.3
Acid insol max.	0.6	0.6		
Fe_2O_3, max.	0.075	0.25	0.1	0.1
Al_2O_3, max.	0.35	0.4	±0.5	±0.5
SiO_2			±0.5	±0.5
CaO			±0.3	±.30
Sulfate, max.	0.05	0.2		
Free carbon, max.	0.1	0.4		
Moisture, max	0.05	0.1		
Cr_2O_3, max.			0.001	0.001
Physical				
Cum. retained on				
8 mesh	0	0		0
12 mesh	2 max.		0	
16 mesh		0.5 max.		
20 mesh		20 max.	20 max.	20 max.
100 mesh		88 min.		10 max.
140 mesh	88 min.			
170 mesh			5 max.	
200 mesh	95 min.	95 min.		

COMMERCIAL CARBONATE MATERIALS USED IN GLASS

	USA Limestone	Bahamas Aragonite	Spain Dolomite	USA Quicklime
$CaCO_3$	98.0	97		
CaO			31.1	56.61
$MgCO_3$	1.3			
MgO		0.23	21.7	40.29
Fe_2O_3	0.12	0.02	0.1	0.13
Al_2O_3	0.08	0.02	0.02	0.29
SiO_2		0.04	0.05	0.57

Particle size (microns) in fillers is listed in the table.

FGD limestone:- ≥ 95% $CaCO_3$, max. 2% SiO_2, 1% Fe_2O_3 (iron content may be beneficial since it catalyses the reaction), 1% Al_2O_3, 1% MgO, 0.02% MnO_2, 1,000 ppm Cl. Reactivity min. of 50% in 30 minutes, 90% in 90 minutes; L.A. abrasion max. of 45; Bond Work Index min. of 9.5 at 200 mesh and max. of 12 at 200 mesh. Fine size required, about 84% -45 µm. Limestone has to be free of wood, flint, clay, plastic, metal, organic material, or other deleterious material.

Glass:- flat glass limestone min. 54.85% CaO, max. 0.8% MgO, 0.6% acid insol., 0.075% Fe_2O_3, 0.35% Al_2O_3, 0.05% sulfate, 0.1% free carbon, and 0.05% moisture; dolomite min. 29.50% CaO & 21.4% MgO, min. 0.6% acid insol., 0.25% Fe_2O_3, 0.4% Al_2O_3, 0.2% sulfate, 0.4% free carbon, and 0.10% moisture. Container glass max. 0.1% Fe_2O_3, 0.001% Cr_2O_3, and 0.1% moisture with the remainder limited by variation rather than absolute values. Critical contaminants are colorants (Cr, Co, Mn), metallics (bronze, Al foil), and refractory particulates (zircon, chromite, corundum).

Lime:- 98.6% $CaCO_3$ and <1% SiO_2.

PCC (typical):- 98%+ $CaCO_3$, 0.5-1.5% $MgCO_3$, 0.1% Fe_2O_3, 0.3-0.8% moisture; dry brightness of 98%; oil absorption 30-50; surface area 8 m^2/g; bulk density 10-30 lbs/ft³. APS 0.5-1.5 µm. USP grade PCC requires: >98% $CaCO_3$, < 0.2% acid insol., <3ppm As, <0.005% F, <0.003% heavy metals (as Pb), <0.001% Pb, <1% Mg & alkali salts; <2% loss on drying.

Soda ash :- >98.6% $CaCO_3$ and <1% SiO_2.

Steel smelting:- high $CaCO_3$, <1% SiO_2, negligible S and P.

Sugar refining:- >96% $CaCO_3$, <1% SiO_2, <1% MgO, and <1% clay, sulfate minerals, and organic matter.

US Pharmacopeia XXII (USP):- min. 98.8% $CaCO_3$; max. 2% loss on drying, 0.2% acid insolubles, 0.0005% fluoride, 3ppm arsenic, 3ppm lead, 0.05% iron, 0.5ppm mercury, 0.002% heavy metals, 1% magnesium & alkali salts, no green color (barium).

LIME: Commercial quicklime is available as lump lime (>2.5"), crushed or pebble lime (0.25 - 2.25"), ground lime (approx. 100% - #8 sieve); pulverized lime (approx. 100% - #20 sieve), and pelletized lime (1" pellets). "Lime" may be high calcium, magnesium, or dolomitic. ASTM C 110 covers residues, consistency, plasticity, soundness, water retention, slaking rate, and settling rate for quicklime and hydrated lime.

CHEMICAL PROPERTIES OF CALCIUM CARBONATE PIGMENTS (%)

	Ground limestone	Precipitated calcium carbonate[1]	Precipitated calcium carbonate[2]	Precipitated calcium carbonate[3]
$CaCO_3$	96.63	98.36	98.43	98.62
$CaSO_4$	-	0.08	0.78	0.63
$MgCO_3$	2.43	0.70	0.37	0.21
Al_2O_3	0.28	0.09	0.07	0.01
Fe_2O_3	0.09	0.07	0.06	0.01
SiO_2	0.37	0.1	0.04	0.02
NaCl	-	-	-	0.10
H_2O loss @ 110°C	0.20	0.60	0.25	0.30
pH (saturated solution)	9.1	9.4	10.3	8.5

caclium carbonate formed through the following reactions:

$$1 \quad Ca(OH)_2 + CO_2 \rightarrow CaCO_3 + H_2O$$
$$2 \quad Ca(OH)_2 + Na_2CO_3 \rightarrow CaCO_3 + 2NaOH$$
$$3 \quad CaCl_2 + Na_2CO_3 \rightarrow CaCO_3 + 2 NaCl$$

Source: Trivedi and Hagemeyer, 1994

Other specific tests include Quicklime for Structural Purposes (C5); Hydrated Lime for Masonary Purposes (C 207); Quicklime and Hydrated Lime for Water Treatment (C 53); Quicklime and Hydrated Lime for Neutralization of Waste Acid (C 400); Quicklime for Sulfite Pulp Manufacture (C 46), and Lime and Limestone Products for Industrial Waste Treatment (C 826).

WORLD CAPACITY: Limestone- extremely large; Lime - 150 M t; Cement - 1,097 M t.

CAPACITY UTILIZATION: NA.

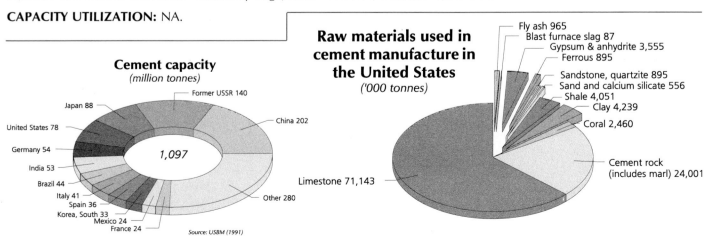

Cement capacity
(million tonnes)

Former USSR 140
Japan 88
United States 78
Germany 54
India 53
Brazil 44
Italy 41
Spain 36
Korea, South 33
Mexico 24
France 24
China 202
Other 280
1,097

Source: USBM (1991)

Raw materials used in cement manufacture in the United States
('000 tonnes)

Fly ash 965
Blast furnace slag 87
Gypsum & anhydrite 3,555
Ferrous 895
Sandstone, quartzite 895
Sand and calcium silicate 556
Shale 4,051
Clay 4,239
Coral 2,460
Cement rock (includes marl) 24,001
Limestone 71,143

MARKET CONDITIONS: Growing regionally.

MARKETING FACTORS: Diverse - construction, paper manufacture, use of plastics, state of the economy, and population growth.

HEALTH & SAFETY: Crystalline silica has been classified as a probable carcinogen by the IARC (see silica for further details). Therefore, because of its crystalline silica content, unless processing has the capability to reduce the crystalline silica content to less than 0.1%, certain carbonate rocks come under the OSHA Hazard Communication Standards, 29 CFR Section 1900.1200 which require labeling and other forms of warning, material safety data sheets, and employee training for products containing identified carcinogens with concentrations greater than 0.1%.

SUBSTITUTES & ALTERNATIVES:
Filler:- ATH, barite, feldspar, kaolin, mica, nepheline syenite, perlite, pyrophyllite, talc, microcrystalline silica, ground silica flour and synthetic silica, wollastonite.
Aggregates:- basalt, chert, diabase, gneiss, granite, traprock, quartzite, sandstone, sand & gravel, schist, slag, volcanic cinder & scoria, etc.
MgO source:- magnesite, seawater or brine magnesia, brucite.

RECYCLING: Calcium values are recycled with glass, and the higher the cullet content of the glass batch, the lower the calcium carbonate or dolomite content. PCC takes advantage of recycled carbon dioxide and heat from the papermaking plant, and lime is used to regenerate feedstocks (causticization in the Solvay pro-

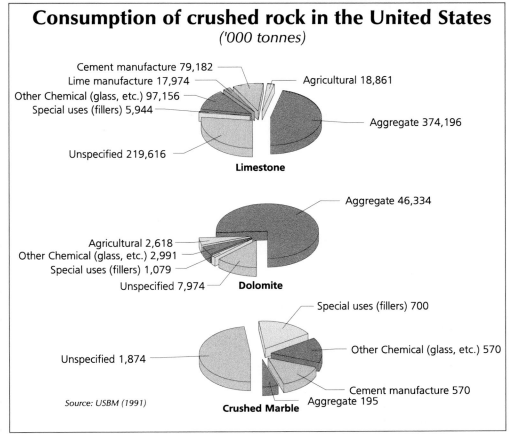

Consumption of crushed rock in the United States
('000 tonnes)

Limestone
- Cement manufacture 79,182
- Lime manufacture 17,974
- Other Chemical (glass, etc.) 97,156
- Special uses (fillers) 5,944
- Agricultural 18,861
- Aggregate 374,196
- Unspecified 219,616

Dolomite
- Aggregate 46,334
- Agricultural 2,618
- Other Chemical (glass, etc.) 2,991
- Special uses (fillers) 1,079
- Unspecified 7,974

Crushed Marble
- Special uses (fillers) 700
- Other Chemical (glass, etc.) 570
- Cement manufacture 570
- Aggregate 195
- Unspecified 1,874

Source: USBM (1991)

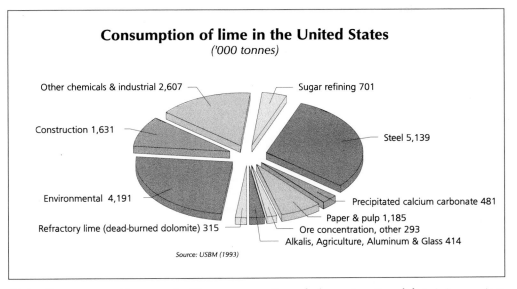

Consumption of lime in the United States
('000 tonnes)

- Other chemicals & industrial 2,607
- Sugar refining 701
- Construction 1,631
- Steel 5,139
- Environmental 4,191
- Precipitated calcium carbonate 481
- Refractory lime (dead-burned dolomite) 315
- Paper & pulp 1,185
- Ore concentration, other 293
- Alkalis, Agriculture, Aluminum & Glass 414

Source: USBM (1993)

cess, Bayer alumina, Kraft paper) and is itself regenerated in several of its processes. Recycled construction debris is increasing. Recycled cement concrete may be used as road base material, although use elsewhere is problematic due to the lower strength of concrete compared with aggregates (the fines produced have a higher absorption and therefore demand more asphalt in asphaltic concrete and mixing water in portland cement).

The amount of asphalt roads recycled is significantly higher than concrete roads since the asphaltic concrete can be rejuvenated with oil additives (up to about 35% of crushed asphalt pavement can be recycled into new asphalt mixtures). In some US states government tenders now stipulate that aggregates must contain a minimum percentage of recycled material.

PRODUCERS & WORLD TRADE: Limestone is produced in virtually all countries. Some trade of filler-grade within Europe and to small consumers. May be shipped considerable distances under certain circumstances, for example, Yucatan, Mexico (cheap production close to tidewater) to Gulf Coast, USA (lack of local supplies and large market). Lime has relatively little trade except convenient cross-border trade. Cement has a very active international market.

Non-aggregate consumption of limestone in the United States

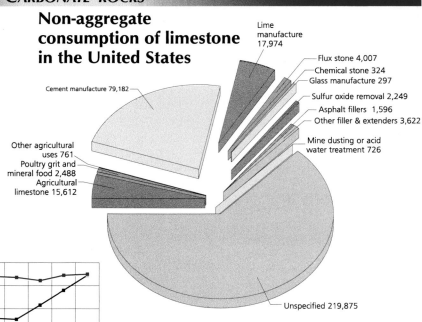

Cement manufacture 79,182
Lime manufacture 17,974
Flux stone 4,007
Chemical stone 324
Glass manufacture 297
Sulfur oxide removal 2,249
Asphalt fillers 1,596
Other filler & extenders 3,622
Mine dusting or acid water treatment 726
Other agricultural uses 761
Poultry grit and mineral food 2,488
Agricultural limestone 15,612
Unspecified 219,875

Cement world production

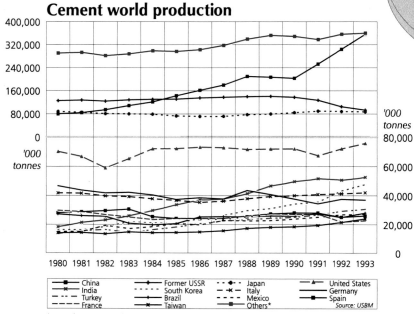

'000 tonnes

'000 tonnes

Legend			
China	Former USSR	Japan	United States
India	South Korea	Italy	Germany
Turkey	Brazil	Mexico	Spain
France	Taiwan	Others*	

Source: USBM

* more than 100 countries

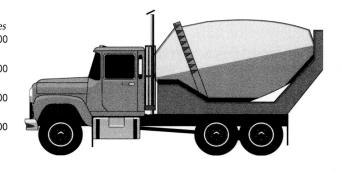

Production of lime including dead-burned dolomite

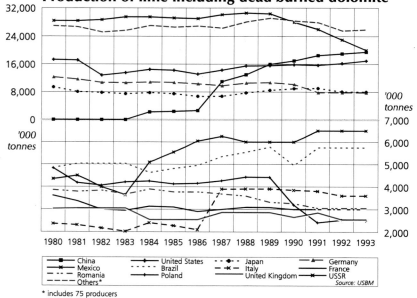

'000 tonnes

'000 tonnes

Legend			
China	United States	Japan	Germany
Mexico	Brazil	Italy	France
Romania	Poland	United Kingdom	USSR
Others*			

Source: USBM

* includes 75 producers

CARBONATE LEADERS

Lime production	Cement production
USSR	China
China	Japan
United States	United States
Germany	Russia
Japan	India
Mexico	Korea, Republic
Brazil	Italy
Italy	Germany
Romania	Turkey
Poland	Brazil
Czechoslovakia	Mexico
France	Spain
United Kingdom	France
Canada	Taiwan
Yugoslavia	Ukraine
Belgium	Iran
South Africa	Thailand
Austria	Indonesia
Turkey	Korea, North
Australia	Egypt

PRICES: Limestone/calcium carbonate:- aggregate/aglime $4-10/t. Glass-grade/FGD/carpet backing $15-25/t. Screened product $60-70/t (bulk), $80-90/t (bags). Coarse grind $35-40/t (rock dust, bulk); $40-45/t (industrial filler, bulk); $50-55/t (industrial filler, bags). Medium grind $35-55/t (bulk); $45-70/t (bags). Calcium carbonate (bags, FOB works) $96-135/t (dry, coarse 9-17 µm); $77-125/t (medium, 4-9 µm); $127-220/t (fine, 0.5 µm); $138-153/t (slurry, fine, 2-3 µm); $204-242/t (coated, fine, 23- µm); $292/t (coated, ultrafine, 0.5 µm). PCC - $272-289/t (technical, 0.5 µm); $640/t (ultrafine, 0.05-0.5 µm). Calcium carbonate USP $507/t (USP, very fine, high purity); $535/t (USP, extra light). Lime $50/t.

Barium carbonate (FOB works) $639/t (precipitated, bulk). Calcium carbide $529/t (Std. generator size, bulk, FOB works). Calcium chloride (ex-works) $208/t (conc., reg. 77-80%, flake, bulk); $275-294/t (paper, plastics, bags); $358/t (anhydrous, 94-97% flake or pellet, bulk); $364/t (anhydrous, 94-97% flake or pellet, bags); $132-143/t (liquid, 32-40% basis, tank car); $154-165t (liquid, 45% basis, tank car). Calcium cyanamide $440-495/t (industrial, anhydrous, drums, ex-works). Calcium iodate $16.40/kg (FCC, drums, FOB works). Calcium iodide $30/kg (50-kg drums, FOB works). Lithium carbonate $4.20/kg. Strontium carbonate $0.82/kg (glass grade, ground, bags, ex-works).

HTS CODES: 2515.00.0000 (rough blocks or slabs of marble, travertine, and other calcareous monumental or building stone); 2515.11.0000 (marble & travertine, crude or roughly trimmed); 2515.12.0010 (marble, merely cut); 2515.12.0020 (travertine, merely cut); 2517.10 (crushed & broken stone); 2518.10.0000 (dolomite not calcined); 2518.20.00000 (calcined dolomite); 2518.30.0000 (agglomerated dolomite, including tarred dolomite); 2522.10 (quicklime); 2522.20 (slaked lime); 2522.30 (hydraulic lime); 2523.10 (cement clinker); 2523.21 (white nonstaining portland cement); 2523.90 (other hydraulic cement); 2805.21.0000 (calcium); 2827.20.000 (calcium chloride); 2836.50.0000 (calcium carbonate); 2849.10.0000 (calcium carbide).

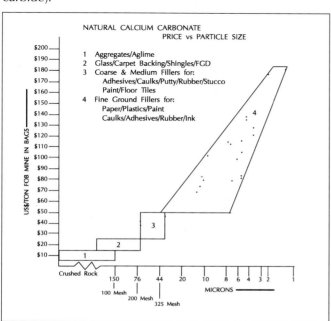

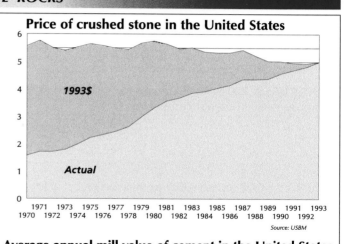

Price of crushed stone in the United States

Source: USBM

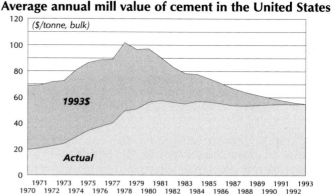

Average annual mill value of cement in the United States

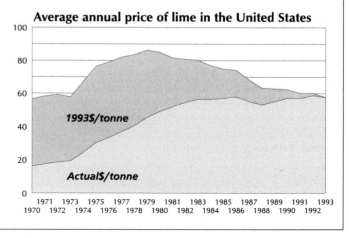

Average annual price of lime in the United States

ETYMOLOGY: Aragonite for Aragon, Spain, where it was first identified. **Brucite** for Archibald Bruce (1777-1818), American mineralogist and first observer. **Calcite** from the Latin *calx, calcis* = *lime*; this is the same origin for chalk and limestone. **Cement** from the Old French *ciment* from Latin *caementum* = *chip of stone used to fill up in building a wall.* **Dolomite** for Deodat Guy Silvain Tancrède Gratet de Dolomieu, French geologist. **Lime** from the Old English; related to Dutch *iljm* & Latin *limus* = *mud*, *linere* = *to smear.* **Marble** from the Greek *marmairein* = *to shine*, *marmaros* = *white glistening stone.* **Portland cement** named for the Isle of Portland, Dorset, England, where a local building stone esembles cement. **Pozzalana** for Pozzuoli near Mount Vesuvius, Italy, where a tuff was extracted by the Romans.

Minerals	Formula	%SrO	Color	SG	H
Celestite	$SrSO_4$	56.4	white/pale blue	3.96	3-3.5

Strontianite, $SrCO_3$, is currently noncommercial.

PROPERTIES & USES: Celestite conc. is converted to $SrCO_3$ via the black ash route forming chemical-grade strontium carbonate:

$$SrSO_4 + 2C \rightarrow SrS + 2CO_2$$
$$2SrS + 2H_2O \rightarrow Sr(SH)_2 + Sr(OH)_2$$
$$Sr(SH)_2 + Na_2CO_3 \rightarrow SrCO_3 + 2NaHS$$
$$NaHS + NaOH \rightarrow Na_2S + H_2O \text{ or}$$
$$SrS + CO_2 \rightarrow Na_2S + H_2O$$

or the direct or soda ash route forming technical grade strontium carbonate:

$$SrSO_4 + Na_2CO_3 \rightarrow SrCO_3 + H_2S$$

and is used as is or as an intermediate chemical source of SrO. $SrCO_3$ is added to TV and CRT glass in order to block X-rays and improve the quality of the glass [color TV faceplates; computer, sonar, and radar screens; guidance and control instruments] and to glazes [ceramics]. Faceplate glass contains 8% by weight of SrO. Strontium is more effective in blocking X-rays than barium, and unlike lead compounds does not brown the glass; strontium also increases the brilliance of the glass and therefore improves the quality of the picture.

10-15% $SrCO_3$ mixed with iron oxide and crystal growth inhibitors is calcined to form $SrFe_{12}O_{19}$ or $SrO\cdot6Fe_2O_3$ strontium (hexa)ferrite which has a high coercive force and thermal and electrical resistivity and so is used as permanent ceramic magnets [anti-lock braking systems or ABS; small d.c. motors; magnetic closures and attachments; loudspeakers]. These magnets retain their magnetism and are not easily affected by electrical currents and high temperatures. Precipitated ferrite powder forms part of photocopier resin matrices.

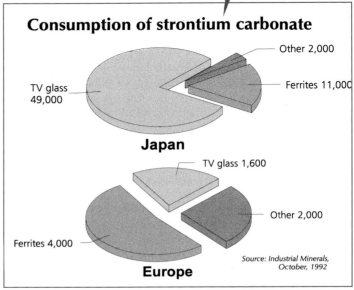

Consumption of strontium carbonate

Japan: TV glass 49,000; Ferrites 11,000; Other 2,000

Europe: TV glass 1,600; Other 2,000; Ferrites 4,000

Source: Industrial Minerals, October, 1992

Since strontium burns with a brilliant red flame at a unique wavelength, Sr chemicals including $SrCO_3$ are used in pyrotechnics [tracer ammunition; military flares; marine distress signals; warning devices; fireworks]. Pyrotechnics work on a reduction-oxidation principle whereby a fuel such as metallic powder or sugar reacts exothermically with an oxidizing agent such as a chlorate or nitrate; the oxidizing agent determines the color of the flame. Flares are required to burn with a specific light intensity for 40 seconds. The average strontium compound content of military flares is 20-40% by weight whereas a Roman Candle firework is 20%.

In metallurgy $SrCO_3$ is used to remove lead during the electrolytic production of zinc (diecasting zinc requires <0.003% lead). The $SrCO_3$ is added to the electrolyte as a slurry where it forms a low solubility, isomorphic salt pair ($SrSO_4/PbSO_4$) which is precipitated and can then be removed thus decreasing the lead content. Consumption averages 0.5-2.0 kg $SrCO_3$/tonne of cathodic zinc produced.

PHYSICAL PROPERITES OF STRONTIUM COMPOUNDS

Compound	Chemical Formula	SrO content	Molecular Weight	SG	Melting Point°C
Carbonate	$SrCO_3$	70.2	147.63	3.70	1,497
Chloride	$SrCl_2$	55.3 (S)	158.53	3.052	873
Chromate	$SrCrO_4$	50.9	203.61	3.895	NA
Nitrate	$Sr(NO_3)_2$	50.0	211.63	2.986	570
Oxalate	$SrC_2O_4\cdot H_2O$	53.5	193.64	NA	NA
Oxide	SrO	100	103.62	4.70	2,430
Peroxide	SrO_2	86.2	119.62	4.56	*
Sulfate	$SrSO_4$	56.4	183.68	3.96	1,605
Sulfide	SrS	73.4 (S)	119.68	3.70	2,000

NA - not applicable; * decomposses on heating

As an intermediate chemical $SrCO_3$ + the relevant acid → nitrate, $Sr(NO_3)_2$ which is nonhygroscopic and produces a brilliant red flame [ammunition tracers; fireworks; flares & distress signals]; → oxalate, $SrC_2O_4\cdot H_2O$ [fireworks]; → sulfate, $SrSO_4$ [pyrotechnics] → chlorate, $SrClO_3$ [pyrotechnics]; → chloride, $SrCl_2$ [desensitizing toothpaste]; → chromate, $SrCrO_4$ [anticorrosive paint, especially on aluminum]; → phosphate, $SrHPO_4$ [fluorescent lighting]; → sulfide, SrS has light-bearing qualities [luminescent & phosphorescent paints]; + TiO_2 @ 2,000°C+ → titanate, $SrTiO_3$ [high-tech ceramics such as semiconductor substrate & piezoelectric application].

High-purity SrO + metallic oxides → superconducting material [R&D]. Reduction of $SrCl_2$ + KCl or SrO + aluminum → strontium metal which is added in small amounts to aluminum to improve castability and machining characteristics [aluminum refining & casting]. Strontium added to molten aluminum improves the castability of the metal and the machinability of the casting thus allowing a broad range of parts to be made from lightweight aluminum [automobiles].

QUALITY & SPECIFICATIONS: Min. 90% $SrSO_4$ for celestite ore which is often associated with barium and calcium which are similar to strontium and therefore difficult to separate. Chemical-grade (via black ash or calcining method) produces strontium carbonate (min. 98% $SrCO_3$) and technical-grade (via the soda ash or direct method) strontium carbonate (min. 97% $SrCO_3$).

Strontium carbonate (glass-grade, typical):- 99.6% $SrCO_3$ + $BaCO_3$, 0.9% $BaCO_3$, 0.1% $CaCO_3$, 0.1% Na_2CO_3, 0.003% Fe_2O_3, total S as SO_3 0.15%; 0% on US 16 screen, 8% on US 140 screen. *Strontium carbonate (ferrite-grade):-* 96-99% $SrCO_3$, <0.2% combined Ca, Na, and Mg; additives need to be controlled <0.2% SiO_2, <0.2% Al_2O_3, <0.1% Fe, and <1% Ba. *Strontium carbonate (electrolytic zinc refining):-* minimum 97% $SrCO_3$, maximum 1.0% Ba, 0.5% Ca, 0.1% Mg, 0.5% Na, 0.01% Fe, 0.0005% Sb, 0.5% SO_3, 0.25% moisture, 3.0% insolubles; maximum 95% retained on 400 mesh.

Strontium nitrate (pyrotechnics):- low moisture content to promote efficient combustion; low sulfur, manganese, ammonia (form mineral acids which catalyze reactions and cause explosions); PS <120 μm. *Strontium chromite:-* low nitrate and chloride content to prevent corrosion.

Typical analysis results of commercial celestite, strontium carbonate, and strontium nitrate are given in the table.

WORLD CAPACITY: 285,000 t (Sr carbonate).

CAPACITY UTILIZATION: 95%.

MARKET CONDITIONS: Growing.

MARKETING FACTORS: Color cathod-ray tube technology and sales of TVs and computer screens and therefore the level of economic development, demand for consumer goods, and the economy. Rather than celestite ore, the production world capacity of strontium carbonate is the limiting factor in the supply of strontium.

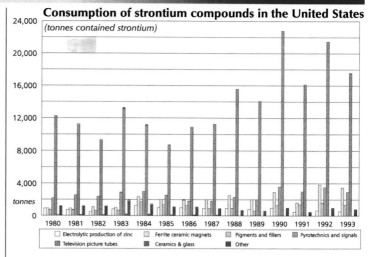

Consumption of strontium compounds in the United States
(tonnes contained strontium)

Legend: Electrolytic production of zinc; Ferrite ceramic magnets; Pigments and fillers; Pyrotechnics and signals; Television picture tubes; Ceramics & glass; Other

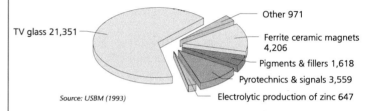

Consumption of strontium compounds in the United States

TV glass 21,351
Other 971
Ferrite ceramic magnets 4,206
Pigments & fillers 1,618
Pyrotechnics & signals 3,559
Electrolytic production of zinc 647

Source: USBM (1993)

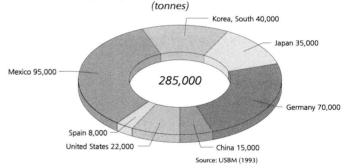

Capacity of strontium carbonate
(tonnes)

285,000

Korea, South 40,000
Japan 35,000
Germany 70,000
China 15,000
United States 22,000
Spain 8,000
Mexico 95,000

Source: USBM (1993)

ANALYSIS OF STRONTIUM CARBONATE AND NITRATE

	Strontium carbonate				Strontium nitrate			
	Chemical(%)	Particle size			Chemical(%)	Particle size	
		Mesh	% retained				Mesh	% retained
$(Sr-Ba)CO_3$	95.00	50	0.42	$Sr(NO_3)_2$	99.5		50	5.9
$BaCO_3$ max.	1.30	100	1.96	Ba	0.17		100	46.1
$CaCO_3$	1.40	140	30.62	Ca	0.0008		140	24.5
$MgCO_3$	0.10	200	31.56	Mg	0.0007		200	11.9
Fe_2O_3	0.03	230	29.34	Fe	0.0010		230	4.9
Al_2O_3	0.01	270	2.24	Al	0.0006		270	0.9
Na	0.50	325	1.7	Na	0.041		325	2.1
Pb	0.00	400	1.04	H_2O	0.03		>325	3.7
Water soluble	0.30	>400	1.12	Water insoluble	0.0064			
Insolubles	1.80			pH	6.0			

Source: Promotora de Industria del Sur (Proinsur), Spain

ANALYSIS OF STRONTIUM CARBONATE BY GRADE (%)

		Grade A	Grade B	Grade C	Grade D
$SrCO_3/BaCO_3$	min.	98	98	98	98
BaO	max.	1.2	1.2	1.2	1.2
CaO	max.	0.17	0.17	0.17	0.17
Na_2O	max.	0.03	0.03	0.03	0.30
Fe_2O_3	max.	0.006	0.006	0.006	0.010
Total S as SO_3	max.	0.50	0.40	0.50	0.40
Insoluble in HCl	max.	0.10	0.10	0.10	0.50
Moisture	max.	0.20	0.05	0.20	0.04
BD loose (kg/l)		0.30-0.50	0.50-0.70	1.20-1.50	1.60-2.00
BD tapped (kg/l)		0.80-0.90	0.90-1.30	1.50-1.80	2.00-2.50
Sieve residue >45µ	max.	1%	1%		
Screen analysis					
>1.00mm	max.			20%	0%
<0.15mm	max.			15%	15
>0.85mm max.	max.				5%

Source: Solvay Barium Strontium GmbH, German

HEALTH & SAFETY: Crystalline silica has been classified as a probable carcinogen by the IARC (see silica for further details). Therefore, because of its crystalline silica content, unless processing has the capability to reduce the crystalline silica content to less than 0.1%, celestite comes under the OSHA Hazard Communication Standards, 29 CFR Section 1900.1200 which require labeling and other forms of warning, material safety data sheets, and employee training for products containing identified carcinogens with concentrations greater than 0.1%.

All color televisions and other devices containing color cathode-ray tubes sold in the United States are required by law to contain strontium in the faceplate glass of the picture tube.

Strontium-90, a radioactive isotope of strontium, is a component of nuclear waste from reactors and nuclear fallout; and, since it generates heat on decay, it presents a difficult disposal problem.

SUBSTITUTES & ALTERNATIVES: TV glass:- barium, lead. **Ferrite magnets**:- barium, lead, Nd-Fe-B magnets. **Pyrotechnics**:- lithium.

RECYCLING: Virtually none except for TV glass. The value of TV faceplate glass is sufficiently high to make recycling a commercial possibility.

PRODUCERS & WORLD TRADE: The supply of celestite is dominated by Mexico which has also expanded its capacity to produce strontium carbonate and other strontium chemicals. Although the number of large-scale consumers is limited, there is considerable international trade in strontium compounds.

PRICES: United States:- Celestite conc. $73/t (Ave. FOB export port); strontium carbonate $0.82/kg (glass grade, ground, bags, ex-works); strontium nitrate $1,133/t (bags, ex-works). Turkey celestite conc. $80-85/t (min. 92% $SrSO_4$) with +$6/t per point above base.

HTS CODES: 2530.90.00.10 (celestite); 2836.92.00.00 (strontium carbonate); 2834.29.20.00 (strontium nitrate); 2816.20.00.00 (strontium oxide, hydroxide, peroxide).

ETYMOLOGY: Celestite from the Latin *caelestis = heavenly* for its faint blue color. **Strontianite** for Strontian, a small town in Argyllshire, Scotland.

STRONTIUM MINERAL LEADERS

Producers	Exporters	Importers
Mexico	Mexico	Germany
Turkey	Turkey	United States
Iran	Iran	Japan
Spain		Korea
Algeria		China
United Kingdom		
Argentina		
Pakistan		

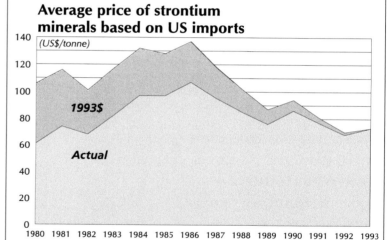

Average price of strontium minerals based on US imports

(US$/tonne) — 1993$ — Actual — 1980 1981 1982 1983 1984 1985 1986 1987 1988 1989 1990 1991 1992 1993

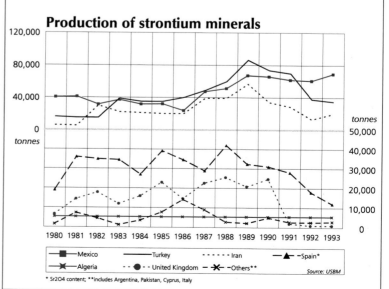

Production of strontium minerals

Mexico — Turkey — Iran — Algeria — United Kingdom — Others**

* Sr2O4 content; **includes Argentina, Pakistan, Cyprus, Italy

Source: USBM

Mineral	Formula	%FeO	%Cr₂O₃	Color	SG	H
Chromite	$FeCr_2O_4$ (Mg & Al substitute)	32.1	67.9	iron-black	4.5-4.8	5.5-6.5

PROPERTIES & USES: Chromite is the sole commercial source of chromium. High-chromium & high iron chromite conc. → ferrochromium, ferrosilicon chromium → stainless, full-alloy steel, high-strength, low-alloy steel, tool steel, & superalloy steel [special steel with Cr_2O_3 content of 18% (stainless) to 30% (ultra-hard cutting steels)].

Roasted chromite + soda ash (+ lime) → sodium chromate (Na_2CrO_4) + sodium dichromate ($Na_2Cr_2O_7 \cdot 2H_2O$) which is ground to 90-98% -75 μm and roasted (1,000-1,500°C), cooled, washed, and treated with sulfuric acid or pressurized CO_2 → 80-85% hydrous sodium bichromate which is converted to a 70% solution known commercially as sodium dichromate [batteries; bleaching waxes and oils; chemical intermediate (see later); copper alloy processing; drilling-mud additive; leather tanning; metal finishing; textile mordant; water treatment; wood preservative].

Sodium dichromate is the most economical and simplest form of chromium in an aqueous soluble form → ammonium bichromate [mordant; catalyst; chromium dioxide for magnetic tapes; porcelain finish; pyrotechnics; sensitizing solutions for lithography and photo-engraving; → barium chromate [pigment for ceramics & paints; safety matches]; → chromic acid [chrome plating; green pigment; ceramic colorant; feedstock for chromic formate, chromic nitrate, zinc chromate, basic lead chromate, chromium dioxide; metallurgy; refractory additive; in copper chromium arsenate (CCA) a wood preservative]; chrome yellow, chrome orange, molybdate orange, zinc yellow, chrome green, chromium oxide green, hydrated chromium oxide green, barium oxide green [pigments (finely divided solid with APS 0.01-1.0 μm)]; → potassium bichromate [feedstock for double metal salts like potassium chrome alum and potassium zinc chromate, and/or strontium chromate; photography; pyrotechnics; safety matches]; ammonium dichromate [fireworks; photo engraving]; → sodium chromate [catalysts; drilling muds; petroleum pipelines; pigment manufacture; textile drying; water treatment; wood preservative. Sodium dichromate + lead compounds (litharge, lead nitrate, basic lead acetate) → soft-textured lead chromate pigments ranging from pale greenish yellows (primrose) to orange/light red depending on chemical composition, crystal structure, and particle size.

Chromite sand is refractory and has good thermal conductivity, resists metal penetration and thermal shock, and has low thermal expansion (steel uses 75-100 kg chromite/tonne of castings produced) [foundry sand for ferrous and nonferrous casting]. Advantages of chromite over silica sand as a foundry sand include greater refractoriness, heat conductivity, and resistance to metal penetration along with lower coefficient of expansion and free silica content. Chromite flour acts as a natural colorant [glass; brick; ceramics].

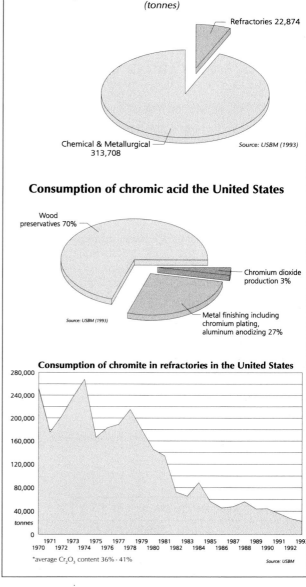

Consumption of chromite in the United States
(tonnes)

Refractories 22,874

Chemical & Metallurgical 313,708

Source: USBM (1993)

Consumption of chromic acid the United States

Wood preservatives 70%

Chromium dioxide production 3%

Metal finishing including chromium plating, aluminum anodizing 27%

Source: USBM (1993)

Consumption of chromite in refractories in the United States

average Cr₂O₃ content 36% - 41%

Source: USBM

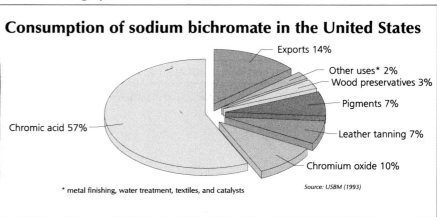

Consumption of sodium bichromate in the United States

Exports 14%

Other uses* 2%

Wood preservatives 3%

Pigments 7%

Leather tanning 7%

Chromium oxide 10%

Chromic acid 57%

* metal finishing, water treatment, textiles, and catalysts

Source: USBM (1993)

Chromite + magnesia ➔ various refractory bricks including chrome-magnesia (70% chromite), mag-chrome (30-40% chromite), co-sintered magnesia-chrome, fused magnesia-chrome [cement; glass; iron & steel; nonferrous metals; power generation].

Chromite ➔ anhydrous chromium iodide or pure chromic oxide ➔ chromium metal (99.996%)

QUALITY & SPECIFICATIONS: *Chromite ore:-* 38-55% Cr_2O_3.

Flour:- 40-44% Cr_2O_3 and low metallic impurities.

Ferrochromium:- grade C ("charge") containing 50-55% Cr derived from high-Fe chromite with Cr:Fe ratio of <1.8; grade B containing 56-64% Cr derived from chromite with Cr:Fe ratio of 1.8-2.5; grade A containing >64% Cr derived from high-Cr chromite with Cr:Fe ratio of >2.5 (becoming the most popular).

Foundry sand:- 44% Cr_2O_3 with max. 26% Fe_2O_3, 4% SiO_2, 0.5% CaO, 0.5% moisture, 0.5% LOI. Fine is 90% min. -390 μm, retained on 75 μm, medium is 95% min. -780 μm, retained on 75 μm, both with an AFS clay content of 0.5% max.

Refractory chromite:- low (30-40%) Cr_2O_3, relatively high (25-32%) Al_2O_3, and low (<15%) Fe; ground to -10 or even -65 mesh.

WORLD CAPACITY: Contained chromium:- 4.2M. t (ore); 2.5M. t (ferrochromium); 257,000 t (chemicals).

MARKET CONDITIONS: Steady; however, use in refractories is declining.

COMPOSITION OF BASIC-REFRACTORY CHROMITE BRICKS (%)

	Magnesia-chrome burned	Magnesia-chrome direct bonded	Magnesia-chrome chemical bonded	Chrome burned	Chrome-magnesia burned
SiO_2	1.8-7.0	1.0-2.6	2.0-8.0	5.0-8.0	3.0-5.0
Al_2O_3	6.0-13.0	3.0-16.0	5.0-14.0	27.0-29.0	8.0-20.0
Fe_2O_3	2.0-12.0	3.0-10.0	2.0-8.0	12.0-20.0	8.0-12.0
CaO	0.6-1.5	0.6-1.1	1.0-2.0	0.4-1.0	0.7-1.1
MgO	50.0-82.0	50.0-80.0	50.0-80.0	15.0-23.0	40.0-50.0
Cr_2O_3	6.0-15.0	7.0-20.0	6.0-15.0	29.0-35.0	18.0-24.0

Chromite capacity
('000 tonnes contained chromium)

Kazakhstan 1,100
India 309
Turkey 300
Finland 190
Zimbabwe 169
Albania 150
Brazil 135
Others* 73
Philippines 60
Madagascar 45
Russia 40
Iran 34
South Africa 1,600
4,205

Source: USBM (1993)

CHROMITE SPECIFICATIONS BY USE (%)

	Met.	Chem.	Ref.	Foundry
Cr_2O_3	>46	>44	30-40	>44
Cr:Fe	>2:1	>1.5	2-2.5:1	2:1
SiO_2	<10	<3.5	6	<4
Al_2O_3			25-30	
CaO				<0.5
Physical	hard/lumpy	lumpy	lumpy/friable	friable

COMPOSITION OF COMMERCIAL CHROMITE ORE (%)

	Philippines Lump ore	Refractory Losil	Finland Chemical conc.	Finland Foundry conc.
Cr_2O_3	31	33	46.0	46.0
$Cr_2O_3+Al_2O_3$ **		58	60	
Al_2O_3			13.8	14.0
Fe max.	12	12	25.6*	25.5*
SiO_2	6.5	3.95	2.1	1.5
MgO			10.3	10.0
CaO			0.14	0.1

* $FeO+Fe_2O_3$ ** min.

TYPICAL QUALITIES FOR CHROMIUM CHEMICALS (%)

	Sodium dichromate	Anhydrous sodium chromate	Sodium chromate tetrahydrate	Chromic acid
Formula	$Na_2Cr_2O_7 \cdot 2H_2O$	Na_2CrO_4	$Na_2CrO_4 \cdot 4H_2O$	CrO_3
% of analysis	100	99.5	100.3	99.9
SO_4 as Na_2SO_4	0.01	0.41	0.3	0.01
Cl as NaCl	0.05	0.02	0.02	10ppm
V as V_2O_5	0.01	0.01	0.01	—
Water insol.	0.01	0.01	0.005	10ppm

FOUNDRY-GRADE CHROMITE (%)

	Elandsdrift (Henry Gould)	Rand Mines (Millsell)	Rand Mines (Winterveld 1)	Rand Mines (Winterveld 2)	Rand Mines (Waterkloof & Montrose)	Samancor
			SOUTH AFRICA			
Cr_2O_3	45.90	46.20	46.00	46.60	46.30	47.05
FeO	25.40	26.50	25.20	25.00	25.00	25.77
Fe	-	-	-	-	-	-
SiO_2	1.30	1.00	1.00	0.80	0.90	0.70
Al_2O_3	15.4	15.50	14.70	15.20	15.20	14.84
$Cr_2O_3+Al_2O_3$	-	-	-	-	-	
MgO	9.8	9.80	10.20	11.20	11.20	10.75
TiO_2	0.55	0.50	0.60	0.50	0.50	0.69
V_2O_5	0.36	0.40	0.40	0.30	0.30	-
CaO	0.33	0.25	0.20	0.23	0.23	0.05
Ni	0.08	-	-	-	-	-
P	0.005	0.003	0.003	0.003	0.003	-
S	0.000	0.002	0.002	0.002	0.002	-
Cr:Fe	-	-	-	-	-	1.60

CHEMICAL-GRADE CHROMITE (%)

	BRAZIL			SOUTH AFRICA			
	Vina Nova	Elandsdrift	Hernic	Lebowa Dev. Corp. (Dilokong)	Rand Mines (Henry Gould)	Rand Mines (Winterveld)	Samancor (Tweefontein)
Cr_2O_3	>49	46.3	46.0	46.92	46.00	45.00	46.80
FeO	-	25.4	-	26.14	26.50	24.70	27.03
Fe	17-19	-	26.0	-	-	-	-
SiO_2	<3	1.20	1.00	0.85	1.00	2.50	0.50
Al_2O_3	11-13	15.4	15.20	14.59	15.50	15.80	15.17
$Cr_2O_3+Al_2O_3$							
MgO	5-7.5	9.8	8.70	9.8	9.80	11.40	9.23
TiO_2	-	0.55	0.54	0.55	0.50	0.40	-
V_2O_5	-	0.36	0.43	-	0.40	0.30	-
CaO	0.1	0.33	0.26	0.21	0.25	0.20	0.16
Ni	-	0.08	-	-	-	-	-
P	-	0.005	0.002	-	0.003	0.005	-
S	-	0.000	0.003	-	0.002	0.002	-
Cr:Fe	>1.7	-	1.55	1.58	1.53	1.60	1.52

REFRACTORY-GRADE CHROMITE (%)

	S. AFRICA					PHILIPPINES			
	Anglo America (Marico)	Rand Mines (Winterveld 1)	Rand Mines (Winterveld 2)	Rand Mines (Winterveld 3)	Samancor (Groothoek&Jagdust)	Benguet (Masinloc 1)	Benguet (Masinloc 2)	Benguet (Masinloc 3)	Benguet (Masinloc 4)
Cr_2O_3	48.3	46.60	46.50	46.94	47.07	31.55	32.18	33.88	35.73
FeO	20.70	24.90	24.50	24.50	25.77	-	-	-	-
Fe	-	-	-	-	-	11.34	10.83	10.79	12.45
SiO_2	0.94	0.70	0.75	0.30	0.56	5.84	5.42	3.30	1.69
Al_2O_3	17.2	15.40	15.60	15.60	14.84	-	-	-	-
$Cr_2O_3+Al_2O_3$	-	-	-	-	-	58.79	60.02	62.21	63.50'
MgO	12.4	11.50	11.50	11.50	10.75	-	-	-	-
TiO_2	0.39	0.50	0.50	0.50	0.69	-	-	-	-
V_2O_5	-	0.30	-	0.30	-	-	-	-	-
CaO	0.01	0.25	0.25	0.25	0.05	-	-	-	-
Ni	-	-	-	-	-	-	-	-	-
P	-	0.003	0.003	0.003	-	-	-	-	-
S	-	0.002	0.002	0.002	-	-	-	-	-
Cr:Fe	2.05	-	-	-	1.60	-	-	-	-

Source: Papp, J.F., 1994

MARKETING FACTORS: Prevailing iron & steel production rates and the demand for stainless steel which are greatly influenced by the general state of the economy. Environmental concerns are growing.

HEALTH & SAFETY: Crystalline silica has been classified as a probable carcinogen by the IARC (see silica for further details). Therefore, because of its crystalline silica content, unless processing has the capability to reduce the crystalline silica content to less than 0.1%, chromite comes under the OSHA Hazard Communication Standards, 29 CFR Section 1900.1200 which require labeling and other forms of warning, material safety data sheets, and employee training for products containing identified carcinogens with concentrations greater than 0.1%.

Hexavalent chromium compounds are generally recognized as toxic with chronic occupational exposure associated with an increased incidence of bronchial cancer. The toxicity of trivalent chromium is unclear (although they are less toxic than hexavalent); lower valency chromium compounds (divalent and less) are generally recognized as benign.

OSHA is reviewing chromium's permissible exposure limit (PEL), with the final ruling due in 1995. Current exposure levels are chromic acid and chromates - 0.1 mg of CrO_7 m³, ceiling; chromium metal and insoluble salt - 0.1 mg of CrO_7 m³, 8-hour time weighted average; soluble chromic and chromous salts - 0.5 mg of CrO_7 m³, 8-hour time weighted average. EPA limits on drinking water is 0.1 ppm chromium.

SUBSTITUTES & ALTERNATIVES: **Foundry sand:**- silica, olivine, zircon. **Metallurgical chrome:**- nickel for stainless steel. **Refractories:**- graphite.

RECYCLING: Chromium is recycled as scrap steel and reused in the steel industry. Little chemical chrome is recycled, although regulations limiting chromium releases are encouraging recycling. There is increased recycling of refractory chrome as disposal costs increase dramatically.

PRODUCERS & WORLD TRADE: Commercial chromite production is confined to a handful of countries with major consumers such as the United States and Japan totally dependent on imports. The Phillipines is noted for the production of refractory-grade chromite.

APPARENT CONSUMPTION OF CHROMITE ORE & CONCENTRATES (TONNES)	
	Apparent Consumption
South Africa	3,288,205
Former USSR	3,059,000
India	815,420
Japan	796,805
China	641,267
United States	554,984
Albania	407,000
Finland	351,301
Former Yugoslavia	280,477
Germany	273,647
Brazil	196,573
Sweden	191,722
Italy	175,771
Turkey	173,501
Czechoslovakia	171,000
Norway	159,457
Poland	159,110
United Kingdom	154,883
Romania	146,700
Greece	89,317
France	85,749
Zimbabwe	62,600
Spain	54,695
Iran	48,300
New Caledonia	46,477
Austria	43,622
Philippines	36,254
Mexico	29,376
Argentina	26,060
North Korea	25,700
Canada	21,309
Pakistan	18,191
Netherlands	16,363
Hungary	16,169
Denmark	14,770
Oman	12,810
Venezuela	11,958
Sudan	11,000

NOTE: Numbers are approximate and rounded for 1990 or thereabouts; absence of a country does not necessarily indicate no production or trade; absence of a number does not necessarily mean zero

Source: British Geological Survey

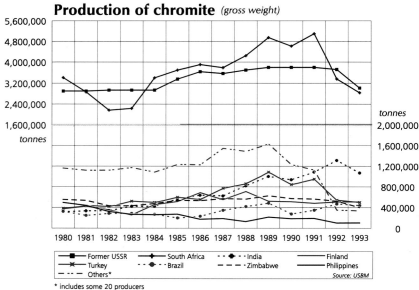

Production of chromite (gross weight)

Legend: Former USSR, South Africa, India, Finland, Turkey, Brazil, Zimbabwe, Philippines, Others*

Source: USBM

* includes some 20 producers

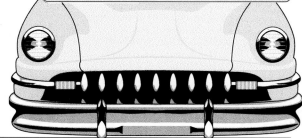

CHROME

PRICES: S. Africa, Transvaal (FOB, wet bulk):- $55-60/t (chemical, 46% Cr_2O_3); $70-75/t (foundry, 45% Cr_2O_3); $75-80/t (refractory, 46% Cr_2O_3); $63-67/t (friably lumpy, 40% Cr_2O_3). Philippines $100-120/t (refractory, conc., FOB). Europe $180-225/t (foundry molding sand, 98% <30 mesh, del. UK). Metallurgical Albanian (lumpy 42-47% min. Cr_2O_3) $60-70/t. Turkish (lumpy 48% Cr_2O_3, 3:1(scale pro rata))$100-105/t. Kazakhstan $65-67/t (40-41% Cr_2O_3 min.); $80-85/t (48% Cr_2O_3 min.).

Chrome green (CP, del. E. of Rockies, bags) $3.70/kg (extra light); $3.74/kg (light); $3.78/kg (medium); $3.82/kg (extra deep). Chrome orange $2.05-2.53/kg (CP, bags, del. E. of Rockies). Chrome yellow $3.08/kg (CP, bags, del. E. of Rockies). Chromic acid $2.68/kg (99.75%, flake, drums, freight equalized). Chromium fluoride $5.83/kg (drums, ex-works). Chromium nitrate (drums, FOB) $3.19/kg; $1.63-1.89/kg (10% metal solution). Chromium oxide $11-12.10/kg (hydrated); $4.18-4.40/kg (pure). Potassium chromate $1.25/kg (purified, crystals, drums, ex-works). Sodium bichromate $0.80/kg (of sodium dichromate dihydrate equivalent content). Sodium chromate 1.54/kg (anhydrous, drums, ex-works); $1.47/kg (tetrahydrate, bags, ex-works).

HTS CODES: 2610.00.0020 (ore <40% Cr_2O_3); 2610.00.0040 (ore >40% but <46% Cr_2O_3); 2610.00.0060 (ore >46% Cr_2O_3); 2849.90.2000 (chromium carbide); 2819.90.0000 (chromium hydroxide); 2833.23.0000 (chromium sulfate); 2841.30.0000 (sodium dichromate); 2841.50.0000 (chromic acid); 3206.20.0010 (chrome yellow); 7202.41.00 (high-carbon ferrochromium); 8112.20.3000 (chromium waste and scrap).

ETYMOLOGY: Chromite from the Greek *chroma = a color* for the brilliant hues of its compounds.

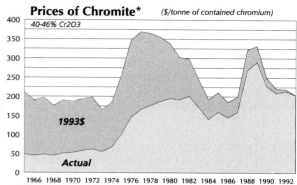

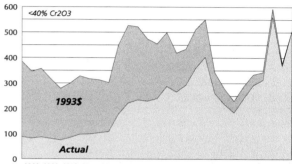

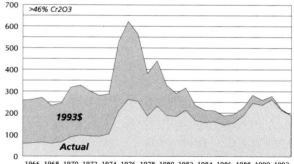

Prices of Chromite* (*$/tonne of contained chromium*)

* US Customs value per tonne of chromium contained in imported material   Source: USBM

CHROMITE ORE & CONCENTRATES LEADERS

Producers	Importers	Exporters
South Africa	Japan	South Africa
Former USSR	China	Former USSR
India	United States	Turkey
Albania	Germany	Albania
Turkey	Former Yugoslavia	Zimbabwe
Zimbabwe	Sweden	Philippines
Finland	Italy	India
Philippines	Czechoslovakia	Madagascar
Brazil	Norway	Finland
Madagascar	Poland	Cuba
Iran	United Kingdom	Netherlands
New Caledonia	Romania	Brazil

WORLD PRODUCTION AND TRADE IN CHROMITE ORE & CONCENTRATES (TONNES)

	Production	Imports	Exports	Apparent Consumption	Net Supplier	Net Consumer
North America		616,042	10,373	605,669		(605,669)
South America	225,000	55,740	34,995	245,745		(20,745)
Central & South America	50,000		49,664	336	49,664	
European Union	50,000	902,246	77,991	874,255		(824,255)
Non-EU Europe	6,021,277	1,174,194	2,033,730	5,161,741	859,536	
Australasia	1,319,366	1,463,115		2,782,481		(1,463,115)
Middle East	91,810			91,810		
Africa	5,209,000		1,350,477	3,858,523	1,350,477	

NOTE: Numbers are approximate and rounded for 1990 or thereabouts

Source: British Geological Survey

CORUNDUM & EMERY

Minerals	Formula	Color	SG	H
Corundum	Al_2O_3	gray/green/red/tan	3.9-4.1	7-9
Emery	corundum+magnetite	gray-black	3.2-4.5	7.25

PROPERTIES & USES: Corundum, natural anhydrous aluminum oxide, is the second hardest mineral known after diamond. It has a blocky sharp grain shape, melting point of 1,950°C, and can be carefully sized for use as a polishing & lapping abrasive [optical grinding, metal burnishing, lapping medium-hardness metals; filler or friction powder]. Emery is an impure corundum with a higher percentage of fused iron oxide. It is used as an abrasive [coated abrasives; bonded abrasives; tumbling or deburring media including dehusking and polishing rice; medium- to low-pressure blasting; stone surfacing and rough grinding of glass; stone sawing and metal polishing]. Non-abrasive uses rely on its hardness, toughness, and chemical inertness [nonskid wear-resistant floors; epoxy coating and grouting; concrete surface hardener; nonskid dusting agent for oily floors]. Its variability in composition (±mullite, titania, silica, magnesia, hematite) and weak internal structure put it at a disadvantage compared with synthetic abrasives such as fused alumina (artificial corundum).

Gemstone varieties are ruby (red), sapphire (blue). Some relatively uncommon varieties of corundum are known as Oriental Amethyst (violet corundum), Oriental Emerald (green corundum), and Oriental Topaz (yellow corundum).

QUALITY & SPECIFICATIONS: Strict control regarding sizing and PSD. *Corundum powders* (typical):- 86.55% Al_2O_3, 7.56% SiO_2, 2.88% TiO_2, 0.45% Fe_2O_3, 0.14% Na_2O, 0.98% MgO, 1.12% Cr_2O_3, 0.32% CaO; APS 4.5-42 µm. Emery:- see table for chemical analysis; sizes for Turkish crude emery:- -240 +50mm, -150 +50mm, and -50 +10mm which are further processed into about 35 grades ranging from 2.36mm to 53 µm plus emery flour.

CORUNDUM LEADERS

Producers	Exporters	Importers
Zimbabwe	Zimbabwe	Canada
S. Africa	S. Africa	France
India		Germany
Former USSR		India
		Japan
		Netherlands
		United Kingdom

EMERY LEADERS

Producers	Exporters	Importers
Turkey	Turkey	Netherlands
Greece	Greece	India
United States	*Re-exporters*	Nigeria
	Netherlands	Canada
	India	United Kingdom
	Nigeria	Germany
	United States	France
		Pakistan
		Japan

SPECIFICATIONS FOR EMERY

	USA Oregon Emery	Turkey Etibank	Turkey Ranar Mineral	Turkey Lutfullah
Al_2O_3	50 - 55	54 - 56	61.02	64
Fe_2O_3	20	25 - 27	24.95	25
SiO_2	28	3 - 5	7.96	4
TiO_2	2	2.5	2.60	3
CaO	-	1.5	0.70	0.2
LOI	-	8.0	2.25	3
Hardness	8 - 9	8 - 9	7.85 - 8.5	8 - 9

Source: Company literature and Holroyd and McCracken, 1994.

WORLD CAPACITY: 50-60,000 t (non-gem variety).

CAPACITY UTILIZATION: 62%.

MARKET CONDITIONS: Continuing to decline.

MARKETING FACTORS: Manufacturing industries such as steel and glass and therefore the economy. Competition from synthetic abrasives will eliminate most markets with emery surviving in niche markets based on competitive pricing.

HEALTH & SAFETY: Other than a dusting problem when used in blasting, there appears to be no health & safety related problems with corundum and emery.

SUBSTITUTES & ALTERNATIVES: Abrasives:- bauxite & alumina (fused alumina), diamonds, diatomite, feldspar, garnet, iron oxide (magnetite), nepheline syenite, olivine, perlite, pumice, silica sand, staurolite, tripoli, silicon carbide, ilmenite.

RECYCLING: Blasting abrasives may be recovered, cleaned, resized, and reused several times.

PRODUCERS & WORLD TRADE: The few remaining producers export a significant proportion of their production.

PRICES: Corundum abrasive grain $1- 2.75/kg; Emery - Europe (CIF) $285-375/t (coarse grain); $375-420/t (medium and fine grain). Turkey, FOB port $34-48/t (crude); $220-460/t (micronized). Polishing emery $1.75-2.75/kg (based on sizing & quantity).

HTS CODES: 2513.21 (emery, natural abrasives, natural garnet, and other natural abrasives, crude); 2513.29 (emery, natural abrasives, natural garnet, and other natural abrasives, other than crude); 6805.10 (natural abrasives on woven textile); 6805.20 (natural abrasives on paper or paperboard) 6805.30 (natural abrasives sheets, strips, disks, belts, sleeves, or similar form).

ETYMOLOGY: Corundum from the Hindi *kurund*, or the Tamil *kurundam*, describing a native stone of India. **Emery** from the French *emeri*, Italian *smeriglio*, and Greek *smiris* or *smeris*; akin to the Greek *myron* = urgent. **Ruby** from the Latin *rubeus* = *red* alluding to its color. **Sapphire** is an ancient name of uncertain origin; possibly Hebraic *sappir* and Sanskrit *sanipruja*; applied by the ancients to lazurite. Also French and Latin *sapphirus* and Greek *sappheiros*.

PROPERTIES & USES: Natural diamond comprises carbon with very minor impurities (<0.2% nitrogen in natural diamond). Synthetic diamond, manufactured by subjecting graphite to high temperatures and pressures in the presence of a catalyst metal (nickel or nickel alloy), contains significant amounts of metal (up to 10% nickel) either as macroscopic or platelike inclusions or as substitutional metal atoms. Physical differences between diamond and metal often create stress in the synthetic diamond which in turn causes birefringence and weakness.

Diamond is unsurpassed in hardness at H10 or Knoop 8,200-8,500 (abrasion resistance), yet it is brittle and tends to shatter under stress; cleavage planes allow diamonds to be split and renders wear resistance directional. Diamond has extremely high thermal conductivity, low thermal expansion, and has modest thermal stability (grafitization begins at 788°C and therefore a coolant is required), a very low coefficient of friction, and is an excellent electrical insulator. Tool and die stones are larger stones of fairly high quality [to true and dress conventional abrasive wheels; turning, boring, and milling tools; wire-drawing dies]; drilling materials are regular shaped crystals used for various drilling activities [exploration drilling (15-100 stones/carat); masonry and concrete drilling (50-200 stones/carat); oilwell drilling (12 stones/carat)]; grits and powders [loose-grained and bonded abrasive; engraving points; lapping compounds; fine finishing tools; wire dies]. Diamond has replaced traditional cutting materials for everything from cataract surgery to cutting uncooked pasta.

PROPERTIES OF GEMSTONES

	Colors	Hardness (Mohs)	SG	Refractive index (brilliance)	Dispersion (fire)
Natural diamond	colorless, yellow, brown, pink, green, gray, black.	10	3.52	2.417*	0.044
Gadolinium gallium garnet	colorless	7	7.05	2.05*	0.038
Yttrium aluminum garnet	colorless	8+	4.65	1.8333*	0.028
Strontium titanate	colorless	5-6	5.13	2.41*	0.19
Paste (lead glass)	colorless	5.5	3.74	1.63*	variable
Cubic zirconia	colorless	8.5	5.4-5.7	2.15*	0.060
Lithium niobate	colorless	6	4.64	2.21-2.30**	0.13
Zircon	colorless, yellow, brown, red, purple, blue, green	7+	4.67	1.926-1.985**	0.139
Topaz	colorless, yellow, brown, red, blue, green	8	3.56	1.612-1.622**	0.014
Quartz	colorless	7	2.65	1.544-1.553**	0.013

* single refraction; ** double refraction.

A diamond makes an excellent gem because of three main characteristics: *resistance to wear* - i.e. its hardness (see above); *rarity* - one carat may require the processing of up to 20t of rock, and only a small percentage of the diamonds recovered is gem quality; in addition, the combination of size, color, and shape renders each diamond virtually unique; *beauty* - comes from its brilliance (refractive index of 2.417), fire (dispersion of 0.044), and scintillation which, according to some, surpasses all rivals [jewelry; investment stone] as shown below.

QUALITY & SPECIFICATIONS: Diamonds are hand sorted into gem, near-gem, and industrial grades.

Gem quality:- assessed by the four "Cs", carat weight, color, clarity, and cut. *Carat weight -* diamonds are weighed within a tolerance of 1/200 by metric carat (0.2 gm) which is divided into 100 points (2,268 carats = 1 pound; 5,000 carats = 1 kg). Stones less than 2 carats are regarded as small gems.

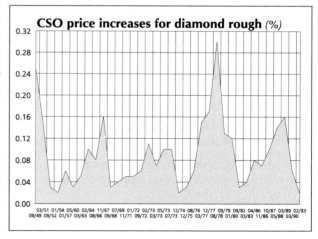

CSO price increases for diamond rough *(%)*

Color - this is generally measured by an instrument like The DiamondLite which compares the target stone with a master set of diamonds. There are several systems used to quantify color, for example the Gemological Institute of America (GIA) has 23 gradations from D (colorless) to Z (yellow).

Clarity, that is the internal quality of a diamond, is a measure of its imperfections, inclusions, and flaws. A diamond may be regarded as flawless if no bubble, carbon spots, feathers, cracks, clouds or blemishes of any kind can be seen using ten-power magnification in a binocular microscope with "dark field" illumination.

STANDARD MICRON SIZES

Size designation (grade number)	Nominal size range (microns)	Max. permissible particle size (microns)
¼	0 - ½	¾
½	0 - 1	1½
1	0 - 2	3
2	1 - 3	4
3	2 - 4	6
4	2 - 6	8
5	4 - 6	8
6	4 - 8	10
8	6 - 10	12
10	8 - 12	14
12	8 - 16	19
15	10 - 20	23
17	12 - 22	25
20	15 - 25	29
25	20 - 30	34
30	22 - 36	40
35	30 - 40	45
45	36 - 54	60
50	40 - 60	67
67	54 - 80	90

US STANDARD (WIRE CLOTH)

Sieve size	Stones per carat	Average diameter (inches)
3½	.32	.223
4	.52	.187
5	.88	.157
6	1.4	.132
7	2.8	.111
8	4.2	.098
10	7	.079
12	12	.066
14	20	.055
16	33	.047
18	57	.039
20	97	.033
25	160	.028
30	282	.023
35	460	.019
40	770	.016
45	1,334	.014
50	2,080	.012
60	3,240	.010
70	6,140	.008
80	10,400	.007
100	17,140	.006
120	20,920	.005
140	49,400	.004
170	83,400	.0035
200	140,000	.0029
230	252,000	.0025
270	384,000	.0021
325	660,000	.0017
400	1,130,000	.0015

Industrial diamond capacity

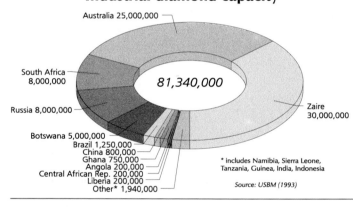

Australia 25,000,000
South Africa 8,000,000
Russia 8,000,000
Botswana 5,000,000
Brazil 1,250,000
China 800,000
Ghana 750,000
Angola 200,000
Central African Rep. 200,000
Liberia 200,000
Other* 1,940,000

81,340,000

Zaire 30,000,000

* includes Namibia, Sierra Leone, Tanzania, Guinea, India, Indonesia

Source: USBM (1993)

DIAMOND GRIT SIZES

Grade #	μm range	Approx. mesh size
½	0-1	50,000
1	0-2	14,000
3	2-4	8,000
6	4-8	3,000
9	8-12	1,800
15	12-22	1,200
30	22-36	800
45	36-54	500/600
60	54-80	400/500

Source: USBS C/S 262/63

The slightest inclusion reduces the value of the stone drastically. There are several clarity grading systems such as the Gemological Institute of America's system which ranges from flawless (F) through very, very slightly included (VVS), very slightly included (VS), slightly included (SI), to imperfect (I). Each division has several subdivisions.

Cut - there are various types, the most popular being the brilliant cut.

Near-gem:- diamonds with substantial impurities and other defects that, depending on market conditions and labor costs, can be either cut into cheap gems or used as industrial diamonds (a.k.a. "Indian goods" since most are cut in India).

Industrial diamonds may be divided into several categories including: *Industrial stones (fine industrials):-* large stones unsuited for gem use because of shape, mechanical imperfections, or color; *Bort:-* a low-grade (small, irregular shape with flaws and imperfections) natural industrial diamond crushed into finer grades and used chiefly in drilling (drilling bort) or as grit, powder, or dust; *Carbonado (black diamond):-* a compact, opaque dark gray to black diamond/graphite/amorphous carbon mixture, with no cleavage; *Ballas (short bort):-* a dense, globular aggregate that is extremely hard and tough.

Diamond grit ranges in size from very coarse (2.0 to 2.4 mm) to fine (38 to 44 μm). Still finer material is diamond micron powders.

Synthetics are available in sizes up to 100 stones per carat (1.2 to 1.4 mm). Based on size (see tables), diamonds are divided into stones (>16-20 mesh), grit (16-20 to 325-400 mesh), and powder or micron (<400 mesh).

DIAMOND LEADERS

Producers

Industrial	Gem	Total Gem + Industrial	Synthetic	Importers	Exporters
Australia	Australia	Australia	United States	Belgium	Belgium
Russia	Botswana	Zaire	South Africa	India	United Kingdom
South Africa	Russia	Russia	Ireland	United Kingdom	South Africa
Botswana	South Africa	Botswana	Russia	Germany	India
Brazil	Namibia	South Africa	Japan	Ireland	Germany
China	Angola	Namibia	Sweden	Italy	Zaire
Ghana	Brazil	Brazil	China	United States	Taiwan
Venezuela	Gabon	Angola	Czechoslovakia	Taiwan	United States
Gabon	CAR	China	Yugoslavia	Israel	Russia
Liberia	China	Others	Romania	Korea	Switzerland
Sierra Leone	Ghana	Ghana	France	France	Japan
CAR	Sierra Leone	Gabon	Greece	Austria	Thailand
Angola	Venezuela	CAR		Spain	Israel
Namibia	Guinea	Sierra Leone		Thailand	Italy

WORLD CAPACITY: 80M. carats (natural), 488M. carats (synthetic).

CAPACITY UTILIZATION: Varies with market.

MARKET CONDITIONS: Increasing rapidly.

APPARENT CONSUMPTION OF DIAMONDS (CARATS)

	Apparent Consumption including synthetics
United States	110,434,220
Ireland	98,560,000
USSR	53,326,000
Australia	37,066,000
India	33,913,598
Italy	30,573,592
Sweden	25,000,000
Japan	23,918,369
Germany	21,267,996
Botswana	16,500,000
China	16,477,550
Korea	15,513,590
Israel	15,298,000
Belgium	13,118,426
France	9,961,931
Brazil	7,051,000
Spain	6,977,477
Austria	6,365,000
Czechoslovakia	5,000,000

NOTE: Numbers are approximate and rounded for 1991 or thereabouts; absence of a country does not necessarily indicate no production or trade; absence of a number does not necessarily mean zero

Source: British Geological Survey and USBM

Synthetic diamond capacity

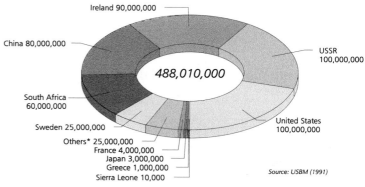

Ireland 90,000,000
China 80,000,000
South Africa 60,000,000
Sweden 25,000,000
Others* 25,000,000
France 4,000,000
Japan 3,000,000
Greece 1,000,000
Sierra Leone 10,000
USSR 100,000,000
United States 100,000,000

488,010,000

Source: USBM (1991)

*5,000,000 each - Germany, Czechoslovakia, Romania, Yugoslavia, Yugoslavia

Production of synthetic diamonds

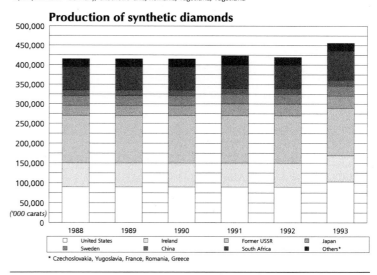

| | United States | | Ireland | | Former USSR | | Japan |
| | Sweden | | China | | South Africa | | Others* |

* Czechoslovakia, Yugoslavia, France, Romania, Greece

MARKETING FACTORS: *Gem quality:*- state of the economy, availability of disposable income, fashion, the success of advertising, interest & exchange rates, inflation rate, etc. The gem diamond trade is largely controlled by De Beers through its Central Selling Organization (CSO). *Industrial quality:*- increasing availability and decreasing prices together with the emphasis on life cycles rather than initial investment have promoted synthetic diamond as an abrasive.

HEALTH & SAFETY: None.

SUBSTITUTES & ALTERNATIVES: Various colored precious and semiprecious stones; paste and cosmetic jewelry; various high-quality abrasives like boron nitride (Knoop 4,500), fused alumina (2,100), & SiC (2,500).

RECYCLING: One of the major strengths of diamond as an abrasive is the fact that it can be recovered, cleaned, resized, and reused many times over with little or no reduction in effectiveness. Some 3 million carats/year are recovered from powders salvaged from grinding wheels, saws, and lapidary compounds. The much higher initial cost of diamond compared with rival abrasives may be justified in certain cases by an increased life cycle based on recycling.

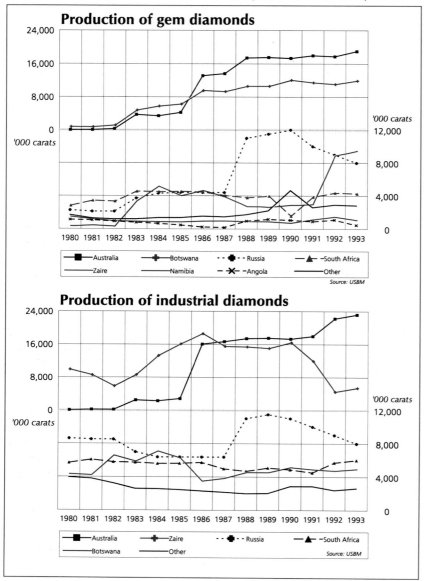

Production of gem diamonds

Legend: Australia, Botswana, Russia, South Africa, Zaire, Namibia, Angola, Other

Source: USBM

Production of industrial diamonds

Legend: Australia, Zaire, Russia, South Africa, Botswana, Other

Source: USBM

PRODUCERS & WORLD TRADE: Australia, Botswana, South Africa, Russia, and Zaire account for more than 90% of the volume, although Botswana, South Africa, and Russia account for the bulk of the value. Diamonds are extremely portable and mobile commodities. All the major producers are exporters, and many countries re-export imported diamonds. The main gem cutting centers are New York, United States; Tel Aviv, Israel; Antwerp, Belgium; Bombay, India; Bangkok, Thailand; other S.E. Asian centers. Value is more important than volume (see prices). Worldwide sales of rough diamonds are valued at more than $5 billion with the CSO controling 80% of the market.

PRICES: Price per carat for gem-quality is x10 near-gems which is x10 industrial diamonds. Prices vary enormously depending on quality and size, and are tightly controlled by DeBeers. Gem prices have increased steadily, as synthetic industrial prices have fallen. *Gems (natural)*:- $600-800 (large, >2 carats), $200-300 (medium, 0.45-2 carats), $50-250 (small, <0.45 carats), $5-50 (near-gems).*Industrial*:- $1-150 (natural); $125 (special, large synthetic); $0.20 (synthetic, crushing bort).

HTS CODES: 7102.10/20/29/30/40 (various grades of industrial diamond); 7105.10 (dust, grit, or powder); 7102.31 (diamonds, unworked or sawn); 7102.10 (diamond, less than ½ carat); 7102.50 (diamond, cut more than ½ carat).

ETYMOLOGY: Diamond from the Latin *adamas* = *unconquerable* or *invincible*; first used in Manilius (AD 16).

PRODUCTION AND TRADE IN DIAMONDS (CARATS)

	Production, natural + synthetic	Imports	Exports	Apparent Consumption including synthetics	Net Supplier	Net Consumer
North America	90,000,000	29,732,333	10,806,693	108,925,640		(18,925,640)
South America	1,759,000	5,751,000	200,000	7,310,000		(5,551,000)
European Union	65,000,000	304,477,114	215,879,474	153,597,640		(88,597,640)
Non-EU Europe	100,500,000	8,870,000	16,429,000	92,941,000	7,559,000	
Africa	47,086,000	-	60,782,531	(13,696,531)	60,782,531	
Australasia	77,006,000	139,632,191	68,745,394	147,892,797		(70,886,797)

NOTE: Numbers are approximate and rounded for 1991 or thereabouts; data is ambiguous due to double counting imports, re-exports, and imports, smuggling, and some data given in currency.

Source: British Geological Survey

DIATOMITE

Siliceous sedimentary rock comprising tiny fossilized skeletal diatoms.

Mineral	Formula	Color	SG	H
Diatomite (raw)	$SiO_2 \cdot nH_2O$	cream - gray	1.95	4.5 - 5
Diatomite (calcined)	SiO_2	white/pink	2.3	5.5 - 6

Strictly, diatomite (a.k.a. diatomaceous earth or kieselguhr) is a rock composed of diatomaceous silica. Moler or moler earth is impure diatomite containing up to 30% clay.

PROPERTIES & USES: Diatomite comprises irregularly shaped diatom frustules with a chemical composition similar to opal or hydrous silica. The structure and ornamentation of the frustules are extremely diverse. Some of the many thousands of species have radial symmetry and resemble wheels, discs, and golf balls; others are bilaterally symmetrical and look like boats, feathers, ladders, or needles. In the typical lace-like patterns, the combined area of the holes ranges from 10 to 30% of the total area. Frustules range in diameter from 5 to 1,000 μm; the majority are in the 50 to 100 μm range. On average 1 inch^3 of diatomite contains 40M. frustules. Calcination (870-1,093°C) and flux calcination (at 1,148°C with soda ash or salt) burn off organic matter, increase SG (from 2.0 to 2.3), H (from 5-5.5 to 5.5-6), and refractive index (from 1.4 to 1.49), reduce surface area through the destruction of fine structure, and decrease the surface area of milled powders (from 10-30 to 0.5-5 m^2/g). Flux calcining converts the iron oxide to a colorless glassy phase and produces a white rather than pink diatomite.

The nature of the particulate structure combined with chemical stability and inertness make diatomite an ideal filter aid [swimming pools; water treatment; dry-cleaning solvents; pharmaceuticals & antibiotics; beer, liquor, and wine; raw sugar liquors and fruit juices; crude fats and vegetable oils; various lubricating and cutting oils; organic and inorganic chemicals; varnishes & lacquers]. In the separation of suspended solids from fluids a woven cloth or screen or tubes or discs of porous powder (the septum or filter mesh) can only trap relatively large particles and are quickly clogged. A fine-powder filter aid like diatomite allows finer particles to be removed before they reach the septum thus yielding an acceptable level of clarity together with a high rate of flow and the maximum filter cycle length (high clarity and fast filtration are mutually opposed achievements). The size and shape of the diatomite particles provide for optimum cake permeability and a high initial liquid flow. The irregular particle structure forms a bed containing 85-90% voids and billions of fine interstices in which impurities are trapped. This includes the spaces between the individual diatoms as well as in the interstices and chambers within the diatom structure itself. In addition, diatomite is lightweight, can be compressed and still retain up to 90% voids, and can remove solid particles 0.1μm in size.

Diatomite's brightness of up to 90%, refractive index of 1.42-1.49, low bulk density, inertness and moderate refractoriness (softening range 1,400-1,600°C), high absorptive capacity, and high surface area allow it to be used as a filler [paint (flatting agent); paper; rubber; chemicals; dental impressions & dentrifices, chemicals, and pharmaceuticals] and anti-blocking agent which separate adjacent sheets and so prevent cold welding [polyethylene film]. In paint, diatomite's fine size and irregular shape roughen the surface thus providing a flatting effect and improving intercoat adhesion, and add toughness and durability to the film. In the production of fine and specialty papers and in linerboard diatomite improves sheet formation and drainage. Since the diatomite tends to absorb the oil, silicone rubber compounds remain soft and millable with good tensile and tear strength [rubber products].

Diatomite may be used as a mild abrasive since it is moderately hard and the hollow structure breaks down under pressure to provide a good polishing action [toothpaste, polish and buffing compounds].

PROS & CONS OF MINERAL FILTER AIDS

Filter aid	Pros	Cons
Diatomite	Wide size range. Fines may be reduced by calcination.	Slightly soluble in dilute acids and alkalis.
Perlite	Wide size range. Equals finest retention of diatomite. Lower bulk density (45-90 kg/m) than diatomite (120-190 kg/m).	More soluble than diatomite in acids & alkalis. May form highly compressive cakes.
Cellulose	Used mainly as a coarse precoat. High purity, excellent chemical resistance. Insoluble in dilute acids.	Expensive.
Carbon	Used to filter very strong alkali solutions.	Available in coarse grades only. Expensive.

Source: Adapted from Matteson & Orr, 1987, Filtration - Principals and Practices.

TYPICAL PHYSICAL PROPERTIES OF DIATOMITE

	Filler						Abrasives		Conditioning Agent	
	Paper Cylinder machine Celite 321A	Paper Fourdrinier Celite 305	Paint High-flatting Celite 281	Paint Semi-gloss Celite 499	Plastic Polyethylene White Mist	Rubber Celite 270	Automobile Polish Super Floss	Buffing Compound Celite HSC	Toxicant Carrier Celite 209	Fertilizer Coating Celite 392
Loose wt., pcf	8.0	-	8.5	8.5	7.5	8.6	8.7	9.0	8.0	7.0
Wet density, pcf	20	24	22	22	23	28	24	19	24	17
Moisture, % max.	6.0	4.0	0.5	0.5	0.5	0.5	0.5	0.5	6.0	6.0
Retained on 150 mesh, %wt	0.5	0.1	Trace	Trace	0	0	0	6	Trace	0.5
Retained on 325 mesh, %wt	8.0	1.0	1.5	Trace	0.05	0.7	0.1	17.6	0.5	5.00
Oil absorption, %wt	210	175	110	105	160	150	105	185	175	210
Color	Lt. Grey	Gray	White	White	White	Pink	White	White	Buff	Buff
pH, max.	7.0	7.0	10.0	10.0	10.0	7.0	9.4	9.5	7.0	7.0
Resistivity	3,000	3,000	13,000	7,400	6,500	30,000	-	-	3,000	4,000
Refractive index	1.40	1.40	1.46	1.46	1.47	1.45	1.47	1.47	1.43	1.43
Surface area. m^2/g	10-20	10-20	0.7-3.5	0.7-3.5	0.7-3.5	4-6	0.7-3.5	0.7-3.5	10-20	10-20
Median particle size, µm	-	-	7.8	6.8	3.5	5.1	5.5	17.5	-	-

	Veg oil Celite 500 Natural	Wine Celite 505 Calcined	Beer & wine Standard Super-Cel Calcined	Beer Celite 512 Calcined	Filter aid Dry cleaning solvents, chem, sugar Hyflo-Super-Cel Calcined	Grape juice Celite 501 Calcined	Industrial & potable water Celite 503 Calcined	Industrial wastes Celite 535 Flux calcined	Swimming pools Celite 545 Flux calcined	Corn sugar Celite 580 Flux calcined	Phosphoric acid Celite 560 Flux calcined
Color	Gray	Pink	Pink	Pink	White	White	White	White	White	White	White
Dry density, pcf	7.0	8.0	8.0	8.0	9.0	9.5	9.5	12.0	12.0	18	16
Wet density, pcf	16	23	18	19	18	18	18	19	19	21	20
Screen analysis, % -150 mesh	2.0	2.0	4	7	6	8	9	10	12	30	40
pH	7.0	7.0	7.0	7.0	10.0	10.0	10.0	10.0	10.0	10.0	10.0
Median pore size, µm	1.5	2.5	3.5	5.0	7.0	9.1	10.0	13.0	17.0	17.0	22.0
Permeability, d'Arcy	0.057	0.16	0.28	0.53	1.20	1.4	2.0	3.1	4.8	4.8	30.0

Source: Breese, 1994

Based on its inertness, high surface area, and low bulking value, diatomite can absorb 2 to 3 times its own weight of liquid and thus acts as a carrier [pesticide & seed inoculates]; free-flowing or anti-caking agents [ammonium nitrate prills; stabilizer; fertilizers], stabilizer [acetylene containers; explosives]; absorbers [pet litter; oil spills; waste treatment], and catalyst carriers [nickel for hydrogenation; vanadium for sulfuric acid production; phosphoric acid for petroleum refining].

Miscellaneous uses include silica source in the manufacture of synthetic silicates [calcium and magnesium silicates]; a source of reactive silica [acetylene gas cylinders]; an additive to improve plastic and hardened properties of portland cement mixtures [concrete, stucco, plaster, grouts, gunite]; a porous ingredient where required [controls combustion after glow in matches]; a thermal and sound insulator and fireproofer (mainly Molar) [industrial fireproofing; in insulating bricks; and loose fill].

QUALITY & SPECIFICATIONS: Commercial diatomite contains 85-94% SiO_2 plus 1-7% Al_2O_3, 0.4-2.5% Fe_2O_3, 0.1-0.5% TiO_2, 0.03-0.2% P_2O_5, 0.3-3% CaO, 0.3-1.0% MgO, 0.2-0.5% Na_2O, and 0.3-0.9% K_2O plus organic matter, soluble salts (0.1-0.2%), and various rock-forming minerals. Natural, calcined, and flux calcined filter-aid grades depend on diatom skeletal constitution and structure and have the characteristics outlined in the tables.

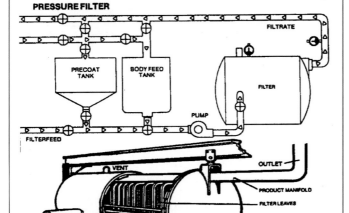

PRESSURE FILTER

ROTARY VACUUM PRECOAT FILTER

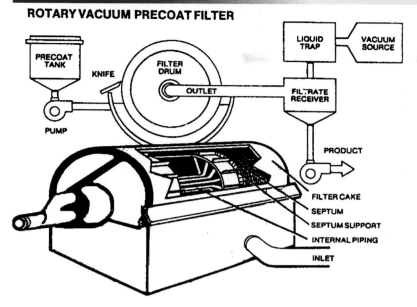

MINIMUM STANDARD CLARITY/FLOWRATE RATIOS
BASED ON STANDARD RAW SUGAR SOLUTION 60° BRIX 80° C

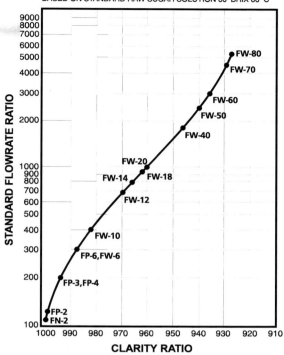

Filter-grade diatomite focuses on particle size distribution and porosity of the filter aid cake since these characteristics determine permeability and flow-rate clarity of the filter cake. In general, natural grades exhibit slower flow rates but the greatest clarity; with calcined grades it is the reverse. The objective is to select a grade or blend of grades that provides an acceptable flow rate and clarity. Filler-grade diatomite is usually produced from baghouse fines and ranges in particle size from 1 to 50 μm.

Water permeability is measured in Darcies defined as "A material having a permeability of 1 Darcy unit passes 1 ml per second per cm^2 of a liquid of 1 centipoise viscosity through a cake of 1 cm thickness at a pressure differential of 1 atmosphere".

WORLD CAPACITY: 2M. t.

CAPACITY UTILIZATION: NA.

MARKET CONDITIONS: Increasing.

MARKETING FACTORS: Wine, beer, fruit juice, etc., swimming pool building, general state of the economy, and population growth.

HEALTH & SAFETY: Crystalline silica has been classified as a probable carcinogen by the IARC (see silica for further details). Therefore, because of its crystalline silica content, diatomite comes under the OSHA Hazard Communication Standards, 29 CFR Section 1900.1200 which require labeling and other forms of warning, material safety data sheets, and employee training for products containing identified carcinogens with concentrations greater than 0.1%. This has implications not only on the production and use of diatomite, but also on the disposal of diatomite and diatomite-bearing material such as spent filter cake.

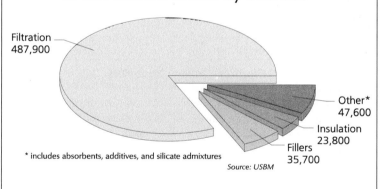

Diatomite sales and exports in the United States by end use

Filtration 487,900
Other* 47,600
Insulation 23,800
Fillers 35,700

* includes absorbents, additives, and silicate admixtures

Source: USBM

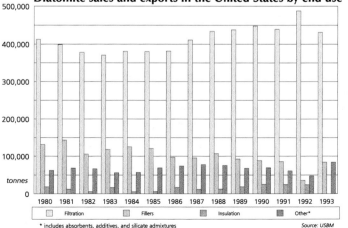

Diatomite sales and exports in the United States by end use

	Filtration	Fillers	Insulation	Other*

* includes absorbents, additives, and silicate admixtures

Source: USBM

SUBSTITUTES & ALTERNATIVES: Absorbent/pet litter:- clays (attapulgite, bentonite, sepiolite), gypsum, zeolites. **Abrasives**:- calcined kaolin, precipitated silica (anti-blocking agents); bauxite & alumina (fused alumina), corundum/emery, diamonds, feldspar, garnet, iron oxide (magnetite), nepheline syenite, olivine, perlite, pumice, silica sand, staurolite, tripoli, and silicon carbide, ilmenite. **Carrier**:- attapulgite, bentonite, kaolin, peat, pumice, pyrophyllite, sepiolite, talc, vermiculite, zeolites. **Filter Media**:- activated carbon/anthracite, asbestos, cellulose, diatomite, garnet, iron oxide (magnetite), perlite, pumice, silica sand, ilmenite plus non-mineral filtration systems like vacuum filtration and cross-flow filtration.

Filler:- ATH, barite, calcium carbonate, feldspar, kaolin, mica, nepheline syenite, perlite, talc, microcrystalline silica, ground silica flour and synthetic silica, wollastonite. **Thermal and sound insulator**:- brick clays, mineral wool, expanded perlite, and exfoliated vermiculite.

Diatomite production

Source: USBM

RECYCLING: In some filter systems, the filter media can be back flushed and cleaned for re-use. However, for the filtration of beer and the like, the diatomite filtercake is rarely re-used.

PRODUCERS & WORLD TRADE: World production and exports of high-quality diatomite are dominated by the United States which sets the standard for quality. Most of the production in Denmark is actually molar, an impure mixture that includes diatomite.

PRICES: United States (FOB plant) $300-450/t (list, filter-aid grade); $262/t (sales average, 1993, filter-aid grade); $360 (list, calcined filter-aid grade); $250-300/t (list, insulation grade); $153/t (sales average, 1993, insulation grade); $280 (list, paint filler grade); $287 (sales average, 1993, filler grade); $230-300/t (insecticide grade); $180-200/t (concrete additive); $1,350/t (superfine grades).

Europe (del. UK) $480-525/t (US calcined, filter aids); $510-570/t (US flux-calcined filter aids).

HTS CODES: 2512.00.0000 (siliceous fossil meals (e.g. kieselguhr, tripolite, and diatomite) and similar siliceous earths, whether or not calcined, of an apparent specific gravity of 1 or less).

ETYMOLOGY: Diatomite from the Latin via Greek *dia = through* and *tome = cutting* in reference to the two generally symmetrical valves of the single-cell diatom. **Kieselguhr** from the German *kiesel = flint* and *guhr = earthy sediment* deposited in water.

DIATOMITE LEADERS

Producers	Exporters	Importers
United States	United States	Germany
Former USSR	Denmark	United Kingdom
France	France	Netherlands
Denmark	Mexico	Canada
Spain	Austria	France
Mexico	Spain	Belgium
South Korea	Italy	Austria
Romania	Germany	Italy
Germany	Belgium	

PRODUCTION AND TRADE IN DIATOMITE (TONNES)

	Production	Imports	Exports	Apparent Consumption	Net Supplier	Net Consumer
North America	689,207	22,141	152,445	558,903	130,304	
South America	47,277	11,101	1,461	56,917		(9,640)
C. America & Carib.	6,000	2,430		8,430		(2,430)
European Union	498,310	167,908	140,639	525,579		(27,269)
Non-EU Europe	330,975	37,257	38,203	330,029	946	
Australasia	69,593	33,007		102,600		(33,007)
Middle East		4,785		4,785		(4,785)
Africa	7,898	8,815	530	16,183		(8,285)

NOTE: Numbers are approximate and rounded for 1990 or thereabouts

Source: British Geological Survey

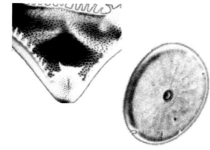
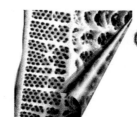

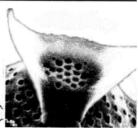

APPARENT CONSUMPTION OF DIATOMITE (TONNES)

	Apparent Consumption
United States	487,230
Former USSR	250,000
France	228,499
Germany	94,334
Spain	80,415
South Korea	54,791
Romania	51,100
Mexico	47,722
United Kingdom	35,958
Italy	29,722
Netherlands	24,532
Canada	23,951
Peru	20,292
Brazil	17,857
Australia	16,192
Belgium	13,809
Argentina	9,038
Denmark	8,527
Austria	7,877
Switzerland	6,801
Portugal	6,798
Costa Rica	6,316
Former Yugoslavia	6,201
Taiwan	5,922
South Africa	5,465
Thailand	4,868
Saudi Arabia	4,785
Colombia	4,506
Algeria	4,389
Finland	3,610
Tunisia	3,183
China	3,100
Greece	2,771
New Zealand	2,654
Japan	2,638
Venezuela	2,587

NOTE: Numbers are approximate and rounded for 1990; absence of a country does not necessarily indicate no production or trade; absence of a number does not necessarily mean zero

Source: British Geolgogical Survey

Average annual value of diatomite by major use

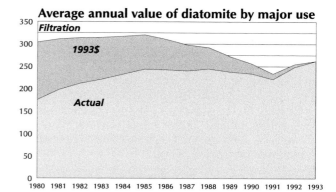

Filtration — 1993$ — Actual

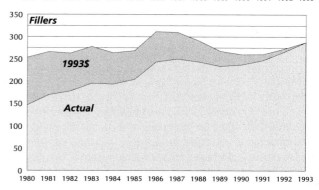

Fillers — 1993$ — Actual

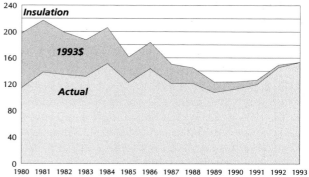

Insulation — 1993$ — Actual

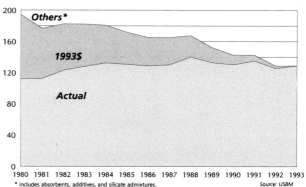

Others* — 1993$ — Actual

* includes absorbents, additives, and silicate admixtures.

Source: USBM

Feldspars are aluminosilicates with varying amounts of K, Na, and Ca in a solid solution series; the main commercial feldspars lie between the sodium (albite) and potash (microcline) rich end members, and the sodium end of the sodium-calcium series (oligoclase).

Minerals	Formula	%Al$_2$O$_3$	%SiO$_2$	%Other	Color	SG	H
Microcline	KAlSi$_3$O$_8$	18.3	64.8	16.9 K$_2$O	gray-white, pinkish	2.56	6-6.5
Albite	NaSi$_3$O$_8$	19.4	68.8	11.8 Na$_2$O	white-gray	2.60-2.62	6-6.5
Oligoclase	(Na, Ca)Si$_3$O$_8$	18.4	64.7	8.7 Na$_2$O	grayish	2.64	6-6.5

Microcline or orthoclase, known as potassium feldspar or potash spar or K spar, is required to contain 10% or more K$_2$O; albite or sodium plagioclase, known as soda spar or Na spar, 7% or more Na$_2$O. Aplite is a fine-grained quartz-feldspar igneous rock used as a feldspar source. Alaskite is an important feldpsar-bearing rock mined in North Carolina, United States.

PROPERTIES & USES: In glassmaking feldspar is used as a source of Al$_2$O$_3$, Na$_2$O, and/or K$_2$O, and SiO$_2$ [borosilicate glass; soda-lime (flat and container) glass; fiberglass; TV tube glass]. The alumina enhances the workability of molten glass, increases the resistance of glass to chemical corrosion, improves the hardness and durability, and inhibits devitrification. The alkalis (which partially replace soda ash) act as a flux and chemically attack the other glass batch minerals such as silica.

In ceramics, feldspar acts as a flux to form a glassy phase in bodies [vitreous and semivitreous china; wall & floor tile; sanitaryware; electrical porcelain; frits, glazes, & enamels]. In both glass and ceramics, feldspar contributes SiO$_2$. High-purity K-spar [high-voltage porcelain insulators; artificial teeth (dental spar)].

With properties such as sub-angular particle shape, H6-6.5, G.E. brightness of 89-92%, refractive index of 1.53, chemical inertness, oil absorption of 16-17 to 21-23 lbs/100 lb (ASTM D-28-31), non-photoreactivity, and low free silica content, fine-ground (APS 4-12 µm) feldspar is a useful filler [latex and oleoresinous exterior and interior paint; plastics; caulks, sealants, adhesives, mastics; elastomers]. The controlled PSD assists flatting and retouchability; the relatively low oil absorption minimizes viscosity increases; and chemical inertness prevents atmospheric degradation and reaction with other raw materials.

Feldspar is also used as a mild abrasive [scouring powders] and welding rod coating.

QUALITY & SPECIFICATIONS: Soda spar is preferred in glass and potash spar in ceramics. *Glass-grade feldspar:*- 4-6% K$_2$O, 5-7% Na$_2$O, 19% Al$_2$O$_3$ with a max. 0.08% Fe$_2$O$_3$; 20-40 mesh (flat glass); ground to -20 to -40 (-850 to 425 µm). *Ceramic- or pottery-grade feldspar:*- 5-14% K$_2$O with a max. 0.07% Fe$_2$O$_3$; -200 mesh (sanitaryware); ground to -200 mesh (-75 µm).

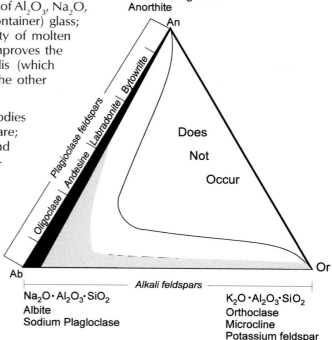

CaO·Al$_2$O$_3$·2SiO$_2$
Calcium Plagioclase
Anorthite
An

Does Not Occur

Plagioclase feldspars
Oligoclase | Andesine | Labradonite | Bytownite

Ab — *Alkali feldspars* — Or

Na$_2$O·Al$_2$O$_3$·SiO$_2$
Albite
Sodium Plagioclase

K$_2$O·Al$_2$O$_3$·SiO$_2$
Orthoclase
Microcline
Potassium feldspar

TYPICAL GLASS BATCH COMPOSITIONS (% BY WEIGHT)

	Container glass	Flat glass	Spec. glass	Insul. f'glass	Textile f'glass
Silica sand	57.0	60.0	65.0	42.0	29.0
Feldspar /Neph. syenite	8.0		11.0	18.0	
Soda ash	19.0	20.0	2.0	4.0	
Limestone	16.0	5.0		15.0	30.0
Dolomite		20.0		11.0	
Boron			22.0	10.0	12.0
Kaolin					29.0

TYPICAL ALUMINA & ALKALI CONTENT BY GLASS (%)

	Al$_2$O$_3$	Na$_2$O	K$_2$O
Container glass - white	1.5	13.0	1
Container glass - green	2.6	12.5	1.5
Flat glass	—	13.7	0.2
Pressed ware	0.3	16.9	—
Boro-silicate glass	2.4	4.2	—
Lead-crystal glass	0.02	1.0	14.9
CRT faceplate	3.5	7.5	10.5
Fiber optics	3.0	14.0	—
Glass ceramics	20.9	—	—
Textile fiberglass			
A-Glass (Al$_2$O$_3$+Fe$_2$O$_3$)	1.5	13.0	—
C-Glass (Al$_2$O$_3$+Fe$_2$O$_3$)	4.0	0.5	8
D-Glass	—	1.0	1.5
E-Glass	14.5	— 0.8 —	
R-Glass	25.0	0.4	0.1
S-Glass	25.0	—	—
AR-Glass	1.0	—	—

SPECIFICATIONS FOR FELDSPAR USED AS A FILLER

	Minspar 3	Minspar 4	Minspar 25	Minspar 7
G.E. bightness	89.6	91.4	91.5	92.2
Weight/solid gallon (lb/gal)	21.61	21.61	21.61	21.61
Bulking value (US gal/lb)	0.0463	0.0463	0.0463	0.0463
Apparent bulk density (lb/ft^3)				
Loose	44	40	40	38
Packed	70	60	60	55
Moisture content	0.1	0.1	0.1	0.1
pH	8.7	9.3	9.3	9.3
Oil absorption (rub out) ASTM D-282-31	16 - 17	18 - 19	19 - 20	21 - 23
Particle size distribution, % finer than				
74μ	99.6	100	100	100
44μ	96	99.95	100	100
30μ	87	94	99	100
20μ	72	88	96	100
10μ	41	60	70	90
5μ	19	30	35	55
Mean particle size, μ	12	8	7	4.8
Specific surface area (m^2/g)	0.8 - 0.9	1.0 - 1.2	1.2 - 1.4	1.5 - 1.6

Source: K-T Feldspar Corp., USA

SPECIFICATIONS FOR COMMERCIAL FELDSPAR

	Glass F-20	Glass C-20	Glass G-40	Glass Aplite*	Pottery NC-4	Pottery C-6	Pottery G-200	Pottery K-200
SiO_2	68.20	68.90	67.70	63.10	68.15	68.70	67.00	67.10
Al_2O_3	22.00	18.75	18.50	22.00	19.00	18.50	18.30	18.30
Fe_2O_3	0.10	0.07	0.1 max	0.10	0.067	0.07	0.08	0.07
CaO	5.60	1.85	0.90	5.60	1.60	0.90	1.02	0.36
MgO	trace	trace	trace	trace	trace	trace	trace	trace
K_2O	3.00	3.85	4.10	3.00	4.00	4.10	10.50	10.10
Na_2O	6.00	7.15	7.00	6.00	7.00	7.20	2.85	3.80
LOI	0.20	0.13	0.25	0.20	0.10	0.25	0.20	0.26
Screen analysis, cum. % retained on:	0	0	0					
16 mesh	0.1	0.4		0				
20 mesh	8.2	8.0		1.5				
30 mesh	12.0			15.0				
40 mesh		49.0	1.75	50.0				
50 mesh	85.5	81.0		97.0				
100 mesh	98.8	96.1	61.0	100.0				
200 mesh			97.5					

* Feldspar Corp. no longer produces aplite

Source: Feldspar Corp., USA

WORLD CAPACITY: 6.1M. t.

CAPACITY UTILIZATION: 90%.

MARKET CONDITIONS: Steady-increasing regionally.

MARKETING FACTORS: Glass & ceramics depend on the construction activity which is driven by the economy. Consumption is affected by increased glass recycling.

HEALTH & SAFETY: In 1987 crystalline silica was classified as a probable carcinogen by the International Agency for Research on Cancer (IARC), a unit of the World Health Organization. This was followed by IARC's Supplement 7 in which crystalline silica was classified in Group 2A, that is probably carcinogenic to humans. Therefore, feldspar comes under

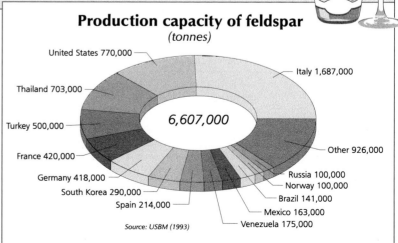

Production capacity of feldspar
(tonnes)

6,607,000

United States 770,000
Italy 1,687,000
Thailand 703,000
Turkey 500,000
France 420,000
Germany 418,000
South Korea 290,000
Spain 214,000
Venezuela 175,000
Mexico 163,000
Brazil 141,000
Norway 100,000
Russia 100,000
Other 926,000

Source: USBM (1993)

the OSHA Hazard Communication Standards, 29 CFR Section 1900.1200 which require labeling and other forms of warning, material safety data sheets, and employee training for products containing identified carcinogens with concentrations greater than 0.1%.

SUBSTITUTES & ALTERNATIVES: Abrasives:- bauxite & alumina (fused alumina), corundum/emery, diamonds, diatomite, garnet, iron oxide (magnetite), nepheline syenite, olivine, perlite, pumice, silica sand, staurolite, tripoli, silicon carbide, ilmenite. **Filler**:- ATH, barite, calcium carbonate, feldspar, kaolin, mica, nepheline syenite, perlite, pyrophyllite, talc, microcrystalline silica, ground silica flour and synthetic silica, wollastonite. **Glass**:- aplite, steel mill slag, cullet, nepheline syenite (container & fiberglass); kaolin (textile-grade fiberglass); calcined alumina or alumina hydrate (specialty glass). **Ceramics**:- aplite, nepheline syenite.

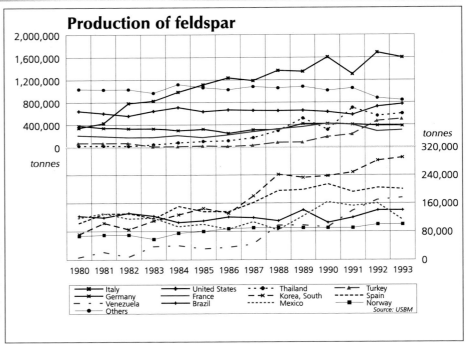

Production of feldspar

Source: USBM

RECYCLING: The use of cullet or recycled glass is increasing which in turn is reducing the need for virgin raw materials in the glass batch. The recycling rate is about 33% in the United States and as high as 90% in some European countries like Switzerland.

PRODUCERS & WORLD TRADE: World production and consumption of feldspar are dominated by Italy and the United States. Despite being a common rock-forming mineral, quality requirements by the ceramics and glass industries mean that there is a considerable international trade in feldspar which competes with nepheline syenite.

PRICES: United States (FOB Spruce Pine, NC, ceramic grade) $67/t (soda spar, 170-250 mesh, bulk); $87/t (soda spar, 170-250 mesh, bags); $126/t (soda spar, 325 mesh, bags). (FOB Monticello, GA, ceramic grade) $105/t (potash spar, 200 mesh, bags). (FOB Spruce Pine, NC, glass grade, bulk) $46/t (soda spar, 30 mesh). (FOB Monticello, GA, glass grade) $88/t (potash spar, 80 mesh, bags). Europe (ex-store UK) $240/t (ceramic grade, powder, 300 mesh, bags); $127.50/t (glass grade, sand, 28 mesh). South Africa (FOB Durban, bags) $140/t (ceramic grade); $235/t (micronized).

HTS CODES: 2529.10 (crude & ground).

A COMPARISON OF ALUMINA SOURCES IN GLASS AND CERAMICS

	Nepheline syenite	Soda-feldspar	Potash-feldspar	Low-iron aplite	Calumite slag
SiO_2	61.40	67.54	67.04	63.71	38.8
Al_2O_3	22.74	19.25	18.02	21.89	10.5
Fe_2O_3	0.06	0.06	0.04	0.09	0.3
CaO	0.70	1.94	0.38	0.48	38.5
MgO	trace	trace	trace	trace	1.4
K_2O	4.95	4.05	12.10	2.37	0.5
Na_2O	9.54	6.96	2.12	5.60	0.4
LOI	0.60	0.13	0.30	0.21	1.1 (S cpds)

PRODUCTION AND TRADE IN FELDSPAR (TONNES)

	Production	Imports	Exports	Apparent Consumption	Net Supplier	Net Consumer
North America	880,000	17,600	29,400	868,200	11,800	
South America	308,000	700	6,600	302,100	5,900	
C. America & Carib.	7,000	7,800	5,000	9,800		(2,800)
European Union	2,564,000	401,650	206,100	2,759,550		(195,550)
Non-EU Europe	676,000	39,200	235,100	480,100	195,900	
Australasia	1,479,400	971,150	754,900	1,695,650		(216,250)
Middle East	65,000	5,500		70,500		(5,500)
Africa	89,300	19,930	6,000	103,230		(13,930)

NOTE: Numbers are approximate and rounded for 1990 or thereabouts.   *Source: British Geological Survey*

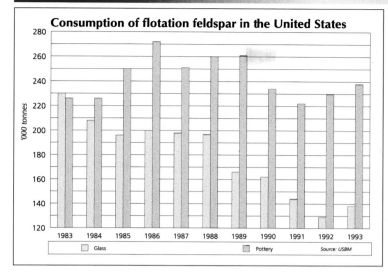

Consumption of flotation feldspar in the United States

'000 tonnes — years 1983–1993. Legend: Glass, Pottery. Source: USBM

ETYMOLOGY: Albite from the Latin *albus = white*, for its color. **Anorthite** from the Greek for *not straight*, because of its triclinic symmetry. **Feldspar** from the Swedish *feldt* or *fält = field* and *spat = spar*, for the spar in the tilled fields overlying granite. **Microcline** from the Greek *mikro = little* and *klinein = to incline* in reference to its characteristic variation of cleavage angle from 90°. **Orthoclase** from the Greek for *straight* and *klasis = fracture* in reference to its cleavage angle of 90°. **Plagioclase** from the Greek *plagios = oblique* and *klasis = fracture* in reference to the oblique angles between its best cleavages.

POSTSCRIPT: Feldspars are the most abundant mineral group constituting 60% of the Earth's crust.

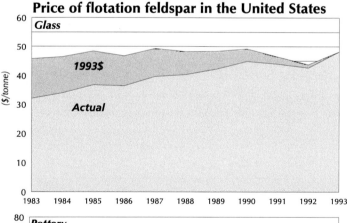

Price of flotation feldspar in the United States

Glass — ($/tonne) 1993$, Actual. Years 1983–1993.

Pottery — ($/tonne) 1993$, Actual. Years 1983–1993.

APPARENT CONSUMPTION OF FELDSPAR (TONNES)

	Apparent Consumption
Italy	1,571,400
United States	720,300
Taiwan	535,500
Germany	465,000
Thailand	368,000
France	308,900
Spain	272,000
South Korea	234,200
India	205,050
Former USSR	200,000
Mexico	147,900
Brazil	108,400
China	108,000
Turkey	103,500
Venezuela	95,700
Japan	75,700
Malaysia	66,800
Iran	65,000
Poland	57,200
United Kingdom	52,500
Philippines	51,250
Egypt	47,300
South Africa	44,000
Portugal	40,300
Colombia	40,000
Former Yugoslavia	35,100
Ecuador	24,000
Argentina	23,500
Finland	20,200
Belgium	19,000
Norway	18,900
Indonesia	16,700
Greece	15,500
Switzerland	14,200
Singapore	13,500
Austria	13,000

NOTE: Numbers are approximate and rounded for 1990 or thereabouts; absence of a country does not necessarily indicate no production or trade; absence of a number does not necessarily mean zero

Source: British Geological Survey

FELDSPAR LEADERS (TONNES)

Producers	Exporters	Importers
Italy	Thailand	Taiwan
United States	China	India
Thailand	Hong Kong	Hong Kong
Germany	France	Italy
France	Turkey	Spain
China	Norway	Germany
South Korea	India	United Kingdom
Spain	Germany	Malaysia
Former USSR	Finland	France
Turkey	Italy	Others
Mexico	South Korea	Singapore
Brazil	Sweden	Belgium

Mineral	Formula	%Ca	%F	Color	SG	H
Fluorite	CaF_2	51.1	48.9	colorless, green, yellow, purple	3.01-3.6	4

Other F-containing minerals are of minor commercial significance and include cryolite (Na_3AlF_6), sellaite (MgF_2), topaz ($Al_2SiO_4(F,OH)_2$), villiaumite (NaF), bastnaesite ((Ce,La)(CO_3)F), and fluorapatite ($Ca_5(PO_4,CO_3)_3F$). Along with chlorine, bromine, iodine, and astatine, fluorine is part of the halogen family.

PROPERTIES & USES: Fluorspar is the dominant commercial source of fluorine.

Acid-grade fluorspar ("acidspar") + heat + conc. sulfuric acid → anhydrous hydrogen fluoride or hydrofluoric acid (70% HF) [acidizing oilwells; brick & stone cleaning; electronic etching; electroplating; enamel stripping; feedstock for F chemicals; glass etching and polishing; master alloy salts; petroleum alkylation; brass, copper, stainless steel pickling]. Calcium sulfate (fluorogypsum) is a byproduct.

HF → chlorofluorocarbons (CFCs) such as trichlorofluoromethane (CCl_3F or CF No.11) and dichlorofluoromethane (CCl_2F_2 or CF No.12 a.k.a. freon) [aerosol propellant; refrigerant; foam blowing agent; solvent]; chlorodifluoromethane ($CHClF_2$ or CF (No.22) [aerosol propellant; feedstock for tetrafluoroethylene, hexafluoropropylene, and bromotrifluoromethane; refrigerant; low-temperature solvent]; trichlorotrifluoroethane ($C_2Cl_3F_3$ or CF No. 113) [dry cleaning solvent; fire extinguisher; refrigerant; solvent drying; foam blowing agent]; dichlorotetrafluoroethane ($C_2Cl_2F_4$ or CF No. 114) [aerosol propellant; foam blowing agent; dielectric fluid]; polytetrafluoroethylene ($C_2F_2)_n$ or P.T.F.E. or Teflon; hydrochlorofluorocarbons (HCFCs) [aerosol propellants; refrigerants; plastic foams]; → fluoropolymers [inert liquids; laser cooling; medical applications], fluoroelastomers which resist hydrocarbons and many organic solvents [seals, gaskets, packing for aerospace and automobiles].

HF → synthetic cryolite (Na_3AlF_6) & aluminum fluoride [molten electrolyte & solvent in aluminum reduction cells (12-29 kg F/tonne virgin aluminum); opal enamel and glass, ceramic body & glazes mixes; specialty refractories; filler in abrasive wheels; insecticide; welding rod coating; aluminum silicates]; → fluosilicic acid* (H_2SiF_2) & fluoroboric acid [electroplating; feedstock for ammonium, cadmium, cupric, iron, lead, nickel, potassium, sodium, stannous, and zinc fluoborate; metal finishing; water fluorination]; → potassium fluoride [insecticide; etching glass; feedstock for fluorine, sodium fluoroacetate, hexafluorobenzene]; → organic fluorides; → sodium bifluoride [glass etching; tin plating]; → sodium fluoride [insecticide; metallurgical flux; wood preservative; dentifrice additive; sterilization in brewery & dairy equipment]; → stannous fluoride [dentifrice additive]; → uranium tetrafluoride [concentrating uranium isotope 235 for nuclear fuel and explosives].

* *fluosilicic acid may be produced as a byproduct of phosphate processing or HF production.*

Anhydrous HF → elemental fluorine → uranium hexafluoride [separation of U^{235} from U^{233} by the diffusion process]; → [stable high dielectric gas in coaxial cables, transformers, radio wave guides]; → halogen fluorides [substitute for HF]; → emulsified perfluorochemicals [blood substitute].

Ternary diagram vertices: H (170), F (116/115), C (110). Labeled points: H 170; 161, 160; FLAMMABLE; 152, 151, 150; 143, 142, 141, 140; 134, 133, 132, 131, 130, TOXIC; ACCEPTABLE 125, 124, 123, 122, 121, 120; 116, FULLY-HALOGENATED (MONTREAL) 110; 115, 114, 113, 112, 111.

PRIMARY USES OF CFCs AND HALONS

Application	CFC 12	CFC 11	CFC 115	CFC 114	CFC 113	Halon 1301	Halon 1201	Typical Use
Stationary air conditioners & refrigeration	x	x	x	x				Refrigerators and freezers in homes & commercial buildings such as food stores, restaurants, and supermarkets; refrigerated trucks and railcars.
Mobile air conditioning	x							Cars and light trucks.
Plastic foams	x	x		x				Rigid insulation for homes, buildings, and refrigerators; flexible foam cushioning, food trays and packaging.
Solvent					x			Microelectronic circuitry, computers, and dry cleaning.
Sterilants	x							Medical instruments and pharmaceutical supplies.
Aerosols	x	x						Essential uses in solvents, medicines, and pesticides.
Miscellaneous	x							Food freezants for shrimp, fish. fruit, and vegetables.
Fire extinguishing						x	x	Computer rooms, telephone exchanges, storage vaults.

Source: Alliance for Responsible CFC Policy; EPA; and Rand Corp.

CFCs: THE NUMBERS GAME

Generally CFCs have complex chemical formulas and names, and so a numbering system has been devised to simplify the nomenclature:

The number on the extreme right is the number of fluorine atoms in the compound; the second number from the right is one more than the number of hydrogen atoms; and the third number from the right is one less than the number of carbon atoms. Where there is a zero, it is omitted. All other available spaces in the molecule are occupied by chlorine atoms. The most symmetrical compound is indicated by the number without any letter, and as isomers become more asymmetrical the letter a, b, or c is added. If a molecule is cyclic the number is preceded by the letter C.

NAMES AND FORMULAS OF THE MOST IMPORTANT CFCs, HFCs, AND HCFCs

CFC-11	Cl_3F
CFC-12	CCl_2F_2
CFC-22	$CHClF_2$
CFC-113	CCl_2FCClF_2
CFC-114	$CClF_2CClF_2$
CFC-115	$CClF_2CF_3$
HFC-22	CH_2F_2
HFC-125	CHF_2CF_3
HFC-134a	CH_2FCF_3
HFC-152a	CH_3CHF_2
HCFC-22	$CHClF_2$
HCFC-123	$CHCl_2CF_3$
HCFC-124	$CHClFCF_3$
HCFC-141b	CH_3CCl_2F
HCFC-142b	CH_3CClF_2
HCFC 225ca	$CHCl_2CF_2CF_3$
HCFC-225cb	$CHClFCF_2CClF_2$

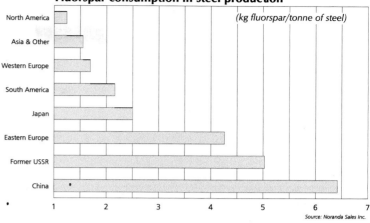

Fluorspar consumption in steel production

(kg fluorspar/tonne of steel)

North America, Asia & Other, Western Europe, South America, Japan, Eastern Europe, Former USSR, China

Source: Noranda Sales Inc.

APPARENT CONSUMPTION OF FLUORSPAR (TONNES)

	Apparent Consumption
China	666,306
Japan	565,249
Former USSR	352,500
United States	351,607
Germany	232,265
Italy	190,791
Hong Kong	185,599
France	184,026
Mexico	178,387
Canada	110,494
Brazil	90,855
United Kingdom	80,465
Spain	76,070
Korea, South	72,320
Norway	56,994
Tunisia	50,298
Korea, North	41,000
Czechoslovakia	40,000
India	31,839
Romania	30,200
Namibia	27,816
Taiwan	25,956
South Africa	23,003
India	22,000
Australia	19,681
Netherlands	16,887
Austria	15,994
Argentina	14,800
Turkey	14,003
Egypt	12,579
Belgium	8,972
Sweden	8,638
Finland	6,709
Kenya	5,144
Costa Rica	4,876
Poland	4,695
Greece	4,682

NOTE: Numbers are approximate and rounded for 1991 or thereabouts; absence of a country does not necessarily indicate no production or trade; absence of a number does not necessarily mean zero

Source: British Geological Survey

Ceramic-grade fluorspar is an opacifier in flint or clear (3% fluorspar) & opal (10-20% fluorspar) glass [food, drug, & toiletries container; ornamental glassware] and enamels (3-10% fluorspar) [stoves, refrigerators, bath tubs, cabinets, cookware], an ingredient in the manufacture of Mg or Ca metal, Mn chemicals, zinc smelting, fiber glass, and welding-rod coatings.

Metallurgical-grade fluorspar ("metspar") is used in steel-making to reduce the surface tension of the slag, to reduce variations in slag viscosity with the melt temperature, to lower the melting point of the slag by forming a eutectic (fluxing), and to improve the fluidity and therefore heat transfer of the slag (the slag removes Si, S, P, and C from the iron) [open hearth, basic oxygen, and electric furnaces; iron foundries]. Nonsteelmaking uses include abrasive wheel bonding agent; calcium carbide; calcium cyanamide].

Minor uses include ornamental purposes such as carved vases, ornaments, figurines, and table tops.

Consumption of fluorspar in the United States
(tonnes)

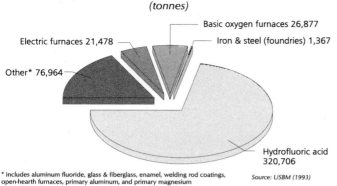

Basic oxygen furnaces 26,877
Electric furnaces 21,478
Iron & steel (foundries) 1,367
Other* 76,964
Hydrofluoric acid 320,706

* includes aluminum fluoride, glass & fiberglass, enamel, welding rod coatings, open-hearth furnaces, primary aluminum, and primary magnesium

Source: USBM (1993)

Consumption of CFCs worldwide
(%)

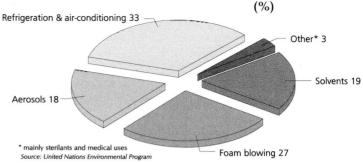

Refrigeration & air-conditioning 33
Other* 3
Solvents 19
Aerosols 18
Foam blowing 27

* mainly sterilants and medical uses
Source: United Nations Environmental Program

QUALITY & SPECIFICATIONS: *Acidspar:*- min. 97% CaF_2 (96% if remaining impurities are acceptable), <1.50% SiO_2, and 0.03-0.10% S as sulfide and/or free S. Other limitations include <10-12 ppm A, ave. 100-550 ppm P, limits on Pb, Cd, Be, $CaCO_3$, and moisture. PS is 100 mesh (flotation product).

Ceramic-grade:- No.1 grade with 95-96% CaF_2, medium grade with 93-94% CaF_2, and No.2 grade with 85-90+% CaF_2; <2.5-3.0% SiO_2, 0.12% ferric oxide, limited calcite, trace lead, and zinc sulfate.

Metspar:- min. 60 effective percent fluorspar, <0.3% sulfide, and <0.50% lead. The effective percent is calculated by multiplying the silica percentage in the chemical analysis by 2.5 and subtracting the result from the calcium-fluoride percentage. Outside the United States, min. requirement is 80% CaF_2 with max. 15% SiO_2. It is usually required to pass through a 1- to 1.5-inch screen, but must contain less than 15% minus $\frac{1}{16}$- inch material (or in briquette form).

CHEMICAL ANALYSIS OF ACID-GRADE FLUORSPAR

	Mexico Fluorita de Mexico	Mexico Las Cuevas	USA Ozark Mahoning	S. Africa Buffalo, GENMIN	S. Africa Chemspar, P-D	Morocco SAEM	Italy Mineraria Silius	Spain Fluoruros SA	UK LaPorte Minerals	China Standard Guarenteed	China Typical
CaF_2	98.09	97.52	97.8	97.58	97.42	98.23	97.58	97.56	97.6	97.00	98.5
SiO_2	0.32	0.89	0.62	0.84	0.34	0.57	0.75	0.98	0.4	1.10	0.8
$CaCO_3$	0.75	0.79	1.33	0.3	0.96	0.66	0.68	0.75	1.3		
S, total	-	0.036	-	0.004	0.011	0.022	0.14	-			
S, sulfide	0.001	0.013	-	0.002	0.008	0.014	0.015	0.013	-		
As, ppm	4	300	2	3	3	1	10	10	2	10	3
P_2O_5, ppm	140	540	0.5	320	260	50	160	180	0.5	300	200
NaCl, total ppm	60	40	-	170	320	200	140	180	-		

WORLD CAPACITY: 7.7M. t. **CAPACITY UTILIZATION:** 75%.

MARKET CONDITIONS: Declining.

MARKETING FACTORS: More efficient use is reducing fluorspar consumption per unit of steel and aluminum produced. The pattern of consumption is influenced by the environmental concern over CFCs which have come under increasing attack as chemicals that damage the stratospheric ozone layer (it should be noted that the main environmentally harmful ingredient is chlorine rather than fluorine). Under the Montreal Protocol, CFC production must end January 1, 1996 (although this will be extended in order to service certain markets). Worldwide production of CFCs in 1991 was just 60% of the 1986 level with the largest reductions being in aerosols (elimination is complete in the United States), foam blowing, and solvents.

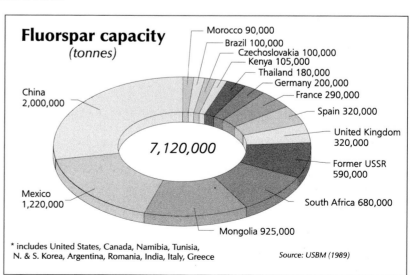

Fluorspar capacity
(tonnes)

7,120,000

China 2,000,000
Mexico 1,220,000
Mongolia 925,000
South Africa 680,000
Former USSR 590,000
United Kingdom 320,000
Spain 320,000
France 290,000
Germany 200,000
Thailand 180,000
Kenya 105,000
Czechoslovakia 100,000
Brazil 100,000
Morocco 90,000

* includes United States, Canada, Namibia, Tunisia, N. & S. Korea, Argentina, Romania, India, Italy, Greece

Source: USBM (1989)

HEALTH & SAFETY: Fluorine contained in some phosphate rock may be a cause for concern. Fluorine evolves as silicon tetrafluoride (SiF_4) and is recovered in the scrubbers as fluosilicic acid (H_2SiF_6) which can be used as a feedstock for aluminum fluoride (synthetic cryolite) or sodium and potassium fluosilicates. CFCs have been blamed for the depletion of the ozone layer, and substitution has mainly centered on related compounds such as hydrochlorofluorocarbons or HCFCs and hydrofluorocarbons or HFCs; these compounds have a lifetime of 2 to 28 years compared with 60 to 400 years for CFCs, and react with OH and therefore may be removed in the lower atmosphere thus limiting accumulation. Consequently, HCFCs and HFCs have an ozone depleting potential of 0.02-0.1 and zero respectively compared with 0.4 to 1.0 for CFCs. In the United States, the EPA has requested manufacturers to continue manufacture until December 1995 in order to service existing air-conditioning equipment.

SUBSTITUTES & ALTERNATIVES: CFCs:- hydrochlorofluorocarbons (HCFCs) and hydrofluorocarbons (HFCs). **Flux**:- borates; dolomitic limestone; ilmenite; manganese; mixtures of iron, aluminum, and calcium oxide; olivine; soda ash.

RECYCLING: Virtually none.

POSSIBLE CFC SUBSTITUTES

CFC-11 substituted by	CFC-12	CFC-113	CFC-114	CFC-115
HCFC 123	HCC134a	HCFC 225ca/cb	HCFC 124	HFC 125
HCFC 141b	HCFC 22	HCFC 141b		
HCFC 22		HCFC 123		

Substance	Ozone depletion potential*	Major uses	Regulatory/use outlook
HCFC-22	0.055	Foam, A/C, refrigeration, aerosols	Clean Air Act bans aerosol use after 1993. EPA likely to ban use in new equipment after 2005.
HCFC-142b	0.065	Foams, refrigeration	EPA likely to ban use in new equipment after 2005.
HCFC-141b	0.11	Foams, solvents	EPA likely to approve for foam only and ban use in new equipment after 2005. Attacks plastic and weakens elastomers. Toxicity question.
HCFC-123	0.02	Foams, A/C, fire fighting	EPA likely to approve for A/C use; Clean Air Act bans use in new equipment after 2015. Attacks plastic and weakens elastomers. Toxicity question.
HCFC-124	0.022	Refrigeration, sterilant	Clean Air Act bans use in new equipment after 2015.
HFC-134a	0	Refrigeration, A/C	No restrictions anticipated.
HFC-125	0	Refrigeration	No restrictions anticipated.
HFC-22	0	Refrigeration, A/C	No restrictions anticipated.

* potentials set relative to CFC-11 which is assigned a value of 1.0.

Source: UNEP.

PRODUCTION AND TRADE IN FLUORSPAR (TONNES)

	Production	Imports	Exports	Apparent Consumption	Net Supplier	Net Consumer
North America	428,297	513,598	301,407	640,488		(212,191)
South America	96,113	14,765	-	110,878		(14,765)
Central America & Carib.	-	5,061	-	5,061		(5,061)
European Union	543,503	373,056	121,350	795,209		(251,706)
Non-EU Europe	417,000	117,629	912	533,717		(116,717)
Australasia	2,096,706	905,037	1,018,486	1,983,257	113,449	
Middle East	-	1,792	-	1,792		(1,792)
Africa	492,101	24,721	399,677	117,145	374,956	

NOTE: Numbers are approximate and rounded for 1990 or thereabouts

Source: British Geological Survey (1991)

PRODUCERS & WORLD TRADE: China, Mexico, Mongolia, and South Africa dominate both production and trade. Production in the United States has virtually ceased due to a combination of increased production costs and the availability of relatively cheap imports, particularly from Mexico and South Africa. A declining use in both the steel industry (metallurgical grade) and in CFCs (chemical grade) has forced a reduction and rationalization of fluorspar production.

PRICES: Mexican, FOB Tampico $100-112/t (acidspar filtercake,); $80-95/ton (metspar). South Africa (acidspar, dry basis) $88-100/t (FOB Durban); $110-110/t (US Gulf port). Chinese $130-137/t (acidspar, wet filtercake, CIF Rotterdam). Europe $135-142/t (metspar, min. 70% CaF$_2$, ex-UK mine); $240-247/t (acidspar, dry basis 97% CaF$_2$, bags, exworks); $217-225/t (acidspar, dry bulk, tankers, ex-works).

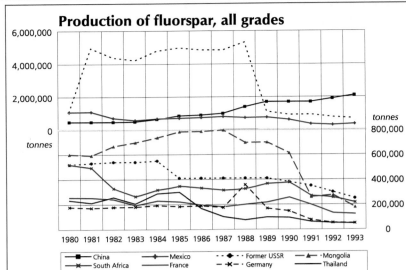

Production of fluorspar, all grades

Source: USBM

China — Mexico — Former USSR — Mongolia — South Africa — France — Germany — Thailand — Other

Ammonium fluoborate $0.72/kg (tech, drums, ex-works, freight equalized). Ammonium fluorosilicate $1.13-1.17/kg (drums, ex-works). Boron trifluoride (FOB works) $11.55-14.63/kg (cylinders); $10/t (bulk). Fluoboric acid $2.25/kg (drums, ex-works, freight equalized). Cryolite $560-600/t (synthetic, bulk).

Lead fluoborate (liquid conc., drums, ex-works, freight equalized) $2.20/kg. Hydrofluoric acid (aqueous, 70%, tank, FOB freight equalized) $1,144/t. Hydrogen fluoride $1.51/kg (anhydrous, tank cars, freight equalized).

Hydrofluosilicic acid $182/t (23% basis, tanks, E. coast, midwest terminals). Lithium fluoride $15.11-15.27/kg (drums, delivered).

Magnesium fluorosilicate, drums, ex-works $1.11-1.13/kg. Magnesium silicofluoride bags, ex-works $0.88/kg. Potassium fluoborate $3.08/kg (tech., drums, ex-works, freight equalized).

Potassium fluoride $3.70/kg (anhydrous, drums, ex-works, freight equalized). Potassium silicofluoride $0.62/kg (bags, freight equalized). Potassium silicofluoride $0.51-0.59/kg (bags, freight equalized).

Sodium fluoborate $3.89/kg (tech., granular, drums, ex-works, freight equalized). Sodium fluoride $1.40/kg (white, 97%, drums, freight equalized).

Fluorocarbons (bulk, tanks, delivered) No. 11 $13.93-14.18/kg (incl. $4.35 Fed. tax); No. 12 $14.92-15.18/kg (incl. $4.35 Fed. tax); No. 22 $2.15-2.17/kg; No. 113 $5.61/kg; No. 114 $6.01/kg.

Fluorspar vase from Derbyshire

FLUORSPAR LEADERS

Producers	Importers	Exporters
China	Japan	China
Mexico	United States	Mongolia
Mongolia	Germany	South Africa
Former USSR	Hong Kong	Mexico
South Africa	Canada	Thailand
France	Italy	Morroco
Spain	Korea, South	Kenya
Italy	Norway	United States
Brazil	Mexico	Spain
Kenya	India	Germany
United Kingdom	France	France
Morroco	Taiwan	Italy
Thailand	Australia	United Kingdom
Germany	Netherlands	Belgium

HTS CODES: 2529.22 (acid-grade, >97% CaF$_2$); 2529.21 (metallurgical-grade, <97% CaF$_2$). 2826.11 (fluorides of ammonium and sodium). 2826.12 (fluorides of aluminum). 2826.20 (fluorosilicates of sodium or potassium). 2826.30 (sodium hexafluoroaluminate or synthetic cryolite). 2903.30 fluorinated, brominated, or iodated derivatives of acyclic hydrocarbons); 2903.30.10 (fluoride). 2903.40.10 (trichlorofluoromethane). 2903.40.20 (dichlorodifluoromethane). 2903.40.30 (trichlorotrifluoromethane).

ETYMOLOGY: Bastnaesite for Bastnäs, Vastmanland, Sweden. **Cryolite** from the Greek *kryos = cold, frost* and *lithos = stone* for its icy appearance. **Fluocerite** containing *fluorine* and *cerium* named *for Ceris*, an asteroid. **Fluorapatite** containing *fluorine* and *apatite*. **Fluorite** from the Latin *fluo = flow*. **Sellaite** for Quintino Sella (1827-1884), Italian mining engineer and mineralogist. **Topaz** from the Greek *Topazion = to seek* and the name of an island in the Red Sea which is difficult to see since it is covered by mist. **Villiaumite** for the French explorer Villiaume who brought the specimen from Guinea.

GARNET

Minerals	Formula	Color	SG	H
Almandine*	$3FeO \cdot Al_2O_3 \cdot 3SiO_2$	dark reddish-brown	7.5	3.9-4.2
Grossular	$3CaO \cdot Al_2O_3 \cdot 3SiO_2$	pale green	7.0	3.5-3.7
Pyrope	$3MgO \cdot Al_2O_3 \cdot 3SiO_2$	deep crimson	6.5-7.5	3.5-3.8
Spessartine	$3MnO \cdot Al_2O_3 \cdot 3SiO_2$	brownish-red	7.0-7.5	4.1-4.3
Andradite**	$3CaO \cdot Fe_2O_3 \cdot 3SiO_2$	dark brown-green	6.5-7.0	3.7-3.8
Uvarovite	$3CaO \cdot Cr_2O_3 \cdot 3SiO_2$	emerald green	7.5	3.4-3.5

* preferred commercial garnet ** commercial garnet

PROPERTIES & USES: Moderately high H, melting point of 1,250°C, sharp sub-rounded to sub-angular chisel-edged fracture, little or no free silica, and a high resistance to physical and chemical attack make garnet a high-quality abrasive [sandpaper, abrasive wheels, polishing/lapping grains, powders, and grits]. Garnet of a consistent size distribution is used in sandblasting [loose-grain abrasive], water-jet equipment [cutting], and as a tumbling media [deburring and polishing] where garnet's equidimensional and blocky particle shape and its relatively high SG (less air pressure required for the same cutting power) are advantageous. Being non-hydroscopic prevents the formation of lumps thus allowing the powder to be free-flowing.

Garnet is used in some non-skid surfaces. Inertness, resistance to degradation (through back-flushing), particle shape and size distribution, and SG (to remain separate from other filter bed layers, usually silica sand and anthracite) are useful in filtration [multi-media filtration systems].

Some varieties of garnet are used as a semi-precious gemstone - almandine (violet red), andradite (black to green), grossular garnet (light yellowish green), hessonite (yellow-brown), pyrope (bright red), pyrope-almandine garnet (red), rhodolite (pinkish-red), and spessartite garnet (orange-pink).

QUALITY & SPECIFICATIONS: Almandite is the preferred garnet due to higher SG and resistance to degradation; andradite is a secondary choice. Chemistry requires a min. garnet content (+97%) plus limits on free silica. In the United States, California's Title 22 hazardous waste standard sets limits on toxic metal content as per the table. GMA Pty, Ltd./Barton Mines Corp. states total chlorides <50ppm, free iron <0.001%, copper <0.01%, and other heavy metals <0.01%. ISO standards for blasting media garnet requires <25ppm water soluble chloride (particularly important when using beach-derived garnet).

H is of little practical consequence since it influences shear rather than impact strength, that is a material may be hard but brittle and therefore shatters relatively easily. Natural crystal sizes are such that a wide range of sizes

BLAST-GRADE GARNET SIZINGS

Cumulative % retained US mesh (typical)	ROM (30x60)	Medium (60#)	Fine (80#)
+600	0 - 2	-	-
+425	10 - 20	0 - 2	-
+300	50 - 75	30 - 45	0 - 15
+212	99 - 100	85 - 95'98 - 100	65 - 85
+150			95 - 100

Source: GMA/Barton Mines Corp.

SIZE RANGES FOR GARNET BY END USE

End use	Size ranges (mm)
Sand blasting	1.1, 0.5, 0.6/0.4, 0.4/0.2, 0.3/0.15
Water filtration	2.5/1.7, 1.1, 1.4/0.6, 0.5, 0.6/0.4, 0.4/0.2
Water jet cutting	1.0/0.3, 0.25/0.18, 0.18, 0.15, 0.18/0.85, 0.12/0.06
Coated abrasives	0.34/0.1, 0.08/0.036
Polishing/lapping	0.15/0.18, 0.10/0.15, 0.030, 0.010

Single grain size indicates mean particle size

HARDNESS OF ABRASIVE MATERIALS

	Knoop hardness (K100)
Quartz	820
Spinel	1,270
Garnet	1,360
Sintered bauxite	1,900
Corundum	2,050
Heat-treated fused aluminum oxide	2,090
$Al_2O_3 + 0.3\% Cr_2O_3$	2,150
Silicon carbide	2,480
Boron carbide	2,760
Cubic boron nitride	7,800
Diamond	8,000

Consumption of almandite garnet in the United States

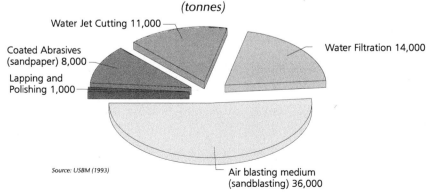

(tonnes)

Water Jet Cutting 11,000
Coated Abrasives (sandpaper) 8,000
Lapping and Polishing 1,000
Water Filtration 14,000
Air blasting medium (sandblasting) 36,000

Source: USBM (1993)

can be produced to tight tolerances ranging from No. 8, 16, 25, 36, 40, 60-80, 100, 150, 250, and 325 to micronized grades from 250 to 37 μm. Blasting:- -1.0 +0.3mm and -.059 +21mm; water filtration:- -4.75 + 1.41mm and a finer grade such as -0.84 + 0.3 or -0.71 +0.25mm; Abrasive cutting;- -0.25 +0.177mm.

Specifications for abrasives are covered by standards set by various organizations such as ANSI Specifications B74.18-1977 (Specifications for Grading of Certain Abrasive Grains on Coated Abrasive Products), ANSI Specifications B74.12-1977 (Specification for Size of Abrasive Grains-Grinding Wheel, Polishing, and General Industrial Uses), U.S. Navy specification MIL-A-22262 (SH), and The Steel Structures Painting Council's SSPC-XAB1X (Mineral and Slag Abrasives).

Garnet for water filtration requires a min. SG of 4.0 (ideally), rounded particle shape sized between 8 and 250 mesh with a uniformity coefficient as near to 1 as possible (UC is the ratio of the size of the grain that has 60% of the sample finer than itself to the effective size that has 10% finer than itself). Specifications in the United States are covered by standards set by the American Water Works Association's B100-89 (Standards for Filtering Materials) specification and tests.

BREAKDOWN FACTORS FOR ABRASIVES

	Breakdown factor* (1 pass)	Breakdown factor* (3 passes)
Aluminum oxide (30 FDT)	0.80	0.61
Garnet RT-60	0.61	0.38
Starblast®	0.77	0.45
Flintshot®	0.68	0.36
Flintbrasive® #3	0.58	0.32

* breakdown factors can range from 1 to 0 with 1 equal to no change after blasting and 0 breaking down completely to dust.

Tests conducted by DuPont Engineering Test Center in 1970. Conditions: 0.64 cm nozzle; 634-655 x 10³ Pa nozzle pressure; 0.64 cm steel plate target..

Ownership trademarks - Starblast® E.I. duPont de Nemours and Co. Ltd.; Flintshot® US Silica Co.

Source: Fulton, 1994

CALIFORNIA WASTE EXTRACTION TEST

	Total Content Allowable (%)	Soluble Content Allowable (mg/l)
Antimony	0.05	15
Arsenic	0.05	5
Barium	1.0	100
Beryllium	0.0075	0.75
Cadmium	0.01	1
Chromium	0.25	500
Chromium (+6)	0.05	5
Cobalt	0.80	80
Copper	0.25	25
Fluoride	1.80	180
Lead	0.1	5
Mercury	0.002	0.2
Molybdenum	0.35	350
Nickel	0.20	20
Selenium	0.01	1
Silver	0.05	5
Thallium	0.07	7
Vanadium	0.24	24
Zinc	0.50	250

Sec. 66700

CLEANING RATE & PROFILE FOR BLAST CLEANING ABRASIVES

	Cleaning rate m²/hr	Abrasive flow rate kg/hr	Profile mm
Aluminum oxide (80/100)	23	245	0.028
Starblast®	22	272	0.028
Biasill®	22	263	0.023
Aluminum oxide (54/70)	21	261	0.033
Garnet RT-80	21	290	0.025
Flint silica	20	331	0.036
Flintshot®	19	318	0.043
Coarse staurolite	19	243	0.038
Garnet RT-60	18	238	0.025
Aluminum oxide (30 FDT)	16	302	0.038
Black Beauty®	15	340	0.038
Rotoblast® G80A (met. grit)	14	318	0.030
Rotoblast® G40A (met. grit)	11	340	0.053
Flintbrasive® #3	11	236	0.043

Tests conducted by DuPont Engineering Test Center in 1970. 100% mill scale on new steel plate. All surfaces to Class 1 white metal. Conditions: 0.95 cm nozzle; 634-655 x 10³ Pa nozzle pressure.

Ownership trademarks - Starblast® and Biasill® E.I. duPont de Nemours and Co. Ltd.; Rotoblast® Pangborn Corp.; Black Beauty® H.B. Reed Corp.; Flintshot® US Silica Co.

Source: Fulton, 1994

TYPICAL CHEMICAL COMPOSITIONS OF GARNET (%)

	W. Australia Beach Sands	Tamilnadu, India Beach Sands	Idaho, USA Alluvial	New York, USA Hard Rock	Czech Rep. Hard Rock
SiO_2	36.10	35.10	38.00	38	36.92
Al_2O_3	20.40	21.60	26.00	26	21.17
FeO	29.80		-	-	36.7
Fe_2O_3	1.70	32.90	30.00	30	
TiO_2	1.80	0.55	-	1	0.06
MnO	1.05	0.53	2.00	1	0.37
CaO	1.55	1.84	2.00	1	0.87
MgO	6.00	7.40	2.00	1	3.92

WORLD CAPACITY: 150,000 t. **CAPACITY UTILIZATION:** 95%.

MARKET CONDITIONS: Steady - increasing.

MARKETING FACTORS: Expanding safety and health legislation/competitive abrasives including synthetic abrasives/manufacturing activity and therefore the economy.

HEALTH & SAFETY: Garnet generally contains less than 0.1% free silica and therefore falls outside OSHA's Hazard Communication Standard. In addition, garnet contains no leachable heavy metals. Garnet meets the guidelines for dry unconfined blasting including the U.S. Navy specification MIL-A-22262 (SH) and the State of California Air Resources Board. Radioactivity is a consideration, particularly from garnet extracted from heavy-mineral deposits (it needs to be undetectable above background levels). The main health & safety concern appears to be nuisance dust. Overall, the market for abrasive-grade garnet may benefit from health and safety concern over alternative abrasives such as silica sand and slags.

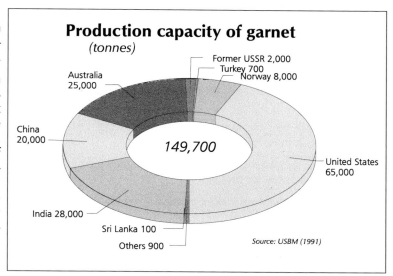

Production capacity of garnet
(tonnes)

149,700

Australia 25,000
China 20,000
India 28,000
Sri Lanka 100
Others 900
Former USSR 2,000
Turkey 700
Norway 8,000
United States 65,000

Source: USBM (1991)

SUBSTITUTES & ALTERNATIVES: Abrasives:- bauxite & alumina (fused alumina), corundum/emery, diamonds, diatomite, feldspar, iron oxide (magnetite), nepheline syenite, olivine, perlite, pumice, silica sand, staurolite, tripoli, and silicon carbide), ilmenite. **Filter media**:- activated carbon/anthracite, asbestos, cellulose, diatomite, garnet, iron oxide (magnetite), perlite, pumice, silica sand, ilmenite.

RECYCLING: One of the major advantages of garnet as an abrasive is the fact that it can be recovered, cleaned, resized, and reused several times. Higher initial costs compared with rival abrasives may be justified in some cases by an increased life cycle based on efficient recycling.

PRODUCERS & WORLD TRADE: Traditionally, garnet has been regarded as a US mineral, although production has become more widespread in recent years with expansions in Australia, China, and India.

HTS CODES: 2513.21 (emery, natural abrasives, natural garnet, and other natural abrasives, crude); 2513.29 (emery, natural abrasives, natural garnet, and other natural abrasives, other than crude); 6805.10 (natural abrasives on woven textile); 6805.20 (natural abrasives on paper or paperboard; 6805.30 (natural abrasives sheets, strips, disks, belts, sleeves, or similar form).

PRICES: United States (FOB Idaho plant, almandine, list) $230-235/t (100, 150, 250 mesh); $215-225/t (30, 50, 60, 60/80 mesh); $200/t (36 mesh); $396/t (5 mesh). $180-400/t (andradite, 12-80 mesh, FOB New York plant). $300+/t (heat-treated, coated abrasive). Europe $300+/t all grades. Australia $140/t (exports, FOB port). India $50-80/t (FOB, bags).

ETYMOLOGY: Almandine for Alabanda, Asia Minor, where garnets were cut and polished. **Andradite** for J.B.d'Andrada e Silva (1763-1838), Brazilian mineralogist and first observer. **Garnet** from the Latin *granatum* = *a pomegranate* since it resembles their red seeds. **Grossular** from the Latin *grossularium* = *gooseberry* for its pale green color. **Hessonite** from the Greek *ésson* = *inferior* in reference to its inferior hardness and color. **Pyrope** from the Greek *pyr* = *fire* and *ops* = eye alluding to its fire-red color. **Rhodolite** from the Greek *rhodon* = *a rose* and *lithos* = *stone*. **Spessartine** for Spessart in northwestern Bavaria, Germany. **Uvarovite** for Count Sergei Semeonovich Uvarov (1786-1855), Russian nobleman, Imperial Academy of St. Petersburg.

GARNET LEADERS

Producers	Exporters	Importers
United States	Australia	France
Australia	China	Germany
India	Sri Lanka	Korea
China	United States	Netherlands
Former USSR		Taiwan
Norway		United Kingdom
Turkey		United States
Sri Lanka		

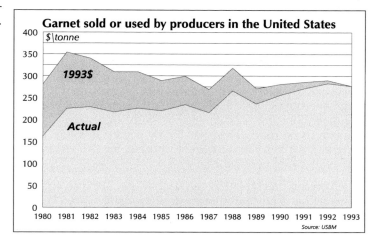

Garnet sold or used by producers in the United States

$\tonne

1993$

Actual

1980 1981 1982 1983 1984 1985 1986 1987 1988 1989 1990 1991 1992 1993

Source: USBM

GRAPHITE

Mineral	Formula	Color	SG	H
Graphite	C	black-steel gray	2.1-2.3	1-2

PROPERTIES & USES: Natural graphite is an excellent conductor of heat & electricity; stable over a wide range of temperatures; highly refractory with a high melting point (3,650°C); compressible and malleable; resists chemical attack, thermal shock, shrinkage, wetting by metals, and oxidation, has a low absorption coefficient for X-rays and neutrons and a low coefficient of friction (good lubricity). Natural graphite is divided into three main types each with a given range of C content, particle size, ash content, and end use:-

Amorphous (actually microcrystalline): carbon range 70-85% [friction materials; metallurgy; pencils; refractories; coatings; lubricants; paints]

High crystalline graphite (lump, vein, or crystalline vein): carbon content 90-99% [batteries; lubricants; grinding wheels; powder metallurgy]

Flake graphite (crystalline flake): carbon range 80-98% [refractories; lubricants; powder metallurgy; pencils; coatings].

Flake graphite provides good oxidation and corrosion resistance and the orientation of the flakes improves structural strength in various carbon-based refractory products [alumina-graphite refractories; mag-carbon brick; crucibles, retorts, molds, ladles, nozzles; continuous casting powders and hot-top compounds for molten metal]. Amorphous graphite may be used in some cases, for example where the refractory needs to be deformable or flexible. The carbon (graphite) content of resin-bonded magnesia-carbon (mag-carbon) brick may be as high as 20-25% and is designed to operate in a high-temperature environment [lining for steel and iron furnaces; slag lines, ladles, and nozzles]. Alumina-graphite refractories have excellent resistance to thermal shock and corrosion attack [continuous casting; shrouding tubes of slab and bloom casters; torpedo ladles]. Low quality flake graphite or amorphous graphite (10-90% of the mix), refractory clay, and silica sand are ground to 350 μm, mixed, formed, and fired to produce crucibles, molds, and ladles [steel, nonferrous, and precious metals industries]. Finely ground (50-75 μm) flake or amorphous graphite mixed with refractory clay (+ talc, silica sand, mica) is used as a foundry facing or coating for molds forming a smooth finish on castings which eases release on cooling.

Because of its high lubricity and resistance to heat up to 310°C, graphite is used in many forms as a lubricant, for example incorporated in piston rings and bearings [automotive and mechanical devices]; dispersed in a carrier such as kerosene or oil with quick drying characteristics in high-temperature environments [oven conveyors]; added to a soapy lubricant [die lubricant, especially galvanized wire]; a solid lubricant film that retains its properties under conditions of high temperature and pressure [anti-seize agent in steel mill and railroad applications], and can constitute 5-10% of some oils and greases [general lubrication applications; packings]. Graphite impregnated organic friction materials assist with heat stability and reduce wear in friction materials [heavy-duty brake and clutch linings]. Amorphous graphite may be incorporated into specialty paint used on metal surfaces exposed to corrosive conditions. Because of its unctuousness, jet color, and opaqueness (marking ability), amorphous and crystalline graphite has long been used in pencils. In fact, this is the origin of the name graphite (this plus its early misidentification as galena (hence plumbago) are the basis for the old fashioned terms "black lead" and "lead pencil". Good electrical conductivity allows graphite to be used where small currents are required over a long period of time [dry-cell zinc-carbon batteries; alkaline batteries], for transferring current [brushes for DC generators and motors, variable HP motors, AC variable speed motors, battery charging generators].

When crystalline graphite is oxidized by chromic acid and dilute sulfuric acid water is deposited between the graphite layers which on rapid heating ➔ *expanded graphite* (100 - 700% of the original volume) [insulating agent in the casting of steel; hot topping material or exothermic powder to cover ingots; combustion modified high resilience foam in furniture and mattresses].

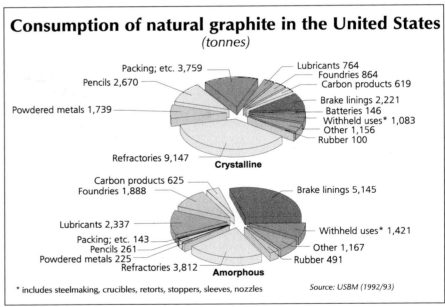

Consumption of natural graphite in the United States
(tonnes)

Packing; etc. 3,759
Pencils 2,670
Powdered metals 1,739
Refractories 9,147
Lubricants 764
Foundries 864
Carbon products 619
Brake linings 2,221
Batteries 146
Withheld uses* 1,083
Other 1,156
Rubber 100
Crystalline

Carbon products 625
Foundries 1,888
Lubricants 2,337
Packing; etc. 143
Pencils 261
Powdered metals 225
Refractories 3,812
Brake linings 5,145
Withheld uses* 1,421
Other 1,167
Rubber 491
Amorphous

* includes steelmaking, crucibles, retorts, stoppers, sleeves, nozzles

Source: USBM (1992/93)

Natural graphite ➔ *graphite foil* (GRAFOIL®) with excellent sealing characteristics and may be calendered, corrugated, wrapped, injected, or molded into various shapes or manufactured into adhesive-backed tape, ribbon, roll, sheet, or laminate [valve and pump gaskets, packings, seals in nuclear steam generation, chemical production, cryogenics, petroleum refining]. Graphite foil remains resilient and flexible over a wide range of temperature (-200 to +1,650°C) and pressure, resists attack from a wide variety of industrial chemicals for extended periods of time.

Pyrolizing polyacrilonitrile fibers and pitch at 700-1,400°C and heating to 2,800°C in an electric furnace ➔ *graphite fibers* [aerospace, sporting goods]. Pyrolitic carbons and graphites are produced from methane or natural gas via vapor deposition techniques in a vacuum furnace at >2,000°C [aerospace rocket exhaust insulating liners].

Synthetic graphite has a higher purity but lower crystallinity than natural graphite. Divided into *primary or electrographite*, essentially pure C produced from calcined petroleum coke & coal tar pitch in an electric furnace, and *secondary synthetic graphite* (powder and scrap), produced by heating calcined petroleum pitch to 2,800°C, synthetic graphite has a similar purity to natural graphite but with a lower density, higher electrical resistance, and higher porosity [aerospace; batteries; carbon brushes; graphite electrodes for electric arc furnaces for the production of steel, aluminum, copper, magnesium, and other metals and alloys; nuclear moderator and reflector]. A particularly pure graphite (synthetic or chemically treated natural) is required to slow down (moderate) and contain (reflect) neutrons produced during the nuclear fission process. Synthetic graphite is not normally used in refractories because of its high porosity (10-15%) compared with natural graphite (2-3%).

Natural and synthetic graphite processed at temperatures of 2,500°C+ ➔ *high-purity graphite* with 99.9% C and the ability to introduce selected promoter elements (boron, silicon, copper, iron, and rare earths) into the carbon/graphite structure. Purification and promoter elements enhance certain properties including consistency of the specifications, lubricity, and conductivity. Purified graphites (99.9% C) include crystalline vein [batteries; carbon parts; lubricants; powder metal]; crystalline flake [graphite foil for the nuclear, industrial liquid, and automotive industries; high-purity refractory brick; high-performance, graphite-based lubricants]; amorphous [lubricant]; synthetic [batteries (zero percent mercury alkaline cells); friction products; lubricants]; petroleum coke [carbon raiser for gray and ductile iron; carbon adjustment in ladle metallurgy; lubricant]. Boron as a promoter element in natural flake graphite improves oxidation resistance which in turn provides a refractory brick with lower deformation and higher strength.

GRAPHITE LEADERS

Producers	Importers	Exporters
China***	Japan	China
Former USSR***	United States	Korea, South
India*	Italy	United States
North Korea**	Germany	Madagascar
Brazil*	Korea, South	Zimbabwe
South Korea**	United Kingdom	Korea, North
Mexico**	Taiwan	Mexico
Turkey***	Canada	Canada
Austria**	South Africa	Germany
Madagascar*	Austria	Brazil
Zimbabwe**	France	Austria
Czechoslovakia**	Poland	United Kingdom
Canada*	Iran	Hong Kong
Romania**	Pakistan	Sri Lanka
Germany*	Hong Kong	Netherlands
Sri Lanka	Spain	Czechoslovakia
Norway*	Turkey	South Africa

*flake **amorphous ***flake & amorphous*

APPARENT CONSUMPTION OF GRAPHITE (TONNES)

	Apparent Consumption
China	446,939
South Korea	131,602
Japan	125,043
Former USSR	75,000
India	49,553
Korea, North	39,000
Brazil	36,702
Italy	29,781
Germany	29,137
Turkey	28,233
Mexico	21,923
Austria	18,783
United States	14,001
Taiwan	13,429
United Kingdom	12,369
Czechoslovakia	10,300
Romania	10,000
Canada	7,202
Poland	4,108
Sri Lanka	4,033
France	3,901
South Africa	3,594
Iran	2,666
Pakistan	2,627
Spain	2,304
Zimbabwe	1,823
Indonesia	1,761
Venezuela	1,646
Denmark	1,579
Australia	1,557
Hungary	1,282
Singapore	1,213
Argentina	1,202
Egypt	1,036

NOTE: Numbers are approximate and rounded for 1991 or thereabouts; absence of a country does not necessarily indicate no production or trade; absence of a number does not necessarily mean zero

Source: British Geological Survey

GRAPHITE SPECIFICATIONS BY APPLICATION

Application	Average carbon (%)	Average flake size	Comments
FOUNDRIES			
Core & mold washes (F)	80-90	200 mesh	
Core & mold washes (A)	70-80	200 mesh	
Foundry facings (A*)	40-70	53 to 75 µm	Low sulfides and readily fusible minerals; quartz, mica advantageous
Sintering	98-99	APS 5 µm	Natural or synthetic
REFRACTORIES			
Crucibles, molds, ladles (F)	85-95	+150 µm	Large flakes, typically 75% +600 µm, 75% +400 µm, or 75% +300 µm. Low iron, mica, carbonaceous material
Refractory bricks (A)	70-80	-20mm & -600 mesh	
Refractory bricks (F)	90-97	+180 to +150 µm	Trend to finer sizes, higher C
Mag-carbon bricks (F)	85-90	+150 to -710 µm	Aspect ratio 20:1, <2% ash preferred
Al graphite refractories (F)	min. 85	-600 to +150 µm	
OTHER			
Brake linings	min. 98	-75 µm	Commonly 60:40 natural/synthetic blends. Low abrasive minerals (quartz & feldspar)
Batteries, dry cell	min. 88	85% -75 µm	Natural or synthetic, no conductors
Batteries, alkaline	min. 98	-75 to 5 µm	(Cu, Co, Ni, Sb, As); <0.5% S
Carbon brushes	95-99	-50 µm	99% C preferred (<1% silica & ash)
Conductive coatings (A)	50-55		Can contain 20-25% silica. Low pyrite (sulfuric acid on weathering) and mica (flaking)
Explosives		-150 µm	No sulfides and moisture
Expandable graphite	min. 90	-2 mm to +250 µm	
Graphite foil	min. 90		Low sodium and leachable chlorides
Lubricants	98-99	106 to 53 µm	Low abrasive minerals (quartz & feldspar), metal sulfides or free
Neutron moderator	99+		<0.04% ash, <1ppm rare earths, boron
Pencils	80-82	Extremely fine	Amorphous or flake

A - amorphous; F - flake

SPECIFICATIONS OF COMMERCIAL GRAPHITE

Source	Crystal size	% C
Madagascar		
Large flake	75% on 40 mesh	85-89.5%
	97% on 60 mesh	to 92-94%
Medium flake	25% on 40 mesh	80-84.9%
	97% on 80 mesh	to 90-92.5%
Fine flake	25% on 40 mesh	75-80%
	& 75% on 60 mesh (max.)	to 89-90%
	95% on 80 mesh (min.)	
Extra fine flake		70-75%
		to 85-90%
China		
Large flake	80% on 50 mesh	85-90%
Medium flake	80% on 80 mesh	85-90%
Small flake	50% on 80 mesh	80-90%
Norway		
Large flake	above 100 mesh	85-95%
Medium flake	150+ mesh	85-95%
Small flake	below 200 mesh	80-95%
Sri Lanka		
Large lump/lump	+10 mm	92-99%
Chippy dust	-5 mm	80-99%
Powders	below 200 mesh	70-99%

ASH CONTENT OF SOME NATURAL GRAPHITE (%)

	Madagascar	Mexico	India
Ash	12	3.8	11.8
SiO_2	44.6	51	56
Al_2O_3	32.8	14.5	20.3
Fe_2O_3	18.8	29.5	14.9
TiO_2	0.5	0.7	1.1
CaO	0.2	1.5	1.5
MgO	2.3	1.5	3
Na_2O	0.1	0.6	0.5
K_2O	0.7	0.7	2
	China	Norway	Canada
Ash	16.9	8.8	23.5
SiO_2	49.7	56.7	64.8
Al_2O_3	19.7	15.6	13.9
Fe_2O_3	19.2	10.5	12.3
TiO_2	1.6	1.1	0.4
CaO	1.9	3.5	3.7
MgO	4.2	6.1	1.4
Na_2O	0.7	3.5	0.6
K_2O	2.6	2.4	2

QUALITY & SPECIFICATIONS: Each graphite type is divided into numerous grades based on a combination of carbon content, PS and PSD, and ash content and ash chemistry and certain uses have specific needs (see below). Grade description may be based on the Chinese nomenclature, e.g. +590 grade has min. 80% on +50 mesh with min. 90% carbon. Flake is divided into coarse flake (-20 to +100 mesh) and fine flake (-100 to +325 mesh). Crystalline has grain sizes ranging from chip or dust through fine and "amorphous lump" to coarse or "crystalline lump". Purified graphite generally contains <0.1% impurities compared with 1-10% ash for crystalline vein, 5-20% for crystalline flake, 0.01-5% for synthetic, 12-35% for amorphous, and 1.0-7.0% for calcined coke.

WORLD CAPACITY: 700,000 t.

CAPACITY UTILIZATION: 90%.

MARKET CONDITIONS: Stable.

MARKETING FACTORS: Steel industry for refractories and asbestos substitution for friction materials all of which depend on the economy. Trend is toward high C content and stricter specifications. R&D is developing new uses and products based on various types of graphite. Blended grades are common, often supplied by a graphite house or specialized trader.

SUBSTITUTES & ALTERNATIVES: Batteries:- lithium, manganese, rare earths. **Carbon raiser in iron & steel:**- calcined petroleum coke, anthracite coal, used carbon electrodes. **Fire retardant:**- ATH, antimony oxide, asbestos, borates, bromine, chromite, diatomite, magnesite & magnesia, perlite, phosphates, pumice, vermiculite. **Friction material:**- asbestos, barite, bauxite & alumina, clays (attapulgite, kaolin, sepiolite), garnet, gypsum, mica, pumice, pyrophyllite, silica, slate, vermiculite, wollastonite, zircon. **Lubricant:**- lithium, mica, molybdenum disulfide (MoS_2), talc. **Refractories:**- andalusite, bauxite, chromite, kyanite, dolomite, magnesite, olivine, pyrophyllite, refractory clays, silica, sillimanite, zircon.

HEALTH & SAFETY: Natural graphite is an inert, nontoxic substance and therefore health & safety concerns are limited to dust control.

RECYCLING: Opportunities for recycling are limited since most graphite is gradually "consumed" during use as a refractory, brake lining. Used electrodes are often salvaged and crushed for reuse either to be reformed into an electrode or as a substitute for amorphous graphite.

PRODUCERS & WORLD TRADE: China is the dominant producer and exporter of flake graphite along with, Brazil, India, Former USSR, Madagascar, Germany, Norway, and most recently Canada. China, S. Korea, Mexico, Czech Rep. , Austria, former USSR, N. Korea, Zimbabwe produce amorphous graphite, and Sri Lanka lump graphite.

PRODUCTION AND TRADE IN GRAPHITE (TONNES)

	Production	Imports	Exports	Apparent Consumption	Net Supplier	Net Consumer
North America	40,488	40,763	38,125	43,126		(2,638)
South America	44,000	2,848	7,298	39,550	4,450	
European Union	8,900	85,414	13,431	80,883		(71,983)
Non-EU Europe	143,377	15,160	9,055	149,482		(6,105)
Australasia	741,409	175,472	200,936	715,945	25,464	
Middle East		2,666		2,666		(2,666)
Africa	26,981	6,546	26,134	7,393	19,588	

NOTE: Numbers are approximate and rounded for 1990 or thereabouts   *Source: British Geological Survey (1991)*

PRICES: Europe (CIF UK port) crystalline $650-850/t (lump, 92/95% C); $400-600/t (large flake, 85/90% C); $300-500/t (medium flake, 85/90% C); $250-500/t (small flake, 80/95% C). Amorphous powder $220-300/t (80/85% C). Swiss border synthetic graphite $2.23/kg (99.95% C). Chinese flake $250-1,250/t; Mexican amorphous $100/t; Sri Lankan lump & chip $750-820/t.

HTS CODES: 2504.10 (natural graphite in powder or in flakes); 2504.90.00 (other); 3801.10 (artificial graphite); 3801.20 (colloidal or semicolloidal graphite).

ETYMOLOGY: Graphite from the Greek *graphein = to write* due to its use in making pencils. **Plumbago** from the Latin *plumbum = lead* since graphite was originally misidentified as galena.

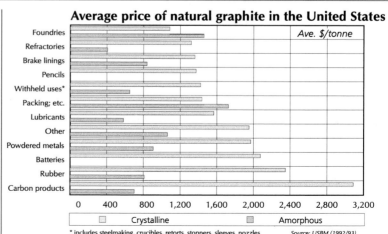

Average price of natural graphite in the United States

Foundries, Refractories, Brake linings, Pencils, Withheld uses*, Packing; etc., Lubricants, Other, Powdered metals, Batteries, Rubber, Carbon products

Ave. $/tonne

0, 400, 800, 1,200, 1,600, 2,000, 2,400, 2,800, 3,200

☐ Crystalline   ☐ Amorphous

* includes steelmaking, crucibles, retorts, stoppers, sleeves, nozzles   *Source: USBM (1992/93)*

Minerals	Formula	%CaO	%SO$_3$	%H$_2$O	Color	SG	H
Gypsum	CaSO$_4$·2H$_2$O	32.6	46.5	20.9	white to gray	2.38	1.5-2.0
Anhydrite	CaSO$_4$	41.2	58.8		white to gray	2.93	3.0-3.5

PROPERTIES & USES: Gypsum and anhydrite, the dihydrate anhydrous forms of calcium sulfate, are often associated together in nature. Anhydrite converts to gypsum via an intermediate mineral, bassanite (CaSO$_4$·½H$_2$O). Alabaster is a fine-grained compact form of rock gypsum used in sculpturing; satin spar is a secondary acicular calcium sulfate mineral; and selenite is a large crystal secondary calcium sulfate mineral with mica-like cleavage. Although anhydrite is the more common calcium sulfate mineral, gypsum is by far the more important commercially. In addition to natural gypsum, synthetic, chemical, or byproduct gypsum is increasingly available, i.e. gypsum produced during the production of phosphoric acid (phosphogypsum), flue gas desulfurization (FGD gypsum), titanium dioxide (titanogypsum), and other products such as citric acid, tartaric acid, lactic acid, and Kevlar. Most is landfilled, although some has replaced natural gypsum.

The common beta form of gypsum ground to -100 mesh calcined at 250°C for 2 hours and then at 300-350°C readily loses 75% of its water of crystallization to form the hemihydrate, CaSO$_4$·½H$_2$O, termed stucco or plaster of Paris.

Dehydration or calcining
$$CaSO_4·2H_2O + heat \rightarrow CaSO_4·½H_2O + 3/2H_2O$$
gypsum → hemihydrate

Hydration or setting
$$CaSO_4·½H_2O + 3/2H_2O \rightarrow CaSO_4·2H_2O + heat$$
hemihydrate → gypsum

When water is added this material can be spread, cast, or molded prior to setting to a rock hard, fire-resistant material which may be prefabricated into wallboard, ceiling board, moldings, etc. [construction] or used as a building plaster [construction] or industrial plaster [molding plaster, white art plaster, pottery plaster, impression dental plaster, metal-casting plaster]. The setting time, which is normally 20 minutes, may be accelerated by the addition of metal salts, set plaster, or anhydrite and retarded by glue or starch (board making requires a setting time of about 5 minutes); additives include aggregates, light-weight aggregates, and/or glass/polymer fiber reinforcement. Plaster may be mixed as a fluid slurry for casting or spraying, worked in a plastic state by screeding or template forming, pressed between dies as semi-wet powder, and carved or machined as a solid.

Alpha-gypsum is harder, stronger, and requires less water than its more common beta gypsum counterpart [specialty plaster (dental, orthopedic); self-levelling floors; investment casting].

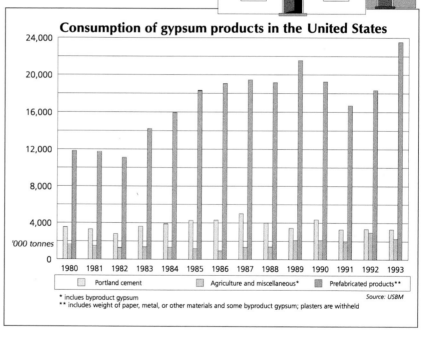

Consumption of gypsum products in the United States

'000 tonnes

Legend: Portland cement; Agriculture and miscellaneous*; Prefabricated products**

* includes byproduct gypsum
** includes weight of paper, metal, or other materials and some byproduct gypsum; plasters are withheld

Source: USBM

Uncalcined gypsum or anhydrite is a source of Ca and sulfate used as a retarder to control set in cement (ave. 3-6% added to clinker) [cement manufacture], as a fertilizer (relatively water soluble form of Ca and S) and a soil conditioner (improves soil structure by loosening heavy, compacted soils and clays to increase permeability and improve aeration, drainage, and penetration and retention of water) [agriculture]. Termed landplaster, gypsum is used as a fertilizer for specific crops like peanuts, legumes, potatoes, and cotton. As a source of Ca and S, gypsum substitutes for sodium sulfate in glassmaking [flat and container glass]; acts as a natural floccing agent to strip suspended particulates blocking sunlight to the oxygen-generating algae in ponds [aquaculture]. Gypsum or anhydrite is inert with good absorbing capabilities [animal feed extender; insecticide carrier]. Together with inertness and lack of abrasiveness, some grades of gypsum (APS 1.4-12 μm) are sufficiently pure to have a brightness of 97%, a refractive index of 1.52-1.58, and oil absorption of 25/26 cc/100g to be used as a filler or dilutent [plastics; adhesives; paint; wood filler; tile grouts & body putties; textiles; modeling clays; food; pharmaceuticals].

QUALITY & SPECIFICATIONS: There are important differences between natural and byproduct gypsum. Natural gypsum varies from <50 to >95% $CaSO_4$ with limestone or insoluble anhydrite being the main contaminant; byproduct gypsum is generally >95% pure with the impurities (in FGD gypsum) fly ash, insoluble salts, trace metals, unoxidized calcium sulfite, and unreacted alkali. Byproduct gypsum varies in particle shape (acicular to blocky) and particle size (<10 to >300 µm) according to how it was formed, whereas natural gypsum is produced as 3-6 inch rocks.

Agriculture:- gypsum as a soil conditioner requires grinding to 80-90% through 100 mesh.

Cement and agricultural:- less stringent.

FGD gypsum:- (on dry weight basis) 95% $CaSO_4 \cdot 2H_2O$, <10% moisture, <0.1% MgO, <0.01% each Cl, Mg, and K, <0.06% Na_2O, < 1.0% Fe_2O_3, <1.0% SiO_2, <0.25% SO_2, <3.5% total metal oxides, pH 5-9, bulk density 68-75, MPS 20 µm.

Filler-grade:- 97% $CaSO_4 \cdot 2H_2O$, brightness of 97%+.

Food & pharmaceutical grades:- (typical) 96.75% $CaSO_4 \cdot 2H_2O$ with max. levels of As (3 ppm), Se (30 ppm), F (30 ppm), heavy metals (10 ppm), iron (100 ppm), lead (10 ppm).

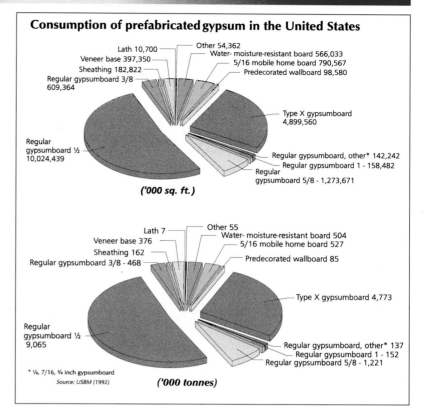

Consumption of prefabricated gypsum in the United States

COMMERCIAL GRADE GYPSUM SPECIFICATIONS

	National Gypsum	Georgia-Pacific	US Gypsum	Japan	Germany	Agriculture grade
Gypsum, min. %	94	90	95	95	80-95	70
Ca sulfite, max. %	0.5	-	2.0	0.25	0.25	
Total sol., max. ppm	-	-	600	1,000	-	
Sodium, max. ppm	250	200	75	-	600	
Chloride, max. ppm	400	200	120	-	100	1.0
Magnesium, max. ppm	250	-	50	-	1,000	
Free water, max. %	1	10	10	10	10	10
pH	6-8	3-9	6.5-8	6.5-8	5-9	
Inerts, max. %	3.0	-	1	-	-	

Source: Ellison & Hammer, 1988.

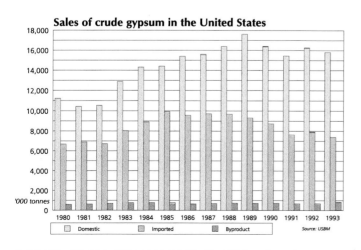

Sales of crude gypsum in the United States

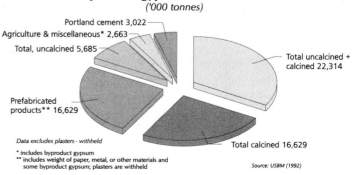

Consumption of gypsum in the United States

FGD gypsum

TYPICAL COMPOSITION OF FLUE GASES

Fuel	Hard coal	Lignite	Oil	Natural gas
Carrier gases % by volume				
N_2	70-80	60-78	75-77	70-72
CO_2	11-15	11-15	11-14	7-10
O_2	4-7	4-7	1-5	1-5
H_2O	3-8	8-24	6-11	1-22
pollutants, ppm				
SO_2	510-1,700	100-2,700	340-1,700	<30
NO_x	200-1,600	100-500	100-1,000	50-1,000
HCl	30-125	12-60		
HF	5-60	0.6-2.2		
CO	100-680	100- 680	4-16	

Gypsum Board Plant

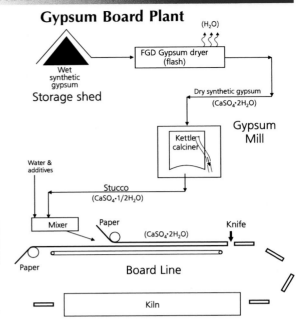

MAIN CHEMICAL REACTIONS IN FGD PLANTS

Formation of the reactive ions

with quicklime
$$CaO + H_2O \rightarrow Ca(OH)_2$$
$$Ca(OH)_2 + H_2O \rightarrow Ca^{2+} + 2\,OH^- + H_2O$$

with limestone
$$CaCO_3 + H_2O \rightarrow Ca^{2+} + CO_3^{2-} + H_2O$$
$$CO_3^{2-} + H_2O \rightarrow HCO_3^- + OH^-$$

Absorption of SO_2 in water
$$SO_2\,(gas) + H_2O \rightarrow H_2SO_3 \rightarrow H^+ + HSO_3^-$$

at higher pH
$$HSO_3^- + OH^- \rightarrow SO_3^{2-} + H_2O$$

pH-dependent reaction of SO_2 in the absorber solution

precipitation of calcium sulfite in alkaline media
$$2\,Ca^{2+} + 2\,SO_3^{2-} + H_2O \rightarrow 2\,CaSO_3 \cdot \tfrac{1}{2}H_2O$$

oxidation of the sulfite to sulfate in acidic media
$$2\,Ca^{2+} + 2\,H^+ + 2\,HSO_3^- + O_2 \rightarrow 2\,Ca^{2+} + 2\,SO_4^{2-} + 4\,H^+$$

Precipitation of calcium sulfate dihydrate
$$Ca^{2+} + SO_4^{2-} + 2\,H_2O \rightarrow CaSO_4 \cdot 2\,H_2O$$

Side reactions
$$Ca(OH)_2 + 2\,HCl \rightarrow 2\,CaCl_2 + 2\,H_2O$$
$$Ca(OH)_2 + 2\,HF \rightarrow 2\,CaF_2 + 2\,H_2O$$

Source: Juergen Umlauf, Saarbergwerke AG, Germany.

Coal Power Station:

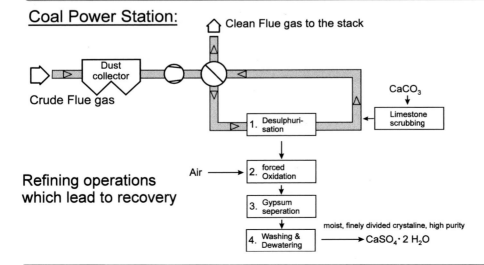

Refining operations which lead to recovery

RULE OF THUMB

Removing
   1t of SO_2

Requires
   1t of lime or 2 tons of limestone

Produces
   6t of 50% solid sludge

   or 3 tons of gypsum

   or 1.5t of acid

   or 1.5t of sulfur

   or 2t of ammonium sulfate

APPARENT CONSUMPTION OF GYPSUM (TONNES)

	Apparent Consumption
United States	20,651,749
China	10,346,122
Iran	8,050,000
France	5,040,206
Former USSR	3,990,200
Japan	3,946,846
United Kingdom	3,016,134
Mexico	2,912,630
Spain	2,559,829
Canada	2,141,159
Germany	1,562,516
India	1,537,994
Egypt	1,250,000
Italy	1,246,619
Brazil	800,000
Poland	766,621
Czechoslovakia	723,000
Colombia	695,791
Greece	643,089
Romania	600,000
Belgium	593,627
Austria	544,365
Taiwan	536,797
Pakistan	521,891
Bulgaria	450,000
South Africa	442,496
Former Yugoslavia	425,673
Argentina	421,670
South Korea	400,895
Portugal	398,018
Switzerland	337,239
Chile	335,678
Turkey	307,903

NOTE: Numbers are approximate and rounded for 1991 or thereabouts; absence of a country does not necessarily indicate no production or trade; absence of a number does not necessarily mean zero

Source: British Geological Survey

Wallboard and plaster:- gypsum >85%, but producers prefer min. 94-95% $CaSO_4 \cdot 2H_2O$; 0.5-2% calcium sulfite. 75-250 ppm Na, 120-400 ppm Cl, 50-250 ppm Mg, 75 ppm K, 10-15% free water, 90% -100 mesh and 75% -200 mesh. In addition, byproduct gypsum requires a low content of fly ash (dark color), < 100 ppm Cl, with low unoxidized sulfite.

WORLD CAPACITY: 106M. t.   **CAPACITY UTILIZATION:** 99%.

MARKET CONDITIONS: Stable.

MARKETING FACTORS: Gypsum is heavily dependent on the construction/renovation industry and therefore the general state of the economy. Gypsum is generally available and is considered a low-cost commodity that is consumed close to the point of production. In fact, many gypsum operations are part of a vertically integrated system to produce wallboard.

HEALTH & SAFETY: Crystalline silica has been classified as a probable carcinogen by the IARC (see silica for further details). Therefore, because of its crystalline silica content, unless processing has the capability to reduce the crystalline silica content to less than 0.1%, gypsum and anhydrite may come under the OSHA Hazard Communication Standards, 29 CFR Section 1900.1200 which require labeling and other forms of warning, material safety data sheets, and employee training for products containing identified carcinogens with concentrations greater than 0.1%.

SUBSTITUTES & ALTERNATIVES: The main threat to natural gypsum is byproduct gypsum from phosphoric acid, FGD, or titanium dioxide plants, although market penetration has been limited to date except for individual cases.

RECYCLING: There are facilities to recycle waste wallboard from construction sites by separating the material into the gypsum and paper components. The rising cost of land fills is encouraging the recycling of byproduct gypsum wherever possible. For example, every tonne of phosphoric acid produced generates 5 tonnes of phosphogypsum.

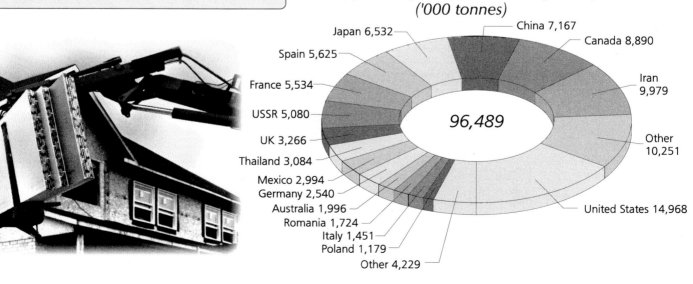

Gypsum production capacity
('000 tonnes)

China 7,167 · Canada 8,890 · Iran 9,979 · Other 10,251 · United States 14,968 · Japan 6,532 · Spain 5,625 · France 5,534 · USSR 5,080 · UK 3,266 · Thailand 3,084 · Mexico 2,994 · Germany 2,540 · Australia 1,996 · Romania 1,724 · Italy 1,451 · Poland 1,179 · Other 4,229

96,489

PRODUCERS & WORLD TRADE: Gypsum is produced in over 100 countries, and despite its relatively low value, international trade is quite common.

PRICES: Crude gypsum $7/t; calcined gypsum $20/t; plaster $125/t; filler grade $80-200/t.

HTS CODES: 2520.10.000 (gypsum; anhydrite); 2520.20.0000 (plasters); 6809.11.0000 (boards, sheets, panels, tiles and similar articles faced or reinforced with paper); 6809.19.0000 (boards, sheets, panels - other); 6809.90.000 (other articles).

ETYMOLOGY: Alabaster from ancient ointment jars called *alabastra* and perhaps Alabastron in Egypt. **Anhydrite** from the Greek *anhydros = dry* or *without water.* **Bassanite** for the Basset group of mines, Redruth, Cornwall, England. **Gypsum** from the Latin *gypsum*, Greek *gypsos = plaster* or *chalk.* **Selenite** from the Greek *selenites (lithos) = moon (stone)* since it was supposed to wax and wane with the moon and/or it has moon-like white reflections.

PRODUCTION AND TRADE IN GYPSUM (TONNES)

Producers / Importers

Producers	Importers
United States	United States
China	Japan
Iran	Belgium
Thailand	Germany
Canada	Taiwan
France	UK
Mexico	South Korea
Spain	Netherlands
Former USSR	Denmark
UK	Norway
Germany	Canada
India	Malaysia
Egypt	Indonesia
Italy	Philippines
Brazil	Finland
Poland	France
Czechoslovakia	Switzerland
Greece	Venezuela
Austria	Portugal
Colombia	New Zealand
Romania	Hong Kong
Pakistan	Singapore
Bulgaria	Italy
Argentina	Ecuador
Yugoslavia	Colombia

Exporters

Exporters	
Thailand	Netherlands
Canada	Syria
Mexico	Jamaica
Spain	Australia
France	Dominican Rep.
Germany	Denmark
United States	Venezuela
Austria	Saudi Arabia
China	Italy
Morocco	Greece
Belgium	UK
Indonesia	Poland
Ireland	

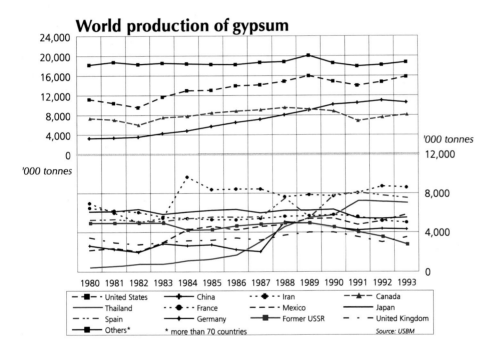

World production of gypsum

'000 tonnes

1980 1981 1982 1983 1984 1985 1986 1987 1988 1989 1990 1991 1992 1993

- ▪ - United States
- ◆ China
- ✦ Iran
- ▲ Canada
- Thailand
- ● France
- Mexico
- Japan
- Spain
- ◆ Germany
- ▪ Former USSR
- United Kingdom
- ■ Others*
- * more than 70 countries

Source: USBM

PRODUCTION AND TRADE IN GYPSUM (TONNES)

	Production	Imports	Exports	Apparent Consumption	Net Supplier	Net Consumer
North America	26,351,000	7,258,534	7,903,996	25,705,538	645,462	
South America	2,779,620	243,930	46,843	2,976,707		(197,087)
Central America & Carib.	500,659	52,692	110,431	442,920	57,739	
European Union	17,692,697	2,966,018	4,751,979	15,906,736	1,785,961	
Non-EU Europe	8,284,018	,775,461	207,563	8,851,916		(567,898)
Australasia	19,970,074	5,961,704	11,560,199	14,371,579	5,598,495	
Middle East	8,608,170	72,654	89,384	8,591,440	16,730	
Africa	2,234,311	72,504	150,611	2,156,204	78,107	

NOTE: Numbers are approximate and rounded for 1991 or thereabouts.

Source: British Geological Survey

Iodine is largely "concentrated" in seawater (0.05 ppm); certain marine organisms like seaweed (up to 0.45% of their own weight on a dry basis); subsurface brines, especially gas-field brines (30 - 1,300 ppm); and caliche nitrate ore in Chile which is cemented with iodine-bearing minerals such as lautarite (CaI_2O_6), dietzeite ($2CaO \cdot I_2O_5 \cdot CrO_3$), and brüggenite ($Ca(IO_3)_2$). Modern commercial production is based on extraction from seawater, brines, and the caliche ore.

IODINE CONTENT OF BRINES

Location		Iodine, ppm
United States	Michigan	30
	California	30-70
	Louisiana	35
	Oklahoma	150-1,200
Japan	Kanto gasfield	50-130
	Okinawa	85

PROPERTIES & USES: Iodine is a gray to purplish black crystalline element that melts at 114°C and sublimes at 184°C to a blue-violet gas. Along with fluorine, chlorine, bromine, and astatine, iodine is part of the halogen family. It has antiseptic & germicide properties [commercial dishwashing detergents; food processing; pharmaceutical/medicines (tincture of iodine); herbicides; sanitary and industrial disinfectants; swimming pools & water supplies], is opaque to X-rays [contrast media for X-rays], and prevents conditions like soft tissue lumpy jaw and foot rot in cattle [animal feed additive]. Iodine is a coloring agent in food coloring [carbonated drinks; powdered drinks, gelatin deserts; pet food] and dyes [various fabrics].

Iodine combines with most elements and dissolves in water. Potassium iodide acts as a heat stabilizer and oxidizer [engraving and lithography; in the manufacture of nylon for tire cord and carpets; for converting rosins, tall oil, and other wood products to more stable forms; photographic emulsions], a catalyst such as in the iodide-promoted rhodium complex [Monsanto acetic acid process; dehydrogenation of butane and butane to butadiene; preparation of stereo-regular polymers], in medicine [expectorant in cough medicine; blood stream X-ray dye to view coronary arteries or kidneys; in the synthesis of amphetamine, methamphetamine, and ethylamphetamine], and as a source of iodine [table salt additive]. Other compounds include silver iodide which is photosensitive [photography]; potassium iodate [feed additive; medicine]; sodium iodide [photography; solvent; feed additive; cloud seeding]; sodium iodate [antiseptic & disinfectant; feed additive]; quartz-iodine [automobile & stadium lights]; ethylenediamine dihydroiodide [feed additive]. Pyrrolidone-base chemicals are replacing CFCs as cleaning solvents.

QUALITY & SPECIFICATIONS: Crude iodine is min. 99.5% I_2 with water, sulfuric acid, iron, and insoluble materials being the main impurities; USP grade min. 99.8% I_2; resublimed 99.9% I_2, with ACS specifications of <0.005% Br_2 & <0.02 total nonvolatile materials.

WORLD CAPACITY: 18,000 t.   **CAPACITY UTILIZATION:** 95%.

MARKET CONDITIONS: Steady-increasing.   **MARKETING FACTORS:** The highly cyclical market and fact that supply depends on natural gas and nitrate production complicate the market for iodine. Therefore, it depends on the level of inventories and developments in medical uses.

APPARENT CONSUMPTIONS OF IODINE (TONNES)

	Apparent Consumption
United States	5,503
Japan	3,104
Former USSR	1,845
United Kingdom	1,568
Italy	875
China	833
France	817
Germany	804
Norway	680
India	664
Spain	564
Chile	289
Netherlands	280
Brazil	176
Mexico	152
Canada	107

NOTE: Numbers are approximate and rounded for 1991 or thereabouts; absence of a country does not necessarily indicate no production or trade; absence of a number does not necessarily mean zero

Source: British Geological Survey

Consumption of iodine by industry in the United States
(tonnes)

Pharmaceuticals 818
Stabilizers (nylon) 91
Inks & colorants 364
Sanitary uses 864
Photography 91
Other 45
Food products 909
Catalysts (rubber) 500
Data for 1983   Source: USBM

Capacity of iodine
(tonnes)

18,040
United States 2,000
Japan 7,500
Chile 6,000
Former USSR 2,000
Indonesia 40
China 500
Source: USBM (1991)

SUBSTITUTES & ALTERNATIVES: Chemical & sanitation:- chlorine, bromine.

HEALTH & SAFETY: Iodine gas has an irritating odor. Several iodine compounds including iodoform and methyl iodide are included on OSHA/MSHA PEL's.

On a positive note, iodized salt is used as a vehicle to introduce iodine to the human diet. Soils deficient in iodine expose the local population to the risk of iodine deficiency disorders (IDD) which in turn causes health problems ranging from goitre (enlargement of thyroid gland) to severe mental disorders. IDD also impairs reproduction in poultry, sheep, goats, and cattle plus lowers the yield of meat, wool, and/or milk. The effects of IDD can be totally eradicated by the introduction of iodine into the diet through edible salt (and salt licks in the case of animals). The concentration of iodine in the salt — generally added as sodium or potassium iodide/iodate — needs to be sufficient to supply 150-200 micrograms of iodine per capita per day (equivalent to one teaspoon per <u>lifetime</u>). This is generally regarded as 40-100 mg iodine per kilogram of salt (iodised salt contains 0.010% - 0.006% iodine).

RECYCLING: Virtually none.

PRODUCERS & WORLD TRADE: Supply, controlled by less than ten countries and dominated by two, is largely based on being a coproduct of natural gas and natural nitrate production. A significant proportion of the production enters international trade.

PRICES: Crude iodine $9.00-9.50/kg (drums, FOB works); USP iodine $37.40/kg. Calcium iodate $16.40/kg (FCC, drums, FOB works). Calcium iodide $$30/kg (50-kg drums, FOB works). Hydriodic acid $18.15-19.90/kg purified, 47-57%, FOB works). Potassium iodide $26.42/kg (USP, drums, delivered); $28.82/kg (ACS grade). Sodium iodide $3630/kg (USP, drums, freight equalized).

HTS CODES: 2801.20.00 (iodine, crude); 2827.60.10 (iodide, calcium & cuprous); 2827.60.20 (iodide, potassium).

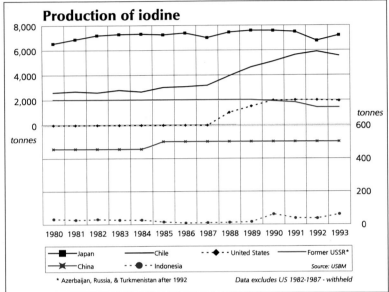

Production of iodine

Japan — Chile - ◆ - United States — Former USSR*
China - ● - Indonesia
Source: USBM
* Azerbaijan, Russia, & Turkmenistan after 1992   Data excludes US 1982-1987 - withheld

ETYMOLOGY: Brüggenite for Juan Brüggen (1887-1953), Chilean geologist. **Dietzeite** for August Dietze who first described the mineral in the 19th century. **Iodine** from the Greek *iodes = violet* alluding to its color. **Lautarite** for the locality at Oficina Lautaro, Antofagasta Province, Chile.

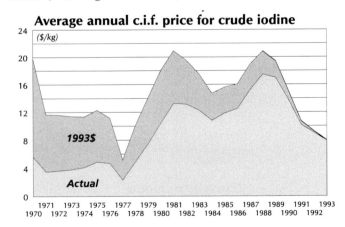

Average annual c.i.f. price for crude iodine

($/kg)

1993$

Actual

IODINE LEADERS

Producers	*Exporters*	*Importers*
Japan	Chile	United States
Chile	Japan	United Kingdom
United States	Switzerland	Germany
Former USSR	Germany	Italy
China	Netherlands	France
Indonesia	United Kingdom	Norway
	Indonesia	India
	Hong Kong	Spain
	Belgium	Netherlands
	France	Japan
	Spain	China
	Italy	Brazil
	Taiwan	Mexico

PRODUCTION AND TRADE IN IODINE (TONNES)

	Production	*Imports*	*Exports*	*Apparent Consumption*	*Net Supplier*	*Net Consumer*
North America	1,999	3,763		5,762		(3,763)
South America	5,700	194	5,411	483	5,217	
European Union		5,726	751	4,975		(4,975)
Non-EU Europe	1,800	810	48	2,562		(762)
Australasia	8,038	1,540	4,863	4,715	3,323	

IRON OXIDE

Minerals	Formula	Color	SG	H	Index of refraction
Hematite	Fe_2O_3	red	4.9-5.3	5.5-6	3.042
Goethite	$\alpha FeOOH \cdot xH_2O$	yellow	3.6-4.0	5-5.5	2.26-2.27
Lepidocrocite	$\gamma FeOOH \cdot xH_2O$	yellow	4.05-4.10	5.0	1.94
Magnetite	Fe_3O_4	brown to black	5.18	5.5-6.5	2.42

These natural iron oxides consist of a combination of one or more ferrous or ferric oxides and impurities such as manganese, clay, or organics. In addition, pyrite and siderite may be calcined to form natural iron oxide pigments.

Synthetic iron oxide is produced in various ways including the following:

➤ Thermal decomposition of iron salts such as ferrous sulfate to produce reds:

Neutralization
$$H_2SO_4 + Fe + H_2O \quad \rightarrow \quad Fe_2SO_4 + H_2\text{-} + H_2O$$

Evaporation/crystallization
$$Fe_2SO_4 + 7H_2O \quad \rightarrow \quad Fe_2SO_4 \cdot 7H_2O$$

Dehydration
$$Fe_2SO_4 \cdot 7H_2O \quad \rightarrow \quad Fe_2SO_4 \cdot H_2O + 6H_2O$$

Without air
$$Fe_2SO_4 \cdot H_2O \quad \rightarrow \quad Fe_2O_3 + Fe_2(SO_4)_3 + 6H_2O + SO_2$$

$$Fe_2(SO_4)_3 \quad \rightarrow \quad Fe_2O_3 + SO_3$$
copperas red

$$SO_3 \quad \rightarrow \quad SO_2 + 1\frac{1}{2}O_2$$

➤ Precipitation to produce yellows, reds, browns, and blacks. For example, Penniman-Zoph process (a.k.a. scrap iron process) to produce yellows:

Nucleation
$$4\,NaOH + 2Fe_2SO_4 \quad \rightarrow \quad 2Fe(OH)_2 + 2Na_2SO_4$$
$$2Fe(OH)_2 + \frac{1}{2}O_2 \quad \rightarrow \quad 2FeOOH + H_2O$$
nucleus

The nucleus is transferred to a precipitator containing Fe_2SO_4, H_2O, and iron in an oxidizing environment at 60-87.8°C; as the iron dissolves, the reaction products precipitate on the nuclei causing the particles to grow:

$$2\,Fe^{++} + \frac{1}{2}O_2 + 3H_2O \quad \rightarrow \quad 2FeOOH + 4H^+$$

and

$$2Fe_2SO_4 + 3H_2O + \frac{1}{2}O_2 \quad \rightarrow \quad 2FeOOH + H_2SO_4$$
$$H_2SO_4 + FeSO_4 + H_2\text{-} \quad \rightarrow \quad Fe_2SO_4 + H_2\uparrow$$

➤ Reduction of organic compounds by iron, e.g. nitrobenzene reduced to aniline in the presence of particular chemicals, will produce specific colors of iron oxide ($AlCl_3$ produces yellows). Reds are produced by calcining yellow or blacks.

The number of possible iron oxide types is increased still further by adjusting the production procedure, calcination, reduction, and blending.

IRON OXIDE CLASSIFICATION

Yellow Natural	Yellow Synthetic	Red Natural	Red Synthetic	Brown Natural	Brown Synthetic	Black Natural	Black Synthetic
					Hematite, goethite, magnetite		
Goethite	Goethite	Hematite	Hematite	Umbers	blend	Magnetite	Magnetite
					Coprecipitated		
Lepidocrocite	Lepidocrocite	Siderite*		Limonite*	hematite-magnetite	Slate (mixed)	
Ochers	Akageneite	Pyrite*		Siderite*	Maghemite		
Siennas				Goethite			
Limonite							* calcined

PROPERTIES & USES: Iron oxide materials yield reproducible pigments that are non-toxic, non-bleeding, relatively inert, weather resistant, mainly opaque, and light fast (i.e. resists the exposure to radiant energy with little chemical or physical change). Within the range of iron oxides, various physical properties influence pigment use including oil absorption (influences binder demand particularly in paint); surface area (depends on the particle shape and/or surface characteristics like porosity, pore size, smoothness, and convolutions); particle size and particle size distribution (influence optical properties); particle shape (spheroidal, cubical, nodular, acicular, or lamellar particles each have a very different effect on a pigmented system); and optical properties (influenced by particle size and shape, that is whether light is absorbed, reflected, or refracted through particle-to-particle interactions).

NATURAL IRON OXIDES (%)

	United States Hematite	Venezuela Hematite	Persian Gulf Hematite	Spain Spanish oxide	Austria Micaceous iron oxide	United States Ocher	France Ocher	Italy Sienna	Italy Sienna, calcined	Cyprus Umber	Cyprus Umber, calcined	United States Magnetite
Fe_2O_3	63.0	96.50	73.0	85.0	90.0	50.0	20.0	62.0	68	45.0	55.0	98.5
SiO_2	12.60	1.50	21.0	6.5	3.5	14.0	50.0	Al silicates	Al silicates	Al silicates	Al silicates	Al silicates
Al_2O_3	4.80	1.50	3.00	1.0	2.40	6.00	18.0	Al silicates	Al silicates	Al silicates	Al silicates	Al silicates
MgO	3.20	0.02	0.33	1.0	1.0	0.20	0.25	Al silicates	Al silicates	Al silicates	Al silicates	Al silicates
CaO	7.50	0.03	0.80	3.00	0.50	0.20	0.25	Al silicates	Al silicates	Al silicates	Al silicates	Al silicates
MnO_2	-	0.02	0.06	-	-	0.62	-	Al silicates	Al silicates	11.0	10.0	Al silicates
LOI @ 1000°C	8.2	0.50	2.50	3.0	0.15	9.00	9.00	15-20	-	10-15	-	-
% H_2O sol. salts	0.8	0.20	<3.00	1-2	0.08	0.50		0.45		0.8	0.4	0.10
Color	Brownish red	Reddish brown	Bright red	Bright red	Brownish red	Brownish yellow	Dull yellow	Brownish yellow	Reddish brown	Greenish brown	Brown	Black
Oil absorption*	15	14	13	17	11	24	32	36	42	44	54	15
APS (µm)	0.8	3.00	0.60	1.50	25	1.0	4.0	0.6	0.7	3.0	0.6	-
Surface area (m²/g)	8.00	6.1	4.7	5.8	0.08	15.4	-	33.4	36.0	101.7	86.9	4.3
SG	3.78	4.90	4.35	4.67	4.80	3.47	2.88	3.58	4.03	3.24	3.74	5.03

* lbs. oil/100 lb. pigment

Source: Podolsky & Keller, 1994

SYNTHETIC IRON OXIDE (%)

	Hematite Decomp. $FeSO_4$	Hematite Ppt.	Hematite Calc. $Fe_2O_3 \cdot H_2O$	Goethite Ppt. & org. reduced	G/H/M blend	Magnetite Ppt.
Fe_2O_3	99.5	97-98	97.5	85-87	94	98-99
SiO_2	0.03	0.05	0.10	0.05	depends	0.12
Al_2O_3	0.02-0.03	0.01	0.01	0.02	on	0.07
LOI @ 1,000°C	0.05-0.20	1.50-2.50	0.70	11.0	blend	-
Color	light-dark red	light-dark red	medium yellow red	light-dark yellow	brown	black
Particle shape	nodular	spheroidal	acicular	acicular	mixed system	cubical
Oil absorption*	12-25	20-25	48	50-55	26	27
APS (µm)	0.25-3.0	0.3-0.9	0.75	0.2-1.5	0.5	0.4
Surface area (m²/g)	2-10	3-10	9-10	5-15	-	7.2
SG	5.15	4.9	4.9	4.03	4.70	4.96

* lbs. oil/100 lb. pigment

Source: Podolsky & Keller, 1994

CONCENTRATIONS OF HEAVY METALS IN IRON OXIDES (PPM)

	Copperas red	Precipitated reds	Precipitated yellows	Synthetic black	Natural red	Raw sienna	Burnt umber
Arsenic	<3	20-60	5-40	3-15	50-100	70-120	100-200
Antimony	5-15	5-20	5-20	10	40-80	*	*
Cadmium	<10	<20	<20	<20	<50	<50	<50
Selenium	<20	<20	<20	<20	<100	<100	<100
Mercury	<5	<5	<5	<5	<5	<5	<5
Lead	1-15	10-140	10-50	50-100	6000+	100-500	400-1100
Barium (acid sol.)	<10	30-120	100-1000	100-1000	100-2000	NA	

*potassium spectral interference

Source: Podolsky & Keller, 1994

Natural iron oxide is used as a low-cost pigment [various paints & stains; printing inks; plastics (vinyls, phenolics, polyurethanes, epoxies); rubber; paper; concrete products and building materials, mortar, brick, and tile; ceramic glazes & frits; animal and pet food; pharmaceuticals and cosmetics; glass feedstock]. Hematite is commonly used in primer paint since its high density, fairly large particle size, and low oil absorption allow heavy loading; in addition, it provides some protection against corrosion [industrial maintenance finishes for railroad equipment, bridge paints, etc.]. Micaceous iron oxide (MIO) or specular hematite, a platelike pigment, utilizes its lamellar film structure to contribute to corrosion control. Natural umbers and siennas have unique color characteristics which cannot be reproduced by synthetics {stains}. Beneficiated natural iron oxide is used in electronics {barium ferrite ($BaFe_{12}O_{19}$); manganese zinc ferrite ($Mn_xZn_y \cdot Fe_2O_4$); magnetic ink].

Compared with natural iron oxides, synthetics tend to have superior uniformity, color purity (chroma), greater tinting strength, and tighter control over color consistency [appliance enamels; automotive paint; interior and exterior paints and wood stains; powder coatings]. Chemical purity can be controlled by the purification of the feed materials thus reducing the heavy metal content, i.e. Sb, As, Cd, Hg, and Se [pharmaceuticals and cosmetics]. As well as beneficiated naturals, synthetics (reds, copperas reds, and calcined yellows because of the chemical purity, high density, and low volatiles) are used to produce various types of ferrites used in permanent magnets [d.c. motors; door closing devices; magnetic resonance imaging; electronics such as speakers]. Ultrafine gamma ferric oxide (for slow recording speeds and high fidelity) or cobalt-treated gamma ferric oxide (to increase the intrinsic coercivity) is used for their magnetic properties [recording tapes/equipment; magnetic ink character recognition (MICR); toner pigments for photocopy and fax machines].

Finely ground hematite is used because of its abrasiveness [jewelers' rouge; ophthalmic polishing] and its high SG [weighting agent in drilling muds; high-density aggregates]. Iron oxide in combination with other elements may be used as catalysts [conversions for ammonia; styrene; butadiene; hydrogen; and formaldehyde].

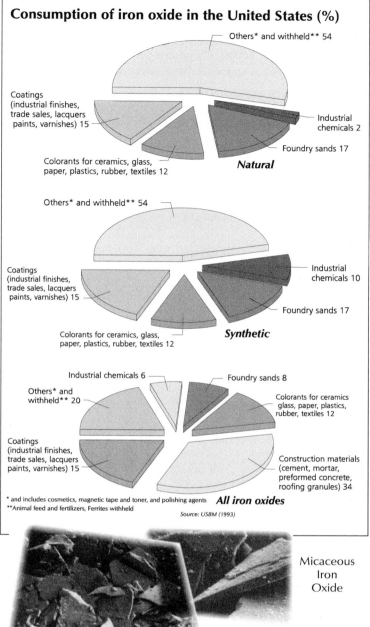

Consumption of iron oxide in the United States (%)

Others* and withheld** 54
Coatings (industrial finishes, trade sales, lacquers paints, varnishes) 15
Industrial chemicals 2
Foundry sands 17
Colorants for ceramics, glass, paper, plastics, rubber, textiles 12
Natural

Others* and withheld** 54
Coatings (industrial finishes, trade sales, lacquers paints, varnishes) 15
Industrial chemicals 10
Foundry sands 17
Colorants for ceramics, glass, paper, plastics, rubber, textiles 12
Synthetic

Industrial chemicals 6
Foundry sands 8
Others* and withheld** 20
Colorants for ceramics glass, paper, plastics, rubber, textiles 12
Coatings (industrial finishes, trade sales, lacquers paints, varnishes) 15
Construction materials (cement, mortar, preformed concrete, roofing granules) 34
* and includes cosmetics, magnetic tape and toner, and polishing agents
**Animal feed and fertilizers, Ferrites withheld
All iron oxides
Source: USBM (1993)

Micaceous Iron Oxide

QUALITY & SPECIFICATIONS: *Pigments:-* For use in paints, natural iron oxide is categorized as A, B, C, D by Fe_2O_3 content, i.e. red >95, 70, 50, & 10%; yellow >83, 70, 50, 10%; brown >87, 70, & 30%; black >95 & 70%; and gray MIO >85%. Other factors include soluble and volatile matter, CaO water-soluble chloride and sulfates; bulk density; oil absorption (rub out); opacity, relative tinting strength; specific surface area; particle size (e.g. -10 or -50 microns). ASTM for ocher requires >17% Fe_2O_3, <1% moisture or volatile matter; for sienna it is >38% Fe_2O_3, <4% moisture and volatiles.

Ferrites:- (hard) min. 98 Fe_2O_3, max. 0.3% SiO_2, 0.25% Cl, 0.5% MnO_2, 0.2% Al_2O_3, 0.1% Cr_2O_3, and 1% moisture with 85% -325 mesh.

API: - SG >5 and -200 mesh.

High-density aggregate:- min. 65% Fe, max. 5% Al_2O_3 + SiO_2, water absorption <4%, low alkali and sulfide reactivity, angular to subangular particle shape, and SG 4.5-5.1.

Pet foods:- Max. 5 ppm As, 20 ppm Pb, and 3 ppm Hg.

Pharmaceuticals & cosmetics:- max. 3 ppm As, 10 ppm Pb, 3 ppm Hg.

WORLD CAPACITY: 350,000 t.
CAPACITY UTILIZATION: NA.

MARKET CONDITIONS: Variable.

MARKETING FACTORS: Construction activity and therefore the strength of the economy.

SUBSTITUTES & ALTERNATIVES: Synthetic iron oxides have taken over many of the markets once served by natural iron oxides.

HEALTH & SAFETY: Most of the iron oxide pigments are relatively non-reactive and contain only traces of heavy metals and toxic elements, usually chemically bound in the form of complex silicates. They have a generally recognized as safe (GRAS) rating by the Food and Drug Administration (FDA).

RECYCLING: Virtually none although much of the feedstock for synthetic iron oxide is derived from scrap metal.

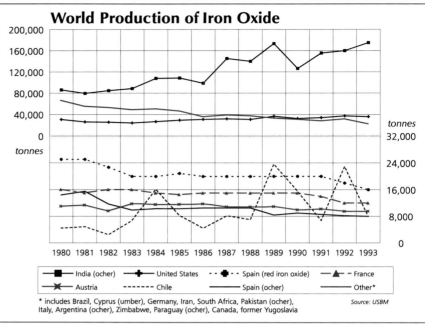

World Production of Iron Oxide

Legend:
- India (ocher)
- United States
- Spain (red iron oxide)
- France
- Austria
- Chile
- Spain (ocher)
- Other*

* includes Brazil, Cyprus (umber), Germany, Iran, South Africa, Pakistan (ocher), Italy, Argentina (ocher), Zimbabwe, Paraguay (ocher), Canada, former Yugoslavia

Source: USBM

PRODUCERS & WORLD TRADE: Traditional suppliers of natural iron oxide like Spain and Cyprus continue to export material, although the ability to produce synthetic products has reduced demand. Austria is noted for micaceous iron oxide production.

PRICES: Natural (FOB) Blacks:- $0.60/kg (natural); $2.00-2.20/kg (synthetic); $2.00 (micaceous). Browns:- $0.35-0.45/kg (natural iron ore); $0.40-0.88/kg (metallic); $1.90-2.00/kg (pure synthetic); $1.30-2.00/kg (burnt sienna - Italy); $1.15-1.60/kg (burned umber - Turkey). Reds:- $1.10/kg (natural); $1.90-2.30/kg (pure synthetic). Yellows:- $0.75-1.25/kg (ocher - USA); $1.40/kg (raw Sienna); $1.65-2.20/kg (synthetic). MIO $0.70-0.80/kg.

Synthetic United States (FOB) Blacks:- $2.00-2.10/kg (precipitated); $1.80-2.10/kg (organic reduction). Browns & tans:- $1.85-2.00/kg (synthetic blends); $2.40-2.50/kg (pet food and cosmetic grades). Reds:- $1.95-2.30/kg (copperas red); $1.95-2.10/kg (precipitated reds); $1.75-4.00/kg (calcined yellows); $1.70-2.10/kg (organic reduction, calcined); $2.25-2.50/kg (pet food and cosmetic grades). Yellows:- $1.65-1.90/kg (regular); $1.85-2.15/kg (low oil). Magnetics:- $2.75-18.00/kg (gamma ferric oxide); $5.50-11.00/kg (magnetite). Ferrite grade:- $2.25-2.50/kg (red iron oxide).

HTS CODES: 2821.10.0010 (synthetic pigments: black); 2821.10.0020 (synthetic pigments: red); 2821.10.0030 (synthetic pigments: yellow); 2821.10.0040 (synthetic pigments: other); 2821.10.0050 (other); 2530.40.0000 (natural micaceous iron oxides); 3206.49.2000 (preparations based on iron oxides); 2530.30.0010 (earth colors - ochers); 2530.30.0020 (earth colors - siennas); 2530.30.0030 (earth colors - umbers); 2530.30.0040 (earth colors - Vandyke brown); 2530.30.0090 (earth colors - not elsewhere specified); 2821.20.0000 (iron oxides - earth colors).

ETYMOLOGY: Akageneite for the Akagene mine, Iwate Prefecture, Japan. **Goethite** for Johann Wolfgang von Goethe (1749-1832), German poet/philosopher. **Hematite** from the Greek *haimatites = bloodlike* alluding to its red color. **Lepidocrocite** from the Greek *lepis = scale* in reference to the scaly or feathery habit, and (Latin) *crocinus = saffron, golden, yellow* for its color. **Limonite** from the Greek *leimon = meadow* since it often occurs in bogs and swamps. **Maghemite** from the first syllables of *magnetite* and *hema*tite referring to magnetism and composition. **Magnetite** from the Middle Latin *magnes = magnet* in reference to its magnetic properties; or from Magnes, a shepherd who first discovered the mineral on Mount Ida when the rock was attracted to the nails in his shoes. **Ocher** from the Latin and Greek *ochra = pale* or *pale yellow* alluding to its color. **Pyrite** from the Greek *pyrites = flint* or *millstone from pyros = a fire* since it gives off sparks when struck. **Sienna** for the town of Sienna in Tuscany, northern Italy. **Umber** for the Umbria district of Italy or possibly Latin *umbra = a shade* or *shadow*.

IRON OXIDE LEADERS

Producers	Importers	Exporters
United States	United States	United States
Spain*	Japan	Spain*
France	Korea	Cyprus (umber)
Austria	United Kingdom	Austria
Chile	Germany	Brazil
Brazil	Canada	Germany
Cyprus (umber)	Mexico	Pakistan (ocher)
Germany		Italy
Iran		
South Africa		
Pakistan (ocher)		
Italy		
*red iron oxide & ocher		

KAOLIN

Minerals	Formula	Color	SG	H
Kaolinite	$Al_4Si_4O_{10}(OH)_8$	white w/ red, brown, blue tint	2.62	1.5-2
Halloysite	$Al_4Si_4O_6(OH)_{12}$	white w/ red, brown, yellow tint	2.6	1.5-2

Kaolin is a white, soft, plastic clay mainly composed of fine-grained platy mineral kaolinite. **Ball clay** is a fine-grained, highly plastic kaolinite admixed with quartz, mica, illite, smectite, chlorite, & colloidal carbonaceous matter. **Chamotte** is a calcined ball clay. **Flint clay** is a smooth, microcrystalline hard-slaking rock with a pronounced concoidal fracture composed mainly of kaolinite; it becomes plastic with prolonged grinding in water. **Fireclay** is a siliceous or aluminous clay composed of a disordered variety of kaolinite that is capable of withstanding high temperatures without deforming (i.e. refractory). **Halloysite** is near kaolinite but containing more hydroxyl and composed of long slender tube-like crystals.

PROPERTIES & USES: Individual kaolins vary in many physical respects, e.g. degree of crystallinity which influences brightness, whiteness, opacity, gloss, film strength, and viscosity; and PS, PSD, and particle shape which affect smoothness, optical properties, rheology. Brightness is measured to slightly different standards of TAPPI or GE (US) or ISO (European). The + or - 2µ is used as the control point for particle size (typical kaolin from Georgia has APS of 0.37µ). Critical types of viscosity are high shear (Hercules) determined by particle packing, and low shear (Brookfield) determined by surface area and therefore particle size. Additional kaolin grades are produced through processing including delamination (breaking up books of kaolin crystals into individual plates) and calcination. Calcined grades have higher SG (2.63), H (6-8), and refractive index (1.62) than regular grades.

Kaolin is a relatively cheap, white or near white mineral filler that is inert over a wide pH range, nonabrasive, with a fine but controllable particle size, low heat & electrical conductivity, and with good brightness and opacity (hiding power) [paper; plastics; paint; rubber; adhesives; sealants, putty, and caulks]. Chemical composition is not critical except as it influences color. Oil absorption is important, particularly for paint and rubber. The same properties plus particle shape, rheology, viscosity, and pH allow kaolin to be used as a paper coating pigment which contributes brightness, gloss, smoothness, and ink reception to the paper surface [printing & writing paper, art paper]. Calcined kaolin is very fine-grained with a brightness of 93-95%, low SG, and enhanced light-scattering power [TiO_2 substitution in paper & paint].

Ball clay in ceramics has high wet and dry strength, long vitrification range, high firing shrinkage, and unfired colors ranging from light buff to various shades of gray.

Kaolin, ball clay, and less so halloysite supply chemical SiO_2 and Al_2O_3 to ceramics (therefore its chemical composition is critical), as well as plasticity, workability, and strength in the pre-fired state, and strength and a light color in the fired body. However, compared with ball clay with its good modulus of rupture and plasticity [earthenware; sanitaryware; wall tiles], kaolin has low plasticity and dry strength but good whiteness [bone china; porcelain bodies]. Halloysite (premium grade) has an unbleached brightness of 91-92% with 0.28% Fe_2O_3 and 0.08% TiO_2 and adds whiteness and translucency to ceramics [porcelain; bone china; technical ceramics; ceramic catalyst support bodies].

Kaolinite-bearing fireclay, flint clay, or chamotte can be shaped and have a PCE of around 30-40 [refractory bricks]. Properties similar to ball clay have nonrefractory uses [vitrified clay pipes; facing bricks; sanitaryware; floor tiles]. The choice ranges in alumina content from calcined kaolin, flint clay, chamotte (35-45% Al_2O_3); andalusite, kyanite, and sillimanite (40-60% Al_2O_3); to synthetic sintered and fused mullite (60-76%+).

Kaolinite contains alumina and silica [cement additive; aluminum sulfate & zeolites production (see below); fiberglass manufacture; catalyst & catalyst carrier] and good bonding and absorption properties [cosmetics, pharmaceuticals; insecticide carrier; animal feed].

Kaolin + aqueous NaOH @ 500-600°C forms an amorphous sodium aluminosilicate → zeolite NaA.

$$2Al_2Si_2O_5(OH)_4 \quad \rightarrow \quad 2Al_2Si_2O_7 + H_2O$$
kaolin   calcined metakaolin

$$12H_2O + 6Al_2Si_2O_7 + 12NaOH \quad \rightarrow \quad Na_{12}((AlO_2))_{12}$$
moderate temperature   zeolite NaA

QUALITY & SPECIFICATIONS: The paper industry divides kaolin into fine at 90% <2µ (Georgia, USA; Brazil; Australia) and coarse at 50% <2µ (Georgia, USA; Cornwall, UK) and requires low viscosity clays (ceramics require a viscous or plastic clay). Bacteria and fungus content needs to be controlled carefully when transported as a slurry.

Filler-grade:- kaolinite >90%, low Fe_2O_3 & TiO_2 (<1%), low abrasive quartz (1-2%) and a brightness of 80%+. Particle size of 50 to 70% <2µ and Brookfield viscosity of <4,000cpe. Details in the table.

Coating grade:- kaolinite 90-100%, low Fe_2O_3 (0.5-1.8%) & TiO_2 (0.4-1.6%), virtually no abrasive quartz, and a brightness of 85%+. Particle size of 80 to 100% <2μ and Brookfield viscosity of <7,000cpe. Rheological properties are particularly critical, i.e. the ability to be dispersed in water to produce slurries with low viscosities at high solid content. Details in the table.

Ceramic grade:- 75-85% kaolinite since other minerals adversely affect color, viscosity, abrasiveness, etc. Kaolin for bone china & porcelain requires a fired brightness of 83-91 @ 1,180°C and <0.9% Fe_2O_3. Strength is a function of PS and therefore fine-grained is used for bone china/some porcelain, intermediate for earthenware bodies, and coarse for sanitaryware.

Refractory grade:- refractory clays are required to withstand temperatures of 1,500°C (PCE 19).

Classed according to suitability for heat duty as low duty (PCE 19-26), moderate duty (PCE 26-31½), high duty (PCE 31½-33), and super duty (PCE 33-34).

Other tests include reheat (permanent linear change), hot load test, panel spalling test, apparent porosity, bulk density, cold crushing strength. Refractory clays may be classified based on Al_2O_3 content; low alkali and iron are preferred (see table).

Fiberglass grade:- used as a source of Al_2O_3 and SiO_2. Typical content is 37% Al_2O_3 and 44% SiO_2 with max. 1% Fe_2O_3, 2% Na_2O, and 1% H_2O.

Cosmetic grade (Light Kaolin BP):- max. 2 ppm arsenic, 20 ppm heavy metals, 350 ppm chlorides; 15 wt% LOI; pH 7.5±0.5.

WORLD CAPACITY: 27m. t.
CAPACITY UTILIZATION: 90%.

MARKET CONDITIONS: Increasing except refractories.
MARKETING FACTORS: Production of paper, plastics, paint and rubber, therefore the state of the economy (construction) and market sophistication.

SUBSTITUTES & ALTERNATIVES: Anti-blocking agent:- calcined kaolin, diatomite, precipitated silica, talc. **Carrier/absorbent**:- attapulgite, bentonite, diatomite, peat, pumice, pyrophyllite, sepiolite, talc, vermiculite, zeolites. **Filler**:- ATH, barite, calcium carbonate, feldspar, mica, nepheline syenite, perlite, pyrophyllite, talc, microcrystalline silica, ground silica flour and synthetic silica, wollastonite. **Foundry**:- bauxite & alumina, chromite, olivine, perlite, pyrophyllite, silica sand, vermiculite, zircon. **Refractories**:- andalusite, bauxite, chromite, kyanite, dolomite, graphite, magnesite, olivine, pyrophyllite, silica, sillimanite, zircon. **Soil amendment**:- bentonite, diatomite, gypsum, perlite, vermiculite, zeolites.

TYPICAL PHYSICAL CHARACTERISTICS OF COMMERCIAL CERAMIC CLAYS (%)

	Kaolin clay	Ball clay
+ 10 μm %	2-20	-
- 2 μm%	35-70	60-86
- 1 μm%	-	45-80
Modulus of rupture (Kgf/cm²)	4-15	20-40
Casting concentration %	55-70	60-65
Casting rate	0.3-2.0	-
Fired brightness	85-92	50-70
Absorption	15-20	3-13
Contraction	5-10	5-15
Fired brightness	87-93	50-70
Kaolinite content	85-97	50-70

Capacity of kaolin
(tonnes)

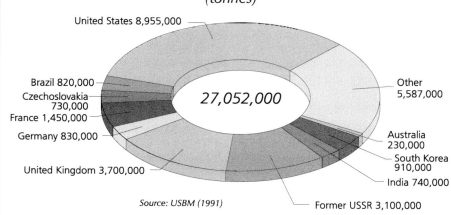

United States 8,955,000
Brazil 820,000
Czechoslovakia 730,000
France 1,450,000
Germany 830,000
United Kingdom 3,700,000
Other 5,587,000
Australia 230,000
South Korea 910,000
India 740,000
Former USSR 3,100,000

27,052,000

Source: USBM (1991)

COMPOSITION OF FLINT CLAYS (%)

	USA plastic	USA semi-flint	USA flint	S. Africa white	S. Africa black
SiO_2	56.10	45.92	44.42	45.8	44.6
Al_2O_3	24.47	35.79	38.63	37.7	37.5
Fe_2O_3	3.64	0.75	0.55	0.55	0,57
TiO_2	1.58	2.28	2.12	1.44	1.44
CaO	0.61	0.06	0.04	0.05	0.14
MgO	1.11	0.36	0.10	0.1	0.1
Na_2O	0.17	0.44	0.30	0.1	0.1
K_2O	2.89	0.41	0.12	0.06	0.26
H_2O	8.39	13.06	13.90		
LOI				14.0	15.1

SPECIFICATIONS OF COMMERCIAL BALL AND CERAMIC CLAY

	UK WBB SKD grade	USA K-T Clays HTP grade	UK WBB Sandblend 90	USA K-T Clays Classic	UK WBB	Germany Stephan Schmidt Westerwald clay	
	Tableware	Tableware	Sanitaryware	Sanitaryware	Porcelain & bone china	Porcelain	Earthenware
SiO_2	50.0	53.6	56.8	61.1	47	66.0	66.0
Al_2O_3	32.9	32.0	1.0	11.0	38	23.0	28.0
Fe_2O_3	1.2	.1.1	27.5	24.6	0.39	1.2	1.2
TiO_2	1.0	1.4	1.3	1.4	0.03	1.6	1.6
CaO	0.2	0.3	0.2	0.3	0.1	0.2	0.2
MgO	0.3	0.3	0.3	0.5	0.22	0.5	0.5
K_2O	1.6	0.7	2.2	1.4	0.8	2.2	2.2
Na_2O	0.2	0.1	0.3	0.2	0.15	0.2	0.2
LOI	12.6	10.5	9.5	9.5	13.0		
Carbon	1.6	-	1.8	-	-		-
pH	4.4	4.8	6.3	5.5			

Source: Watts Blake Bearne & Co. plc, UK; K-T Clay Co., USA

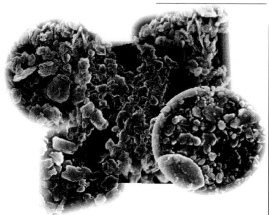

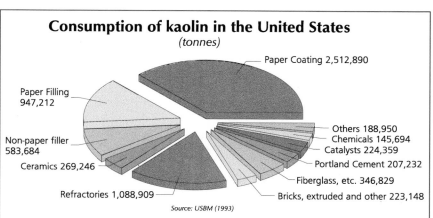

Consumption of kaolin in the United States
(tonnes)

Paper Coating 2,512,890
Paper Filling 947,212
Non-paper filler 583,684
Ceramics 269,246
Refractories 1,088,909
Others 188,950
Chemicals 145,694
Catalysts 224,359
Portland Cement 207,232
Fiberglass, etc. 346,829
Bricks, extruded and other 223,148

Source: USBM (1993)

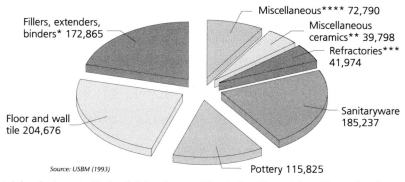

Consumption of ball clay in the United States

Fillers, extenders, binders* 172,865
Floor and wall tile 204,676
Miscellaneous**** 72,790
Miscellaneous ceramics** 39,798
Refractories*** 41,974
Sanitaryware 185,237
Pottery 115,825

Source: USBM (1993)

* includes adhesives, animal feed, asphalt tile, paint, paper filling, plastics, rubber, asphalt emulsions, wallboard, etc.;
** includes electrical porcelain, fine china/dinnerware, and miscellaneous ceramics;
*** includes firebrick, blocks, and shape, high-alumina brick and specialties;
**** includes heavy clay products, absorbents, waterproofing seals, brick (common), flue lining, and uses unknown.

HEALTH & SAFETY: Crystalline silica has been classified as a probable carcinogen by the IARC (see silica for further details). Therefore, because of its crystalline silica content, unless processing has the capability to reduce the crystalline silica content to less than 0.1%, kaolin may come under the OSHA Hazard Communication Standards, 29 CFR Section 1900.1200 which require labeling and other forms of warning, material safety data sheets, and employee training for products containing identified carcinogens with concentrations greater than 0.1%.

RECYCLING: The increased recycling of paper largely influences the market for pulp rather than mineral fillers and coaters, and in addition much of the recycled paper is newsprint which uses little if any kaolin. When recycled, paper is de-inked and any mineral filler or coating pigment is separated as a mixed and dirty slurry which is currently discarded. Therefore, a kaolin-filled and coated paper that is recycled will require a fresh supply of kaolin for its second life. Little fiberglass is recycled; broken pottery is reused in certain limited cases, and although refractory linings have been recycled for some time, clay-based refractories are not the target.

DEFINITIONS OF CALCINED CLAYS AND REFRACTORY ALUMINAS (%)

	Fireclay	Chamotte	Low alumina, low density calcined clay	Low alumina, medium density calcined clay	High alumina, high density calcined clay	Non-calcined andalusite	Mulcoa type clay	Calcined diaspore
Al_2O_3	<40	38-47	40-42	40-43	40-46	57-59	60-70	70.1
Fe_2O_3	>2	1.8-1	0.75-2.2	2.0	0.5-1.5	1 - 1.2	<1	1.07
Alkali			1.3 - 1.8	1.3 - 1.9	0.4 - 1.2			
Density, g/m^3			2.40 - 2.48	2.40 - 2.43	2.5 - 2.7		2.6 - 2.85	
Application			Low temp. (1,200°C)	Medium temp. (1,370°C)	Higher temp. (1,400 - 1,650°C)			

→ increasing Al_2O_3

SPECIFICATIONS FOR COMMERCIAL CALCINED REFRACTORY CLAYS

	H.J. Schmidt, Germany	H.J. Schmidt, Germany	ECC Int'l, UK	Commercial Minerals, Australia	ECC Minerals, S. Africa	AGS, France	Negev Ceramics, Israel	C-E Minerals, USA (Mulcoa 47)
Al_2O_3	29.30	36.60	42.00	42.00	44.00	45.00	46.00	47.80
Fe_2O_3	2.32	3.00	1.10	2.25	0.70	1.20	1.00	0.98
TiO_2	1.55	2.48	0.07	2.30	1.50	1.60	2.90	1.78
SiO_2	64.30	55.60	54.50	51.00	53.10	51.10	49.35	49.30
CaO	0.25	0.35	0.06	0.20	trace	0.30	0.30	0.03
MgO	0.42	0.42	0.31	0.20	0.15	0.30	0.20	0.04
K_2O	2.34	1.35	2.00	0.10	0.20	0.40	0.05	
Na_2O	0.17	0.13	0.10	0.10	0.07	0.10	0.20	
Others								.
Bulk density, g/cm^3	2.45	2.56	2.70	2.47	-	2.49	2.45	2.64
PCE	-	-	34-35	-	-	35	34-35	35
Refractoriness, °C	-	-	1750-1770	1,750	-	1,780	-	

	Negev Ceramics, Israel	Mineraçao Curimbaba, Brazil	Christy Minerals, USA	C-E Minerals, USA (Mulcoa 60)	C-E Minerals, USA (Mulcoa 70)	Mineraçao Curimbaba, Brazil	PSM, Brazil	Christy Minerals, USA
Al_2O_3	50.00	50.70	54.60	59.20	69.20	69.30	70.00	70.10
Fe_2O_3	1.50	2.56	1.71	1.31	1.33	2.57	1.60	1.07
TiO_2	2.90	2.01	2.40	2.25	2.61	2.93	4.50	3.43
SiO_2	44.85	42.70	38.71	38.30	27.90	24.20	23.20	20.74
CaO	0.30	0.12	0.44	0.04	0.06	0.17	0.30	0.32
MgO	0.20		0.43	0.05	0.04			0.29
K_2O	0.05	1.30	0.66	0.04	0.05	0.60	0.10	2.07
Na_2O	0.20	0.14	0.05	0.07	0.07	0.08	0.05	0.08
Others			0.18					
Bulk density, g/cm^3	2.50	2.51-2.61	-	2.80	2.85	2.6-2.77	1.6-1.07	-
PCE	35-36	-	36	37	39	-	-	38
Refractoriness, °C	-	1,760	-	-	-	1,865	1,865	-

Source: Company literature, Industrial Minerals, August 1993

TYPICAL SPECIFICATIONS FOR COMMERCIAL PAPER-GRADE KAOLIN

	#2 High Brightness Coating	#1 High Brightness Coating	#1 Fine High Brightness Coating	#2 Standard Coating	#1 Standard Coating	#1 Fine Coating	Delam Coating	Air Float Filler	Fine Filler	Fine High Brightness Filler	Delam Filler
TAPPI Brightness, %	89.5-90.5	89.5-91.0	90.0-92.0	85.5-86.5	86.5-87.5	86.5-88.0	87.5-89.0	80-81	81-83	84.5-85.5	86-88
Particle size, %<2μm	80-84	90-92	96-100	80-84	90-92	94-97	n/a	62.7	82-95	82-95	n/a
Surface area, m^2/g	12	13	22	12	13	22	14	15	22	22	13
325 mesh residue, max. %	0.01	0.01	0.01	0.01	0.01	0.01	0.01	0.4	0.3	0.3	0.01
Moisture, max. %	1.0	1.0	1.0	1.0	1.0	1.0	1.0	2.0	slurry	slurry	1.0
pH (28% solids)	6.0-7.5	6.0-7.6	6.0-7.7	6.0-7.8	6.0-7.9	6.0-7.10	6.0-7.11	5.0-7.5	60.-8.0	6.0-8.0	6.0-7.5
Brookfield, 20 rpm, cps	350	350	350	350	350	350	350	n/a	n/a	n/a	n/a

Source: Trivedi & Hagemeyer, 1994

SPECIFICATIONS OF COMMERCIAL PAPER-GRADE KAOLIN (GEORGIA, USA)

Trade name	Middle Georgia Filler Clay Kaofill	East Georgia Filler Clay EG-21	Middle Georgia Coating Clay KaoGloss	Middle Georgia Coating Clay Kaobrite	Middle Georgia Delaminated Clay Kaowhite
Brightness, GE	82.0 - 83.5	80.0 - 82.06	86.5 - 87.5	86.5 - 86.6	88.0 - 90.0
Particle size <2μ	40 min.	86 - 92	90 - 93	80 - 83	n/a
Particle size +10μ	0 - 8	0 - 2	0	0	n/a
Viscosity, 70% solids,					
Viscosity, 70% solids,			250 (solid)	250 (solid)	350 (solid)
Brookfield CPS, 20 RPM #1 spindle			300 (slurry)	300 (slurry)	350 (slurry)
Screen residue, % 200 mesh					
Rotary dried (acid)	0.003 - 0.10	0.05 0.1	0.003 - 0.01	0.003 - 0.02	
Spray dried (predispersed)	0.002 - 0.04		0.001 - 0.01	0.001 - 0.01	0.001 - 0.01
Slurry (predispersed)	0.002 - 0.04	0.05 - 0.1	0.001 - 0.01	0.001 - 0.01	0.001 - 0.02
% 325 mesh					
Rotary dried (acid)	0.010 - 0.25	0.17 - 0.3	0.005 - 0.15	0.005 - 0.15	
Spray dried (predispersed)	0.005 - 0.15		0.001- 0.02	0.001 - 0.02	0.001 - 0.02
Slurry (predispersed)	0.005 - 0.15	0.17 - 0.3	0.001 - 0.02	0.001 - 0.02	0.001 - 0.02
Moisture, %					
Rotary dried (acid)	2 - 4	0.5 - 1.5	2 - 4	2 - 4	
Spray dried (predispersed)	0.5 - 1.5		0.5 - 1.5	0.5 - 1.5	0.5 - 1.6
pH					
Rotary dried (acid)	3.5 - 5.5	3.5 - 5.0	3.5 - 4.5	3.5 - 4.6	
Spray dried (predispersed)	6.5 - 7.5		6.5 - 7.5	6.5 - 7.5	6.5 - 7.5
Slurry (predispersed)	6.5 - 7.5	6.5 - 7.5	6.5 - 7.5	6.5 - 7.5	6.5 - 7.5
Solids, %					
Slurry (predispersed)	69 - 71	70 - 71	71 - 71	72 - 71	67 - 68

Source: Thiele Kaolin Company

SPECIFICATIONS OF COMMERCIAL PAPER-GRADE KAOLIN (CORNWALL, UK)

China Clay Grade	Brightness (ISO)	Yellowness	Mass % -2μ	Mass % + 10μ	Mass % + 53μ (300 BSS mesh "residue)	Viscosity conc. (mass % solids for 500 mPas)	pH	Mass & moisture	Mass % slurry solids	Typical slurry viscosity mPas (Brookfield)
Supreme	87.5 ± 0.7	4.2 ±0.5	94 min.	0.2 max.	0.02 max.	67.5 ±1.0	5.0 ±0.5	10 ±2	-	-
Supreme Slurry	87.5 ± 0.7	4.2 ±0.5	94 min.	0.2 max.	0.02 max.	67.5 ±1.0	7.5 ±0.5	-	65.0 ± 1	600
SPS	85.5 ± 0.7	4.7 ±0.5	80.0 ±3.0	0.2 max.	0.02 max.	69.0 ±1.0	5.0 ±0.5	10 ±2	-	-
SPS Slurry	85.5 ± 0.7	4.7 ±0.5	80.0 ±3.0	0.2 max.	0.02 max.	69.0 ±1.0	7.5 ±0.5	-	66.5 ±1	350
NCC	85.5 ± 0.7	4.7 ±0.5	74.0 ±3.0	1.0 max.	0.02 max.	70.0 ±1.0	5.0 ±0.5	10 ±2	-	-
Dinkie B	83.0 ± 0.7	5.5 ±0.5	63.0 ±3.0	2.0 max.	0.02 max.	68.5 ±1.0	5.0 ±0.5	10 ±2	-	-
Dinkie B Slurry	83.0 ± 0.7	5.5 ±0.5	63.0 ±3.0	2.0 max.	0.02 max.	68.5 ±1.0	7.5 ±0.5	-	66.5 ±1	350
Grade B	82.5 ± 0.7	5.2 ±0.5	50 typical	8 typical	0.05 max.	-	5.0 ±0.5	10 ±2	-	-
Grade B Slurry	82.5 ± 0.7	5.2 ±0.5	50 typical	8 typical	0.02 max.	-	7.5 ±0.5	-	66.0 ±1	350
Grade C	81.0 ± 0.7	5.7 ±0.5	50 typical	8 typical	0.05 max.	-	5.0 ±0.5	10 ±2	-	-
Grade D	79.5 ± 0.7	6.2 ±0.7	50 typical	8 typical	0.05 max.	-	5.0 ±0.5	10 ±2	-	-
Grade E	76.5 ± 1.0	8.0 max.	25 typical	25 typical	0.05 max.	-	5.0 ±0.5	10 ±2	-	-
Alphatex (calcined)	90.5 ± 0.5	4.0 ±0.5	91.0 ±2.0	-	0.01 typical	-	5.0 typical	0.5 typical	-	-

Source: ECCI

PRODUCERS & WORLD TRADE: Major producers of refined kaolin are the United States, United Kingdom, Brazil, and Australia. These are the main exporters serving high quality markets including paper, plastics, and paint. Much of the balance is low- to medium-quality kaolin used in refractories, ceramics, etc.

HTS CODES: 2507.00.0000 (kaolin and other kaolinitic clays, whether or not calcined); 2508.30.0000 (fire clay); 2508.40.0010 (common blue and other ball clay); 2508.70.0000 (chamotte or dinas earth); 6806.20.0000 (expanded clays and mixtures).

CHEMISTRY OF COMMERCIAL CLAYS

	Kaolin (coarse coating) Georgia, USA	Kaolin (fine coating) Georgia, USA	Kaolin (fine coating) Brazil	Kaolin (coarse coating) Cornwall, UK	Kaolin (ceramic) Germany	Ball Clay Dorset, UK	Ball clay Tennessee, USA	Brick clay Weald Clay, UK	Flint Fireclay USA	Plastic Fireclay USA
SiO_2	45.2	45.0	46.0	47.2	48.3	44.4	56.7	64.45	52.27	62.4
Al_2O_3	39.2	38.0	37.0	37.6	36.3	33.6	25.8	16.55	44.30	34.56
Fe_2O_3	0.58	1.0	1.8	0.68	0.5	1.28	1.1	2.13	1.56	2.01
TiO_2	0.53	1.6	0.98	0.04	0.3	0.8	1.6		1.41	1.42
MgO	0.08	0.09	0.07	0.20	0.10	0.5	0.5	0.97	1.41	0.74
CaO	0.06	0.06	0.02	0.08	0.1	0.3	0.2	1.07	0.81	1.14
Na_2O	0.03	0.29	0.08	0.08	1.6			0.34	0.88	1.58
K_2O	0.02	0.13	0.0	1.39	0.1			2.30	0.51	0.88
S								0.21		
CO_2								0.55		
H_2O	13.3	14.0	14.3	12.7				4.69		
Organic content								0.70		
LOI						17.2	12.4	6.08		

Source: Pickering and Murray, 1994 (kaolin), Eduard Kick GmbH (ceramic clay); Watts Blake Bearne (UK) and K-T Clay (USA)(ball clay); Redland Bricks (brick); ACS (fireclay)

KAOLIN LEADERS

Producers	Exporters
United States	United States
United Kingdom	United Kingdom
Former USSR	Germany
South Korea	Czechoslovakia
Brazil	Brazil
Germany	France
Colombia	China
Czechoslovakia	Spain
China	Netherlands
Romania	Australia
Spain	Belgium
France	Malaysia

Importers

Japan	Netherlands
Germany	Belgium
Finland	France
Italy	Sweden
Taiwan	Spain
Canada	Austria

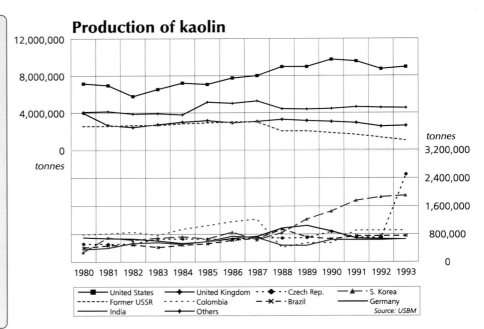

Production of kaolin

Legend: United States, United Kingdom, Czech Rep., S. Korea, Former USSR, Colombia, Brazil, Germany, India, Others
Source: USBM

PRODUCTION AND TRADE IN KAOLIN (TONNES)

	Production	Imports	Exports	Apparent Consumption	Net Supplier	Net Consumer
North America	9,913,742	614,070	2,827,473	7,700,339	2,213,403	
South & Central America	1,578,230	57,786	292,446	1,343,570	234,660	
European Union	4,900,133	3,456,146	3,750,877	4,605,402	294,731	
Non-EU Europe	3,735,809	2,033,425	506,907	5,262,327		(1,526,518)
Australasia	2,967,503	2,341,219	905,271	4,403,451		(1,435,948)
Middle East	178,223	2,061		180,284		(2,061)
Africa	311,602	49,399		361,001		(49,399)

NOTE: Numbers are approximate and rounded for 1990 or thereabouts;

Source: British Geological Survey and USBM

Price of kaolin in the United States (per tonne)

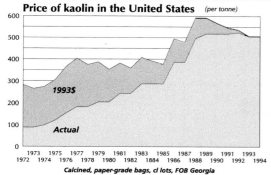

Calcined, paper-grade bags, cl lots, FOB Georgia

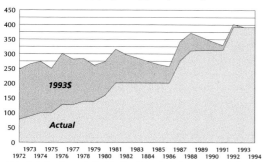

Delaminated, water-washed, calcined, paint grade, 1 micron average, cl FOB Georgia

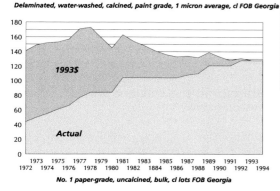

No. 1 paper-grade, uncalcined, bulk, cl lots FOB Georgia

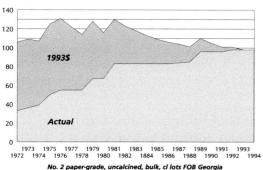

No. 2 paper-grade, uncalcined, bulk, cl lots FOB Georgia

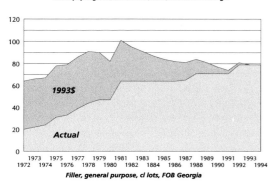

Filler, general purpose, cl lots, FOB Georgia

APPARENT CONSUMPTION OF KAOLIN (TONNES)

United States	6,937,952	Thailand	232,803
Former USSR	1,978,000	Austria	229,640
South Korea	1,478,543	Turkey	218,626
Germany	1,401,061	Poland	192,664
Japan	1,297,504	Czechoslovakia	181,100
Finland	974,943	Greece	158,502
Italy	703,451	Bulgaria	157,767
Taiwan	673,712	Egypt	149,000
Brazil	558,619	South Africa	132,421
Colombia	547,803	Iran	125,246
Spain	515,793	Portugal	118,322
France	507,175	Norway	106,511
Canada	506,432	Switzerland	102,766
United Kingdom	458,077	India	92,210
Romania	415,500	Bangladesh	91,531
Belgium	375,983	Australia	85,633
Sweden	372,811	Paraguay	74,000
Netherlands	325,234	Pakistan	68,674
Former Yugoslavia	274,865	Argentina	63,698
Mexico	259,328	Malaysia	52,652
China	234,400		

NOTE: Numbers are approximate and rounded for 1990 or thereabouts; absence of a country does not necessarily indicate no production or trade; absence of a number does not necessarily mean zero

Source: British Geological Survey

PRICES: Kaolin (bulk, FOB Ohio):- $15/t (crude); $30 - 40/t (dried, -30 to -200 mesh). Kaolin (FOB Georgia):- $20 - 49/t (dry-ground, air-floated soft, bulk); $79/t (general purpose filler grade, bulk); $95 (No. 4 coating-grade, bulk); $95/t (No. 3 coating, bulk); $98/t (No. 2 coating, bulk); $128/t (No. 1 coating, bulk); $392/t (delaminated, water-washed, paint grade, 1µ APS, bulk).Kaolin (FOT, ex-Cornwall, UK):- $75 - 112/t (filler); $112 - 180/t (coating).Calcined kaolin (FOB Georgia):- $398/t (water-washed calcined, paint grade, bags); $507/t (calcined, paper-grade, bags). NF powder (FOB Georgia):- $790/t (colloidal, bags). Kaolin (FOB Georgia):- $55 - 65/t (sanitaryware, bags); $120/t (tableware, bags).Kaolin (FOT, ex-Cornwall, UK):- $60 - 120/t (ceramic); $120 - 185/t (porcelain).Ball clay (FOB, Tennessee):- $72/t (air-floated, bags); $39/t (crushed, moisture repellent, bulk). Ball Clay (FOB UK):- $37 - 97/t (air-dried, shredded, bulk); $75 - 97/t (refined, noodled, bulk); $112 - 172/t (pulverized, air fluid, bags).Westerwald clays (FOB Germany):- $52 - 143/t (dried & ground, bulk); $16 - 59/t (shredded, bulk).Calcined refractory clay (CIF N. Europe):- $97 - 135/t (40-47% Al_2O_3); $105 - 115 (Chinese, 40% Al_2O_3).

ETYMOLOGY: Kaolin from the Chinese *Kau-ling = high ridge*, a village in northwest Jiangxi Province, China, where deposits of white kaolin have long been exploited to make fine white porcelain known as china. **China clay** is commercial term for kaolin (used in the United Kingdom) derived from its origin in China. **Ball clay** is from the tradition of rolling the clay to the cart and thus forming a ball weighing 13-22 kg (30-50 lb) with a diameter of about 25 cm (10 inches). **Halloysite** for Baron Omalius d'Halloy (1707-1789), Belgian geologist and first observer.

Minerals	Formula	%Li$_2$O	Color	SG	H
Spodumene	LiAlSi$_2$O$_6$	8.0	grayish-green	3.15-3.20	6.5-7.0
Petalite	LiAlSi$_4$O$_{10}$	4.9	white to dark gray	2.42	6-6.5
Lepidolite	K(Li,Al)$_3$(Si,Al)$_4$O$_{10}$ (OH,F)$_2$	6.2	mauve	2.8-3.0	2.5-4.0
Amblygonite	LiAlPO$_4$(F,OH)	10.3	white/gray	3.0-3.1	5.5-6
Bikitaite	LiAlSi$_2$O$_6$H$_2$O·	11.8	white to colorless	2.29-2.34	5
Eucryptite	Li$_2$O·Al$_2$O$_3$·2SiO$_2$	11.9	light gray	2.67	6.5
Montebrasite	LiAlPO$_4$F	7	gray to grayish white	3.03	5.5-6

Lithium is contained in the clay mineral hectorite (see bentonite) and the lithium-iron mica zinnwaldite.

CHEMICAL COMPOSITION OF LITHIUM-RICH BRINES (G/L)

	Chile Atacama	Bolivia Uyuni	Argentina Hombre Muerto	USA Silver Peak	USA Gt. Salt Lake	Jordan Dead Sea
Li	1.96	1.15	0.91	0.3	0.05	0.02
K	21.9	20.0	5.5	0.8	6.3	7.0
SO$_4$	23.3	NA	11.3	0.71	20.0	0.6
Mg	12.3	24.0	2.4	0.4	NA	0.3
Boric acid	4.8	4.6	1.9	-	-	-

PROPERTIES & USES: Lithium-rich minerals and brines are the commercial sources of lithia (Li$_2$O) either as spodumene (4-7% Li$_2$O), petalite (3.5-4% Li$_2$O), lepidolite (3-4% Li$_2$O), amblygonite (8-9% Li$_2$O), or bikitaite (6-8% Li$_2$O) concentrate or as lithium carbonate (LiCO$_3$) [intermediate chemical].

Lithia as a spodumene, petalite, or lepidolite concentrate (which also contributes Al$_2$O$_3$) or a chemical (generally lithium carbonate) is used in the glass and ceramics industries to decrease viscosity and improve forming properties [various types of glass including fiberglass; frits and glazes]; increase the thermal shock resistance through the formation of the lithium aluminosilicate beta phase (spodumene is SiO$_2$·Li$_2$O·Al$_2$O$_3$·8SiO$_2$) which has a remarkably low coefficient of expansion [pyro-ceramics such as oven-to-table ware; frits and glazes including lead free glazes; electrode glass]; reduce firing temperatures and flux consumption and increase furnace throughput [container glass; glass tableware; whiteware; fully vitrified ceramics]; improve product strength by forming contracted or condensed glass [safety glass; glaze for electrical porcelain and certain dinnerware]; and improve the stability and electrical properties of glass exposed to radiation [black & white TV face plate glass (shielding effect); radiation glasses]. In fiberglass manufacture, lithia reduces viscosity which helps reduce platinum bushing temperatures and therefore equipment wear. Photochromic glass, i.e. glass that darkens under ultraviolet light, is an alkali aluminosilicate glass containing silver halide, the light-sensitive agent. The addition of lithium carbonate controls the alkalinity of the glass and the solubility of the silver halides.

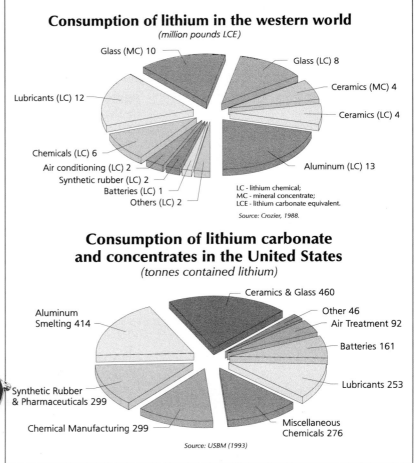

Consumption of lithium in the western world
(million pounds LCE)

Glass (MC) 10
Glass (LC) 8
Ceramics (MC) 4
Ceramics (LC) 4
Lubricants (LC) 12
Chemicals (LC) 6
Air conditioning (LC) 2
Synthetic rubber (LC) 2
Batteries (LC) 1
Others (LC) 2
Aluminum (LC) 13

LC - lithium chemical;
MC - mineral concentrate;
LCE - lithium carbonate equivalent.

Source: Crozier, 1988.

Consumption of lithium carbonate and concentrates in the United States
(tonnes contained lithium)

Ceramics & Glass 460
Other 46
Air Treatment 92
Batteries 161
Lubricants 253
Miscellaneous Chemicals 276
Chemical Manufacturing 299
Synthetic Rubber & Pharmaceuticals 299
Aluminum Smelting 414

Source: USBM (1993)

TYPICAL CHEMICAL COMPOSITION OF LITHIUM ORE CONCENTRATES (%)

	USA	Canada Tanco	Canada Tanco	Canada Tanco spodumene -200 mesh	Australia Gwalia	Australia Gwalia	Australia Gwalia	Zimbabwe Bikita
	Concentrate	Standard	Glassmakers		Concentrate	Fine*	Glass grade	
Li_2O	6.3	7.25 min.	6.80 min.	7.10 min.	7.60	7.50	5.00	7.20 min.
Fe_2O_3	1.4	0.07 max.	0.01 max.	0.12 max.	0.07	0.10	0.10	0.04 max.
SiO_2					64.50	64.00	75.00	-
Al_2O_3		26.00	25.00	25.00	26.00	27.00	18.50	-
K_2O		0.20	0.25	0.20	0.12	0.20	0.35	0.10 max.
Na_2O		0.30	0.35	0.30	0.31	0.20	0.25	0.20 max.
CaO					0.05			
P_2O_5		0.25	0.2	0.35	0.12	0.25	0.35	-
F								
TiO_2					0.01			
Rb_2O_3								
% passing								
20 mesh (820 μm)							100.0	
32 mesh (500 μm)					100			
65 mesh (210 μm)					98.0			
150 mesh (105 μm)							5.0 max.	
115 mesh (125 μm)						99.5		
200 mesh (75 μm)					38.0	88.0		

	Zimbabwe Bikita petalite Standard	Zimbabwe Bikita petalite Low alkali	Zimbabwe Bikita lepidolite	Canada Tanco amblygonite	Canada Tanco montebrasite
Li_2O	4.20 min.	4.40 min.	4.1	7.75 min.	7.0
Fe_2O_3	0.04 max.	0.03 max.	0.06	0.10 max.	0.2 max.
SiO_2					
Al_2O_3				27.50 min.	26.0
K_2O	0.30 max.	0.40 max.	8.0		
Na_2O	0.50 max.	0.15 max.	0.5		
CaO					
P_2O_5	-		-	20.0 min.	8.0
F			4.0		
TiO_2					
Rb_2O_3			3.6		

used for a variety of glass, ceramic, and metallurgical applications

Although lithia can be supplied in various forms depending on a combination of technical and economic factors, the main forms and their principal end uses are amblygonite [glass dinnerware; porcelain enamels; lithium chemicals]; eucryptite [electrical ceramics]; lepidolite (which also contributes alumina) [opal, flint, borosilicate, black & white TV face-plate glass]; montebrasite [ceramic tiles; specialty glass]; petalite [specialty glass; glazes and enamels; whiteware bodies]; spodumene (which also contributes alumina) [pyro-ceramics; tableware, specialty glass such as high-stressed windows, neon sign tubing, sealed beam headlights].

$LiCO_3$ is used in aluminum reduction cells where it improves the conductivity of the molten bath and so reduces the operating temperature, increases the efficiency of power and carbon anode and cryolite use, and decreases F emissions (by retaining the F as lithium fluoride in the bath) [aluminum smelting]. Purified $LiCO_3$ is used in the chemotheraputic treatment of manic depression [pharmaceuticals].

$LiCO_3$ feedstock → lithium acetate [organic synthesis; medicines; catalyst]; → lithium aluminate [flux in high-refractory porcelain enamel]; → lithium amide [fragrances; anti-histamines]; → lithium borate [ceramics; glass; glazes]; → lithium bromide [absorption in refrigeration and industrial drying; dry cell batteries for low-temperature use; hypnotics & sedatives]; → lithium chloride [brazing fluxes; tracer ammunition; dry cell batteries; dehumidifiers; feed for lithium metal and lithium perchlorate; heat-exchange fluid]; → lithium fluoride [ceramics; heat exchange media; welding and soldering flux]; → lithium hydroxide [lithium batteries; liquid dyes; lithium stearate and soaps for lubricants; wood preservatives]; → lithium hypochlorite [bactericide in swimming pools; sanitizing agent in food & drink; laundry bleach]; → lithium nitrate [colorant in pyrotechnics; glass etching; heat transfer medium]; → lithium nitride [additive for synthetic diamonds]; → lithium silicate [flux in glazes and enamels; welding rod coating; base for inorganic base coatings]; ➔ lithium sulfate [pharmaceuticals; photographic development; high-strength glass].

Lithium chloride ➔ lithium metal (the lightest solid element with an SG of 0.534 @ 20°C) [lithium-aluminum and lithium-magnesium alloys (2-3% Li by weight); oxygen and sulfur scavenger in copper & bronze smelting; catalyst for synthetic rubber; battery anodes] ➔ organo-lithium compounds [pharmaceuticals]; ➔ lithium hydride [hydrogen source; purifier of silicon for electronics; neutron shield] ➔ lithium aluminum hydride [organic synthesis].

QUALITY & SPECIFICATIONS: Assessed on lithium content, either Li_2O content or lithium carbonate equivalent (LCE).

High-grade spodumene conc.:- min. 7.5% Li_2O, <0.1% Fe_2O_3, -250 µm; *glass-grade*:- min. 5% Li_2O, <0.2% Fe_2O_3, 0.1% moisture, <810/>150 µm. *Petalite conc.*:- min. 4.40 Li_2O and max. 0.05% Fe_2O_3. *Lepidolite conc.* min. 4.0% Li_2O and max. 0.1% Fe_2O_3. Typical compositions of commercial concentrates are given in the table.

WORLD CAPACITY: 120M lbs. LCE: 30M. Lbs brine-based chemicals; 75M. lbs ore-based chemicals; 15M. lbs. ore-based lithia.

CAPACITY UTILIZATION: 75%+

MARKET CONDITIONS: Stable. Expansion depends on alumina production and its development of new uses.

MARKETING FACTORS: The aluminum, glass, and ceramics industries which are dependent on construction activity and therefore the state of the economy. R&D is finding new uses for lithium including the development of a cell in which a lithium alloy anode, a solid polymer electrolyte, and carbon-oxide cathode form a flexible tape 0.02″ thick. There has been a shift in supply away from hard-rock mines (spodumene) toward extraction from brines; production from brines in South America will soon dominate supply.

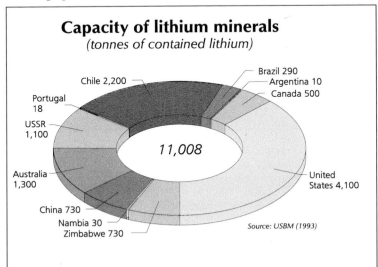

Capacity of lithium minerals
(tonnes of contained lithium)

- Chile 2,200
- Brazil 290
- Argentina 10
- Canada 500
- Portugal 18
- USSR 1,100
- Australia 1,300
- China 730
- Nambia 30
- Zimbabwe 730
- United States 4,100

11,008

Source: USBM (1993)

APPARENT CONSUMPTION OF LITHIUM MINERALS, CARBONATE, AND OXIDE (TONNES Li_2O)	
	Apparent Consumption
United States	9,882
United Kingdom	3,829
Germany	2,829
Japan	2,700
Former USSR	1,189
China	793
Italy	685
France	658
South Korea	475
Brazil	424
Netherlands	278
Spain	245
Belgium	242
Australia	201
South Africa	140
Chile	127
Canada	119

NOTE: Numbers are approximate and rounded for 1991 or thereabouts; absence of a country does not necessarily indicate no production or trade; absence of a number does not necessarily mean zer0.

Source: British Geological Survey

HEALTH & SAFETY: Crystalline silica has been classified as a probable carcinogen by the IARC (see silica for further details). Therefore, because of its crystalline silica content, unless processing has the capability to reduce the crystalline silica content to less than 0.1%, certain lithium minerals may come under the OSHA Hazard Communication Standards, 29 CFR Section 1900.1200 which require labeling and other forms of warning, material safety data sheets, and employee training for products containing identified carcinogens with concentrations greater than 0.1%.

SUBSTITUTES & ALTERNATIVES: Glass & ceramics:- nepheline syenite, feldspar, borates, lead. **Soaps & lubricants**:- Ca and Al compounds.

RECYCLING: Virtually none.

PRODUCERS & WORLD TRADE: The United States, Zimbabwe, Australia, Canada, and Chile are the main producers and exporters of lithium. Production in the United States based on spodumene will decline over the next decade to be replaced by lithium derived from brines in South America, particularly Chile and Argentina.

PRICES: Europe Petalite 4.2% Li_2O (bulk, FOT Amsterdam). Spodumene conc. >7.5% Li_2O $385/t (FOT Amsterdam, Netherlands); $375-419/t (FOB W. Virginia, USA). Spodumene, glass grade, >5% Li_2O $175/t (FOT Amsterdam, Netherlands); $176-198/t (FOB, W. Virginia, USA).

NEON

World production of lithium

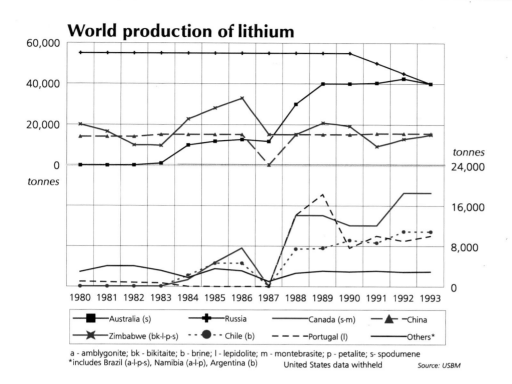

a - amblygonite; bk - bikitaite; b - brine; l - lepidolite; m - montebrasite; p - petalite; s- spodumene
*includes Brazil (a-l-p-s), Namibia (a-l-p), Argentina (b)   United States data withheld   *Source: USBM*

Lithium bromide $15.30-16.68/kg (anhydrous, drums, delivered). Lithium carbonate $4.19/kg granular, bags, delivered). Lithium chloride $10.63/kg (anhydrous, delivered); $8.93/kg (solution, drums, delivered). Lithium fluoride $15.11-15.27/kg (drums, delivered). Lithium hydride $64.13/kg (FOB plant). Lithium hydroxide monohydrate $5.69/kg (drums, delivered). Lithium hypochlorite $3.41/kg (ex-works). Lithium nitrate $7.52/kg (technical, drums). Lithium sulfate $79.15/kg (anhydrous, delivered). Lithium metal $61.50/kg (Producers ingot price, 99.9%).

HTS CODES: 2825.20.00.00.0 (lithium oxide and hydroxide); 2836.91.00.10.4 (lithium carbonate, USP grade); 2836.91.00.50.5 (lithium carbonate, other).

ETYMOLOGY: Amblygonite from the Greek *amblys = dull, obtuse* and *gonia = angle,* in reference to cleavage angle. **Bikitaite** for Bikita, Zimbabwe. **Eucryplite** from the Greek *eu = good,* and concealed due to its mode of occurrence embedded in albite. **Hectorite** for Hector, California, United States. **Lepidolite** from the Greek *lepis = scale* and *lithos = stone* because of its micaceous structure. **Montebrasite** for Montebras, Creuse, France. **Petalite** from the Greek *petalon = leaf* and *lithos = stone* alluding to its leaflike cleavage. **Spodumene** from the Greek *spodoun = to reduce to ashes* refers either to its ash-gray color or the ash-colored mass formed when heated before the blowpipe. **Zinnwaldite** for Zinnwald, Bohemia, itself named for the local tin (German *Zinn*) veins.

LITHIUM LEADERS

Production (minerals)	Imports (oxides)	Imports (carbonate)	Exports (oxides)	Exports (carbonate)
United States	UK	Germany	United States	United States
Former USSR	Germany	Japan	China	Chile
Australia	Japan	United States	Germany	Germany
China	France	UK	UK	China
Canada	Italy	Canada	Former USSR	UK
Portugal	Brazil	Italy	Belgium	Former USSR
Chile	South Korea	France	Netherlands	Netherlands
Brazil	Belgium	South Korea	France	
Argentina	Netherlands	Netherlands		
	South Africa	Belgium		
	Spain	Spain		
	Australia	Brazil		
		Taiwan		
		Sweden		

WORLD PRODUCTION AND TRADE IN LITHIUM MINERALS, CARBONATE, AND OXIDE (TONNES Li$_2$O)

	Production	Imports	Exports	Apparent Consumption	Net Supplier	Net Consumer
North America	15,839	1,739	7,578	10,000	5,839	
South America	3,526	374	3,346	554	2,972	
European Union	45	10,769	2,003	8,810		(8,765)
Non-EU Europe	1,500	99	311	1,288	212	
Australasia	4,500	3,349	3,608	4,242	258	
Africa	735	135	726	144	591	

NOTE: Numbers are approximate and rounded for 1991 or thereabouts; absence of a country does not necessarily indicate no production or trade; absence of a number does not necessarily mean zero.

Source: British Geological Survey

Minerals	Formula	%MgO	%CaO	%CO$_2$	Color	SG	H
Magnesite, crystalline	MgCO$_3$	47.8	-	52.2	white-black + gray, blue	3..02	3.5-4.0
Magnesite, cryptocrystalline	MgCO$_3$	47.8	-	52.2	white-buff + yellow	2.9-3.0	3.5-5.0
Dolomite	CaCO$_3$·MgCO$_3$	21.9	30.4	47.7	white to black	2.8-2.9	3.5-4.0
Brucite	Mg(OH)$_2$	69.1	-	30.9	white, bluish	2.39	2.5

PROPERTIES & USES: Commercial magnesia (MgO) is largely derived from natural magnesite or from the magnesium sulfate and magnesium chloride contained in seawater and certain brines and bitterns; dolomite and brucite are secondary commercial sources. Magnesite has two main physical forms — crystalline magnesite with a marble-like crystalinity often occurring in large deposits and the more important commercially; cryptocrystalline magnesite (a.k.a. bone magnesite), a massive variety generally found in smaller but purer deposits.

Raw magnesite has some limited markets based on being a source of MgO [pasture improvement/fertilizer; batch raw material for glass & ceramics; feedstock for magnesium metal]; white, relatively soft, and chemically inert [filler in paint, paper, plastics, rubber]; being relatively absorbent and fairly unreactive [carrier for germicides and pesticides; anticaking agent or surface coating in table salt, ammonium nitrate fertilizers, explosives]. Most magnesite is calcined to produce caustic calcined (at 800-1,000°C) magnesia and dead-burned or sintered (above 1,450°C) magnesia.

Magnesia in various forms is the starting point for a variety of magnesia-based products. Chemical grade magnesia [feedstock for Mg chemicals; glass; ceramics; magnesium-phosphate cements; Mg-based oil additives] or caustic calcined magnesia is chemically active and alkaline [stack gas scrubbing; water and sewage treatment; pharmaceuticals & medicine; acid neutralization for example in rayon manufacture], both contain Mg in a concentrated form [animal feed supplement; fertilizer; magnesium metal production], and is refractory [basic refractories]. Caustic calcined magnesia is electrofused to produce fused MgO in two main grades - electrical [insulator in water heating elements, welding machines, or general heating systems; sheathed heating elements for appliances such as iron, washing machines, ovens] and refractory [specialty refractories such as premium-grade carbon-magnesia refractories used in hot spots in BOF, electric arc, and other high-temperature furnaces]. Fused magnesia is the highest grade of periclase with a density of 3.58 (close to the theoretical maximum) and crystallite sizes considerably higher than those of deadburned magnesia which in turn provides superior refractory performance. Fused magnesia + fused alumina → fused synthetic spinels, MgAl$_2$O$_4$, used as a refractory [Al & Mg metal contact; lining cement kilns; lining induction furnaces].

Chemical-grade MgO → precipitated magnesium carbonate, MgCO$_3$ [pharmaceuticals; thermal insulator; glass & ceramics; rubber; paints; fertilizers]; → magnesium sulfate, MgSO$_4$ (Epsom Salts) [pharmaceuticals; chemicals; dyes; paper sizing; explosives; fertilizers]; → magnesium hydroxide, Mg(OH)$_2$ [antacid ingredient; pulp & paper; chemicals; water treatment].

Electrolysis of magnesium chloride or the silicothermic reaction of dolime → magnesium metal, the lightest of the structural metals [alloys; die casting and wrought products; chemical desulfurization of iron & steel; (nodular or ductile iron production); desiccant for methanol; energy storage; feedstock for chemical production; pyrotechnics; reducing agent for the fluoride or chloride in the production of Be, Ti, Zr, Hf, and U]. Magnesium has the highest strength to weight ratio of any of the commonly used metals, is dimensionally stable, welds easily by conventional methods, and produces superior damping capacity. Its alloys can be machined fast and are highly impact and dent resistant. Dead-burned magnesia (a.k.a. magnesia clinker or periclase) is hard, dense, chemically non-reactive. It resists

COMPARISON OF COMMON ALKALIS

Alkali	Kgs required to neutralize 1 tonne 98% H$_2$SO$_4$
96% MgO	424
98% CaO	580
Mg(OH)$_2$ powder	627
Mg(OH)$_2$ slurry	1,027
NaOH slurry	1,634
Ca(OH)$_2$ slurry	1,628
Na$_2$CO$_3$ slurry	3,280

Source: Queensland Metals Corp.

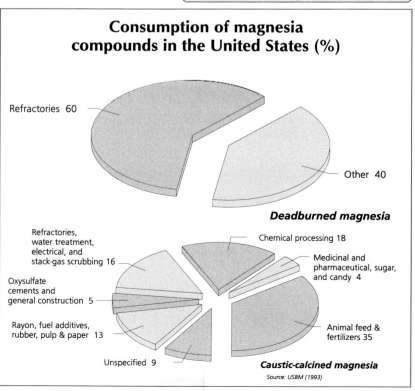

Consumption of magnesia compounds in the United States (%)

Refractories 60

Other 40

Deadburned magnesia

Refractories, water treatment, electrical, and stack-gas scrubbing 16

Oxysulfate cements and general construction 5

Rayon, fuel additives, rubber, pulp & paper 13

Unspecified 9

Chemical processing 18

Medicinal and pharmaceutical, sugar, and candy 4

Animal feed & fertilizers 35

Caustic-calcined magnesia

Source: USBM (1993)

chemical (slag) attack, is highly refractory with the highest melting point (2,800°C) of all refractory oxides, withstands mechanical abrasion and is used as a basic refractory such as mag-chrome or mag-carbon bricks as well as castable refractories and gunning mixes [iron & steel; nonferrous metal smelting; glass melting; cement production].

Brucite, natural $Mg(OH)_2$, is a white mineral with a brightness of 93% and fire retardant and smoke suppressant properties [plastics; paints; roof coatings] and high MgO content [feedstock].

QUALITY & SPECIFICATIONS: Specifications vary enormously depending on origin and end use.

Natural magnesite:- 85-95% MgO, 0.5-2.5% CaO, 0.5-4% SiO_2, 0.5-9% Fe_2O_3, 0.1-1% Al_2O_3, and 0.1-0.5% B_2O_3; BD 3.1-3.45.

Synthetic magnesia:- 96-99+% MgO with 0.4-2.5% CaO, 0.2-1% SiO_2, 0.05-1.5% Fe_2O_3, 0.05-0.1% Al_2O_3, and 0.02-0.1% B_2O_3; BD 3.3-3.45.

Caustic-calcined magnesia:- 80-90% MgO, max. 3.5% SiO_2, 2.5% CaO, and 5% LOI.

Caustic-calcined fertilizer grade:- min. 80% MgO.

Animal feed grade:- min. 85% MgO.

Dead-burned magnesia:- 90-95% MgO with max. 4-6% SiO_2, 3.5% CaO, 1-2% Al_2O_3, 1-2% Fe_2O_3, 0.5% LOI.

First grade refractory:- min. 96-99% MgO, <0.2% Fe_2O_3, lime:silica of 3:1 or 4:1, BD 3.44, boron (<0.01%).

Second quality refractory:- min. 95% MgO, <1% Fe_2O_3, lime:silica of 2:1, low boron; BD 3.4.

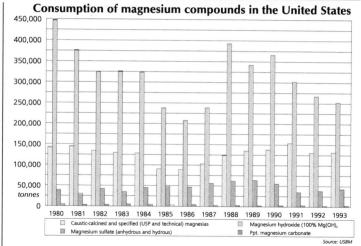

Consumption of magnesium compounds in the United States

Legend: Caustic-calcined and specified (USP and technical) magnesias; Magnesium sulfate (anhydrous and hydrous); Magnesium hydroxide (100% Mg(OH)₂); Ppt. magnesium carbonate

Source: USBM

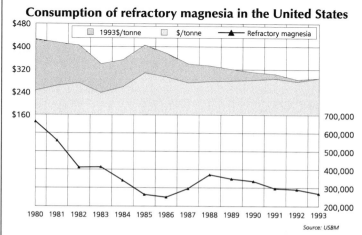

Consumption of refractory magnesia in the United States

Legend: 1993$/tonne; $/tonne; Refractory magnesia

Source: USBM

CHEMICAL COMPOSITION OF COMMERCIAL MAGNESITE AND MAGNESIA (%)

First grade

	UK	Eire	Netherlands	Italy	Israel	USA	Mexico	Japan	Greece*
MgO	97.0	96.8	98.5	96.8	99.2	96.6	99.0	98.6	97.0
CaO	1.9	2.3	0.65	2.3	0.55	2.3	0.7	1.0	1.85
SiO_2	0.4	0.6	0.17	0.55	0.05	0.7	0.1	0.3	0.5
Fe_2O_3	0.2	0.2	0.45	0.15	0.2	0.2	0.1	0.06	0.60
Al_2O_3	0.2	0.2	0.07	0.20	0.03	0.2	0.1	0.05	0.03
B_2O_3	0.05	0.04	0.01	0.05	0.001	0.02	0.003	0.08	<0.01
CaO:SiO_2	5.0	4.0	3.8	4.0	11.0	3.0	7.0	3.0	3.7
BD, g/cc	3.43	3.44	3.44	3.42	3.46	3.42	3.40	3.41	3.42

Second grade

	Greece*	Turkey*	Yugoslavia*	Austria**	Spain**	China**	Korea**	Korea** flotation	USA regular	Japan	UK
MgO	95.70	96.60	95.50	91.00	94.50	92.40	95.10	91.90	98.00	99.58	93.50
CaO	2.20	1.50	2.00	2.40	0.80	1.25	1.60	1.80	0.70	0.18	1.80
SiO_2	1.30	1.25	1.70	0.50	1.30	3.50	1.20	4.00			
Fe_2O_3	0.64	0.35	0.60	5.70	2.70	1.00	1.30	1.10	0.20	0.06	1.60
Al_2O_3	0.06	0.04	0.20	0.20	0.80	1.60	0.60	0.70	0.20	0.01	1.00
B_2O_3	<0.01	<0.01	<0.01	<0.01	<0.01	<0.01	<0.01	<0.01	0.02	0.01	0.18
CaO:SiO_2	1.70	1.20	1.20	4.80	0.60	0.36	1.30	0.45	1.00	0.67	1.00
BD, g/cc	3.45	3.40	3.35	3.30	3.35	3.20	3.25	3.15	3.32	3.46	3.10

* cryptocrystalline natural; ** macrocrystalline natural; others - seawater.

Source: Coope, 1987.

COMPOSITION OF COMMERCIAL FUSED MAGNESIAS (%)

	France electrical low grade	USA electrical medium	USA electrical low	UK refractory	Japan ceramic	Canada refractories
MgO	92-96	94	96	96.8	99.9	97.0
SiO_2	2-4.5	4.0 max	3.1	0.45	0.05	0.50
CaO	1.5-2.5	2.1 max.	0.8	2.45	0.05	1.8
Fe_2O_3	<0.02	0.25 max.	0.07	0.12	0.04	0.65
BD, g/cm^3	2.34-2.48	2.38	2.39	3.58	3.585	3.50

Fused MgO:- electrical grade - low levels of sulfur, boron, and trace metals; refractory grade- 94-97% MgO, 1-2% CaO, 0.5-0.8% Fe_2O_3, 0.2-0.8% Al_2O_3, and 0.5-3.5% SiO_2. BD 3.50 or higher.

Chemical grade MgO:- min. 96-98% MgO, max. 1.2% CaO, 0.6% SiO_2, 0.4% Fe_2O_3, 0.2% sulfate (typical seawater).

Pharmaceutical:- min. 96% MgO, max. 1.5% CaO, 0.1% acid insolubles, 0.05% Fe, 3ppm As, 40ppm heavy metals, 10% LOI.

COMPOSITION OF SYNTHETIC ALUMINA-MAGNESIA SPINELS (%)

	USA	USA	UK	Germany
MgO	29.26	26.80	30.1	27.0
Al_2O_3	70.00	70.00	68.8	72.2
Fe_2O_3	0.09	0.70	0.06	0.03
SiO_2	0.10	2.0	0.11	0.10
CaO	0.36	0.50	0.25	0.28
BD, g/cm^3	NA	3.578	3.57	3.54

WORLD CAPACITY: (contained MgO) 7.2 M. t (magnesite) &1.7M. t (seawater/brines); magnesium metal 530,000 t.

CAPACITY UTILIZATION: NA.   **MARKET CONDITIONS:** Steady.   **MARKETING FACTORS:** Iron/steel/economy.

HEALTH & SAFETY: Crystalline silica has been classified as a probable carcinogen by the IARC (see silica for further details). Therefore, because of its crystalline silica content, unless processing has the capability to reduce the crystalline silica content to less than 0.1%, certain magnesium minerals may come under the OSHA Hazard Communication Standards, 29 CFR Section 1900.1200 which require labeling and other forms of warning, material safety data sheets, and employee training for products containing identified carcinogens with concentrations greater than 0.1%.

SUBSTITUTES & ALTERNATIVES: Animal feed and supplement:- dolomite, limestone, talc. **Refractories:-** andalusite, bauxite, chromite, kyanite, dolomite, graphite, olivine, pyrophyllite, refractory clays, silica, sillimanite, zircon. **Magnesium metal:-** aluminum & zinc. **Neutralizing reagent:-** caustic soda, lime, soda ash.

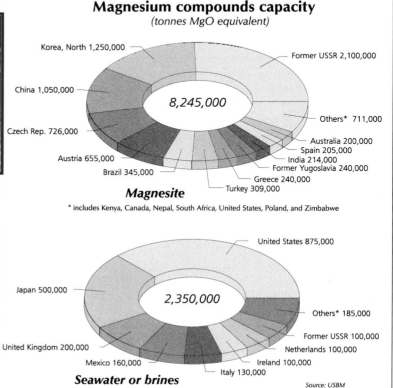

Magnesium compounds capacity
(tonnes MgO equivalent)

Korea, North 1,250,000
Former USSR 2,100,000
China 1,050,000
Czech Rep. 726,000
8,245,000
Others* 711,000
Australia 200,000
Spain 205,000
India 214,000
Former Yugoslavia 240,000
Austria 655,000
Greece 240,000
Brazil 345,000
Turkey 309,000

Magnesite
* includes Kenya, Canada, Nepal, South Africa, United States, Poland, and Zimbabwe

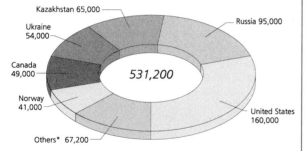

Magnesium metal capacity

Kazakhstan 65,000
Russia 95,000
Ukraine 54,000
Canada 49,000
531,200
Norway 41,000
United States 160,000
Others* 67,200

* includes France, Japan, Brazil, Italy, China, Serbia & Mont., and India

United States 875,000
Japan 500,000
2,350,000
Others* 185,000
Former USSR 100,000
Netherlands 100,000
United Kingdom 200,000
Ireland 100,000
Mexico 160,000
Italy 130,000

Seawater or brines
* includes Israel, South Korea, France, Norway, and China

Source: USBM

APPARENT CONSUMPTION OF MAGNESITE & MAGNESIA (TONNES)

MAGNESITE	Apparent Consumption	MAGNESIA	Apparent Consumption
North Korea	1,416,400	United States	767,994
Former USSR	1,400,000	Japan	681,997
China	1,059,611	Former USSR	542,392
Turkey	1,037,897	Germany	452,710
Austria	947,010	United Kingdom	225,550
Greece	613,593	France	205,136
India	541,141	Poland	174,000
Brazil	400,000	South Korea	132,192
Spain	386,858	Netherlands	113,552
Australia	368,827	Italy	88,209
Former Yugoslavia	240,036	South Africa	80,000
Canada	221,341	Venezuela	79,734
Czechoslovakia	217,000	Taiwan	79,350
South Africa	118,282	India	73,956
Philippines	114,164	Mexico	71,811
United Kingdom	71,114	Former Yugoslavia	65,597
United States	63,361	Hungary	50,729
Romania	58,100		

* magnesia production taken as 70% of production capacity

NOTE: Numbers are approximate and rounded for 1991 or thereabouts; absence of a country does not necessarily indicate no production or trade; absence of a number does not necessarily mean zero.

Source: British Geological Survey

RECYCLING: Refractory linings from iron and steel or glass furnaces have been recycled for some time, although fired magnesia and mag-chrome products tend to be less amenable to recycling than acid refractories. Degradation of some chemical and physical properties generally limits use to a lower grade of product such as safety lining bricks used in BOF vessels. Resin or pitch-bonded magnesia bricks are more difficult to recycle, particularly if metallic additives are used in the binders. Used magnesia refractories may be utilized outside the refractory industry (termed "down-cycling") as a general aggregate, roofing granules, abrasives, or a slag conditioner in the steel industry. The effect of recycling on magnesia consumption is limited by the fact that about 50% of the magnesia is consumed during its service life in a refractory lining and a further 25% will be sufficiently contaminated as to make recycling impossible.

PRODUCERS & WORLD TRADE: Sales and trade in crude magnesite are extremely limited, and for the most part commerce is conducted with produced or manufactured products.

PRICES: Greek raw magnesite, max. 3.5% SiO_2 $45-50/t (FOB East Mediterranean).

Magnesia:- $250/t (natural, 85% MgO). Chinese, deadburned, lump $64-74/t 90-92% Mg); $100-120/t (94-95% MgO). Magnesia, dead-burned 340-450/t (first grade); $90-220/t (second quality). Magnesia, United States, ex-works $364/t (deadburned, bulk); $406/t (deadburned, bags); $403/t (synthetic, technical, chemical grade, bulk); $449/t (synthetic, technical, chemical grade, bags); $256-292/t (natural, technical, 85% 150 mesh, bulk); $292/t (natural, technical, 90% 325 mesh, bulk); $1.85.kg (technical, light, neoprene grade, bags). Caustic calcined $340-360/t (first grade); $140-200/t (second grade); $130-145/t (calcined, agricultural, CIF N. Europe); $210-405/t (calcined, natural, industrial grade, CIF N. Europe).

Fused magnesia $1,000-1,200/t. Brucite $330-350/t (filler grade).

Magnesium bromide hexahydrate $5.50/ kg (drums). Magnesium carbonate (ex-works, bags, freight equalized) $1.60-1.72/ kg (light, technical); $1.63-1.76/kg (USP, light); $1.83 (USP, heavy). Magnesium chloride, bags, ex-works $0.28-0.33/kg (anhydrous, 92% flake or pebble, drums); $0.32/kg (hydrous, 99% flake). Magnesium fluorosilicate, drums, ex-works $1.11-1.13/kg. Magnesium hydroxide 1.75/ kg. Magnesium metal, 99.8% ingots, FOB Freeport, TX $3.21-3.37/kg. Magnesium nitrate $0.70/kg (technical). Magnesium oxide bags, ex-works, freight equalized $3.63/kg (USP, light); $3.40/kg (heavy). Magnesium phosphate tribasic technical FOB $2.20/kg. Magnesium silicofluoride bags, ex-works $0.88/kg. Magnesium sulfate (Epsom salts) ex-works $0.37-0.4/kg (10% Mg, technical, bags); $0.35/kg (bulk); $0.40-0.42/kg (USP, crystal, bags); 0.6/kg (USP, crystal, bags).

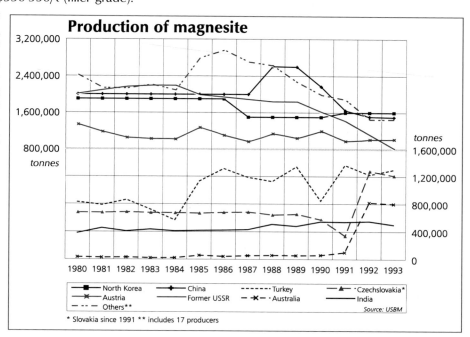

Production of magnesite

Legend: North Korea, China, Turkey, *Czechoslovakia*, Austria, Former USSR, *Australia*, India, Others**

* Slovakia since 1991 ** includes 17 producers

Source: USBM

MAGNESITE/MAGNESIA/MAGNESIUM METAL LEADERS

Producers (magnesite)	Producers (magnesia)	Producers (magnesium metal)	Importers (magnesite)	Exporters (magnesite)	Importers (magnesia)	Exporters (magnesia)
China	United States	United States	Philippines	China	Former USSR	Greece
North Korea	Japan	Russia	United Kingdom	North Korea	Germany	Austria
Former USSR	United Kingdom	Kazakhstan	Canada	Turkey	Japan	Turkey
Turkey	Mexico	Ukraine	Romania	Czechoslovakia	United States	United States
Austria	Italy	Canada	Greece	Spain	France	Italy
Greece	Netherlands	Norway	Ireland	United States	Poland	Japan
India	Former Yugoslavia	France	Sweden	Hong Kong	Austria	Germany
Brazil	Ireland	Japan	Singapore	Netherlands	United Kingdom	Spain
Spain	Israel	Brazil	South Africa	Australia	Netherlands	Mexico
Australia	South Korea	Italy	Thailand	Greece	South Korea	Canada
Czechoslovakia	France	China	Italy	Italy	Italy	Ireland
Former Yugoslavia	Norway	Serbia & Mont.	Malaysia	Former Yugoslavia	Canada	Netherlands
Canada		India	Germany	Belgium		

HTS CODES: 2518.20.0000 (calcined dolomite); 2519.10.0000 (crude magnesite); 2519.90.1000 (dead-burned/fused magnesia); 2519.90.2000 (caustic-calcined magnesia); 2519.90.5000 (magnesia, other); 2530.20.1000 (kieserite, natural); 2530.20.2000 (epsom salts, natural); 2816.10.0000 (magnesium hydroxide and peroxide); 2827.31.0000 (magnesium chloride); 2833.21.0000 (magnesium sulfate); 8104.11.000 (unwrought magnesium); 8104.19.0000 (unwrought magnesium alloys); 8104.90.0000 (wrought magnesium); 8104.20.0000 (magnesium waste and scrap).

ETYMOLOGY: Brucite for Archibald Bruce (1777-1818), American mineralogist and first observer. **Calcite** from the Latin calx, calcis = lime; this is the same origin for chalk and limestone. **Dolomite** for Deodat Guy Silvain Tancrède Gratet de Dolomieu, French geologist. Lime from the Old English; related to Dutch iljm & Latin limus = mud, linere = to smear. **Epsomite/Epsom Salts** for Epsom, a town near London, England. **Magnesite** applied to a series of magnesium salts by J.C. Delanethrie in 1795; D.L.G. Karsten first restricted it to the natural carbonate in 1808. **Magnesium** from the Latin magnesia, a mineral said to be brought from Magnesia, a district in Thessaly, Greece. **Periclase** from the Greek peri = around and klasis = fracture due to its perfect cubic cleavage.

PRODUCTION AND TRADE IN MAGNESIA (TONNES)

	Production	Imports	Exports	Apparent Consumption	Net Supplier	Net Consumer
North America	724,500	369,071	230,738	862,833		(138,333)
South America		100,983	40,735	60,248		(60,248)
European Union	392,000	1,130,845	654,842	868,003		(476,003)
Non-EU Europe	87,500	940,934	270,391	758,043		(670,543)
Australasia	385,000	712,665	93,300	1,004,365		(619,365)
Middle East	49,000	2,200	43,627	7,573	41,427	
Africa	21,514	82,464		103,978		(82,464)

Production is taken as 70% of capacity of seawater/brine magnesia; trade includes magnesia derived from magnesite

NOTE: Numbers are approximate and rounded for 1991 or thereabouts

Source: British Geological Survey

PRODUCTION AND TRADE IN MAGNESITE (TONNES)

	Production	Imports	Exports	Apparent Consumption	Net Supplier	Net Consumer
North America	220,000	73,297	8,595	284,702		(64,702)
South America	418,769	9,100		427,869		(9,100)
European Union	956,375	201,578	31,250	1,126,703		(170,328)
Non-EU Europe	4,063,380	99,430	229,004	3,933,806	129,574	
Australasia	5,134,891	198,938	1,738,053	3,595,776	1,539,115	
Middle East	2,000			2,000		
Africa	131,503	21,000	1,500	151,003		(19,500)

NOTE: Numbers are approximate and rounded for 1990 or thereabouts

Source: British Geological Survey

Minerals	Formula	%Mn	Color	SG	H
Braunite	$2Mn_2O_3 \cdot MnSiO_3$	64.3	brownish-black	4.75-4.82	6-6.5
Manganite	$Mn_2O_3 \cdot H_2O$	62.5	iron-black/dark steel gray	4.2-4.4	4
Pyrolusite	MnO_2	60-63	iron-black/dark steel gray	4.8	2-2.5
Psilomelane	$BaMn_9O_{18} \cdot 2H_2O$	45-60	iron-black/dark steel gray	3.7-4.7	5-6
Rhodochrosite	$MnCO_3$	48	red-rose to brown	3.3-3.6	3.5-4.5

PROPERTIES & USES: Manganese is used to scavenge sulfur and oxygen from molten steel resulting in a variety of finished products with a manganese content ranging from 1% for carbon steels, as much as 10% for stainless steel, up to 14% for extremely hard and abrasion-resistant steels. This metallurgical use, supplied by manganese ore concentrates and/or ferromanganese & silicomanganese derived from the ores, accounts for some 95% of manganese consumption. Nevertheless, there is a great multitude of nonmetallurgical uses for manganese.

Ground manganese ore acts as a source of manganese, an important micronutrient [animal feed additive; fertilizer], a colorant [bricks, cement, pottery, porcelain, tiles], an oxidizer [chemical production such as hydroquinone used in photographic developers; medicines], a colorizer, decolorizer, and chemical scavenger [glass], a slag former [welding rod coating & flux], and a material that enhances the adherence properties of frits [ceramics], and feedstock for Zn-Mn soft ferrites [electronics]. Battery-active grades of natural, activated, and synthetic (chemical or electrolytic) manganese dioxide are used as a depolarizer in dry-cell batteries, that is to oxidize the hydrogen (to form water) formed during the generation of electrical energy from an electrolyte solution which if allowed to build up would reduce the electrical flow. Activated manganese dioxide is produced by heating ground ore to 600-800°C and adding sulfuric acid to form a porous, hydrated, and chemically active product. Chemical manganese dioxide (CMD) is obtained by the thermal decomposition of a manganese compound other than an oxide (the SEDEMA process). Electrolytic manganese dioxide (EMD) is prepared by anodic oxidation of manganese sulfate (see below) in sulfuric acid solution.

Manganese ore (MnO_2 reduced) or manganese carbonate (calcined) → manganous oxide (MnO) [animal feed additive; ceramic glazes; electrolytic zinc production; fertilizer; ferrites; welding flux]. MnO + nitric acid → manganese nitrate [feedstock for manganese dioxide (synthetic battery grade)]; → manganese carbonate (see below).

Manganese ore (reduced) + sulfuric acid → manganese sulfate [animal feed additive; fertilizer (citrus trees); food supplement; fungicide; paint additive; textile dye; intermediate manganese chemical]. Manganese sulfate → electrolytic manganese metal or EMM [alloying agent]; → manganese carbonate [animal feed additive; catalyst in polymerization of olefins; feedstock for manganese acetate, linoleate, naphthenate, octoate, tallate, resinate, and stearate and battery-grade manganese dioxide; Mn-Zn ferrites for electronics; fuel oil S scavenger; glass & ceramics; welding rod coating & flux]; → manganese ethylene bisdithiocarbamate (Maneb - $(CH_2NH\ Ca_2)2Mn$) [fungicide]; → manganous hydroxide [intermediate in the production of manganese acetate, borate, citrate, dioxide, octoate, fluoride, glycerophosphate, and phosphate].

Manganese ore + KOH and oxidation/roasting to potassium manganate followed by electrochemical oxidation → potassium permanganate [bleach; catalyst for organic synthesis; circuit board cleaning; disinfectant; gas purification; plant growth regulator; water treatment & sewage odor control; mineral processing; chemical oxidizing agent; welding rod coatings].

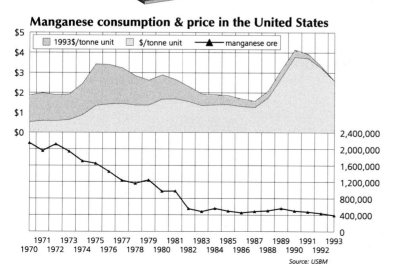

Manganese consumption & price in the United States

Source: USBM

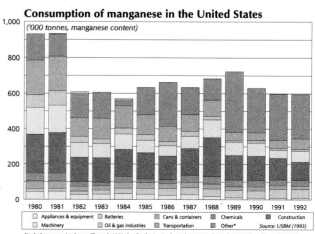

Consumption of manganese in the United States

('000 tonnes, manganese content)

Appliances & equipment · Batteries · Cans & containers · Chemicals · Construction · Machinery · Oil & gas industries · Transportation · Other*

Source: USBM (1993)

*includes processing losses. Through 1988 the distribution is about the same as for end uses in the table exclusive of batteries and chemicals. Beginning in 1989, includes nonidentified uses in steel equal to 30% of total steel shipments.

CHEMICAL COMPOSITION OF COMMERCIAL MANGANESE CONCENTRATES (%)

	Brazil Chemical	Gabon Battery	Morocco Chemical	S. Africa Metallurgical	Ghana Carbonate N grade	Australia Met. lump	Australia Siliceous intermediates	Australia Chemical	Netherlands* Glass Mangalox A	Netherlands* Ceramics" Mangalox B
Mn	51	54.85	55.42	48	30.8	49	43	52		
MnO_2	76.5	83.64	85.85	12.13	nil				79	69
MnO		3.04	1.51		39.77				1	3
Fe	3.2		0.53		1.04	3.3	7	3		
FeO				1.34						
Fe_2O_3		2.64	0.76						3	5.5
SiO_2	2.6	1.06	4.28	4.6	12.68	6	13	3.5	3.5	5
Al_2O_3	5.7	4.67	0.86		2.15	4	7	3.5	4.5	9
CaO	0.23	traces		2.3	4.75				0.05	0.2
MgO	0.32	0.05		0.4	3.5				0.35	0.2
BaO		0.37	2.37		trace	0.7	0.7	1.5	2.8	0.4
TiO_2		traces			0.1				0.3	0.3
S			0.012	0.03					0.01	-
SO_3		0.025			0.15				-	0.05
P_2O_5		0.19			0.137				-	0.25
P	0.15	0.08	0.039	0.05	0.06	0.09	0.075	0.08	0.09	-
As_2O_3		absent				0.025				
Cu		0.03	0.21		trace					
CuO									0.06	0.07
Pb		absent	0.98		trace					
Zn		0.01								
ZnO					0.07				-	0.06
SnO					0.005					
K_2O	2.05	0.56			0.17	1.7	1.4	0.8		
Na_2O	0.07	0.05			0.05					
Co		0.095								
CoO									0.04	0.15
Ni		0.05								
NiO									0.05	0.1
CO_2		0.41		2.5	33.68				0.02	-
$Mo + H_2O$		2								
Combined H_2O				0.75						
Water of crystall.									3	5
Insols.		0.12								
LOI	15.5									

* Jan de Poorter BV

Manganese ore + HCl (or the reduction of rhodochrosite) → manganese chloride [catalyst for organic chlorination reactions; cotton dyeing; flux in magnesium metal refining; fungicide; intermediate product in the production of manganese carbonate]. Manganese chloride → methylcyclopentadienyl manganese tricarbonyl or MMT [anti-knock compound in gasoline; combustion improver in distillate fuels]; → manganese metal via electrolytic method [alloying agent]; → manganese naphthenate, oxalate, and oleate [paint and varnish dryers].

QUALITY & SPECIFICATIONS: Ore is divided into manganese ore (>35% Mn) and manganiferous ore (5-35% Mn) which may be further subdivided into ferruginous manganese ore (10-35% Mn) and manganiferous iron ore (5-10% Mn).

Metallurgical-grade:- (typical) min. 48% Mn and max. 6% Fe, 11% Al_2O_3 + SiO_2, 0.18% As, 0.19% P, and 0.3% Cu+Pb+Zn.

Chemical-grade:- min. 35% manganese.

Battery-grade:- categorized by manganese dioxide content of 70-85%. Dry-cell EMD is min. 92% MnO_2 with max. 2% H_2O, 0.02% Fe, 0.0005% Cu, and 0.0009% Pb.

Fertilizer & feed grade:- 30-60% Mn.

Ferrites:- very low levels of CaO, K_2O, Na_2O, BaO, and SiO_2.

Hydroquinone:- 80-88% MnO_2 and -300 to 325 mesh.

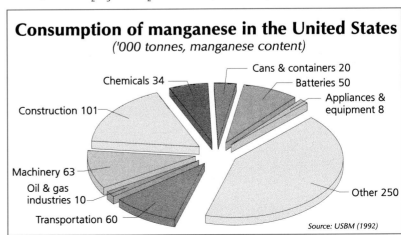

Consumption of manganese in the United States
('000 tonnes, manganese content)

Chemicals 34
Cans & containers 20
Batteries 50
Construction 101
Appliances & equipment 8
Machinery 63
Oil & gas industries 10
Transportation 60
Other 250

Source: USBM (1992)

Consumption in the United States
(tonnes, gross weight)

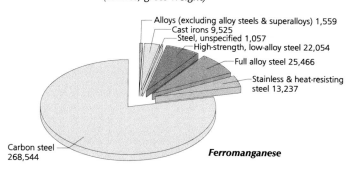

Alloys (excluding alloy steels & superalloys) 1,559
Cast irons 9,525
Steel, unspecified 1,057
High-strength, low-alloy steel 22,054
Full alloy steel 25,466
Stainless & heat-resisting steel 13,237
Carbon steel 268,544

Ferromanganese

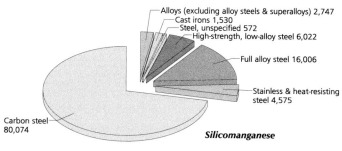

Alloys (excluding alloy steels & superalloys) 2,747
Cast irons 1,530
Steel, unspecified 572
High-strength, low-alloy steel 6,022
Full alloy steel 16,006
Stainless & heat-resisting steel 4,575
Carbon steel 80,074

Silicomanganese

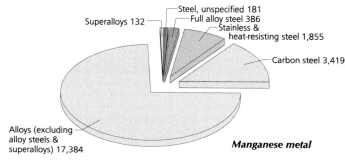

Superalloys 132
Steel, unspecified 181
Full alloy steel 386
Stainless & heat-resisting steel 1,855
Carbon steel 3,419
Alloys (excluding alloy steels & superalloys) 17,384

Manganese metal

superalloys (ferromanganese only) and miscellaneous & unspecified data withheld

WORLD CAPACITY: 10.4M. t.

CAPACITY UTILIZATION: 80%.

MARKET CONDITIONS: Stable, growing regionally.

APPARENT CONSUMPTION OF MANGANESE ORE (TONNES)	
	Apparent Consumption
Former USSR	7,605,000
China	4,456,034
South Africa	2,250,719
Japan	1,646,663
Brazil	1,576,094
India	1,045,967
Czechoslovakia	951,900
France	701,753
Norway	682,147
Poland	575,223
North Korea	489,000
Mexico	460,322
South Korea	393,118
Germany	357,525
Italy	354,532
Australia	332,008
United Kingdom	317,909
Spain	262,314
Romania	260,000
United States	225,722
Gabon	220,000
Former Yugoslavia	177,599
Belgium	164,002
Taiwan	141,392
Argentina	71,844
Singapore	70,315
Venezuela	64,702
Canada	62,831
Hungary	51,860

NOTE: Numbers are approximate and rounded for 1990 or thereabouts; absence of a country does not necessarily indicate no production or trade; absence of a number does not necessarily mean zero

Source: British Geological Survey

MARKETING FACTORS: Overwhelmingly influenced by the iron & steel industry which is linked to automobile production and construction activity which are tied to the state of the economy. Resources are concentrated in relatively few countries with the major consuming regions — North America, Europe, and Japan — largely dependent on imports.

HEALTH & SAFETY: Crystalline silica has been classified as a probable carcinogen by the IARC (see silica for further details). Therefore, because of its crystalline silica content, unless processing has the capability to reduce the crystalline silica content to less than 0.1%, manganese minerals may come under the OSHA Hazard Communication Standards, 29 CFR Section 1900.1200 which require labeling and other forms of warning, material safety data sheets, and employee training for products containing identified carcinogens with concentrations greater than 0.1%.

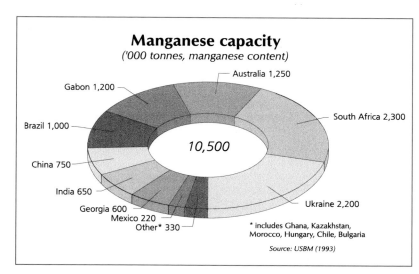

Manganese capacity
('000 tonnes, manganese content)

Australia 1,250
Gabon 1,200
Brazil 1,000
China 750
India 650
Georgia 600
Mexico 220
Other* 330
South Africa 2,300
Ukraine 2,200

10,500

* includes Ghana, Kazakhstan, Morocco, Hungary, Chile, Bulgaria

Source: USBM (1993)

MANGANESE ORE LEADERS

Producers	Importers	Exporters
Former USSR	Japan	Gabon
South Africa	Czechoslovakia	South Africa
China	France	Australia
Gabon	Norway	Brazil
Brazil	Poland	Former USSR
Australia	North Korea	India
India	China	Ghana
Mexico	South Korea	United States
Ghana	Germany	Indonesia
Hungary	Italy	Mexico
Romania	United Kingdom	France
Former Yugoslavia	United States	Netherlands
Austria	Spain	Morocco

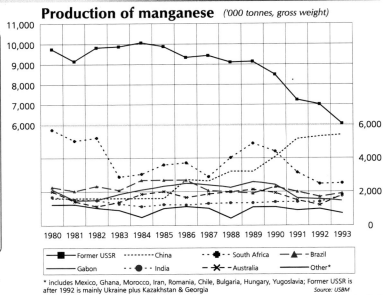

Production of manganese *('000 tonnes, gross weight)*

Legend: Former USSR; China; South Africa; Brazil; Gabon; India; Australia; Other*

* includes Mexico, Ghana, Morocco, Iran, Romania, Chile, Bulgaria, Hungary, Yugoslavia; Former USSR is after 1992 is mainly Ukraine plus Kazakhstan & Georgia   *Source: USBM*

SUBSTITUTES & ALTERNATIVES: None for most major uses.

RECYCLING: Virtually none to recover manganese specifically although some was generated through the reprocessing of ferrous and nonferrous scrap and steel slag.

PRODUCERS & WORLD TRADE: Production is dominated by metallurgical grade ore, although Brazil, Gabon, Ghana, Morocco, and India are noted for nonmetallurgical grades.

PRICES: Manganese acetate, drums, delivered $2.64/kg (dihydrate); $2.42/kg (tetrahydrate). Manganese carbonate, chemical grade, 46% Mn, ex-works $3.19/kg. Manganese chloride, anhydrous, drums $2.66/kg.

Manganese dioxide ex-works $242/t (natural, African, 74-76% MnO_2, bags); $275-419/t (natural, African, 84% MnO_2, bags); $1.54-1.92/kg (synthetic, crystalline, battery grade, 90-92% MnO_2, bags); $1.80/kg (synthetic, crystalline, chemical ferrite grade, bags).

Manganese metal, electrolytic No. 1, chip, bulk $2.32/kg. Manganese sulfate $524/t (29.5% Mn, powder and mini granular, FOB Mobile, AL, bags); $595/t (32% Mn, granular, ex-works, bags). Potassium permanganate, free flowing $2.66/kg (bulk, hopper trucks); $2.95/kg (50-kg drums); $1.43/kg (150-kg drums).

HTS CODES: 2602.00.0040 (manganese ores and concentrates <47% manganese); 2602.00.0060 (manganese ores and concentrates >47% manganese); 2820.10.0000 (manganese dioxide); 2820.90.0000 (other manganese oxides); 2841.60.0010 (potassium permanganate); 2841.60.0050 (other manganates and manganites of metal); 7202.11.50 (high-carbon ferromanganese); 7202.30.00 (silicomanganese); 8111.00.3000 (manganese waste and scrap); 8111.00.4500 (other unwrought manganese).

ETYMOLOGY: Braunite for Kammerath Braun, of Gotha, Germany. **Manganese** from the Greek *mangania = magic*. **Manganite** for its manganese content. **Pyrochlore** from the Greek *pyros = a fire* and *chloros* = green since it turns green on ignition. **Psilomene** from the Greek *psilos = naked, bare* and *melas = black* alluding to its appearance. **Pyrolusite** from the Greek *pyros = a fire* and *lusite = to wash* due to its use to decolorize glass. **Rhodochrosite** from the Greek *rhodochros = rose colored* alluding to its color.

PRODUCTION AND TRADE IN MANGANESE ORE (TONNES)

	Production	Imports	Exports	Apparent Consumption	Net Supplier	Net Consumer
North America	358,000	539,059	148,184	748,875		(390,875)
South America	2,545,229	134,450	923,917	1,755,762	789,467	
European Union	9,654	2,343,700	119,017	2,234,337		(2,224,683)
Non-EU Europe	8,757,041	2,630,039	965,144	10,421,936		(1,664,895)
Australasia	7,391,669	3,205,107	2,023,079	8,573,697		(1,182,028)
Middle East	35,000	11,235		46,235		(11,235)
Africa	7,282,593	17,527	4,802,086	2,498,034	4,784,559	

NOTE: Numbers are approximate and rounded for 1990 or thereabouts;

Source: British Geological Survey

Minerals	Formula	Color	SG	H
Muscovite	$KAl_2(AlSi_3O_{10})(OH,F)_2$	white, black, brown, green	2.76-2.88	2.8-3.2
Phlogopite	$KMg_3(AlSi_3O_{10})(OH,F)_2$	white, colorless brown, copper red	2.78-2.90	2.5-3.0

The term mica covers a number of hydrous aluminosilicates with muscovite (a.k.a. potash or white mica) and to a lesser extent phlogopite (a.k.a. amber mica) the most important commercially. Other micas are biotite (magnesium-iron mica), lepidolite (potassium-lithium mica), roscoelite (vanadium-potassium-magnesium mica), zinnwaldite (lithium-iron mica). Vermiculite, that is hydrated biotite, is covered in a separate chapter.

Commercial mica may be supplied as *sheet mica*, that is large crystals which can be cut, punched, or stamped accurately. More commonly it is supplied as *flake* or *scrap mica* consisting of smaller sized particles (generally derived from a flotation process) which may be finely ground dry or wet to produce ground mica or micronized mica. Micas may also be synthesized, for example, fluor-phlogopite ($KMg_3AlSi_3O_{10}F_2$) is a *synthetic mica* manufactured by heating a properly proportioned mixture of dry, pulverized potash, feldspar, potassium silicofluoride, magnesia, alumina, and silica in a furnace at 1,360°C and allowing the melt to cool slowly over several days. *Built-up mica* (termed *micanite*) is made from mica splittings which are arranged so that they overlap in layers of uniform thickness. Alternative layers of mica and a cementing agent like shellac are built up and then bonded together by heat and pressure. It is often bonded to another material like fiberglass cloth to form a composite sheet. *Reconstituted mica* (*mica flakes*) is produced by partially exfoliating high-quality scrap mica and feeding it as pulp to a modified papermaking machine to produce a continuous sheet or mica paper. This is impregnated with a binder and cut to length. *Glass-bonded mica* is made by pressing and heating a mixture of ground mica and powdered borosilicate glass which anneals.

PROPERTIES & USES: Muscovite mica splits into thin, tough, flexible, chemically resistant, and elastic sheets that are thermally stable up to about 500°C. Phlogopite has similar properties and uses but can operate at temperatures of 900-1,000°C.

Muscovite is virtually colorless and transparent and resists chemical and thermal attack [optical filters; stove windows; retardation plates in helium-neon lasers; gauge glass in e.g. high-pressure steam boilers; gap separators in computer recording heads]. Electrical properties include low conductivity and power loss plus high dielectric strength (muscovite is 1,500-3,000 and phlogopite 1,000-1,500 volts/mil), dielectric constant (muscovite 6-8 & phlogopite 5-6), and resistivity (muscovite 10^{15}-10^{16} and phlogopite 10^{12}-10^{14} ohm/cm) [condensers; transformers; rheostats; fuses; incandescent bulbs; insulating material in vacuum tubes].

Flake and dry-ground mica is used to feed the production of micanite, mica paper, glass-bonded mica which substitute for natural sheet mica.

Ground mica may be dry ground (APS 1.2 mm to 150 μm), wet ground (APS 90 to 45 μm), or micronized (APS

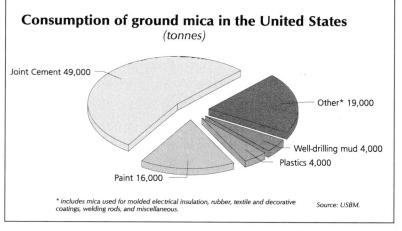

Consumption of ground mica in the United States
(tonnes)

Joint Cement 49,000
Other* 19,000
Well-drilling mud 4,000
Plastics 4,000
Paint 16,000

* includes mica used for molded electrical insulation, rubber, textile and decorative coatings, welding rods, and miscellaneous.

Source: USBM.

<53 μm). In addition to size differences, dry ground mica forms a non-lustrous highly delaminated product with a high aspect ratio whereas wet grinding produces thin, flat platelets with a high luster and good slip. Dry-ground mica is inert, flexible, and nonabrasive with finer grades providing brightness (about 75%), suspension properties, and weather resistance; mica reduces chalking, cracking, and shrinking, and has good lubricating, elastic, and reinforcing properties [joint cement; textured interior plasters; stucco coatings; textured stone and roof paint; rubber; and plastics]. The platy structure of coarse (1.2 mm to 420 μm) dry-ground mica is utilized as a lost-circulation material designed to seal off openings and fractures encountered when drilling through porous and fractured rock formation [drilling muds]. Dry-ground mica is used as a surface coating [welding rods, cores and molds for metal casting, and electric cables; concrete, tile, and stucco surfaces; wallpaper; artificial snow on Christmas cards]. Mica is used as an absorbent [explosives; disinfectants; fire extinguishers].

When it is critical to retain the characteristic laminar crystalline structure and reduce particle size to the 90 to 45 μm range, mica is wet ground or steam micronized. This material has application as a specialized filler [plastics; rubber], as an anti-sticking and antifriction powder [between the inner tube and casing of tires], and as a lubricant [substituting for graphite in special greases in soft packings].

Surface treated grades include pearlescent pigments (e.g. titanium-coated). The large surface area of the flakes is utilized in drilling muds [oil and gas drilling].

PARTICLE SIZE DISTRIBUTION OF GROUND MICA PRODUCTS

Sieve analysis mesh	% finer than µm	Dry-ground				Wet ground					Micronized
		Oilwell-Fine	Oilwell-Coarse	Joint cement	Welding rod	High K_2O	Plastics	Rubber	170 mesh	325 mesh	Paint
¼-inch	6,400										
6	3,360		0-10								
7	2,800		25-55		100						
14	1,200				98						
16	1,190										
20	850	trace									
28	600										
32	500	10-30			60						
35	475					trace					
44	355			40	100						
60	250	10-50		100	10	5 - 0	1.0				
80	180										
100	150	10-70	25-65	99		10	30.0	100	0.0	0.0	
140	106	10-30	10-20				50.0		0.5-1.0		
150	105			95				99.9			
200	74			85		10mx.		85	5.0mx.	1.0mn.	
270	53			75			80.0	80			100
325	44			70			15.0	75	7.0-14.0	3.0-10.0	99.9
-325	44					40-75	5.0		75.0-85.0	90mn.	
BD (kg/l)	0.4-0.6		0.18-0.26	0.26		0.18	0.2mx.	0.2mx.	0.22mx.		

Source: Chapman, 1980 & company literature

INDIAN STANDARD GRADES FOR MUSCOVITE BLOCKS, THINS AND FILMS

Designation		Usable rectangle area		Minimum dimension one side usable	
Old	New	Sq. inch	Sq. cm.	inch	cm
OOEE Sp.	630	100+	645.2+	4	10.2
OEE Sp.	500	80-100	516.1-645.2	4	10.2
EE Sp.	400	60-80	387.1-516.1	4	10.2
E Sp.	315	8-60	309.7-387.1	4	10.2
Sp.	250	36-48	232.3-309.7	3.5	8.9
1	160	24-36	154.8-232.3	3	7.6
2	100	15-24	96.8-154.8	2	5.1
3	63	10-15	64.5-96.8	2	5.1
4	40	6-10	38.7-64.5	1.5	3.8
5	20	3-6	19.4-38.7	1	2.5
5.5	16	2.25-3	14.5-19.4	0.875	2.2
6	6	1-2.25	6.4- 14.5	0.75	1.9
7	5	0.75-1	4.8-6.4	0.625	1.6

O-over; E-extra; Sp.-special

Source: Modified from Indian Standard Institute

CHEMICAL COMPOSITION OF MICA (%)

	Muscovite	Phlogopite
SiO_2	44-47	37-43
Al_2O_3	30-38	12-17
Fe_2O_3	0.2-5	0.2-2
K_2O	8.5-11.5	8.5-11.5
Na_2O	0.1-0.8	0.3-0.8
TiO_2	0-0.9	0-1.5
BaO	-	0-0.7
MgO	0.3-1.5	23-29
CaO	0.1	0.1-0.5
Li_2O	0.1-0.8	0-0.1
F	0-0.15	0.5-5.0
P	traces	traces
S	traces	traces
LOI	4-5	1-3

QUALITY & SPECIFICATIONS: Sheet mica may be graded on the basis of color and visual quality and on the maximum usable rectangle that can be cut from a single lamina, and may be divided into 4 categories:

Block mica: a knife-dressed sheet mica of which at least 95% by weight has a thickness of not less than 0.008 inch (0.20 mm), with the remainder having a minimum thickness of 0.007 inch (0.18 mm). The minimum usable area is generally 1 square inch; *Thins*: dressed sheet having a thickness in the 0.002-0.007 inch (0.05-0.18 mm) range; *Film mica*: superior in quality to block mica and overlaps thins, with a size range of 0.0008-0.007 inch (0.02-0.18 mm); *Splittings*: mica laminae with a maximum thickness of 0.0012 inch (0.03mm) and a maximum usable area of 0.75 square inch.

QUALITY CLASSIFICATION OF MUSCOVITE MICA, 0.018 CM MIN. THICKNESS

ASTM Classification	V-1	V-2	V-3	V-4	V-5	V-6	V-7	V-7a	V-8	V-9	V-10	V-10a
Visual Quality	Clear	Clear & slightly stained	Fair stained	Good stained	Stained A quality	Stained B quality	Heavy stained	Densely stained	Black dotty	Black spotted	Black stained	Densely black & red stained
AIR INCLUSIONS												
Crystall. Discolor.	X	✔	✔	✔	✔	✔	✔	✔	✔	✔	✔	✔
Very Slight	X	✔	✔	✔	✔	✔	✔	✔	✔	✔	✔	✔
Slight	X	X	✔	✔	✔	✔	✔	✔	✔	✔	✔	✔
Medium	X	X	X	✔	✔	✔	✔	✔	✔	✔	✔	✔
Heavy	X	X	X	X	X	X	✔	✔	✔	✔	✔	✔
STAINS												
Cloudy Stains	X	X	X	X	X	✔	✔	✔	✔	✔	✔	✔
Lt. black & red date (Mineral)	X	X	X	X	X	X	✔	✔	✔	✔	✔	✔
Black Stains (Mineral)	X	X	X	X	X	X	X	X	X	✔	✔	✔
Red Stains (MIneral)	X	X	X	X	X	X	X	✔	X	X	✔	✔
Black & Red Stains (Mineral)	X	X	X	X	X	X	X	✔	X	X	X	✔
Green Stains (Veg. type)	X	X	X	X	X	✔	✔	✔	✔	✔	✔	✔
Clay Stains	X	X	X	X	X	✔	✔	✔	X	X	✔	✔
WAVINESS												
Nearly Flat	✔	✔	✔	✔	✔	✔	✔	✔	✔	✔	✔	✔
Slight	X	X	X	✔	✔	✔	✔	✔	✔	✔	✔	✔
Medium	X	X	X	✔	✔	✔	✔	✔	✔	✔	✔	✔
Heavy	X	X	X	X	X	✔	✔	✔	X	X	X	✔
HARDNESS												
Hard	✔	✔	✔	✔	✔	✔	✔	✔	✔	✔	✔	✔
Soft	X	X	X	X	X	X	S	✔	X	X	X	S
Stones & holes	X	X	X	X	X	X	X	X	X	X	X	X
Buckles	X	X	X	X	X	X	S	✔	X	X	X	X
Reeves	X	X	X	X	X	X	X	X	X	X	X	X
Ridges	X	X	X	X	X	X	S	✔	X	X	X	X
Tears	X	X	X	X	X	X	X	X	X	X	X	X
Cracks	X	X	X	X	X	X	X	X	X	X	X	X
Hairline cracks	X	X	X	X	X	X	X	X	X	X	X	X
Wedge	X	X	X	X	X	X	X	X	X	X	X	X
Tangle sheet	X	X	X	X	X	X	X	X	X	X	X	X
Herringbone	X	X	X	X	X	X	X	✔	X	X	X	X
Sand Blast	X	X	X	X	X	X	S	✔	X	✔	✔	✔

INDIAN GRADES OF MUSCOVITE

V-1	Ruby clear
V-2	Ruby clear and slightly stained
V-3	Ruby fair stained
V-4	Ruby good stained
V-5	Ruby stained 'A'
V-6	Ruby AQ
V-7	Ruby stained 'B'
V-8	Ruby BQ
V-9	Ruby heavy stained
V-10	Ruby densely stained
V-11	Black dotted
V-12	Black spotted
V-13	Black/red stained
V-14	Green/brown 1st quality
V-15	Green/brown 2nd quality
V-16	Green/brown stained or BQ

Source: Mica Manufacturing Co. Pvt. Ltd., Calcuta, India.

Indian categories are summarized in the tables. ASTM specifications are covered by ASTM-D351-62 (stain, inclusions, and imperfections); ASTM-D2131-65 (characteristics for mica product manufacture); ASTM-D748-59 (requirements for electrical, physical, and visual properties of sheet mica for capacitors). ASTM quality classification of muscovite block based on size is given in the table.

WORLD CAPACITY: 300,000 t.
CAPACITY UTILIZATION: 88%.

MARKET CONDITIONS: Sheet:- declining; ground:- increasing.
MARKETING FACTORS: Construction/use of plastics/economy.

HEALTH & SAFETY: Crystalline silica has been classified as a probable carcinogen by the IARC (see silica for further details). Therefore, because of its crystalline silica content, unless processing has the capability to reduce the crystalline silica content to less than 0.1%, mica will come under the OSHA Hazard Communication Standards, 29 CFR Section 1900.1200 which require labeling and other forms of warning, material safety data sheets, and employee training for products containing identified carcinogens with concentrations greater than 0.1%.

SUBSTITUTES & ALTERNATIVES: Sheet mica:- alumina ceramics, fused quartz, and organic polymers. **Carrier**:- attapulgite/sepiolite, bentonite, diatomite, kaolin, peat, pumice, pyrophyllite, talc, vermiculite, zeolites. **Electrical**:- synthetic mica. **Filler**:- ATH, barite, calcium carbonate, diatomite, feldspar, kaolin, mica, nepheline syenite, perlite, talc, microcrystalline silica, ground silica flour and synthetic silica, wollastonite. **Lubricant**:- Graphite, Lithium, molybdenum disulfide (MoS_2), Talc.

RECYCLING: Virtually none.

PRODUCERS & WORLD TRADE: Production is dominated by scrap mica, in particular material recovered from flotation, often as a byproduct of feldspar or spodumene production. Sheet mica supply is largely confined to India and to a lesser extent South Africa and Argentina; phlogopite is produced almost exclusively in Canada with minor tonnages from Madagascar.

PRICES: Muscovite sheet mica, clear $5-59/kg (FOB S. African port). Europe ex-works, UK $330-450/t (dry ground); $$900-1,200/t (wet ground); $450-540/t (micronized). Indian, CIF N. Europe $225-300/t (dry ground); $465/t (wet ground); $375-560/t (micronized). FOB Madras, India $263/t (mine scrap for mica paper). United States FOB plant $220-440/t (dry ground); $560-1,210/t (wet ground); $572-836/t (micronized); $340-400/t (flake). South Africa FOB Durban $325-355/t (20-60 mesh). Phlogopite $5.50/kg (splittings).

APPARENT CONSUMPTION OF MICA (TONNES)

United States	118,272
Former USSR	45,150
Germany	16,058
United Kingdom	15,758
Norway	7,067
Canada	6,146
Mexico	5,576
France	5,291
Australia	4,521
Iran	2,755
Spain	2,565
South Korea	2,508
South Africa	1,762
Czechoslovakia	1,500
Italy	1,491
Netherlands	1,356
Singapore	1,063
Former Yugoslavia	904
Hong Kong	904
Poland	893
Indonesia	814
Sweden	559
Greece	557
Sri Lanka	509
Ireland	507

NOTE: Numbers are approximate and rounded for 1990 or thereabouts; absence of a country does not necessarily indicate no production or trade; absence of a number does not necessarily mean zero

Figures include splittings, waste, ground, and/or unmanufactured

Source: British Geological Survey

Capacity of mica
(tonnes)

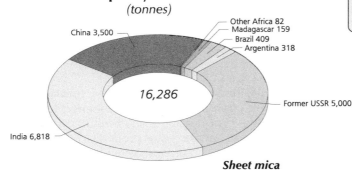

Sheet mica

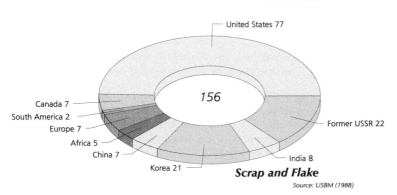

Scrap and Flake

Source: USBM (1988)

MICA LEADERS

Producers	Importers	Exporters
United States	Japan	China
Former USSR	United Kingdom	Canada
China	Germany	India
Canada	United States	France
France	Norway	Belgium
India	France	United States
Mexico	Netherlands	United Kingdom
Taiwan	South Korea	Turkey
Norway	Canada	Finland
Australia	Italy	Malaysia
Malaysia	Spain	Norway
Iran	Belgium	Madagascar
Spain	Czechoslovakia	Netherlands
Sri Lanka	Singapore	Brazil
South Africa	Taiwan	Germany
Zimbabwe	Australia	Sri Lanka
Brazil	Hong Kong	Spain
Morocco	Poland	Zimbabwe

TYPICAL USES OF MICA

Grade	Sieve Size (mesh)	Typical Uses
Coarse flakes	6	Oilwell drilling, artificial snow
Med-coarse flakes	10	Christmas ornaments, display material
Fine-coarse flakes	16	Concrete block fillers, refractory bricks, gypsum boards, asphalt roofing felts, shingles
Coarse-fine powder	30	Metal annealing, absorbent in explosives, disinfectants, automotive components
Med-fine powder	60	Welding electrodes, cables & wires, foundry works, pipeline enamels, mastics, lubricants, adhesives
Fine powder	100	Texture paints, acoustical plasters, ceiling tiles
Superfine powder	325	Paints, plastics, rubber products, paper

Source: Industrial Minerals, November, 1992

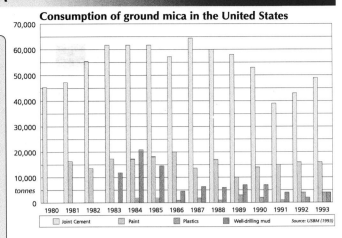

Consumption of ground mica in the United States

Legend: Joint Cement, Paint, Plastics, Well-drilling mud. Source: USBM (1993)

HTS CODES: 2525.10.0010 (split block mica); 2525.10.0020 (mica splittings); 2525.10.0050 (other crude mica); 2525.20.0000 (mica powder); 2525.30.0000 (mica waste); 6814.10.0000 (plates, sheets and strips of agglomerated or reconstituted mica, whether or not on a support); 6814.90.0000 (other worked mica and articles of mica).

ETYMOLOGY: Biotite for Jean Baptiste Biot (1774-1862), the French physicist who studied its optical aspects. **Lepidolite** from the Greek *lepis = scale* and *lithos = stone* because of its micaceous structure. **Mica** from the Latin *micare = to shine* or *to glitter* or the Latin *mica = a crumb* or *grain*. **Muscovite** from Muscovy glass, when first described from Muscovy Province, Russia. **Phlogopite** from the Greek *phlogistos = to burn* or *inflame* alluding to its reddish tinge. **Roscoelite** for Henry Enfield Roscoe (1833-1915), a chemist from Manchester, England, who firstprepared pure vanadium. **Vermiculite** from the Latin *vermiculare = to breed worms* alluding to its appearance after exfoliation and Greek *lithos = stone*. **Zinnwaldite** for Zinnwald, Bohemia, itself named for the local tin (German *Zinn*) veins.

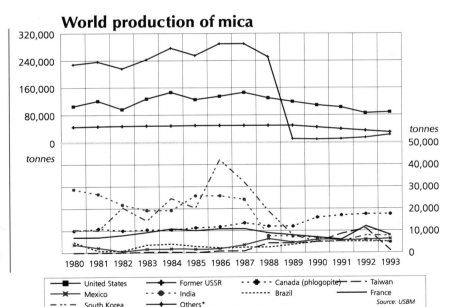

World production of mica

Legend: United States, Former USSR, Canada (phlogopite), Taiwan, Mexico, India, Brazil, France, South Korea, Others*

Source: USBM

* includes Iran, South Africa, Sri Lanka, Morocco, Argentina, Madagascar (phlogopite), former Yugoslavia, Zimbabwe, Spain, Peru, Mozambique, Namibia, Sudan, and Tanzania (sheet).

PRODUCTION AND TRADE IN MICA (TONNES)

	Production	Imports	Exports	Apparent Consumption	Net Supplier	Net Consumer
North America	130,357	16,955	17,318	129,994	363	
South America	1,529	552	1,516	565	964	
Central America & Carib.		261		261		(261)
European Union	11,060	53,126	23,735	40,451		(29,391)
Non-EU Europe	50,602	9,185	11,518	48,269	2,333	
Australasia	44,768	36,077		80,845		(36,077)
Middle East	2,000	302		2,302		(302)
Africa	4,786	792	4,498	1,080	3,706	

NOTE: Numbers are approximate and rounded for 1990 or thereabouts

Figures include splittings, waste, ground, and/or unmanufactured

Source: British Geological Survey

Nepheline syenite is a fine-grained igneous rock comprising 48-54% albite ($NaAlSi_3O_8$) and 18-23% microcline ($KAlSi_3O_8$) feldspar plus 20-25% nepheline ((Na,K) $AlSiO_4$).

PROPERTIES & USES: Nepheline syenite is used as a source of Al_2O_3, Na_2O, and/or K_2O in certain glasses [borosilicate glass; soda-lime (container) glass; fiberglass; TV tube glass]. The alumina enhances the workability of molten glass, increases the resistance of glass to chemical corrosion, improves the hardness and durability, and inhibits devitrification. The alkalis (which partially replace soda ash) act as a flux and chemically attack the other glass batch minerals such as silica.

In ceramics, a low fusibility temperature and high fluxing capacity allow nepheline syenite to act as an efficient vitrifying agent, that is as a flux to form a glassy phase in the ceramic body [vitreous and semivitreous china, wall & floor tile, sanitaryware, electrical porcelain, frits, glazes, & enamels]. This in turn reduces the amount of flux required, lowers the firing temperatures, and allows faster firing. The long firing range of nepheline syenite contributes to the physical strength of the finished ceramic body.

With properties such as H5-5.5, brightness of 90-95%, refractive index of 1.53, low tint strength, chemical inertness, oil absorption of 21-22 lbs/100 lb., and low free silica content, fine-ground (APS 8-16 μm) nepheline syenite is a useful filler [antiblocking agent; adhesives; caulks and sealants; coatings including latex and alkaloid paints, metal primers, wood stain, sealers, and undercoats; powder coatings for appliances, wheel covers, lawn furniture, etc.; elastomers; foam carpet-backing; plastics including PVC, epoxy, and polyester resin systems]. The low resin demand of nepheline syenite allows high loading rates in plastics, and is categorized as "Generally Recognized As Safe" (GRAS) for indirect food contact (nepheline syenite is transparent to microwaves). In paint, control of the particle top size gives a smooth surface to satin, eggshell, and flat interior wall paints. Nepheline syenite can be used in powder coatings at levels of up to 30%. Nepheline syenite is also used as a mild abrasive [scouring powders].

TYPICAL ALUMINA & ALKALI CONTENT BY GLASS (%)

	Al_2O_3	Na_2O	K_2O
Container glass - white	1.5	13.0	1
Container glass - green	2.6	12.5	1.5
Flat glass	—	13.7	0.2
Pressed ware	0.3	16.9	—
Boro-silicate glass	2.4	4.2	—
Lead-crystal glass	0.02	1.0	14.9
CRT faceplate	3.5	7.5	10.5
Fiber optics	3.0	14.0	—
Glass ceramics	20.9	—	—
Textile fiberglass			
A-Glass ($Al_2O_3+Fe_2O_3$)	1.5	13.0	—
C-Glass ($Al_2O_3+Fe_2O_3$)	4.0	0.5	8
D-Glass	—	1.0	1.5
E-Glass	14.5	0.8	
R-Glass	25.0	0.4	0.1
S-Glass	25.0	—	—
AR-Glass	1.0	—	—

TYPICAL GLASS BATCH COMPOSITIONS (% BY WEIGHT)

	Container glass	Flat glass	Spec. glass	Insul. f'glass	Textile f'glass
Silica sand	57.0	60.0	65.0	42.0	29.0
Feldspar /Neph. syenite	8.0		11.0	18.0	
Soda ash	19.0	20.0	2.0	4.0	
Limestone	16.0	5.0		15.0	30.0
Dolomite		20.0		11.0	
Boron			22.0	10.0	12.0
Kaolin					29.0

A COMPARISON OF ALUMINA SOURCES IN GLASS AND CERAMICS

	Nepheline syenite	Soda-feldspar	Potash-feldspar	Low-iron aplite	Calumite slag
SiO_2	61.40	67.54	67.04	63.71	38.8
Al_2O_3	22.74	19.25	18.02	21.89	10.5
Fe_2O_3	0.06	0.06	0.04	0.09	0.3
CaO	0.70	1.94	0.38	0.48	38.5
MgO	trace	trace	trace	trace	1.4
K_2O	4.95	4.05	12.10	2.37	0.5
Na_2O	9.54	6.96	2.12	5.60	0.4
LOI	0.60	0.13	0.30	0.21	1.1 (S cpds)

Consumption of nepheline syenite in Canada

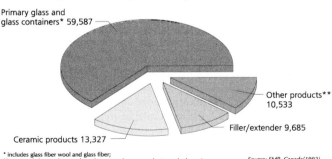

Primary glass and glass containers* 59,587

Other products** 10,533

Filler/extender 9,685

Ceramic products 13,327

* includes glass fiber wool and glass fiber;
** structural clay products, pulp and paper and paper products, amd other minor uses

Source: EMR, Canada(1992)

In Russia nepheline syenite concentrate + limestone in a coal-fired sinter kiln → aluminum metal [containers & packaging; electrical goods; structural materials including construction, aerospace, automobiles]. Byproducts include sodium carbonate [glass; soap & detergents; pulp & paper, sodium chemical feedstock], potassium carbonate [specialty glass, potassium chemical feedstock], and calcium silicate [can constitute up to 40% of portland cement]. The materials list and the principal reactions involved are shown on the next page.

CHEMICAL COMPOSITION OF COMMERCIAL NEPHELINE SYENITE

	Norway North Cape Nefelin Glass grade	Norway North Cape Nefelin Amber grade	Canada Unimin Glass grade (A-30)	Canada Unimin Glass grade 333	Canada Unimin Ceramic grade (A-200, 270, and 400)	Norway North Cape Nefelin Ceramic grade	Canada Unimin Filler grade (Minex 3 & 2)
SiO_2	57.00	56.50	60.3	59.7	60.7	57.00	59.99
Al_2O_3	23.80	22.50	23.7	23.5	23.3	23.80	23.7
Fe_2O_3	0.10	0.40	0.1	0.4	0.07	0.12	0.08
TiO_2	0.10	-					0.001
CaO	1.30	2.50	0.3	0.5	0.7	1.10	0.37
Na_2O	7.90	7.50	10.4	10.2	9.8	7.80	10.6
K_2O	9.00	8.20	5.0	5.0	4.6	9.10	4.8
MgO	n.a.	n.a.	trace	0.1	0.1	n.a.	0.02
BaO	0.30	n.a.	-	-	-	0.30	n.a.
SrO	0.30	n.a.	-	-	-	0.30	n.a.
P_2O_5	0.10	n.a.	-	-	-	-	n.a.
F	<40ppm	<40ppm	n.a.	n.a.	n.a.	<40ppm	n.a.
Cl (water soluble)	<0.15ppm		n.a.	n.a.	n.a.	<18ppm	n.a.
Cl (total)	<100ppm	<100ppm	n.a.	n.a.	n.a.	<75ppm	n.a.
Loss on ignition	1.2		0.3	0.6	0.7		0.37

Source: Company literature

CHEMICAL REACTIONS:

$$4CaCO_3 + (Na,K)_2O \cdot Al_2O_3 \cdot 2SiO_2 \xrightarrow[1,300°C]{} (Na,K)_2O \cdot Al_2O_3 + 2Ca_2SiO_4 + 4CO_2$$

$$2(Na_2K)AlO_2 + CO_2 + 3H_2O \rightarrow 2Al(OH)_3 + (Na,K)_2CO_3$$

SPECIFICATIONS OF NEPHELINE SYENITE FOR THE GLASS INDUSTRY

	Nepheline syenite Low-iron	Nepheline syenite High-iron
SiO_2	±0.5%	±0.5%
Fe_2O_3	0.1% max.	0.35%
Al_2O_3	±0.5%	±0.5%
CaO+MgO		
CaO	±0.5%	±0.5%±
Na_2O+K_2O	±0.5%	±0.5%
ZrO_2		
Cr_2O_3	0.001% max.	0.001% max.
Moisture	0.10% max.	0.10% max.
Physical		
On US 20	-	-
On US 30	0	0
On US 40	1% max.	1% max.
Through		
US 200	5% max.	5%
US 140		

Container glass companies also stipulate that unwanted refractory particles in feldspathic sands, aplite, and nepheline syenite include:

quartz grains larger than US 16 mesh (1.19mm);

clay particles like kaolin and spinel larger than US 20 (0.84mm) or more than 50 particles larger than US 30 mesh (0.59mm) per 10 pounds of sample;

aluminum silicate such as kyanite, mullite, sillimanite, andalusite larger than US 30 mesh (0.59mm) or more than 10 grains larger than US 40 mesh (0.42mm) per 10 pounds of sample;

refractory minerals like corundum larger than US 40 mesh (0.42mm);

zircon, cassiterite, or chrome particles larger than US 60 mesh (0.25mm).

Raw materials	Tons
Nepheline concentrate	3.9 - 4.3
Limestone for	
alumina manufacture	6.0 - 7.8
cement	6.0
Coal * for	
alumina manufacture	1.67 - 1.70
cement	1.3 - 1.6
Steam heat	4.68 - 4.12 g-cal
Electric power for	
alumina	1,050 to 1,190 kW-hr
cement	700 to 860 kW-hr
Products	
Alumina	1.0
Sodium carbonate	0.62 to 0.76
Potassium carbonate	0.18 - 0.28
Portland cement	9.0 - 11.0

*min. 7,000 kcal/kg

QUALITY & SPECIFICATIONS: *Glass:-* min. 23% Al_2O_3 and 14% combined alkalis with max. 0.1% Fe_2O_3 (low-iron grade for flint glass) or 0.35% Fe_2O_3 (high-iron grade for amber glass and fiberglass); PS in the range of 40 to 200 mesh. *Ceramics:-* max. 0.07% Fe_2O_3; PS is typically 200, 270, and 400 mesh. Need to fuse on firing to a uniformly white body without specking. *Filler-grade:-* PS is 100% -200 mesh, 99.98% -325 mesh, 98% -30 μm, 92% -20 μm, 65% -10 μm, and 37% -5 μm.

WORLD CAPACITY: 3.5M. t.

CAPACITY UTILIZATION: 50%.

MARKET CONDITIONS: Steady - increasing regionally. Supply is dominated by Canada and Norway with the former USSR producing large tonnages for various end uses.

MARKETING FACTORS: Glass & ceramics depend on the level of construction activity which is driven by the economy. Consumption is affected by increased glass recycling.

HEALTH & SAFETY: Because of its crystalline silica content, nepheline syenite comes under the OSHA Hazard Communication Standards, 29 CFR Section 1900.1200. This requires labeling and other forms of warning, material safety data sheets, and employee training for products containing identified carcinogens with concentrations greater than 0.1% (crystalline silica has been classified as a probable carcinogen by the IARC). See silica for further details.

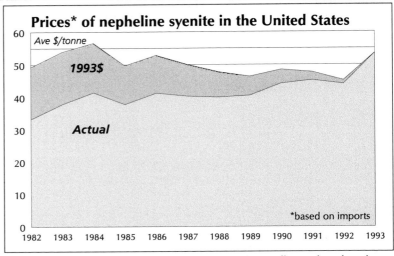

Prices* of nepheline syenite in the United States

SUBSTITUTES & ALTERNATIVES: Abrasives:- bauxite & alumina (fused alumina), corundum/emery, diamonds, diatomite, feldspar, garnet, iron oxide (magnetite), olivine, perlite, pumice, silica sand, staurolite, tripoli, and silicon carbide), ilmenite. **Ceramics**:- aplite, feldspar. **Fillers**:- ATH, barite, calcium carbonate, feldspar, kaolin, mica, perlite, pyrophyllite, talc, microcrystalline silica, ground silica flour and synthetic silica, wollastonite. **Glass**:- aplite, steel mill slag, cullet, feldspar (container & fiberglass); kaolin (textile-grade fiberglass); calcined alumina or alumina hydrate (specialty glass).

RECYCLING: The use of cullet or recycled glass is increasing which in turn is reducing the need for virgin raw materials in the glass batch. The recycling rate is about 33% in the United States and as high as 90% in some European countries like Switzerland.

PRODUCERS & WORLD TRADE: Canada and Norway are virtually the only commercial producers of nepheline syenite and therefore the main exporters. In addition, both deposits are owned and operated by one US company. Production in the Former USSR is largely used as a chemical source and rarely affects world trade.

HTS CODES: 2529.30.0000 (nepheline syenite); 2529.30.0050 (other leucite; nepheline and nepheline syenite).

PRICES: Canada, FOB $40/t (glass, low-iron, 30 mesh, bulk); $36-37/t (glass, high-iron, 30 mesh, bulk); $113/t (ceramic, 200 mesh, bagged); $130-260-85/t (filler grade, bagged). Norwegian (CIF UK port) $105/t (glass grade, 0.5mm, bulk); $121.50/t (ceramic grade, 45μ, bulk); $165/t (ceramic grade, 45μ, bags).

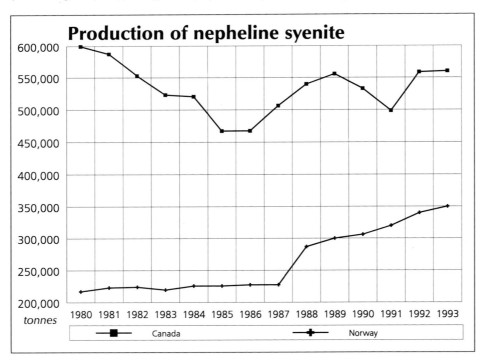

Production of nepheline syenite

Canada — Norway

ETYMOLOGY: Leucite from the Greek *leukos = white* reflecting its white or gray color. **Nepheline** from the Greek *nephele = cloud* alluding to the cloudy appearance developed on immersing nepheline in strong acid.

NEPHELINE SYENITE LEADERS

Producers	Exporters
Fomer USSR	Canada
Canada	Norway
Norway	

Importers	
United States	Taiwan
Netherlands	Spain
Germany	Japan
Italy	Sweden
United Kingdom	Greece
Australia	Portugal
Singapore	Ireland
France	

NITROGEN COMPOUNDS

Although mining caliche ore in Chile yields sodium and potassium nitrates and iodine, the overwhelming commercial source of nitrogen-based products is synthetic ammonia (NH_3) via the Haber-Bosch process. Natural gas (CH_4) is compressed to 300-600 psi and desulfurized. In the presence of nickel catalysts and at $815°C$ ($1,500°F$), the gas reacts with high-pressure steam to yield "process gas", a mixture of hydrogen, carbon dioxide, and carbon monoxide. The process gas enters a secondary reformer containing nickel catalysts; compressed air is injected and the oxygen in the air is consumed in exothermic reactions with hydrogen, carbon monoxide, and residual methane from the primary reformer. The gas contains sufficient nitrogen from the injected air for the ammonia synthesis. The process gas reacts with steam to produce additional hydrogen and convert the carbon monoxide to carbon dioxide which is separated as a by-product. Traces of carbon dioxide and monoxide are removed by methanation to produce a pure hydrogen. The remaining gas mixture or "synthesis gas" consists of hydrogen and nitrogen in the correct ratio for ammonia synthesis which takes place at high temperature and pressure and over a catalyst of iron oxide promoted by aluminum oxide, with potassium, calcium, or magnesium oxide.

$$N_2 + 3H_2 \rightarrow 2NH_3$$

The production of 1 tonne anhydrous ammonia requires 680,000-708,000m³ (24-25 MCF) natural gas feedstock and 425,000-453,000m³ (15-16 MCF) process gas.

PROPERTIES & USES: Nitrogen (N) is a primary nutrient (along with P & K) which encourages vigorous plant growth and increases yields. However, elemental N can only be taken up by plants in the soluble nitrate or ammonium form, that is chemically bonded or fixed nitrogen [fertilizer]. Ammonia (NH_3) [direct application fertilizer; chemical feedstock; cleaning agent; curing agent in leather; pulp & paper; rubber; sodium carbonate production], either anhydrous or aqueous (ammoniacal liquor), contains approx. 82% nitrogen (82-0-0).

$NH_3 + CO_2 \rightarrow$ urea, $CO(NH_2)_2$ (46-0-0) [prilled direct application fertilizer; animal feed; urea-formaldehyde resin; melamine production; textile treatment] + ammonium nitrate $\rightarrow$ urea-ammonium nitrate (UAN) solutions (45% ammonium nitrate, 35% urea, and 20% water = 32% N) [direct application fertilizer and fluid mixes]. Note: urea has the highest nitrogen content (45-46%) of any solid nitrogen fertilizer and is the world's leading nitrogen fertilizer.

NH_3 + relevant acid $\rightarrow$ ammonium nitrate (33.5-0-0) [fertilizer; ANFO explosives], ammonium sulfate (21-0-0) [fertilizer], diammonium phosphate or DAP (18-46-0) [fertilizer], monoammonium phosphate or MAP (16-2-0) [fertilizer], ammonium chloride (ammoniac sal) [galvanizing; batteries].

Note: most ammonium sulfate is now a by-product. About 4 tonnes of ammonium sulfate is produced per tonne of caprolactan (the intermediate for nylon 6 fiber and plastics); and in the steel industry sulfuric acid is used to remove ammonia from coking coal.

NH_3 + air $\rightarrow$ nitric acid [stainless steel pickling; chemical intermediate]. NH_3 + nitric acid $\rightarrow$ ammonium nitrate [fertilizer; explosives (nitroglycerine); glass & frits; charcoal briquettes; metal treatment; water treatment]; $\rightarrow$ adipic acid [nylon & polyurethane resins]; $\rightarrow$ nitrobenzene [$\rightarrow$ aniline]; $\rightarrow$ toluene diisocyanate [flexible urethane foams].

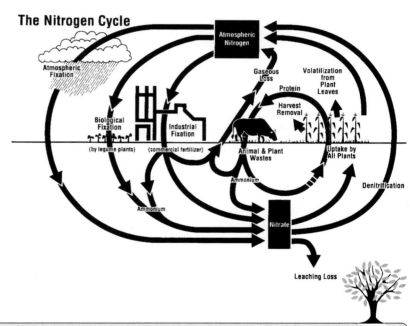

The Nitrogen Cycle

NITROGEN PRODUCTS

Fertilizer	Formula	%N	%P	%S	Production route
Anhydrous ammonia	NH_3	82	-	-	$N_2 + 3H_2 \rightarrow 2NH_3$
Ammonium nitrate	NH_4NO_3	33.5	-	-	$NH_3 + HNO_3 \rightarrow NH_4NO_3$
Ammonium sulfate	$(NH_4)_2SO_4$	21		24	$2NH_3 + H_2SO_4 \rightarrow (NH_4)_2SO_4$
Diammonium phosphate (DAP)	$(NH_4)_2HPO_4$	18	46	-	$NH_3 + NH_4H_2PO_4 \rightarrow (NH_4)_2PO_4$ (DAP)
Monoammonium phosphate (MAP)	$NH_4H_2PO_4$	12	52	-	$NH_3 + H_3PO_4 \rightarrow NH_4H_2PO_4$ (MAP)
Urea	$CO(NH_2)_2$	46	-	-	$CO_2 + 2NH_3 \rightarrow NH_2COONH_4$ ammonium carbomate $\rightarrow CO(NH_2)_2 + H_2O$

SPECIFICATION OF NITRATE-BASED PRODUCTS FROM CHILE (%)

Nitrates: Specifications	Sodium nitrate (16-0-0) NaNO₃	Sodium potassium nitrate (15-0-14) NaNO₃+KNO₃	Magnesium sodium nitrate NaNO₃+MgO	Sodium nitrate (industrial grade) NaNO₃	Technical sodium nitrate NaNO₃	Refined sodium nitrate NaNO₃	Potassium nitrate prilled (13.5-0-44) KNO₃	Potassium nitrate standard (13.5-0-45) KNO₃
Chemical analysis								
Nitrogen (N), min.	16%	15%	15%				13.50%	13.50%
Sodium nitrate (NaNO₃)	96.8-97.9%	64-66%		98%	99.20%	99.60%		
Potassium oxide (K₂O)	0.4-1.2%	14% min.	0.50%				44% min.	45% min.
Potassium nitrate (KNO₃)		30-32%						
Sodium (Na)	26%	18%	24%					
Magnesium oxide (MgO)	0.10%	0.10%	5.5% min.					
Sulfur (S)	0.10%	0.10%	0.10%					
Sodium chloride (NaCl)				0.8% max.	0.3% max.	0.13% max.		
Chloride (Cl)	1% max.	0.8% min.	1% min.					
Iron (Fe)								
Sodium nitrite (NaNO₂)				0.05% max.	0.005% max.	0.005% max.		
Sodium sulfate (Na₂SO4)				0.35% max.	0.10% max.	0.10% max.		
Moisture (H₂O)	0.15% max.	0.50%		0.15% max.	0.15% max.	0.15% max.	0.50% max.	0.10% max.
Insolubles	0.15%	0.15%		0.15% max.	0.02% max.	0.02% max.	0.10% max.	0.04% max.
Sodium tetraborate (Na₂B₄O₇)					0.03% max.	0.03% max.		
Boric acid (H₃BO₃)		0.30%						
Boron (B)	0.035% max.			0.025% max.				
Screen (Tyler mesh)								
plus 8 (2.38 mm)	10%	20%	20%	8%	5%	5%	45%	
plus 10 (1.68 mm)	70%	70%	70%	65%	45%	45%	86%	
plus 14 (1.19 mm)	96%	97%	97%	96%	90%	90%	99%	
plus 35 (0.42 mm)								3%
plus 100 (0.149)								62%
plus 150 (0.105 mm)								83%
plus 200 (0.074 mm)								91%
minus 20 (0.841 mm)	1.50%	1.00%	1.00%	2%	8%	8%	0.10%	

Source: SQM Nitratos S.A.

NH₃ → acrylonitrile [acrylic and nylon fiber; nitrile rubber]. NH₃ → sodium azide [detonators for high explosives; air bag propellent]; cyamides & cyanides [gold leaching; dyes; photography fumigant; insecticide; steel hardener]; hydrazine; hydroxylamine.

QUALITY & SPECIFICATIONS: Urea contains 46% N, ammonium nitrate 33.5% N, ammonium sulfate 21% N, MAP 13% N & 52% P, and DAP 18% N & 20% P, aqueous ammonia min. 29.4% NH₃. Products from Chile are summarized in the table.

WORLD CAPACITY: 144M. t (anhydrous ammonia).

CAPACITY UTILIZATION: 78%.

MARKET CONDITIONS: Steady and increasing in Latin America, Australasia, and Africa.

MARKETING FACTORS: Fertilizer use will increase with population growth, the need for more efficient food production, and nutrient balance. DAP futures are traded on the Chicago Board of Trade.

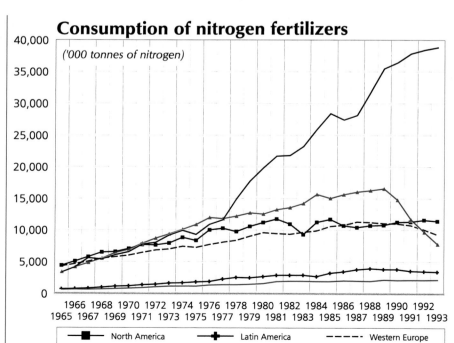

Consumption of nitrogen fertilizers

('000 tonnes of nitrogen)

Legend: North America; Latin America; Western Europe; East Europe & FSU; Africa; Asia-Pacific

Western Europe includes the former West Germany and East Europe & FSU includes the former East Germany. Asia Pacific includes West Asia. Source: FAO Fertilizer Yearbook.

HEALTH & SAFETY: Anhydrous ammonia is not a poison and has no cumulative toxic effects on the human body. However, ammonia vapor is considered to be "life threatening" when exposure levels reach 2,500-6,500 ppm for up to 30 minutes or "rapidly fatal" if exposure levels reach 5,000-10,000 ppm for up to 30 minutes. It is not combustible except when its concentration in the air is 16 to 25% at 849°C (1,560°F) or higher. It does require special handling since anhydrous ammonia turns to a colorless, pungent, hazardous gas under atmospheric conditions. Regulations on handling in the US are issued by OSHA. The industry reference for storage and handling is K61.1 drawn up by The Fertiliser Institute (TFI) and issued by the American National Standards Institute (ANSI). In 1990 the US Department of Transportation classified anhydrous ammonia as a non-flammable gas linked to a required "inhalation hazard" label and as a Division 2.2 non-flammable, non-poisonous compressed gas for domestic shipments. However, international shipments were classified as Division 2.3 "poisonous gas" consistent with United Nations regulations. Ammonia is stored in carbon steel cylindrical tanks at atmospheric pressure and -2°C (-28°F) and shipped in tank railcars or trucks under pressure as a liquid, or by refrigerated barges and ocean vessels, or by pipeline.

SUBSTITUTES & ALTERNATIVES: None in fertilizers (primary nutrient).

RECYCLING: Virtually none.

PRODUCERS & WORLD TRADE: Chile is the sole producer of natural nitrates. By far the bulk of production is derived as a byproduct of natural gas production in more than 50 countries.

PRICES: Anhydrous ammonia (wholesale, USA) $220/t fertilizer, tanks, del. midwest terminals; $220/t (fob Gulf Coast). Aqueous ammonia (USA, freight equalized, E. of Rockies) $287 - 347/t (basis 29.4% NH_3, tanks).

Urea (46% N) $150/t (agricultural, granular, barges, FOB Gulf Coast); $176-182/t (agricultural, granular, FOB Midwest terminals); $230/t (industrial, bulk, FOB Gulf Coast). DAP $163-172/t (fertilizer grade, min. 18% N, 20% P, bulk, FOB Florida works); $265-275/t (feed grade, 18% N, 20% P, bulk, FOB Florida works); $1,315-1,350/t (tech. grade, bags, ex-works, freight equalized); $1,340-1,390/t (food grade, bags, ex-works, freight equalized). DAP (FOB N. Africa) $170/t. MAP $137-145/t (fertilizer grade, min. 13% N, 52% P, bulk, FOB Florida works); $1,342-1,390/t (tech. grade, bags, ex-works, freight equalized); $1,375-1,425 (food grade, bags, ex-works, freight equalized).

Ammonium bicarbonate $730-745/t (drums, ex-works). Ammonium chloride $396-462/t (white, technical, fine granular, bags); $913/t (USP, granular drums). Ammonium nitrate $165-170/t domestic, fertilizer grade 33.5%N, bulk, S.E. USA del.). Ammonium pentaborate $2,090/t (granular, bags, ex-works). Ammonium sulfate $94-116/t (granular, bulk, ex-works); $42-50/t (standard, commercial, FOB works); $146/t (technical, bags, ex-works). Ammonium sulfide $507/t (liquid, 40-44%, tanks, 100% basis, freight equalized). Ammonium thiosulfate $286/t (photographic, 60% tanks, FOB works). Nitric acid (100% basis) $204-215/t (40°Be, 42°Be, tanks, ex-works); $380/t (94.5-98% HNO_3, tanks, ex-works).

Capacity of anhydrous ammonia by region
('000 tonnes)

South America 2,458
C. America & Carib. 2,168
European Union 16,075
North America 22,680
Africa 4,209
Middle East 5,842
Non-EU Europe 42,048
141,864
Australasia 46,384

Capacity of anhydrous ammonia
('000 tonnes)

China 24,058
United States 16,066
Former USSR 27,968
India 10,551
Rumania 4,645
Netherlands 3,874
Canada 3,629
Germany 3,574
Indonesia 3,484
Mexico 2,985
Poland 2,740
France 2,304
141,866
Other 33,938
Japan 2,050

Source: USBM (1989)

Downstream nitrogen compounds produced in the United States
('000 tonnes nitrogen)

Caprolactum 77
Acrylonitrile 300
Nitric acid, direct use 388
Ammonium sulfate 461
Urea 3,268
9,618
Ammonium phosphates 2,459
Ammonium nitrate 2,665

Source: USBM (1993)

Calcium cyanamide $440-495/t (industrial, anhydrous, drums, ex-works). Lithium nitrate $7.52/kg (technical, drums).

Potassium cyanide $3.87-4.0/kg (drums, >20,000 lb, FOB works). Potassium nitrate $358/t (fertilizer grade, standard, bulk, del. S.E. USA); $364/t (fertilizer grade, prilled, bulk, del. S.E. USA); $600/t (technical, prilled, bags, ex-works).

Sodium cyanide $1.43/kg (briquettes or granular, 99% min. drums, delivered). Sodium nitrate (Chile, natural) $180/t (ex-store). Sodium nitrate (USA, imported) $236/t (commercial, bags, Gulf Coast warehouse); $212/t (commercial, bulk, Gulf Coast warehouse); $154/t (agricultural, bulk, Gulf Coast warehouse); $760-820/t (USP, bags, FOB, freight equalized).

Strontium nitrate $1,133/t (bags, ex-works).

Production of ammonia ('000 tonnes of contained nitrogen)

Legend: North America; South America; C. America/Caribbean; European Union; Non-EU Europe; Australasia; M. East/Africa

Source: USBM

HTS CODES: 2814.10 (ammonia, anhydrous); 2834.21.0000 (nitrates of potassium); 2834..22.0000 (nitrates of bismuth); 2834.29.1000 (other, nitrates of calcium); 2834.29.2000 (other, nitrates of strontium); 2914.20 (ammonia, aqueous); 3105.10.0000 (mineral or chemical fertilizers containing two or three of the fertilizing elements nitrogen, phosphorus, and potassium); 3105.20.0000 (mineral or chemical fertilizers containing the three of the fertilizing elements nitrogen, phosphorus, and potassium); 3105.30.0000 (diammonium phosphate - DAP); 3105.40.0010 (monoammonium phosphate - MAP); 3105.40.0050 (other ammonium phosphate).

ETYMOLOGY: Ammonia from the Temple of Jupiter, *Ammon*, Libya where it was first produced by distilling camel's dung.

Time-price relationships for ammonia and natural gas in the United States

Ammonia ($/ton) — 1993$ / Actual

Natural Gas ($/m. BTU) — 1993$ / Actual

Source: USBM

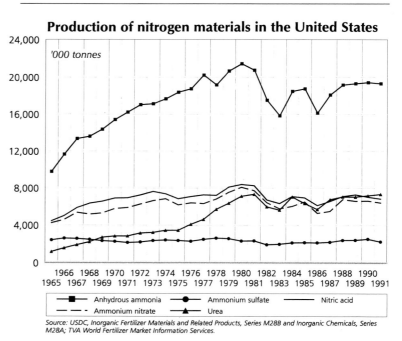

Production of nitrogen materials in the United States

'000 tonnes

Legend: Anhydrous ammonia; Ammonium sulfate; Nitric acid; Ammonium nitrate; Urea

Source: USDC, Inorganic Fertilizer Materials and Related Products, Series M28B and Inorganic Chemicals, Series M28A; TVA World Fertilizer Market Information Services.

OLIVINE

Minerals	Formula	% MgO	SiO₂	Color	SG	H
Olivine	$(MgFe)_2SiO_4$	32	47.6	pale green to green	3.2-4.3	6.5-7

Olivine forms part of a solid solution series ranging from forsterite ($2MgO \cdot SiO_2$) to fayalite ($2FeO \cdot SiO_2$) with forsterite generally accounting for 85% of commercial olivine. Dunite, an igneous rock comprising almost entirely of olivine, may also be a commercial source of olivine. Synthetic olivine is produced in Canada by calcining asbestos mine tailings.

PROPERTIES & USES: Olivine is a source of magnesia and silica [metallurgy; fertilizer]. Olivine may be added directly to the blast furnace charge as lump, a sinter feed, or mixed with low-silica iron ore fines and pressed into pellets [slag conditioner for blast furnace & electric arc furnace]. Benefits of olivine in the blast furnace include: alkali recirculation reduction within the furnace by forming stable magnesium alkali silicates; its higher reaction temperature reduces low temperature breakdown and swelling of the burden thus maintaining permeability and reducing coke consumption; and compared with dolomite it has a higher MgO content (requires less material for a given MgO level), MgO:SiO₂ ratio (allows MgO levels to be raised without changing the basicity of the slag), and lower LOI (conserves the energy required to drive off unwanted carbon dioxide). Used as a sinter feed, olivine reduces the sintering temperature by up to 100°C and so increases the sinter furnace capacity by 10-15%; olivine-fluxed pellets swell less, reduce more quickly, and have a narrow melting range.

Olivine is refractory (fusion temperature of 1,665-1,743°C) with a low and uniform coefficient of thermal expansion, good resistance to thermal shock, spalling, and slag attack, and a high green strength [magnesia (forsterite) refractory bricks; spraying, ramming, and gunning mixes; precast refractory linings for incinerators]. The refractory properties plus its low silica content and strong resistance to metal attack mean that olivine can replace silica sand as a foundry sand [aluminum; brass; bronze; manganese steel]. Additional benefits include: the basicity of olivine which enhances the bentonite's bonding properties thus reducing clay demand and its low and uniform expansion rate which eliminates the need for cushioning agents and thus allows recycling. Olivine has extremely high heat retention properties [brick cores heat-storage units].

Olivine is inert, contains <1% free silica, has a moderately high H and SG with a conchoidal fracture yielding an angular grain shape and a light-colored dust [loose-grain shot blasting abrasive; filtration media; weighting agent in concrete oil-production platforms]. Olivine may replace silica sand as a blasting abrasive because of the reduced risk of silicosis and the higher SG providing a higher force of impact; unlike slags, olivine does not leave a black, dusty surface. The light color of the dust allows olivine to be used as a filler [specialty paints; asphalt, and mastics; roofing tile formulations]. Olivine contributes magnesia and iron as nutrients to the soil [fertilizer]. As a local rock, olivine may be crushed and used as an aggregate [ballast; construction; concrete].

QUALITY & SPECIFICATIONS: Typically contains 45-51% MgO with 40-43% SiO₂, 7-8% Fe₂O₃, 0.2-0.8% CaO, and 1.8-2% Al₂O₃+TiO₂, MnO, Cr₂O₃, NiO, and CoO. LOI is critical since this indicates the presence of hydrated minerals such as chlorite and serpentine. Sizes range from lump or aggregate (10-45mm) through sand to flour (-200 or -325 mesh).

Blast furnace grade:- lump (10-40mm) for direct feed to the blast furnace and 0-6mm or 0-3mm to the sinter stream with an average MgO content of 47-48%. *Foundry grade (general):-* mainly AFS 20, 30, 60, 90, 120, and flour. *Foundry grade (for brass, bronze, and aluminum):-* AFS 100, 140, 180. *Filler grade:-* 0-0.8mm and 0-0.02mm. *Fertilizer grade:-*<0.1 mm. *Blasting grit:-* see table.

WORLD CAPACITY: 6.5M. t. **CAPACITY UTILIZATION:** 70%.

MARKET CONDITIONS: Steady-declining.

MARKETING FACTORS: Iron & steel/ferrous and nonferrous foundries which are driven by the economy and technological changes. New uses (plastics).

OLIVINE FOR BLASTING

Grade	Size range (mm)	Surface profile on mild steel
AFS 20	1.7-0.355	medium
AFS 30	1.0-0.18	fine
Special	1.0-0.15	fine
AFS 60	0.5-0.125	less than fine
AFS 90	0.25-0.09	less than fine

Source: Scangrit, UK.

CHEMICAL COMPOSITION OF COMMERCIAL OLIVINE

	Norway Dunite	Norway A/S Olivin Standard	Norway A/S Olivin Refractory	Austria Magnolithe	Italy Nouva Cives	Sweden Handol	USA Washington Olivine Corp.	USA N. Carolina Unimin	Japan Toho
MgO	47-51	48-50	49-51	49-51	41-43	46	49.4	50.5	max. 47
SiO₂	41-43	42-43	41.5-42.5	39-41	42-44	41	41.2	40.1	min. 42
Fe₂O₃	6.5-7.7	6.8-7.3	6.5-7.0	8-9	1.2-2.7	8.2	7.1	6.7	2
Al₂O₃	0.5-1.0	0.5-0.8	0.4-0.5						
CaO	0.05-0.06	0.05-0.1	0.05-0.1	0.4 max.	1.5-2.6	0.8	0.2	0.2	0.4
Oxides				NA	NA	2	1.8	1	max. 8.5
LOI	0.2-1.5	0.7-1.5	0.2-0.5	NA	NA	1.8	0.7	0.7	max. 2.5

* Al₂O₃, TiO₂, MnO, Cr₂O₃, NiO, CaO, K₂O, Na₂O

Consumption of olivine in North America
(tonnes)

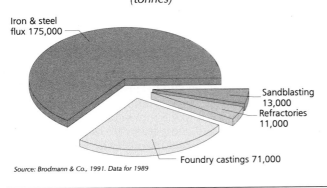

Iron & steel flux 175,000

Sandblasting 13,000
Refractories 11,000

Foundry castings 71,000

Source: Brodmann & Co., 1991. Data for 1989

Consumption of olivine in Japan
(tonnes)

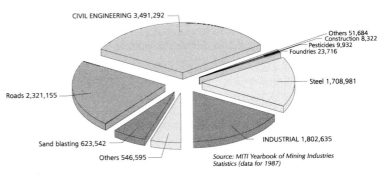

CIVIL ENGINEERING 3,491,292

Others 51,684
Construction 8,322
Pesticides 9,932
Foundries 23,716

Steel 1,708,981

Roads 2,321,155

INDUSTRIAL 1,802,635

Sand blasting 623,542

Others 546,595

Source: MITI Yearbook of Mining Industries Statistics (data for 1987)

Price history of olivine (\$/tonne)

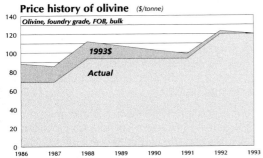

Olivine, foundry grade, FOB, bulk — 1993\$ / Actual

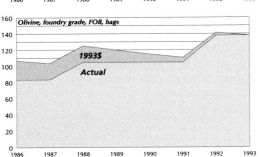

Olivine, foundry grade, FOB, bags — 1993\$ / Actual

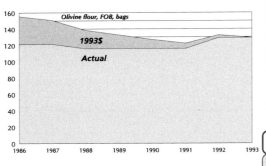

Olivine flour, FOB, bags — 1993\$ / Actual

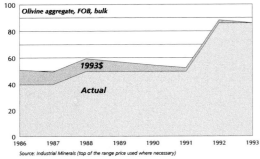

Olivine aggregate, FOB, bulk — 1993\$ / Actual

Source: Industrial Minerals (top of the range price used where necessary)

HEALTH & SAFETY: Crystalline silica has been classified as a probable carcinogen by the IARC (see silica for further details). A major advantage of olivine over silica sand as an abrasive and foundry sand is the low content of free silica.

SUBSTITUTES & ALTERNATIVES: Other sources of magnesia include magnesite (47.8% MgO) and dolomite (20% MgO). **Fertlizer:**- dolomite, magnesite, and magnesium sulfate. **Foundry:**- bauxite & alumina, chromite, clays (kaolin & bauxite), perlite, pyrophyllite, silica sand, vermiculite, zircon. **Night storage heaters:**-magnetite. **Refractories:**-andalusite, bauxite, chromite, kyanite, dolomite, graphite, magnesite, pyrophyllite, refractory clays, silica, sillimanite, zircon. **Slag conditioner:**- dolomite.

RECYCLING: Virtually none except for blasting. One of the advantages of olivine as an abrasive is the fact that it can be recovered, cleaned, resized, and reused. Higher initial costs compared with rival abrasives may be justified in some cases by an increased life cycle based on recycling.

PRODUCERS & WORLD TRADE: Large-scale production of olivine is limited to a handful of countries dominated by Norway.

PRICES: United States, FOB mine/plant \$69-109/t (AFS 30-180, bulk); \$77-177/t (AFS 30-180, bags); \$117/t (flour, bags); \$50-78 (aggregate, bulk). Europe \$13.50-20/t (CIF, crushed, bulk); \$66-88/t (dry graded, refractory aggregate, ex-works, bags); \$66-88/t (foundry sand, del. UK, bags or bulk); \$96-111 (sand for tundish spray, bags).

ETYMOLOGY: Dunite for Dunedin, New Zealand. **Fayalite** for Fayal Island in the Azores and Greek *lithos* = stone. **Forsterite** for Adolarius Jacob Forster (1739-1806), English mineral collector. **Olivine** from the Latin *oliva = olive* alluding to its olive green color.

OLIVINE LEADERS

Producers	Exporters	Importers
Norway	Norway	Germany
Spain	United States	France
Japan	Sweden	Netherlands
Former USSR	Spain	United Kingdom
Italy	Japan	Belgium
United States	Italy	Finland
Mexico		Canada
Sweden		Taiwan
Austria		Korea

Peat is a biomass composed of a group of accumulated organic residues resulting from the incomplete decomposition of plant debris in very moist and anaerobic conditions, i.e. a peat bog (see ASTM definition below).

PROPERTIES & USES: Peat has an SG of 0.1-1.6 (depending on water content), low density, high porosity; it is fibrous and elastic, resistant to decomposition, pH of 2.8-4.0, with an ability to absorb liquids and odors, lacks nutrient [general soil improvement; potting soil ingredient; fertilizer carrier; mushroom beds & earthworm culture medium; seed inoculant; flower packing]. Absorbing properties and high ionic exchange capacity make peat a natural filter and cleaner [industrial and residential waste treatment; oil spill cleaning; bulking agent in composting]. Peat has a fairly high calorific value (4,700-5,100 kcal/kg), low ash content (0.5-2.5%), and low pollutant content [milled or briquetted fuel]. Solvents and/or pyrolysis yields peat wax, resin, and asphalt → semi-coke, activated carbon [drinking water & wastewater treatment; sugar & corn syrup decolorizing; gas phase uses such as air purification, solvent recovery, evaporation control].

QUALITY & SPECIFICATIONS: Subjective classification based on degree of decomposition (von Post's scale from undecomposed or H1 to completely decomposed or H10); biological origin (from high fiber Sphagnum, Hypnum, Reed-sedge, or Humus), and ash content. General division into horticultural (H1-H5) and fuel peat (H6-H10). Standard size for shipping sphagnum moss is 4 ft³ bale compressed 2:1.

ASTM D 2607-69 (Standard Classification of Peats, Mosses, Humus, and Related Products) assigns nomenclature to peat and peat moss, i.e. "The term peat refers only to organic matter of geological origin, excluding coal, formed from dead plant remains in water and in the absence of air. It occurs in a bog, swampland, or march, and it has an ash content not exceeding 25% by dry weight. Fibers are defined as plant material retained in an ASTM No. 100 (150 µm) sieve, that is material 0.15 mm or larger, consisting of stems, leaves, or fragments of bog plants, but containing no particles larger than 0.15" (12.7 mm). It excludes fragments of other materials such as shells, stones, sand, and gravel."

Classification is based on five major types according to generic origin and fiber content. Percentages of fiber are based on oven-dried weight at 105°C, not on a volume basis.

VON POST'S CLASSIFICATION OF PEAT BY DEGREE OF HUMIFICATION

Humification von Post's Scale	Description
H1	Completely undecomposed peat which, when squeezed, releases almost clear water. Plant remains easily identifiable. No amorphous material present.
H2	Almost completely undecomposed peat which, when squeezed, releases almost clear or yellowish water. Plant remains still easily identifiable. No amorphous material present.
H3	Very slightly decomposed peat which, when squeezed, releases muddy brown water, but no peat passes between the fingers. Plant remains still identifiable, and no amorphous material present.
H4	Slightly decomposed peat which, when squeezed, releases very muddy dark water. No peat passes between the fingers but the plant remains slightly pasty and has lost some of the identifiable features.
H5	Moderately decomposed peat which, when squeezed, releases very "muddy" water with a very small amount of amorphous peat escaping between the fingers. The structure of the plant is quite indistinct, although it is still possible to recognize certain features. The residue is strongly pasty.
H6	Moderately decomposed peat with a very indistinct plant structure. When squeezed, about one third of the peat escapes between the fingers. The residue is strongly pasty but shows the plant structure more distinctly than before squeezing.
H7	Strongly decomposed peat. Contains a lot of amorphous material with very faint recognizable plant structure. When squeezed, about one-half of the peat escapes between the fingers. The water, if any is released, is very dark and almost pasty.
H8	Very strongly decomposed peat with a large quantity of amorphous material and very dry indistinct plant structure. When squeezed, about two-thirds of the peat escapes between the fingers. A small quantity of pasty water may be released. The plant material remaining in the hand consists of residues such as roots and fibers that resist decomposition.
H9	Practically fully decomposed peat in which there is hardly any recognizable plant structure. When squeezed, almost all of the peat escapes between the fingers as a fairly uniform paste.
H10	Completely decomposed peat with no discernible plant structure. When squeezed, all the wet peat escapes between the fingers.

Sphagnum Moss Peat (Peat Moss) - The oven-dried peat shall contain a minimum of 66.66% sphagnum moss fiber by weight. These fibers shall be stems and leaves of sphagnum and have recognizable fibrous and cellular structure.Hypnum Moss Peat - The oven-dried peat shall contain a minimum of 33.33% fiber content by weight of which hypnum moss fibers shall comprise over 50%. These fibers shall be stems and leaves of sphagnum and have recognizable fibrous and cellular structure.Reed-Sedge Peat - The oven-dried peat shall contain a minimum of 33.33% fiber content by weight of which reed-sedge and other non-moss fibers shall comprise over 50%.Peat Humus - The oven-dried peat shall contain less than 33.33% fiber by weight. Other Peat - All forms of peat not classified herein.

WORLD CAPACITY: 217M. t.

CAPACITY UTILIZATION: 99%.

MARKET CONDITIONS: Stable-declining.

MARKETING FACTORS: Environmental factors including oil spills and various clean up operations. The need to increase agricultural yield per unit of area based on increased urbanization. Recreation habits, for example the popularity of gardening and the shipment of exotic plants such as orchids.

HEALTH & SAFETY: Crystalline silica has been classified as a probable carcinogen by the IARC (see silica for further details). Therefore, because of its crystalline silica content, unless processing has the capability to reduce the crystalline silica content to less than 0.1%, peat will come under the OSHA Hazard Communication Standards, 29 CFR Section 1900.1200 which require labeling and other forms of warning, material safety data sheets, and employee training for products containing identified carcinogens with concentrations greater than 0.1%.

Peat consumption in the United States
(*tonnes*)

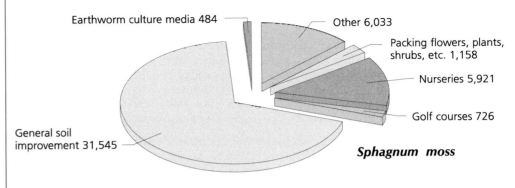

Earthworm culture media 484 — Other 6,033 — Packing flowers, plants, shrubs, etc. 1,158 — Nurseries 5,921 — Golf courses 726 — General soil improvement 31,545

Sphagnum moss

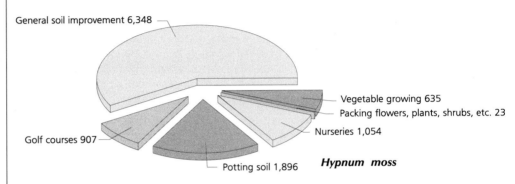

General soil improvement 6,348 — Vegetable growing 635 — Packing flowers, plants, shrubs, etc. 23 — Nurseries 1,054 — Golf courses 907 — Potting soil 1,896

Hypnum moss

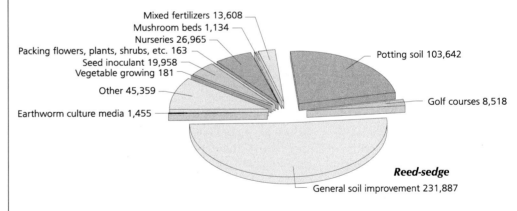

Mixed fertilizers 13,608 — Mushroom beds 1,134 — Nurseries 26,965 — Packing flowers, plants, shrubs, etc. 163 — Seed inoculant 19,958 — Vegetable growing 181 — Other 45,359 — Earthworm culture media 1,455 — Potting soil 103,642 — Golf courses 8,518 — General soil improvement 231,887

Reed-sedge

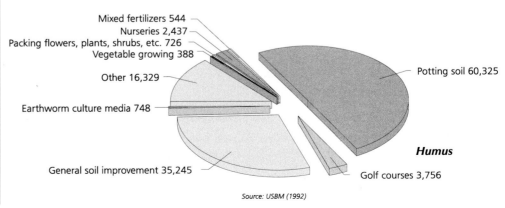

Mixed fertilizers 544 — Nurseries 2,437 — Packing flowers, plants, shrubs, etc. 726 — Vegetable growing 388 — Other 16,329 — Earthworm culture media 748 — Potting soil 60,325 — General soil improvement 35,245 — Golf courses 3,756

Humus

Source: USBM (1992)

SUBSTITUTES & ALTERNATIVES: Carrier:- attapulgite/sepiolite, bentonite, diatomite, kaolin, peat, pumice, pyrophyllite, talc, vermiculite, zeolites. **Soil amendment**:- bentonite/kaolin, diatomite, gypsum, perlite, vermiculite, zeolites, various fibrous plant materials like straw and composted material. **Fuel**:- wood, oil, natural gas, and coal (fuel).

RECYCLING: Virtually none apart from composting.

PRODUCERS & WORLD TRADE: Production is dominated by the former USSR, Finland, Ireland, and Canada which have a large domestic demand, particularly as a fuel source, and export horticultural grades.

HTS CODE: 2703.00 (peat (including peat litter) whether or not agglomerated); 6815.20 (articles of peat).

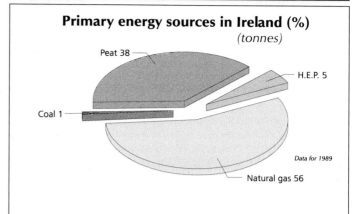

Primary energy sources in Ireland (%)
(tonnes)

Peat 38; H.E.P. 5; Coal 1; Natural gas 56

Data for 1989

World demand for peat

Agriculture 154,545; Fuel 27,337

Source: USBM (1993)

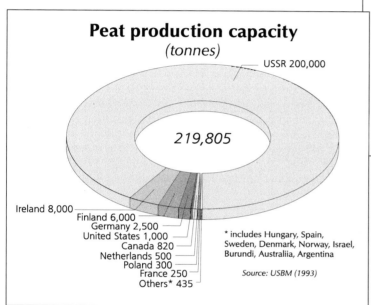

Peat production capacity
(tonnes)

219,805

USSR 200,000
Ireland 8,000
Finland 6,000
Germany 2,500
United States 1,000
Canada 820
Netherlands 500
Poland 300
France 250
Others* 435

* includes Hungary, Spain, Sweden, Denmark, Norway, Israel, Burundi, Australiia, Argentina

Source: USBM (1993)

PRICES: United States Sphagnum moss $30/t (bulk); $113/t (packaged or baled). Hypnum $26.45/t (bulk); $75.65/t (packaged or baled). Reed-sedge $19/t (bulk); $23.20/t (packaged or baled). Humus $19/t (bulk); $10.77/t (packaged or baled).

ETYMOLOGY: Peat from the Anglo-Latin *peta = piece of turf.*

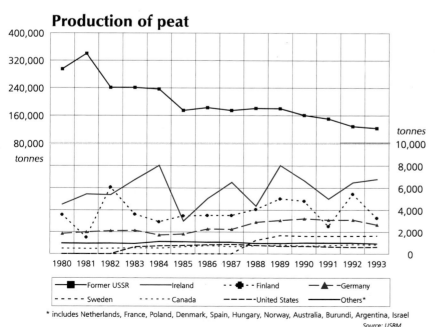

Production of peat

Former USSR — Ireland — Finland — Germany — Sweden — Canada — United States — Others*

* includes Netherlands, France, Poland, Denmark, Spain, Hungary, Norway, Australia, Burundi, Argentina, Israel

Source: USBM

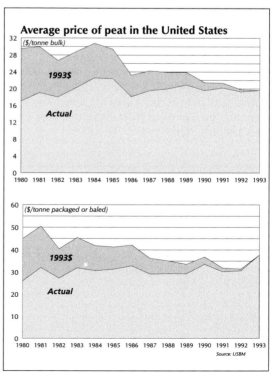

Average price of peat in the United States

($/tonne bulk) — 1993$ — Actual

($/tonne packaged or baled) — 1993$ — Actual

Source: USBM

Perlite is a light gray glassy volcanic rock with a vitreous, pearly luster and a characteristic concentric or perlitic fracture. It is distinguished petrologically from other natural glasses by a silicic (rhyolitic) composition plus chemical water held within the glass structure; a typical chemical composition is 70-75% SiO_2, 12-18% Al_2O_3, 4-6% K_2O, and 2-5% combined water.

PROPERTIES & USES: As is, perlite has limited uses [abrasive in polishes and cleansers; silica source; slag coagulant]. However, when heated quickly to 870-1,100°C perlite softens and expands to 10-20 times its original volume changing from a rock (BD density 1,159 kg/m^3) to a lightweight frothy material (BD 80-180 kg/m^3). It has similarities with vermiculite (see below). Perlite is a white to gray material which comprises microscopic bubbles and pores with a surface area of 1 to 10 m^2/gm, has low thermal and acoustic conductivity, chemical inertness, and noncombustibility and therefore is used as a lightweight aggregate [insulation board, plaster and concrete; roof insulation boards; acoustical ceiling tiles; silicone-treated loose-fill cavity insulation; industrial thermal insulating materials; cryogenic storage vessels; loose-cover heat insulation in foundries; charcoal BBQ base]. Loosely packed lightweight aggregates have a unit weight of 1,281-1,602 kg/m^3 compared with 2,002 kg/m^3 or more for crushed rock. Perlite (or vermiculite) treated with asphalt emulsion or a silicone for water resistance is utilized as a cavity fill for thermal insulation in cement block and other masonry structures.

Perlite's inertness, pH of 6.5-8.0, and cellular structure mean that it can absorb several times its own weight of liquid [carrier for herbicides, insecticides, and fertilizers; soil conditioner & rooting medium]. The inertness combined with the ability to mill expanded perlite with particle-size control in the micron range provide an outlet as a commercial filter [water treatment; removing algae and bacteria from beer; refining fruit juice, syrup, sugar, and waxes] and as a lost-circulation inhibitor [drilling muds]. Perlite's H7, low BD, and brightness of 80-85% allow it to be used as a filler and texturizer [paint; plastics; synthetic and natural rubber; wallboard core].

QUALITY & SPECIFICATIONS: Crushed and screened perlite may be produced as 8/12, 12/16, 16/30, 30/50, 50/100 mesh, and -50 mesh which through blending provide more than 20 grades. When expanded, grades vary from coarse at -20 mesh to fine at - 100. Typical bulk density required for expanded perlite in different applications (kg/m^3): formed products like acoustical ceiling tiles 56 (bubbles of 50-100 mesh); low-temperature insulation 32-64; roof insulation boards 64; cavity fill insulation 96; horticulture 96-128 (bubbles 8-50 mesh); filler and filters 112-192; plaster & concrete aggregate 120-136. A series of testing procedures have been established by the Perlite Institute, ASTM, ISO, and other organizations including PI 110-77 (Sampling of Perlite), PI 307-77 (Perlite Ore Expansibility Test), C 332-82 (Lightweight Aggregates for Insulating Concrete), C 520-81 (density of Granular Loose Fill Insulations).

Filter grades require testing for compliance with world-wide codex standards; USFCC limits are: 3% loss on drying (powdered form); 7% LOI (glassy form); pH of 5-9 in filtrate from 10% suspension; <10ppm As or Pb.

WORLD CAPACITY: 2.7M. t.

CAPACITY UTILIZATION: 60%.

MARKET CONDITIONS: Stable.

MARKETING FACTORS: Construction activity and therefore the economy; climatic conditions. Perlite has the advantage over pumice of being able to be shipped in its compacted form and then expanded close to the point of consumption.

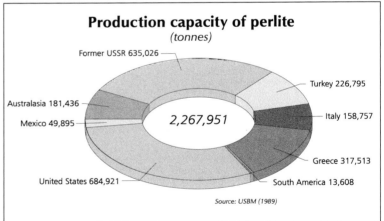

Production capacity of perlite
(tonnes)

Former USSR 635,026
Turkey 226,795
Italy 158,757
Australasia 181,436
2,267,951
Mexico 49,895
Greece 317,513
United States 684,921
South America 13,608

Source: USBM (1989)

CHEMICAL COMPOSITION OF COMMERCIAL PERLITE (%)

	USA Arizona	USA New Mexico	Greece Milos	Italy Sardinia	Hungary	Bulgaria
SiO_2	73.6	74.1	73-74	72.8	73.5	72-75
Al_2O_3	12.7	13.3	12-15	13.8	13.0	13-15
Fe_2O_3	0.7	1.8	0.7-1.2	2.1	1.8	1.5
CaO	0.6	1.5	0.7	0.9	1.5	1.0
MgO	0.2	0.4	0.3	0.4	0.4	0.6
K_2O	5.0	3.8	3.0-4.8	5.6	3.8	4.8
Na_2O	3.2	3.5	3.4-4.1	3.3	3.5	2.7
TiO_2	0.1	0.05	0.06	0.3	-	-
H_2O	3.8	3.0	2.5	NA	3.0	3-6

TYPICAL GRAIN SIZE OF PERLITE & VERMICULITE FOR PEAT COMPOST MIXTURES

Material	Grain size (mm)	% Peat mix	Application
Vermiculite	2-5	-	Quick germination of large seed
Vermiculite	1-3	50	Slow germination of fine seed
Vermiculite	2-5	50	Softwood cuttings
Perlite	2-5	50	Hardwood cuttings
Perlite	0-2	85	Transplant mix for seed blocks
Perlite	1-3	80	Potting mix for bedding plants
Perlite	2-5	75	Potting mix for house plants
Vermiculite	2-5	75	Potting mix for house plants
Perlite	0-2	80*	Soil conditioning for sandy and clay soils

* only a mixture of loam used for this application.

Source: Silvaperl Products Ltd., UK.

SPECIFICATION FOR PERLITE

	Silvaperl Ltd. PO5 Ultrafine
SiO_2	73
Al_2O_3	15
Fe_2O_3	2
Na_2O	3
K_2O	5
CaO+MgO	1
Others	1
pH	6.5-7.5
Organic matter	nil
Moisture content (packed)	nil
Particle size (mm)	0-0.5

Source: Silvaperl Products Ltd, UK

MINERALOGICAL COMPARISON OF PERLITE AND VERMICULITE

	Perlite	Vermiculite
Description	Glassy volcanic rock Metastable amorphous Al-silicate	Hydrated Mg-Al-Fe-sheet silicate of variable composition
Mineral structure	Macro-micro concentric "onion-like" structures formed by shrinkage	Biotite sheet structure but separated by a double layer of water molecules
Color	Light gray to black	Bronze to yellow brown
Mohs hardness	5.5-7.0	2.1-2.8
Expansion characteristics	When contained water vaporizes the heat-softened grains swell into light, fluffy cellular particles.	When contained water vaporizes individual layers are forced apart at right angles to the plane of cleavage. This gives a "concertina" effect.
Expansion temp.	760-1,100°C	870-1,100°C
Expansion ratio	10-20	12-20(volume)

Source: Industrial Minerals

Expanded perlite consumption in the United States
(tonnes)

Source: USBM (1993)

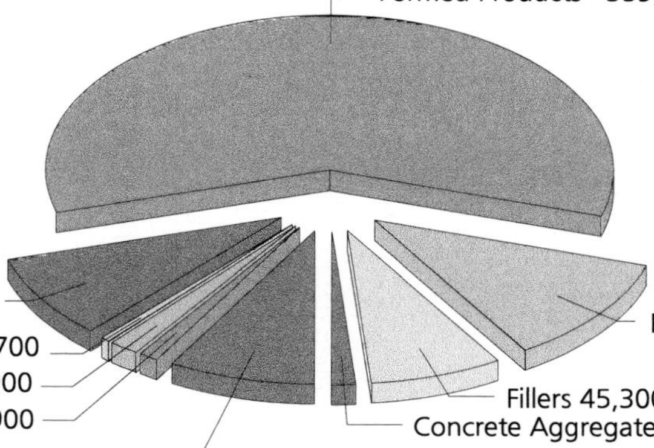

- Formed Products* 359,800
- Filter Aid 70,000
- Fillers 45,300
- Concrete Aggregate 8,400
- Others*** 51,000
- Plaster Aggregate 5,900
- Masonary and cavity-fill insulation 9,900
- Low-temperature insulation 4,700
- Horticultural Aggregate** 52,600

* includes acoustic ceiling tile, pipe insulation, roof insulation board, and unspecified formed products

** includes fertilizer carriers

*** includes chimney mix, fines, fireproofing, high-temperature insulation, oil-water absorbents, paint texturizer, pool base, refractories, specialty aggregate, waste disposals, and various nonspecified industrial uses.

HEALTH & SAFETY: Crystalline silica has been classified as a probable carcinogen by the IARC (see silica for further details). Therefore, because of its crystalline silica content, perlite will come under the OSHA Hazard Communication Standards, 29 CFR Section 1900.1200 which require labeling and other forms of warning, material safety data sheets, and employee training for products containing identified carcinogens with concentrations greater than 0.1%.

SUBSTITUTES & ALTERNATIVES: Animal feed supplement:- clays (bentonite, sepiolite), talc, vermiculite, zeolites. **Filler:**- ATH, barite, calcium carbonate, feldspar, kaolin, mica, nepheline syenite, pyrophyllite, talc, microcrystalline silica, ground silica flour and synthetic silica, wollastonite. **Fire retardant:**-ATH, antimony oxide, asbestos, borates, bromine, chromite, diatomite, magnesite & magnesia, phosphates, pumice, vermiculite. **Filter media**:- activated carbon/anthracite, asbestos, cellulose, diatomite, garnet, iron oxide (magnetite), perlite, pumice, silica sand, ilmenite. **Foundry**:- bauxite & alumina, chromite, clays (kaolin & bauxite), olivine, pyrophyllite, silica sand, vermiculite, zircon. **Insulation**:- asbestos, diatomite, foamed glass, metals, or cement, perlite, pumice, vermiculite, wollastonite, zeolites. **Lightweight aggregate**:- clay (expanded), pumice, shale (expanded, vermiculite, zeolites. **Soil Amendment**:- bentonite/kaolin, diatomite, gypsum, peat, vermiculite, zeolites. **Thermal and sound insulators**:- brick clays, diatomite, mineral wool, exfoliated vermiculite.

RECYCLING: Virtually none except for some limited reuse of lightweight aggregates following demolition.

PRODUCERS & WORLD TRADE: Perlite production is dominated by the western United States, in particular New Mexico. Turkey and Greece are also significant producers.

PRICES: United States $30/t (crude perlite sold to expander); $197/t (expanded perlite); $210-410/t (filter aid grade, explant). Europe &3-87/t (raw crushed graded, loose in bulk, CIF N. Europe); $345-510/t (Aggregate, expanded, ex-works, UK).

HTS CODE: 2530.10.0000 (vermiculite, perlite and chlorites, unexpanded).

ETYMOLOGY: Perlite from the French *perle = pearl* due to its pearly luster and form when hammered.

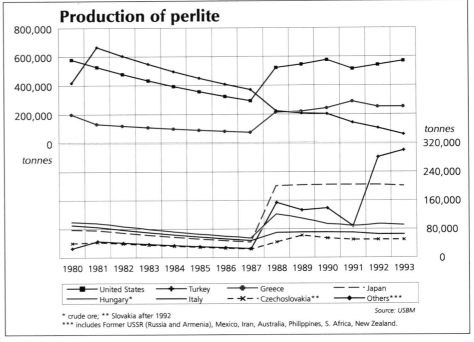

Production of perlite

Legend: United States, Turkey, Greece, Japan, Hungary*, Italy, Czechoslovakia**, Others***

* crude ore; ** Slovakia after 1992
*** includes Former USSR (Russia and Armenia), Mexico, Iran, Australia, Philippines, S. Africa, New Zealand.

Source: USBM

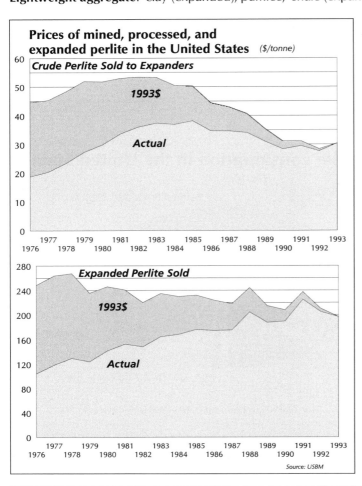

Prices of mined, processed, and expanded perlite in the United States *($/tonne)*

Crude Perlite Sold to Expanders — 1993$ — Actual

Expanded Perlite Sold — 1993$ — Actual

Source: USBM

PERLITE LEADERS		
Producers	**Exporters**	**Importers**
United States	United States	Canada
Turkey	Turkey	Netherlands
Greece	Greece	Belgium
Japan	Hungary	Spain
Hungary	Italy	United Kingdom
Italy	Czech. Rep.	Germany
Czech. Rep.	Armenia	France
Mexico		Taiwan
Armenia		

PHOSPHATE ROCK

Minerals	Formula	Color	SG	H
Hydroxy-fluorapatite	$Ca_5(PO_4)_3(OH,F)$	green or bluish green, yellowish to colorless	3.17-3.23	5
Fluorapatite	$Ca_5(PO_4,CO_3,OH)_3(F,OH)$	dark or lighter-nodules	3.1-3.2	5
Wavellite	$Al_3(PO_4)_2(OH)_3 \cdot 5H_2O$	white to greenish white	2.81	5

Other minor and/or potential sources include basic (Thomas converter) slag, guano, crandallite ($CaAl_3(PO_4)_2(OH)_5 \cdot H_2O$) and millisite $(Na,K)CaAl_6(PO_4)_4(OH)_9 \cdot 3H_2O$. Hydroxy-fluorapatite is common in most igneous deposits and carbonatites, fluorapatite (a.k.a. francolite or carbonate apatite) in marine sediments (phosphorites).

PROPERTIES & USES: Phosphate (P) is a primary nutrient (along with K and N) and converts energy to a usable form for food and fiber. However, P is highly insoluble and must be converted to the plant-available form, orthophosphate (H_2PO_4).

Phosphate rock + sulfuric acid → normal superphosphate (0-18-0 to 0-20-0) [fertilizer] or merchant grade, wet-process phosphoric acid, H_3PO_4 (0-52-0 to 0-54-0) → superphosphoric acid (0-68-0 to 0-72-0) [deep-sea traded phosphates; liquid mixed fertilizers - see below; high-analysis superphosphate (54% P_2O_5)].

Phosphoric acid + soda ash → sodium phosphate monobasic or monosodium phosphate (NaH_2PO_4) [boiler water treatment; dyes; photography; textile processing; industrial cleaner] → sodium acid pyrophosphate ($Na_2H_2P_2O_7$) [acid detergent formulations; deflocculant in drilling muds; electroplating baths; baking additive]; → sodium tripolyphosphates (STPP, $Na_5P_3O_{10}$) [detergent builder; deflocculant in drilling muds; electroplating baths; alkaline cleaning]; → sodium metaphosphate ($NaPO_3$) [dental polishing agent; sequestering agent; water softener].

Sodium phosphate dibasic or disodium phosphate (Na_2HPO_4) [ceramic glazes; dyes; fertilizers; pharmaceuticals; fireproofing; leather tanning; baking powder; processed cheese; water treatment] → aluminum phosphate [ceramics; cosmetics; dental cements; refractory bonding agent]; → monobasic (see above); → sodium phosphate tribasic or trisodium phosphate (Na_3HPO_4) [boiler water treatment; dyes; photographic developers; paint remover; cleaning formulations; sugar purification; water softening; feedstock for calcium and zinc phosphate, tribasic]; → tetrasodium pyrophosphate (Na_4P_2O7) [boiler water treatment; soap & detergent builder; deflocculant in drilling muds; alkaline cleaning formulations; dyes; processed cheese; electroplating baths; synthetic rubber manufacture].

Phosphoric acid + potassium carbonate → potassium phosphate monobasic [baking powder; fertilizer; medicine; feed for KTPP]; → potassium phosphate dibasic [buffer in antifreeze; fertilizer; feed for KTPP]; → potassium phosphate tribasic [builder for liquid soap; fertilizer; water softening]. Potassium tripolyphosphate (KTPP) [detergent builder; deflocculating agent; sequesterant; water softener].

PHOSPHATE FERTILIZERS

	% P_2O_5
Phosphate rock	26 - 31
Nitrophosphate (NP)	15 - 30
Single Superphosphate (SSP)	16 - 21
Triple superphosphate (TSP)	43 - 48
Diammonium phosphate (DAP	56 - 53
Monoammonium phosphate (MAP)	56 - 61

TYPICAL HEAVY DUTY POWDERED DETERGENT FORMULATIONS

	High Phosphate	Low Phosphate	Non-Phosphate
Zeolite A	—	20	25-30
STPP	30	5	—
Soda ash	15	25	15
Silicates	17	7	10
Salt cake	31	36	22
LAS & other actives	7	7	10
CMC	—	—	1

Source: PQ Corp.

PHOSPHATE PRODUCTS

Fertilizer	Nutrient content	Source/Production	Comments
Phosphate rock	5-30% P_2O_5	Only feedstock for phosphorus fertilizers	Highly insoluble - requires treatment with strong acids like sulfuric to yield a soluble product.
Phosphoric acid		Phosphate rock plus sulfuric acid	The basic building block for phosphorus fertilizers.
Normal Superphosphate	19-20% P_2O_5	Phosphate rock plus phosphoric acid	Less popular than TSP.
Triple Superphosphate	46% P_2O_5	Phosphate rock plus phosphoric acid	The basic building block for phosphorus fertilizers.
Monoammonium phosphate	12-50-0	Phosphoric acid plus ammonia	
Diammonium phosphate	18-46-0	Phosphoric acid plus ammonia	
Nitrophosphates	14-22% N 10-22% P_2O_5	Phosphate rock plus ammonia plus nitric acid	

CRITICAL QUALITY CHARACTERISTICS FOR PHOSPHATE ROCK

Property	Practical Levels and Factors	Remarks
Texture	Relatively soft, porous phosphate particles that are easiliy handled in mechanical feeders are preferred. Hard, coarsely textured particles or highly crystalline apatte show low acidulation and may create dust problems.	Preferred textures common to sedimentary rather than igneous or metamorphosed rocks.
Alteration	Weathering and calcining	May have low reactivity because of decreased porosity and surface area and/or thermally induced recrystallization.
Variability	Homogeneity, cements, replacements, secondary overgrowth	Reduces phosphate content and influences chemical composition (see below).
P_2O_5	Content of up to 42%.	
$CaO:P_2O_5$ ratio	From 1.32 to 1.61.	Most critical factor. Needs to be lowest possible in order to reduce sulfuric acid consumption. Over 1.6 uneconomical.
Iron and Aluminum	Generally require <3-4% Fe_2O_3 or Al_2O_3 with a P_2O_5/R_2O_3 ratio of 20 preferred. Practical levels are 0.1-2% Fe_2O_3 or 0.2-3% Al_2O_3 with 60-90% passing through to the acid.	Forms complex phosphates. Influences acid viscosity and forms postprecipitation sludge in P acid, scale formation in super P acid, insoluble P compounds in liquid or solid ammonium P products, and unwanted agglomeration in nongranular solid ammonium polyp.
Magnesium	Mg in apatites varies from 0.05% to 1.5% MgO. Desired P_2O_5/MgO level is 78. 0.2-0.6% MgO	Forms complex colloidal phosphates with Al and F which "blinds" the cloth and impedes filtration; affects downstream product quality. May have nutrient value.
Fluorine	P_2O_5:F ratio ranges from 6 to 11 in apatites; Si:F ratio should be high. 2-4% F. 25-75% passes through to the acid.	Liberated partly as HF; part held by filter and part contributes to sludge. F generated during concentration. Could modify crystal formation. May be a byproduct.
Silica	1-10% SiO_2. 5-40% passes into the acid.	In high proportions causes erosion problems. Converts HF to less aggressive fluosilicic acid. Also forms complexes with AL, Na, Mg, & Fe.
Si:F ratio	Low Si:F ratio usually yields P acid high in F	
Strontium/ lanthanides	Typical levels are, for example, 0-3% SrO	Inhibits recrystallization of hemihydrate gypsum. Insoluble compounds formed in 40 wt.% P_2O_5 acid.
Chlorine	0-0.05%. 100% passes through to the acid.	Above 0.03% can promote severe corrosion with certain materials.
Carbonate	0.7-8%.	Increases sulfuric acid consumption.
Organics	0.1-1.5% C. 15-70% passes through to the acid.	Stabilizes foams during acidulation. Impairs filtration by "blinding" cloth. Discolors acid.
Minor elements	Includes Mn, Fe, Zn, Ti, and Cu	Can contribute postprecipitation of insoluble phosphates. Potentially micronutrients.
Toxic elements	Requires low Cd, Hg, Cr, As, Pb, Se, U, and V content. For example, <0.8-255 ppm Cd.	Significant proportion passes through into acid and downstream products. Toxic metals.
Uranium	35-400 ppm U_3O_8. 75-80% passes through to the acid.	Is recoverable and may be a byproduct.

Sources: G. H. McClennan, IFDC, Muscle Shoals, AL and Phosphorus & Potassium, No. 146

Note: 1 t of P_2O_5 as wet wet process acid consumes 3.3-3.4 t of 70% BPL phospahte rock. Byproducts include phosphogypsum [waste (landfill); wallboard; soil amendment; ammonium sulfate] (see gypsum); sodium fluorosilicate [fluoridate water; glass & enamel frits; metallurgy; insecticide & rodenticide]; fluosilicic acid [feed for production of ammonium, calcium, copper, magnesium, potassium, and sodium fluosilicate (see fluorspar)].

Phosphate rock + phosphoric acid ➔ triple superphosphate or TSP (0-44-0 to 0-46-0) [fertilizer]. Phosphoric acid or TSP + ammonia ➔ monoammonium phosphate or MAP (11-48-0) [fertilizer] and diammonium phosphate or DAP (18-46-0) [fertilizer]. Phosphate rock + nitric acid ➔ nitrophosphates [fertilizers]. All the above products contain water-soluble P and may be used alone or combined (±potash) to form mixed or compound fertilizers. Note: The production of 1 tonne of DAP requires 1.6 tonnes of 70% BPL phosphate rock, 0.45 tonnes of ammonia, and 0.47 tonnes of P_2O_5 as wet process acid (0.90 tonnes of 53% P_2O_5 wet process acid).

Phosphate rock smelted with coke and silica → elemental P (P_4) [smoke bombs; incendiary bombs & shells; roach & rodent poison].

Elemental P → red phosphorus [safety matches; pyrotechnics]; → pure and food-grade phosphoric acid [food & beverage additive; toothpaste]; → phosphorus acid [water treatment]; → phosphorus oxychloride [phosphate esters for flame retardants and plasticizers in plastics & urethanes]; → phosphorus pentoxide [catalyst; drying agent; leather tanning; medicine; paint remover; dehydrating agent; sulfur trioxide stabilizer; sugar refining]; → phosphorus pentasulfide [catalyst; lubricant; ore flotation agent; rubber additive]; → phosphorus trichloride [pesticide intermediate; flame retardant; plasticizer & antioxidant in plastics; paint additive]; → phosphorus trisulfide [matches]; → sodium tripolyphosphate [detergents; food]; → cobalt phosphate [pigment; animal feed supplement].

QUALITY & SPECIFICATIONS: The P_2O_5 content of phosphate varies from 4-42% P_2O_5 with the term phosphate rock applied to any rock containing more than 20% P_2O_5 the content of which is the main method of quantifying grade; tricalcium phosphate, $Ca_3(PO_4)_2$, or bone phosphate of lime (BPL), may also be used. These terms are related as follows:

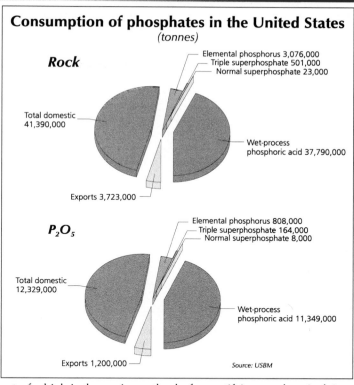

Consumption of phosphates in the United States
(tonnes)

Rock

Elemental phosphorus 3,076,000
Triple superphosphate 501,000
Normal superphosphate 23,000
Total domestic 41,390,000
Wet-process phosphoric acid 37,790,000
Exports 3,723,000

P_2O_5

Elemental phosphorus 808,000
Triple superphosphate 164,000
Normal superphosphate 8,000
Total domestic 12,329,000
Wet-process phosphoric acid 11,349,000
Exports 1,200,000

Source: USBM

%P_2O_5 x 2.1853 = %BPL

%P_2O_5 x 0.4364 = % P

% BPL x 0.4576 = % P_2O_5

%BPL x 0.1997 = % P

%P x 5.0073 = % BPL

%P x 2.2914 = % P_2O_5

Most commercial phosphate rocks contain fluorapatite, that is $Ca_{10}(PO_4)_6F_2$. However, the apatite structure is amenable to many substitutions, particularly Mg, Sr, and Na for Ca; OH and Cl for F; As and V for P; and CO_3 + F for PO_4. The extent of this substitution greatly influences the characteristics of the rock (see table). Many of the sedimentary rocks are francolite or carbonate apatites with the general empirical formula:

$$Ca_{10-a-b}Na_aMg_b(PO_4)_{6-x}(CO_3)_xF_{0.4x}F_2$$

As X or the extent of carbonate substitution increases, so does the reactivity. X may be zero to 1.2 in commercial phosphate rock. Pure fluorapatite contains 42.2% P_2O_5 and carbonate substitution can reduce this to a minimum of 34%. Some rocks show a substantial substitution of OH for F, e.g. guano Nauru and Christmas Island and igneous deposits in Brazil.

WORLD CAPACITY: 188.5M. t phosphate rock.
CAPACITY UTILIZATION: 65%.

MARKET CONDITIONS: Steady and increasing in Latin America, Australasia, and Africa.

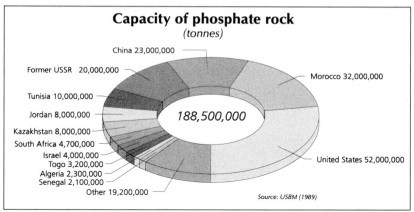

Capacity of phosphate rock
(tonnes)

China 23,000,000
Former USSR 20,000,000
Tunisia 10,000,000
Jordan 8,000,000
Kazakhstan 8,000,000
South Africa 4,700,000
Israel 4,000,000
Togo 3,200,000
Algeria 2,300,000
Senegal 2,100,000
Other 19,200,000
Morocco 32,000,000
United States 52,000,000

188,500,000

Source: USBM (1989)

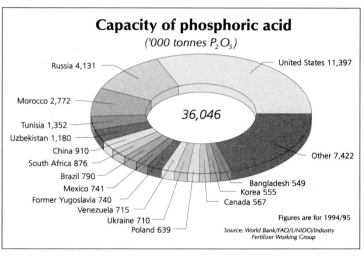

Capacity of phosphoric acid
('000 tonnes P_2O_5)

Russia 4,131
Morocco 2,772
Tunisia 1,352
Uzbekistan 1,180
China 910
South Africa 876
Brazil 790
Mexico 741
Former Yugoslavia 740
Venezuela 715
Ukraine 710
Poland 639
United States 11,397
Other 7,422
Bangladesh 549
Korea 555
Canada 567

36,046

Figures are for 1994/95

Source: World Bank/FAO/UNIDO/Industry Fertilizer Working Group

CHEMICAL COMPOSITION OF COMMERCIAL PHOSPHATE CONCENTRATES (%)

	Jordan 70/72% TCP Sed.	USA Florida 77% BPL Sed.	USA Idaho Sed.	Morocco Youssoufiaun Sed.	Togo Sed.	Mexico Baja California Sed.	Finland Siilinjärvi Igneous	Brazil Goiasfertil Igneous	Brazil Fosfago Igneous	Brazil Tapira Igneous	Nauru calcined Guano
P_2O_5	32.5	35.31	32.3	34.14	36.85	29	35.3	37.04	36.73	35.41	39.92
CaO	50.00	50.10	45.85	53.84	51.69	46.14	NA	49.77	49.21	51.44	54.42
CO_2	4.7	2.98	2.1	2.9		5.33	6.9	0.86	0.58	3.81	2.04
MgO	0.45	0.23	0.17	0.46	0.03	0.77	1.3	0.16	0.06	0.63	-
K_2O	0.03	0.08	0.61	0.09	0.05	0.32	0.04		0.005		trace
Na_2O	0.45	0.4	0.46	0.89	0.27	0.73	0.1		0.002		0.45
Al_2O_3	0.5	1.02	2.13	0.33	1	1.96	0.2	0.54	0.26	0.08	
Fe_2O_3	0.35	1.03	0.95	0.15	1.3	2.15	0.5	2.39	2.55	1.20	
SiO_2	5.35	3.05	9.87	2.72	2.99	6.78	0.5	1.66	1.42	1.60	0.4
F	3.65	3.87	2.99	4.25	3.75	2.95	2.5	2.02	2.47	1.30	2.62
SO_3								0.16	0.17		
SrO								0.96	0.76		
MnO									0.07		
BaO								1.05	0.58		
TiO_2								1.84		1.05	

* beach sands, beneficiated, not calcined

MARKETING FACTORS: Fertilizer use will increase with population growth, the need for more efficient food production, and nutrient balance. Legislation banning the use of STPP in detergents in North America, Europe, Japan and elswhere has severely reduced the non-fertilizer demand for phosphates. Although its harmful effects on water systems have been challenged, the advanced reduction in demand is likely to continue.

ENVIRONMENTAL/HEALTH & SAFETY: Crystalline silica has been classified as a probable carcinogen by the IARC (see silica for further details). Therefore, because of its crystalline silica content, unless processing has the capability to reduce the crystalline silica content to less than 0.1%, phosphate rock will come under the OSHA Hazard Communication Standards, 29 CFR Section 1900.1200 which require labeling and other forms of warning, material safety data sheets, and employee training for products containing identified carcinogens with concentrations greater than 0.1%.

The production of 1 tonne of P_2O_5 as phosphoric acid yields 5 tonnes of byproduct phosphogypsum which is expensive to dispose of and often difficult to utilize commercially. In Florida, for example, it is estimated that there will be 900 million tonnes of stockpiled phosphogypsum. There is concern over waste or excess phosphorus from phosphate-based fertilizers and/or phosphate-built detergents promoting excessive algal growth in lakes which in turn results in eutrophication. Cadmium and fluorine contained in some phosphate rock may be a concern.

Phosphoric acid is usually shipped in bulk in rubber (or steel or glass) lined tanks by truck, rail, or ship.

SUBSTITUTES & ALTERNATIVES: Detergents:- zeolite, silcates, citrates. **Fertilizers:-** none (primary nutrient).

RECYCLING: Virtually none.

PRODUCTION & WORLD TRADE: The United States and the Former USSR are the largest producers of phosphate rock, although most is consumed domestically. Producers in North Africa lead by Morocco have the greatest influence on supply since the bulk of their production enters international trade.

PRICES: Phosphate rock (FOB mine, USA domestic) $17.90/t (<60% BPL); $22.50/t (60-66% BPL); $25-30/t (66-68% BPL land pebble, washed, run-of-mine, Florida); $19.50/t (66-70% BPL); $34.50/t (70-72% BPL); $30.50/t (72-74% BPL). Phosphate rock (ex-vessel, Tampa, FL, 66-68% BPL land pebble, run-of-mine, Florida) $33/t. Phosphate rock (FAS Morocco) $46 (70-72% BPL); $48.50 (75-77% BPL). Phosphate rock (FAS, Sfax, Tunisia) $32-38 (65-68% BPL).

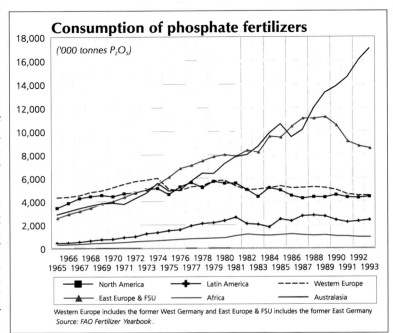

Consumption of phosphate fertilizers

('000 tonnes P_2O_5)

Legend: North America; Latin America; Western Europe; East Europe & FSU; Africa; Australasia

Western Europe includes the former West Germany and East Europe & FSU includes the former East Germany
Source: FAO Fertilizer Yearbook.

Phosphoric acid (USA, commercial and technical grade, freight equalized) $670/t (75%,); $704/t (80%); $748 (85%). Phosphoric acid (USA, food grade, freight equalized) $715/t (75%,); $748/t (80%); $792 (85%). Phosphoric acid (USA, ex-works) $2.70 unit ton (52-54% apa, agricultural grade); $3.05 unit ton (min 70% apa, super grade). Phosphoric acid (FOB, N. Africa) $260-300/t (52-54% apa, agricultural grade).

DAP $163-172/t (fertilizer grade, min. 18% N, 20% P, bulk, FOB Florida works); $265-275/t (feed grade, 18% N, 20% P, bulk, FOB Florida works); $1,315-1,350/t (tech. grade, bags, ex-works, freight equalized); $1,340-1,390/t (food grade, bags, ex-works, freight equalized). DAP (FOB N. Africa) $170/t. MAP $137-145/t (fertilizer grade, min. 13% N, 52% P, bulk, FOB Florida works); $1,342-1,390/t (tech. grade, bags, ex-works, freight equalized); $1,375-1,425 (food grade, bags, ex-works, freight equalized).

Magnesium phosphate tribasic technical FOB $2.20/kg. Phosgene $1,210-1,475/t (1-t on returnable cylinders). Phosphorus $2,200/t (white (yellow), solid, drums, freight equalized); $2,000/t (tanks, fob plant). Phosphorus oxychloride $1,300/t (tanks, freight equalized). Phosphorus pentoxide $1,870-2,375/t (drums). Phosphorus pentsulfide $1,650/t (powder, drums). Phosphorus trichloride $1,540/t (ex-works, drums); $1,012/t (ex-works, tanks).

Sodium phosphate (ex-works, freight equalized) $1,578/t (anhydrous, dibasic, technical, bags); $1,678/t (anhydrous, dibasic, food grade, bags); $1,617/t (monobasic, technical, bags); $1,738/t (monobasic, food grade, bags); $1,590/t (tribasic, technical, bags); $1,884/t (tribasic, food grade, bags). Sodium tripoly phosphate (STPP) (USA ex-works, freight equalized) $935/t (technical, bags); $865/t (technical, bulk); $1,144/t (food grade, bags). Tetrapotassium pyrophosphate (TKPP) $1.55-1.83/kg (E. USA freight equalized); $132-1.39 (liquid, bulk).

Production of phosphate rock

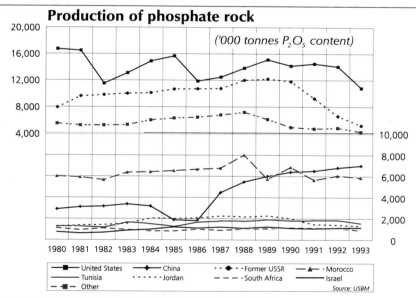

('000 tonnes P_2O_5 content)

Legend: United States, China, Former USSR, Morocco, Tunisia, Jordan, South Africa, Israel, Other

Source: USBM

APPARENT CONSUMPTION OF PHOSPHATE ROCK

(tonnes, gross weight)

United States	39,840,761
Former USSR	34,886,000
China	21,630,721
Morocco	9,517,400
Tunisia	5,656,693
Brazil	3,886,745
India	3,341,011
France	3,268,049
Mexico	2,882,726
Belgium	2,195,078
Spain	2,088,262
South Africa	2,072,382
Netherlands	2,024,219
South Korea	1,559,966
Japan	1,543,302
Poland	1,410,800
Canada	1,258,290
Australia	1,107,983
Iraq	1,100,000
Former Yugoslavia	1,066,386
Germany	1,037,875
Israel	981,000
Senegal	931,300
Indonesia	900,452
Philippines	877,332
Jordan	876,977
Italy	851,157
Turkey	817,119
Egypt	746,911
Greece	713,185
New Zealand	708,618
Sweden	644,150
Finland	635,789
Norway	620,089
United Kingdom	548,126
North Korea	536,400
Romania	495,000
Austria	440,217
Taiwan	420,425

NOTE: Numbers are approximate and rounded for 1990 or thereabouts; absence of a country does not necessarily indicate no production or trade; absence of a number does not necessarily mean zero.

Source: British Geological Survey and USBM

PRODUCTION AND TRADE IN PHOSPHATE ROCK (TONNES, GROSS WEIGHT)

	Production	Imports	Exports	Apparent Consumption	Net Supplier	Net Consumer
North America	46,947,350	3,993,427	6,959,000	43,981,777	2,965,573	
S. & C. America	3,931,829	380,245		4,312,074		(380,245)
European Union		13,308,236	236,762	13,071,474		(13,071,474)
Non-EU Europe	37,439,534	6396,704	1,948,899	41,887,339		(4,447,805)
Australasia	24,075,274	10,724,911	1,161,722	33,638,463		(9,563,189)
Middle East	11,000,100	16,600	7,766,123	3,250,577	7,749,523	
Africa	38,118,382	168,475	18,520,116	19,766,741	18,351,641	

NOTE: Numbers are approximate and rounded for 1990 or thereabouts;   *Source: British Geological Survey and USBM*

Price or value of phsophate rock in the United States
(Exports, $/tonne f.o.b. mine)

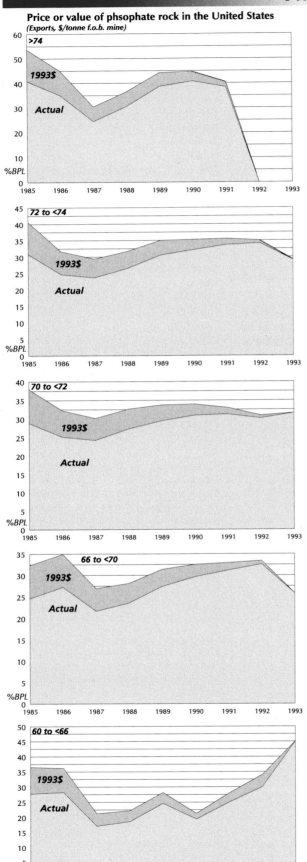

HTS CODES: 2510.10.0000 (natural calcium phosphates, unground); 2510.20.0000 (natural calcium phosphates, ground).2809.20.0010 (phosphoric acid); 2835.25.0000 (dicalcium phosphate); 2804.70.0000 (phosphorus); 3103.10.000 (normal superphosphate); 3103.10.0020 (triple superphosphate, >40% P_2O_5); 3105.10.0000 (mineral or chemical fertilizers containing two or three fertilizing elements nitrogen, phosphorus, and potassium); 3105.20.0000 (mineral or chemical fertilizers containing the three fertilizing elements nitrogen, phosphorus, and potassium); 3105.30.0000 (diammonium phosphate - DAP); 3105.40.0010 (monoammonium phosphate - MAP); 3105.40.0050 (other ammonium phosphate); 3105.51.0000 (mineral or chemical fertilizers containing the two fertilizing elements phosphorus and potassium).

ETYMOLOGY: Apatite from the Greek *apate* = deceit since it was often mistaken for other minerals. **Crandallite** for Milan L. Crandell Jr., American engineer, Knight Syndicate, Provo, Utah and Greek *lithos* = stone. **Fluorapatite** containing *fluorine* and *apatite*. **Francolite** for Wheal (= mine) Franco, Tavistock in Devon, England, Greek *lithos* = stone. **Millisite** for F.T. Mills, of Lehi, Utah, the first observer. **Phosphate** from the Greek for *phos* = light and *phoros* = bearer due to its spontaneous combustion. **Wavellite** for William Wavell (d.1829), English physician, Horwood Parish, Devon, UK, and Greek *lithos* = stone.

TYPICAL PHOSPHORIC ACID ANALYSIS

	Filter acid	Concentrated Acid
P_2O_5	28	52
F-	2.4	1
Cl-	0.15	0.01
SiO_2	1.2	0
Fe_2O_3	1.1	1.85
Al_2O_3	1.1	1.85
Na_2O	0.25	0
F bound in SiF_6	2.05	
F in HF	0.35	

PHOSPHATE LEADERS

Producers	Exporters	Importers
United States	Morocco	France
Former USSR	United States	India
China	Jordan	Mexico
Morocco	Togo	Netherlands
Tunisia	Former USSR	Belgium
Jordan	Israel	Spain
Brazil	Syria	South Korea
South Africa	Senegal	Japan
Togo	South Africa	Poland
Israel	Algeria	Canada
Senegal	Tunisia	Australia
Syria	Netherlands	Former Yugoslavia
Algeria	China	Germany
Iraq	Egypt	Indonesia
Egypt	Finland	Italy

Minerals Commercial name	Formula	Equivalent Wt %			
		K	**KCl**	**K₂O**	**K₂SO₄**
Arcanite	K_2SO_4	44.88	—	54.06	100.00
Carnallite*	$KCl \cdot MgCl_2 \cdot 6H_2O$	14.07	26.83	16.95	—
Glaserite	$3K_2SO_4 \cdot Na_2SO_4$	35.29	—	42.51	78.63
Kainite*	$4KCl \cdot 4MgSO_4 \cdot 11H_2O$	15.71	29.94	19.26	—
Langbeinite Sulfate of potash magnesia (SOPM)	$K_2SO_4 \cdot 2MgSO_4$	18.84	—	22.69	41.99
Leonite	$K_2SO_4 \cdot 2MgSO_4 \cdot 4H_2O$	21.33	—	25.69	47.52
Polyhalite	$K_2SO_4 \cdot MgSO_4 \cdot 2CaSO_4 \cdot 2H_2O$	12.97	—	15.62	28.90
Sylvite* Muriate of potash (MOP)	KCl	52.44	100.00	63.17	—
Sylvinite*	$KCl + NaCl$	—	—	10-35	—

* main commercial minerals

These minerals are often intercrystallized and mixed with other evaporite minerals including halite (NaCl), anhydrite or gypsum ($CaSO_4$), and epsomite ($MgSO_4 \cdot 2H_2O$).

PROPERTIES & USES: Potassium (K) is a primary nutrient (along with P and N) which adds color and flavor to plants and increases disease resistance. K is supplied commercially as potash, i.e. potassium-bearing minerals, ores, and processed products [direct application fertilizer; compound fertilizer]. Processed potash ore ➔ potassium chloride (natural sylvite, KCl) or muriate of potash (MOP) containing 60-62% K_2O [most common K fertilizer; drilling mud additive]; ➔ potassium-magnesium sulfate or natural langbeinite ($K_2SO_4 \cdot 2MgSO_4$ with 22% K_2O) [specialty fertilizers].

KCl + sulfuric acid ➔ potassium sulfate (K_2SO_4 with 50-53% K_2O) [fertilizer for specialized crops; medicine; glass; accelerator for gypsum products] ➔ potassium aluminum sulfate (potash alum); potassium bisulfate [fertiliser; food preservative]; potassium formate; potassium persulfate [bleaching agent; photography; polymerization initiator]; potassium sulfide.

KCl + nitric acid ➔ potassium nitrate or saltpetre (KNO_3 with 44-46% K_2O) [fertilizer; explosives; pyrotechnics; glass & ceramics; plastics; drugs; tobacco] ➔ potassium oxide.

KCl + NaOH ➔ caustic potash, KOH [liquid fertilizer; oil & gas; metal treatment; batteries; soaps; textile bleaching; printing inks; water treatment] ➔ potassium alumate [dyeing; printing; paper sizing]; ➔ potassium bromate/bromide [oxidizing agent; permanent wave compounds; flour]; ➔ potassium fluosilicate [enamel frits; synthetic mica; insecticide]; ➔ potassium iodide [medicine; photography; salt additive]; ➔ potassium laurate [emulsifying agent; base for liquid soap & shampoo]; ➔ potassium manganate [potassium permanganate feedstock - see below; bleaching agent; disinfectant; batteries; photography; printing; water purification]; ➔ potassium silicate.

POTASH PRODUCTS

Fertilizer	Nutrient content	Source/Production
Potassium chloride KCl Chloride or MOP	60-62% K_2O	Natural product is sylvite (KCl)
Potasiium sulfate K_2SO_4 Sulfate or SOP	50-53% K_2O	Reacting potassium chloride with various sulfate-bearing minerals such as langbeinite ($2MgSO_4 \cdot K_2SO_4$) in New Mexico and kieserite ($MgSO_4 \cdot H_2O$) in Germany or with sulfuric acid.
Potassium nitrate KNO_3	44-46 % K_2O	Produced synthetically by reacting KCl with nitric acid; natural mixture with sodium nitrate from Chile (14% K2O) sodium nitrate from Chile (14% K_2O) Niter
Potassium magnesium sulfate $K_2SO_4 \cdot MgSO_4$ SOPM, sulfate of potash magnesia	22% K_2O 18% MgO 22% S	Natural product is langbeinite ($2MgSO_4 \cdot K_2SO_4$) mined in US. Synthetic such as Kali & Salz "Patentkali" which is mixture of K_2SO_4 and $MgSO_4 \cdot H_2O$ bonded by langbeinite.

Potassium manganate ➔ potassium permanganate [bleach; catalyst; manufacture of saccharin; zinc refining; descaling steel; welding rod coating; dye; water treatment].

KCl ➔ potassium carbonate, K_2CO_3 [specialty glass, e.g. TV tubes, optical glass; ceramics; dehydrating agent; eletroplating baths] ➔ potassium acetate [crystal glass; acetone; dehydrating agent; pH control]; ➔ potassium bicarbonate [baking powder; medicine; dry chemical for fire fighting]; ➔ potassium bromide; ➔ potassium chlorate [matches & explosives]; ➔ potassium cyanide [gold/silver recovery; fumigant; heat treatment of steel; electroplating; insecticide; photography; paper manufacture]; ➔ potassium peroxide [breathing apparatus]. Potassium carbonate + phosphoric acid ➔ potassium phosphate monobasic [baking powder; fertilizer; medicine; feed for KTPP]; ➔ potassium phosphate dibasic [buffer in antifreeze; fertilizer; feed for KTPP]; ➔ potassium phosphate tribasic [builder for liquid soap; fertilizer; water softening]. Potassium tripolyphosphate (KTPP) [detergent builder; deflocculating agent; sequesterant; water softener].

QUALITY & SPECIFICATIONS: Concentration is generally based on K_2O content which may be derived from the following calculations:

$$KCl \times 0.61 = K_2O \qquad K_2O \times 1.64 = KCl \qquad K_2O \times 1.2046 = K$$

Muriate of potash (KCl) has a min. 60% K_2O (50%, 40%, and 30% K_2O grades are available in some parts of the world), and potassium sulfate has a min. 50% K_2O and max. 2.5% Cl. Grain sizes are standard (99.5 weight % +200 Tyler mesh), coarse (98 weight % +28 Tyler mesh), and granular (98.5 weight % +20 Tyler mesh). If potash is to be mixed with say DAP, it must be compacted and crushed to equal the particle size of the other ingredients.

WORLD CAPACITY: 39.5M. t K_2O.

CAPACITY UTILIZATION: 62%.

MARKET CONDITIONS: Steady and increasing in Latin America, Australasia, and Africa.

MARKETING FACTORS: Fertilizer use will increase with population growth, the need for more efficient food production, and nutrient balance.

SUBSTITUTES & ALTERNATIVES: Fertilizers:- none (primary nutrient).

RECYCLING: Virtually none, although TV face plate glass is being recycled.

PRODUCTION & WORLD TRADE: Canada and the Former USSR are the largest producers of potash and both are major exporters along with Israel, Jordan, and Germany. Asia is a major importer of potash.

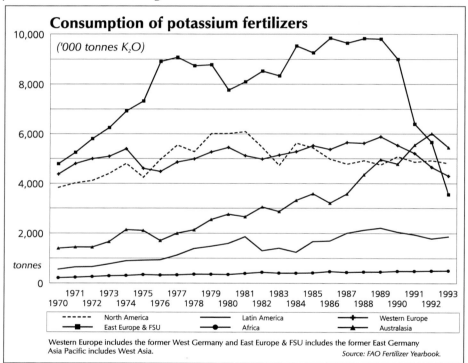

Consumption of potassium fertilizers ('000 tonnes K_2O)

North America; East Europe & FSU; Latin America; Africa; Western Europe; Australasia

Western Europe includes the former West Germany and East Europe & FSU includes the former East Germany
Asia Pacific includes West Asia.
Source: FAO Fertilizer Yearbook.

PARTICLE-SIZE GRADES OF MURIATE OF POTASH, LANGBEINITE, AND SULFATE OF POTASH

Grade	Min. K_2O equiv. wt %	Mesh (Tyler)	Millimeters	Type of potash
Granular	61, 50, 22	-6 to +20	3.35-0.85	Muriate & sulfates
Blend*	60	-6 to +14	3.35-1.18	Muriate
Coarse	60	-8 to +28	2.4-0.6	Muriate
Standard	60, 50, 22	-28 to +65	1.2-0.21	Muriate & sulfates
Special Standardized	60	-35 to +150	0.4-0.11	Muriate & sulfates
Soluble/Suspension	62	-35 to +150	0.4-0.11	Muriate
Chemical	63	NA	NA	Muriate

Approximate particle size range

* blend is a new grade with midpoint between 8 and 10 mesh introduced by Canadian producers

Source: after Searls, 1985 and Williams-Stroud, et al, 1994

Potash production capacity
(tonnes K2O)

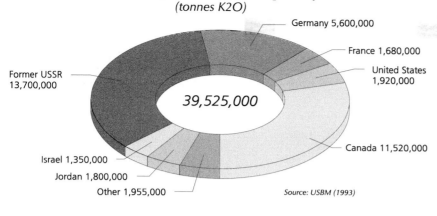

Germany 5,600,000
France 1,680,000
United States 1,920,000
Former USSR 13,700,000
39,525,000
Canada 11,520,000
Israel 1,350,000
Jordan 1,800,000
Other 1,955,000

Source: USBM (1993)

HTS CODES: 2815.20 (potassium hydroxide); 2834.21.0000 (potassium nitrate); 2835.24 (potassium phosphates); 2836.40 (potassium carbonates); 2839.20 (potassium silicates); 3105.90.0010 (potassium-sodium nitrate mixtures); 3104.10 (crude salts, sylvinite, etc.); 3104.20 (potassium chloride); 3104.30 (potassium sulfate); 3104.90.00.10 (magnesium-potassium sulfate); 3104.90.00.90 (other potassic fertilizer); 3105.10.0000 (mineral or chemical fertilizers containing two or three of the fertilizing elements nitrogen, phosphorus, and potassium); 3105.20.0000 (mineral or chemical fertilizers containing the three fertilizing elements nitrogen, phosphorus, and potassium); 3105.51.0000 (mineral or chemical fertilizers containing the two fertilizing elements phosphorus and potassium).

PRICES: Muriate of potash (FOB Saskatchewan, Canada, 60-62.4% min. K_2O) $76/t (standard); $80/t (coarse); $83/t (granular). Muriate of potash (FOB Vancouver) $106/t (standard). Muriate of potash (FOB Carlsbad, NM, USA, bulk) $99-110/t (coarse); $89/t (granular). Muriate of potash (60% K_2O, CIF UK port) $118-138/t (standard); $135-141/t (granular).

Potash production and exports in Canada

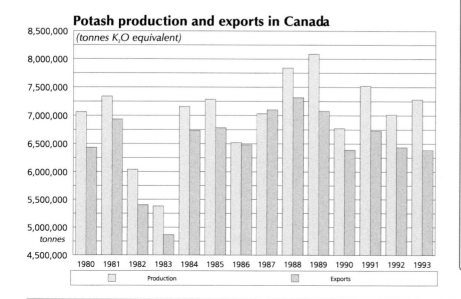

(tonnes K_2O equivalent)

Production | Exports

1980 1981 1982 1983 1984 1985 1986 1987 1988 1989 1990 1991 1992 1993

	Apparent Consumption
APPARENT CONSUMPTION OF POTASH (TONNES OF PRODUCT)	
Former USSR	10,100,000
United States	8,964,385
Germany	3,252,201
France	3,090,906
China	2,101,638
Brazil	1,855,048
India	1,848,573
Japan	1,198,618
Poland	1,185,606
Belgium	1,171,711
United Kingdom	975,488
Italy	759,609
Hungary	684,500
Malaysia	635,339
Spain	591,698
Canada	580,307
South Korea	475,218
Israel	473,056
Czechoslovakia	469,600
Indonesia	449,358
Norway	446,889
Former Yugoslavia	415,456
Cuba	365,000
Colombia	328,439
Netherlands	319,450
Australia	306,250
Romania	296,200
Denmark	295,417
Finland	250,653
Ireland	233,076
South Africa	229,811
Bulgaria	223,200
Austria	213,961
Philippines	182,191
Taiwan	175,799
Sweden	169,023
New Zealand	154,123
Venezuela	139,458
Thailand	133,014
Turkey	129,169
Morocco	87,833
Syria	87,000
Costa Rica	85,141
Mexico	79,553
Switzerland	75,236

NOTE: Numbers are approximate for 1990 and are rounded; absence of a country does not necessarily indicate no production or trade; absence of a number does not necessarily mean zero.

Source: British Geological Survey, USBM, Canada EMR

Potassium acetate $2.14/kg (NF, granular, drums, FOB works). Potassium bicarbonate $2,596-2,794/t (ACS grade, drums, FOB works); $1.87/kg (USP, granular, bags). Potassium bromate $3.94/kg (granular, powder, ex-works). Potasium bromide $$2.42-2.46/kg (NF, granular, powder, drums, FOB works). Potassium carbonate $396/t (liquid, 47% K_2CO_3, tank, truck, or tank cars, ex-works); $858/t (anhydrous, bulk, truck, bulk car, ex-works); $880/t (anhydrous, bags, ex-works); $946/t (anhydrous, drums, ex-works); $880-$1,010/t (granular purified). Potassium chlorate $0.32/kg (crystal, drums, exworks); $0.66/kg (powder, drums, ex-works); $0.88/kg (purified, granular, drums, FOB shipping point). Potassium chloride $115-138/t (chemical grade, 99.95% KCl, bulk, FOB works; $1.19/kg (USP crystal or granular, drums); $1.23/kg (USP, powder, drums). Potassium cyanide $3.87-4.0/kg (drums, >20,000 lb, FOB works).

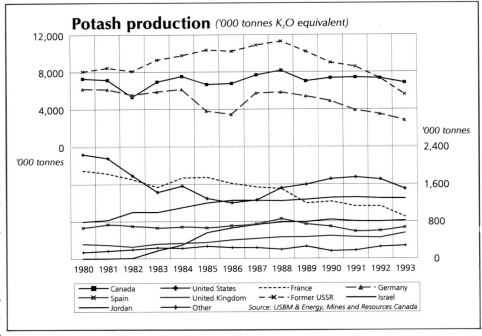

Potash production ('000 tonnes K_2O equivalent)

Legend: Canada, United States, France, Germany, Spain, United Kingdom, Former USSR, Israel, Jordan, Other. Source: USBM & Energy, Mines and Resources Canada

Potassium hydroxide $3.28-3.43/kg (USP, pellets, drums, ex-works, freight equalized). Caustic potash $320/t (liquid, 45% basis, tanks, ex-terminal); $390/t (liquid, 45% basis, tanks, ex-terminal, W. Coast USA); $998/t (regular, flake, 88-92%, ex-works). Potassium iodide $26.44/kg (USP, drums, delivered); $28.82/kg (ACS grade). Potassium-magnesium sulfate $88/t (standard); $75/t (40% K_2SO_4, 50% $MgSO_4$). Potassium nitrate $358/t (fertilizer grade, standard, bulk, del. S.E. USA); $364/t (fertilizer grade, prilled, bulk, del. S.E. USA); $600/t (technical, prilled, bags, exworks).

Potassium permanganate (ex-works) $2.66/kg (free-flowing bulk, hopper, trucks); $2.95/kg (50-kg drums); $2.86/kg (150-kg drums); $3.17/kg (USP, 50 kg). Potassium persulfate $2,070/t (225-lb drums, >24,000 lb, FOB plant); $2,005/t (bags, >24,000 lb, FOB works).

Potassium silicate (ex-works) $529/t (solution, 29.8-30.2°Be, 2.5 ratio*, tank cars); $727/t (solution, 29.8-30.2°Be, 2.1 ratio*, drums); $702/t (40-40.5°Be, 2.1 ratio*, tank cars); $898/t (40-40.5°Be, 2.1 ratio*, drums); $732/t (electronics, 20-30.4°Be, 2.1 ratio*); $927/t (electronics, 30-30.4°Be, 2.1-2.2 ratio*, drums); $1,276/t (solid or glass, 2.5 ratio*, drums).

POTASH LEADERS

Producers	Exporters	Importers
Former USSR	Canada	United States
Canada	Germany	China
Germany	Former USSR	India
United States	Israel	Brazil
Israel	United States	Belgium
France	Spain	France
Spain	Belgium	Japan
United Kingdom	United Kingdom	Poland
Brazil	France	Italy
Italy	South Korea	Hungary
China	Italy	Malaysia
	Taiwan	South Korea

PRODUCTION AND TRADE IN POTASH (TONNES OF PRODUCT)

	Production	Imports	Exports	Apparent Consumption	Net Supplier	Net Consumer
North America	15,096,667	7,376,167	12,848,589	9,624,245	5,472,422	
South America	151,667	2,457,894	137,724	2,471,837		(2,320,170)
C. America & Carib.		575,986		575,986		(575,986)
European Union	12,213,333	5,529,229	7,002,671	10,739,891	1,473,442	
Non-EU Eurpe	15,000,000	4,635,290	4,968,780	14,666,510	333,490	
Australasia	33,333	8,087,105	330,969	7,789,469		(7,756,136)
Middle east	3,586,667	104,747	3,115,302	576,112	3,010,555	
Africa		665,044		665,044		(665,044)

NOTE: Numbers are approximate and rounded for 1990 or thereabouts

Source: British Geological Survey, USBM, Canada EMR

Prices of potash in the United States by type and grade

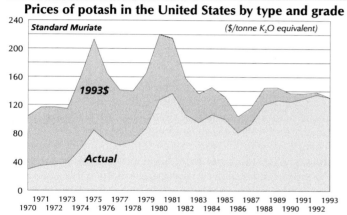

Standard Muriate ($/tonne K₂O equivalent)

1993$

Actual

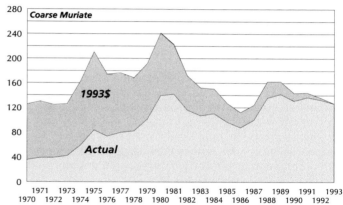

Coarse Muriate

1993$

Actual

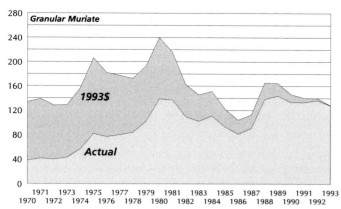

Granular Muriate

1993$

Actual

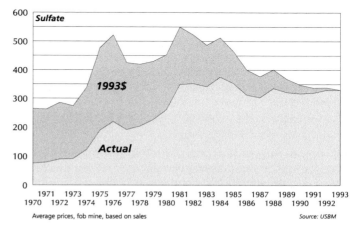

Sulfate

1993$

Actual

Average prices, fob mine, based on sales

Source: USBM

Sales of potash in of North America by grade
(tonnes of K₂O equivalent)

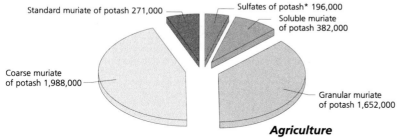

Standard muriate of potash 271,000
Sulfates of potash* 196,000
Soluble muriate of potash 382,000
Coarse muriate of potash 1,988,000
Granular muriate of potash 1,652,000

Agriculture

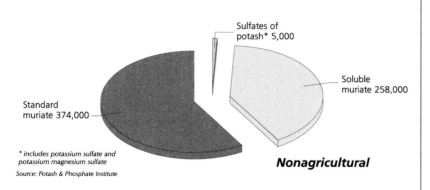

Sulfates of potash* 5,000
Standard muriate 374,000
Soluble muriate 258,000

Nonagricultural

* includes potassium sulfate and potassium magnesium sulfate

Source: Potash & Phosphate Institute

Potassium sulfate $198/t (agricultural, min. 50% K₂O, standard, bulk, FOB works); $2,200-2,860/t (300-lb drums, granular, purified).

Potassium tetraborate (ex-works) $3.08/kg (granular, bags); $3.19/kg (granular, drums); $3.41/kg (powder, bags); $3.52/kg (powder, drums). Tetrapotassium pyrophosphate (TKPP) $1.55-1.83/kg (E. USA freight equalized); $1.32-1.39/kg (liquid, bulk).

* *ratio by weight of SiO₂:K₂O.*

ETYMOLOGY: Arcanite from Medieval Latin alchemical name, *Arcanum duplicatum = double secret.* **Carnallite** for Rudolph von Carnall (1804-1874), Prussian mining engineer, Greek *lithos = stone.* **Kainite** from the Greek *kainos = new, recent* alluding to its recent (secondary) formation. **Langbeinite** for A. Langbein, German chemist of Leopoldshall. **Leonite** for Leo Strippelmann, director of the salt work at Westerregeln, Germany. **Polyhalite** from the Greek *polys = much* or *many* and *hals = salt* due to the component salts. **Potash** from *pot* and *ash*, originally prepared by evaporating the lixivium of wood ashes in iron pots (see soda ash). **Sylvite** is the old chemical name *Sal digestivus Sylvii* or digestive salt of Francois Sylvius de la Boë (1614-1672), Dutch chemist and physician of Leyden.

PUMICE & SCORIA

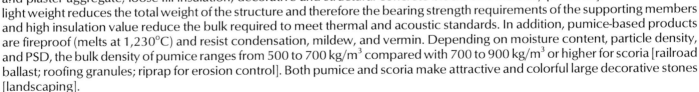

Pumice is a light-colored (white, gray, pink, yellow, or brown), highly vesicular volcanic glass generally composed of 60-70% SiO_2, 12-14% Al_2O_3, 1-2% Fe_2O_3, plus alkalis. The finer-grained equivalent is pumicite or volcanic ash. Typically pumice vesicles are <1mm in size separated by thin walls. Scoria or cinder is similar but is rusty red to black in color with larger vesicles and thicker walls than pumice, heavier, porous, and contains 50-60% SiO_2.

PROPERTIES & USES: The cellular nature and composition mean that pumice fragments generally have an SG of <1.0 (and will float on water), good thermal and sound insulation properties, very low permeability, and adequate compressive strength and modulus of elasticity [lightweight structural concrete and members; stucco and plaster aggregate; loose-fill insulation; decorative and structural concrete blocks and masonry products]. The light weight reduces the total weight of the structure and therefore the bearing strength requirements of the supporting members and high insulation value reduce the bulk required to meet thermal and acoustic standards. In addition, pumice-based products are fireproof (melts at 1,230°C) and resist condensation, mildew, and vermin. Depending on moisture content, particle density, and PSD, the bulk density of pumice ranges from 500 to 700 kg/m^3 compared with 700 to 900 kg/m^3 or higher for scoria [railroad ballast; roofing granules; riprap for erosion control]. Both pumice and scoria make attractive and colorful large decorative stones [landscaping].

Since pumice and pumicite are inert (pH 7.2), extremely brittle with a sharp conchoidal fracture, and H5-6, they can be used as a mild abrasive [hand soaps and household scouring compounds and cleansers; stone-washed jeans; hand-rubbed satin finishing; leather buffing; erasers; grill cleaners; micronized polishing powders for teeth; cosmetic skin removal (pumice stone); polishing compounds for TV tube glass, electronic circuit boards, metal, plastics; matches and striking surfaces]. These abrasive products include sawn and shaped blocks, granules, and powders. In stone washing, the pumice needs to float in the laundry machine (hence it requires low density and permeability), and be hard enough to survive but soft enough not to damage the fabric; this is generally achieved with clean, light-colored pumice containing few lithic fragments.

When the vesicles are interconnected, the pumice is permeable and highly absorbent, and when they are isolated the rock is highly porous but very impermeable. This porosity, together with a large surface area and chemical inertness allow pumice to be used as absorbent [catalyst carrier; floor sweep products; acid-washing; grease collector in gas-fired grills; soil substitute (hydroponic growth medium) and additive; chemical, herbicide, fungicide, and pesticide carrier]. In acid-washing the pumice is impregnated with bleaching chemicals (hence it requires high porosity and permeability) and then tumbled dry with finished garments; as the pumice contacts the fabric, the chemicals are released (see stone washing above).

Fine-ground high-purity pumice is near white, hard, lightweight, chemically inert, and can be processed into various particle sizes suitable for fillers [nonskid coating and filler in paint; asphalt mixes]. Fine-ground pumice is a pozzalan, that is a material that reacts with the calcium hydroxide formed in cement to form compounds with cementitious properties [additive to portland cement]. The fine particle size, particle shape, chemical inertness, low cost, and expandability allow pumice to be used as a filter media [water; juices, beverages; oils; fuels].

QUALITY & SPECIFICATIONS: *Construction grade:-* (Italy) includes 0-3mm, 3-7mm, 7-10mm, and 10-12mm, 0-15mm, and 0-18mm plus blends; BD 550-750kg/m^3. *Lightweight aggregates:-* generally sold in sizes from 8 mm downward. Specifications in structural concrete (designated in ASTM C 331) specify unit weights of oven-dry material from 880 kg/m^3 for fine aggregate to 1,120 kg/m^3 for coarse aggregate.

CHEMICAL ANALYSIS OF COMMERCIAL PUMICE

	USA Hess Pumice Products(Idaho)	USA New Mexico	Turkey Soylu Madencilik (Nevsehir)	Turkey Dost (Nevsehir)	Japan S. Kyushu	Italy Pumex SpA (Lipari)
SiO_2	70.5	74.2	72.50	67.80	73.08	71.75
Al_2O_3	13.5	12.52	12.59	14.00	13.84	12.33
Fe_2O_3	1.1	1.62	0.90	3.00	1.16	1.98
FeO	0.1					0.02
H_2O	3.4					
Na_2O	1.6		3.62	3.40	2.76	3.59
K_2O	1.8		4.71	3.10	2.61	4.47
CaO	0.8	0.44	0.80	1.50	1.34	
TiO_2	0.2					0.11
SO_3	0.1					
MgO	0.5	0.17			0.28	0.12
As (ppm)	<0.05					
Pb (ppm)	1.0000					
LOI			-	4.30	4.77	

Abrasive-grade:- ranges from -6 mesh for cleaning to -300 mesh for polishing; purity demands may be as high as 99.85% or 99.95% with an average particle size of 75, 150, 250, and 350 μm. Thin vesicle walls are preferred.

Acid-wash stone:- coarse granular +1.9 cm in size.

WORLD CAPACITY: 12M. t.

CAPACITY UTILIZATION: 90%.

MARKET CONDITIONS: Declining.

MARKETING FACTORS: Construction activity and therefore the economy. The popularity of stone-washed garments has been a boost to the pumice market.

HEALTH & SAFETY: Crystalline silica has been classified as a probable carcinogen by the IARC (see silica for further details). Therefore, because of its crystalline silica content, pumice will come under the OSHA Hazard Communication Standards, 29 CFR Section 1900.1200 which require labeling and other forms of warning, material safety data sheets, and employee training for products containing identified carcinogens with concentrations greater than 0.1%.

SUBSTITUTES & ALTERNATIVES: Abrasives:- bauxite & alumina (fused alumina), corundum/emery, diamonds, diatomite, feldspar, garnet, iron oxide (magnetite), nepheline syenite, olivine, perlite, silica sand, staurolite, tripoli, and silicon carbide), ilmenite.**Filler**:-ATH, barite, calcium carbonate, feldspar, kaolin, mica, nepheline syenite, perlite, pyrophyllite, talc, microcrystalline silica, ground silica flour and synthetic silica, wollastonite. **low-density fillers**:- hollow microspheres of glass and plastics. **Filter media**:- activated carbon/ anthracite, asbestos, cellulose, diatomite,

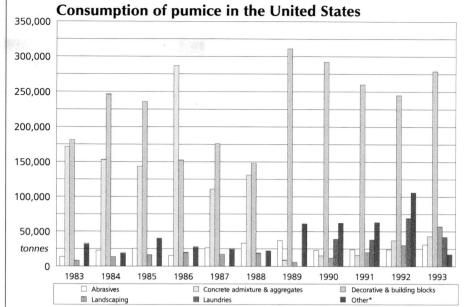

Consumption of pumice in the United States

Legend:
- ☐ Abrasives
- ☐ Concrete admixture & aggregates
- ☐ Decorative & building blocks
- ▨ Landscaping
- ▨ Laundries
- ■ Other*

* includes absorbents, agricultural (horticultural, dilutents, fillers, filter aids, insulating medium, granules. Source: USBM

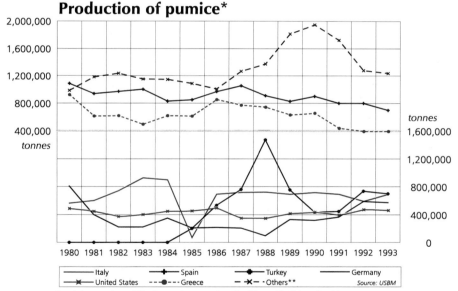

Production of pumice*

Legend:
- Italy
- Spain
- Turkey
- Germany
- United States
- Greece
- Others**

Source: USBM

* excludes pozzolan. **leading producers are: Iran, Guadeloupe, Martinique, Dominica

PUMICE LEADERS

Producers	Exporters	Importers
Italy	Italy	Netherlands
Spain	Greece	United Kingdom
Turkey	Spain	Japan
Germany	United States	Singapore
United States	Turkey	Canada
Greece	Iceland	Taiwan
Iran	Guadeloupe	Hong Kong
Guadeloupe	Martinique	Germany
Martinique	Dominica	China
Dominica	Ecuador	

Source: Hess Pumice Products

garnet, iron oxide (magnetite), perlite, Silica sand, ilmenite. **Lightweight aggregate**:- clay (expanded), perlite, shale (expanded), vermiculite, zeolites. **Pozzolans**:- diatomite, fly ash. **Thermal sound insulators**:- brick clays, diatomite, mineral wool, expanded perlite.

RECYCLING: Virtually none.

PRODUCERS & WORLD TRADE: The main producers of pumice are in the Mediterranean region of Europe — Italy, Spain, Greece, and Turkey — and the western United States. Italy is by far the world's largest producer of pozzolan.

PRICES: United States (based on average for US sales) $109/t (abrasives); $44/t (laundries); $27/t (landscaping); $21/t (concrete admixtures & aggregates); $13/t (decorative building blocks).

HTS CODES: 2513.11.0000 (crude or irregular pieces including crushed pumice); 2513.19.0000 (pumice, other).

ETYMOLOGY: Pumice from the Latin *pumex = pumice* or *porous stone* or from *spuma = foam*.

POSTSCRIPT: A cubic yard of loose dry pit-run pumice from New Mexico weighs about 850 pounds.

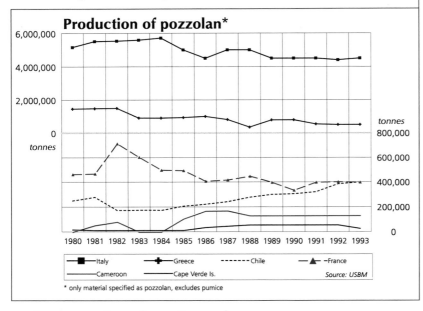

Production of pozzolan*

Legend: ■ Italy, ✦ Greece, ------ Chile, ▲ France, — Cameroon, — Cape Verde Is.

Source: USBM

* only material specified as pozzolan, excludes pumice

Average value of pumice and pumicite f.o.b. mine or mill in the United States

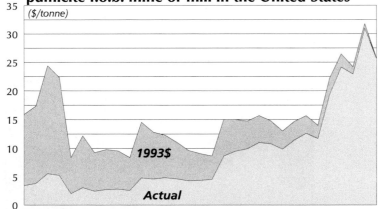

($/tonne)

1963 1964 1965 1966 1967 1968 1969 1970 1971 1972 1973 1974 1975 1976 1977 1978 1979 1980 1981 1982 1983 1984 1985 1986 1987 1988 1989 1990 1991 1992 1993

Price of pumice in the United States ($/tonne)

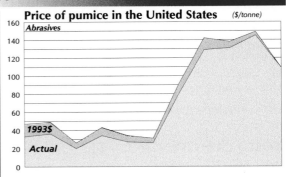

Abrasives

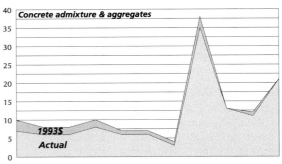

Concrete admixture & aggregates

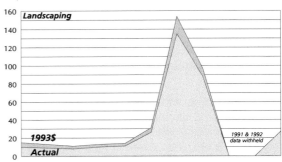

Landscaping

1991 & 1992 data withheld

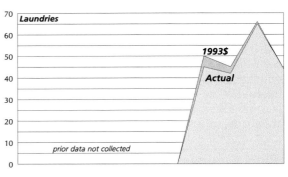

Laundries

prior data not collected

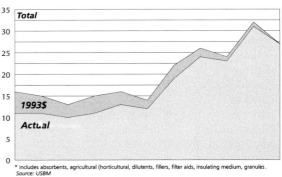

Total

* includes absorbents, agricultural (horticultural, dilutents, fillers, filter aids, insulating medium, granules.
Source: USBM

PYROPHYLLITE

Mineral	Formula	%Al₂O₃	%SiO₂	Color	SG	H
Pyrophyllite	$Al_2O_3 \cdot 4SiO_4 \cdot H_2O$	28.3	66.7	white/pale yellow, green	2.8-2.9	1-2

Pyrophyllite is a hydrous aluminum silicate, the aluminum analog of talc. Related products include pyrophyllite-bearing rocks such as roseki comprising pyrophyllite, sericite, kaolinite, and quartz (mainly Japan and Korea); agalmatolite, a rock composed of pyrophyllite, muscovite, diaspore, kyanite, and quartz (Brazil); and wonderstone, a rock containing up to 90% pyrophyllite with associated chloritoid, rutile, and epidote (South Africa).

PROPERTIES & USES: Pyrophyllite is a "soft, slippery, and sallow" mineral with distinctive physical and chemical characteristics. However, the properties of its associated minerals need to be taken into account when assessing its commercial properties (e.g. quartz adds abrasiveness, kyanite refractoriness, sericite lubricity). Pyrophyllite is refractory (PCE of 27-28) and at 1,200°C decomposes to cristobilite and mullite with a corresponding increase in H from 1-2 to 7-8. It has low values for thermal conductivity, coefficient of expansion, hot load deformation, reversible thermal expansion, and bulk density, excellent reheat stability, and resists corrosion from molten metals and slags, and exhibits low heating shrinkage [alumina-silica monolithic refractories (gunning, ramming, and castable mixes); insulating firebricks and monoliths; metal pouring refractories ladle, tundish, cupola liners); foundry mold coatings].

Pyrophyllite partly substitutes as a source of Al_2O_3 and SiO_2 for traditional feldspar/silica used in ceramics where it is reported to lower the firing temperature, reduce shrinking and cracking, and improve thermal shock resistance [electrical porcelain; glazes; wall and floor tiles; pottery; semi-vitreous dinnerware; vitreous chinaware] and have low electrical conductivity [electrical porcelain]. In addition, the finished product has good mechanical strength with a high degree of vitrification.

CHEMICAL COMPOSITION OF COMMERCIAL PYROPHYLLITE (%)

	USA	Canada Newfound-land	Japan	S. Korea Nohwado Minkyung Industrial	S. Korea Nohwado Minkyung Industrial Fire brick & fiberglass	S. Korea Nohwado Minkyung Industrial	S. Korea Nohwado Minkyung Industrial White cement	China Quingtian	Australia Pambila	Brazil
	Ceramics		Refractory	Clay (filler)		Tile			High-grade	
SiO₂	57.58	63.1	75.76	65-71	73-77	76-80	83-87	64.8	65.8	63.64
Al₂O₃	33.31	27.4	17.68	21-27	18-19	15-19	9-12	29.6	28.2	25.59
Fe₂O₃	0.33	0.8	0.57	0.15-0.25	0.15-0.30	0.15-0.30	0.15-0.30	0.4	0.11	-
CaO	trace		0.28	-				0.1	0.28	-
MgO	trace		0.02	-				0.04	0.01	0.01
K₂O	3.90	3.10	0.96	-				NA	0.96	2.48
Na₂O	0.06	0.2	0.15	-				0.02	0.1	0.29
TiO₂	NA		0.31					NA	0.18	
LOI	5.56	4.9	4.38	4-5	3.8-4.5	3.3-3.8	2.9-3.4	4.0	NA	

COMPOSITION OF PYROPHYLLITE (%)

Refractory grade (low-sericite)

Minerals		Chemistry		Screen Analysis Cum% retained (US sieve)	
Pyrophyllite	40 - 50	SiO₂	75.0	4	17.0
Quartz	30 - 45	Al₂O₃	19.3	8	40.0
Sericite	5 - 15	Fe₂O₃	0.8	16	57.8
Kaolin	1 - 3	Na₂O	0.1	30	72.5
		K₂O	0.1	50	80.8
		CaO	0.1	100	84.4
		LOI	3.9	200	88.6
				325	92.0

Ceramic grade (high sericite)

Minerals		Chemistry		Particle size (%µm)	
Pyrophyllite	20 - 30	SiO₂	80.9	40	90
Quartz	50 - 60	Al₂O₃	13.8	30	78
Sericite	20 - 25	Fe₂O₃	0.2	20	58
Kaolin	5 - 10	TiO₂	0.1	10	28
		Na₂O	0.4	5	10.6
		K₂O	2.3	2	1.6
		LOI	2.3	1	nd

Source: Guillo and Thompson, 1994

CHARACTERISTICS OF BRAZILIAN AGALMATOLITE

	Sericite-agalmatolite	Diaspore-pyrophyllie-agalmatolite	Quartz-kyanite-agalmatolite
Rock type	Soft, compact	Soft, compact	Hard, crystalline
Luster	Waxy	Waxy	Crystalline
Color	White, gray, greenish	Yellow, dark specs	White to gray
Hardness	2.5 - 3.0	3.0	Variable
SG	2.7 - 2.8	2.9 - 3	2.9 - 3.0
Inertness/chemical stability	Good	Good	Good
Thermal stability	Up to 1,400°C		Refractory
Melting point	1,530°C (PCE 21)	1,615-1,640°C"(PCE 28-29)	Refractory
Acid resistance	Excellent	Partial decomp. in sulfuric acid	
Bulk density	Excellent @ 0.55 t/m³	Good @ 0.63 t/m³	Low @ 0.67 t/m³
Oil absorption (g/100g)	30, 40	28, 40, 44	38
Surface tention	Low good water wetability		Very high
Uses	Filler/filter	Filler/filter/ceramics	Filler/ceramics

Source: Pimenta & Damiani, 1988.

TYPICAL WHITEWARE SEMIVITREOUS WARE COMPOSITIONS

	Kaolin	Ball clay	Flint	Feldspar	Tremolitic talc	Pyrophyllite	Calcium carbonate
Wall tile (1)	18	18	10	-	12	40	2
Wall tile (2)	-	24	17	-	35	16	8
Wall tile (3)	-	28	-	3	61	7	1
Floor tile	25	7	-	52	-	16	-
Electrical porcelain	30	16	-	35	-	19	-

Pyrophyllite has a neutral PH and is inert, nonabrasive, absorbent with good flowability which allow it to be used as a dilutent, extender, vehicle, and carrier for liquids [fungicide, insecticide, herbicide; fertilizer] and as an anti-caking agent [animal feed]. Other advantages include its compatibility with both acid and alkaline poisons, its fluffy characteristics allow it to settle and cover the foliage; and the electrostatic charge picked up in the blowers causes it to adhere to the underside of the leaves.

Some grades are sufficiently white to be fine ground and used as a filler [wallboard, wallboard cement and mastics; texture paint; plastics; paper; rubber; vinyl tiles]. Since it can be easily machined to tight tolerances, is a good electrical insulator, and provides a perfect seal, pyrophyllite may form the reaction vessel for synthetic diamond production. Calcined and crushed pyrophyllite exhibits many of the characteristics required for road construction (high PSV and AIV) plus anti-skid properties and high luminance factor [aggregates].

In Japan and Korea, roseki may be processed to roseki clay or pyrophyllite clay [feedstock for fiberglass; filler in paper; insecticide carrier] or may be a source of pure pyrophyllite. Agalmatolite represents a range of metamorphic rocks with or without pyrophyllite (see table). Depending on the exact mineralogy, agalmatolite is white, cream, gray to greenish in color, inert, has a brightness of up to 95%, an SG 2.7-3.0, and H 2.5-3 making it a usefull filler [adhesives; rubber; plastics; paint & putty; paper; powder and bar soap; bitumen; cosmetics]; is thermally stable and refractory (melting point >1,500°C) [refractories]; has good ceramic properties [wall tiles; porcelain; insulators]; and is absorbent [insecticide, herbicide, fertilizer carrier].

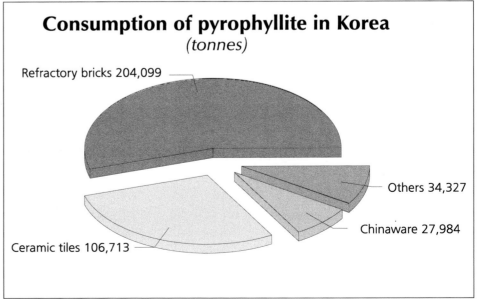

Consumption of pyrophyllite in Korea
(tonnes)

Refractory bricks 204,099
Ceramic tiles 106,713
Others 34,327
Chinaware 27,984

PYROPHYLLITE

QUALITY & SPECIFICATIONS: Since pyrophyllite is generally intimately associated with minerals such as kyanite, diaspore, quartz, and alunite, the commercial products have a varied chemical analysis. This mineral mixture influences the grade and consumption pattern of the product.

Refractory:- low sericite and alkali content, <1% coloring oxide ($Fe_2O_3+FeO+TiO_2$); *ceramics:-* high sericite, low iron, and relatively high alkali content; *carrier or dilutent:-* if it works, use it.

Korea, *clay filler:-* 21-27% Al_2O_3; *fiberglass and refractory:-* 18-21% Al_2O_3; *ceramic:-*15-19% Al_2O_3; *white cement:-*9-12% Al_2O_3.

Japan, roseki *glassfiber-grade:-*19-20% Al_2O_3,*refractory grade:-* 5-18% Al_2O_3 with low alkalis.

WORLD CAPACITY: 2.2M. t. **CAPACITY UTILIZATION:** 95%.

MARKET CONDITIONS: Steady. **MARKETING FACTORS:** Construction/iron & steel/economy.

HEALTH & SAFETY: Crystalline silica has been classified as a probable carcinogen by the IARC (see silica for further details). Therefore, because of its crystalline silica content, unless processing has the capability to reduce the crystalline silica content to less than 0.1%, pyrophyllite will come under the OSHA Hazard Communication Standards, 29 CFR Section 1900.1200 which require labeling and other forms of warning, material safety data sheets, and employee training for products containing identified carcinogens with concentrations greater than 0.1%.

SUBSTITUTES & ALTERNATIVES: Carrier/absorbent:- attapulgite, bentonite, kaolin, peat, pumice, pyrophyllite, sepiolite, talc, vermiculite, zeolites. **Filler:-** ATH, barite, calcium carbonate, feldspar, kaolin, mica, nepheline syenite, perlite, pumice, talc, microcrystalline silica, ground silica flour and synthetic silica, wollastonite. **Refractories:-** andalusite, bauxite, chromite, kyanite, dolomite, graphite, magnesite, olivine, pyrophyllite, refractory clays, silica, sillimanite, zircon.

RECYCLING: Virtually none.

PRODUCERS & WORLD TRADE: Pyrophyllite production and consumption are dominated by Japan and Korea with the United States a significant contributor.

PRICES: Australia $100-110/t (FOB Port Kembla); $230/t (milled filler grade, min. 21 t container, FOB Sydney). Brazil $45/t (agalmatolite). Japan ¥7,000-8,000 ($70-80)/t. Korea (FOB Nohwado port) $110-150/t (clay filler, 21-27% Al_2O_3); fiberglass, refractory 18-21% Al_2O_3); $27-42/t (ceramic, 15019% Al_2O_3); $15-24/t (white cement, 9-12% Al_2O_3). South Africa $253/t (paper grade, micronized, FOB Durban). United States $70-120/t.

ETYMOLOGY: Agalmatolite from the Greek *algalma = image* and *lithos =* stone as it was carved by the Chinese. **Pyrophyllite** from the Greek for *pyro = a fire, phyllo = a leaf,* and *lithos = stone* referring to the effect of heat separating the laminae in foliated varieties. **Roseki** from the Japanese for *waxy stone* referring to its wax-like appearance. **Sericite** from the Greek for *silky* alluding to its silky luster.

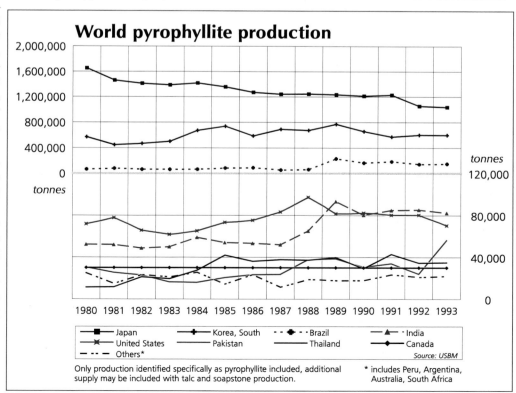

World pyrophyllite production

Source: USBM

Only production identified specifically as pyrophyllite included, additional supply may be included with talc and soapstone production. * includes Peru, Argentina, Australia, South Africa

PYROPHYLLITE LEADERS

Producers	Exporters	Importers
Japan	Japan	Japan
South Korea	South Korea	China
Brazil	Brazil	Sri Lanka
India	Canada	Indonesia
United States	Australia	United Kingdom
Pakistan	South Africa	Germany
Thailand		Netherlands
Canada		
Peru		
Argentina		
Australia		
South Africa		

RARE EARTHS

Minerals	Formula	%REO	Dominant RE type	Color	SG	H
Bastnasite	$CeFCO_3$	75	cerium group	light yellow to brown	5.0	4.5
Xenotime	YPO_4	61	yttrium group	pale yellow/brownish green	4.5	4.5
Monazite	$(Ce,Y)PO_4$	71	cerium group	yellowish to reddish brown	5.0	5.0

Rare earths, the 15 lanthanide elements plus yttrium (and possibly scandium and thorium), may be divided into the cerium or "light" (a.k.a. cerics) and the yttrium or "heavy" (a.k.a. yttrics) rare earths. REs with an even atomic number tend to be more plentiful than their odd-numbered neighbors and are preferred for commercial use. Although REs occur in many minerals, those listed above are the most important commercially.

THE RARE EARTHS

Cerium Group "Light" RE	Atomic No.	Oxide	Yttrium Group "Heavy" RE	Atomic No.	Oxide
lanthanum (La)	57	La_2O_3	yttrium (Y)	39	Y_2O_3
cerium (Ce)	58	CeO_2	terbium (Tb)	65	Tb_4O_7
praseodymium (Pr)	59	Pr_6O_{11}	dysprosium (Dy)	66	Dy_2O_3
neodymium (Nd)	60	Nd_2O_3	holmium (Ho)	67	Ho_2O_3
promethium (Pm)*	61	none	erbium (Er)	68	Er_2O_3
samarium (Sm)**	62	Sm_2O_3	thulium (Tm)	69	Tm_2O_3
europium (Eu)	63	Eu_2O_3	ytterbium (Yb)	70	Yb_2O_3
gadolinium (Gd)	64	Gd_2O_3	lutetium (Lu)**	71	Lu_2O_3
Also included:					
thorium (Th)	90	ThO_2	scandium (Sc)	21	Sc_2O_3

*naturally radioactive; ** radioactive isotopes Sm 147 and Lu 176

PROPERTIES & USES: Hydrometallurgical processing and chemical purification of the ore yield rare-earth elements (REE) as salts such as the chloride, carbonate, nitrate, fluoride, and halide which may be calcined to form rare-earth oxides (REO) or reduced through electrolysis or metalthermic reduction to the rare-earth metal (REM).

In metallurgy, REMs, either individually or combined as mischmetal (51-53% Ce, 22-25% La, 15-17% Nd, 3-4% Pr, 2-3% Sm, 3% Tb, 3% Y, and 5% iron) improve cold formability and hot workability, weld integrity, and resistance to impact, high-temperature oxidation, and hydrogen cracking in specialized steels such as high-strength, low-alloy (HSLA) steel [automobiles; pipelines; deep-wells], high-carbon steel [ball bearings; plow blades], superalloys, stainless steel, and armorplate [aerospace; military]. Mischmetal added to pyrophoric alloys gives tracer shells their fiery tail [military ammunition]; small quantities of La and Ce added to a galvanizing zinc alloy enhance fluidity, wetability, and the elimination of intergranular corrosion [galvanized steel]; and selected REs extend the life of Ni and Co alloys used to protect structural materials subject to intense cyclic heat and oxidation [jet-engine exhaust nozzles; reaction vessels and heat exchanges]. REs are replacing toxic materials such as Cr, Zn, Cd, and nitrates in aqueous corrosion protection coatings.

DISTRIBUTION OF RARE EARTHS IN COMMERCIAL MINERALS

	USA Mountain Pass, CA Bastnasite	China Baiyunebo, Nei Monggol Bastnasite	Australia Capel, WA Monazite	Australia N. Stradbroke Is., Qld. Monazite	Australia Mt. Weld Monazite	USA Green Cove Springs, FL Monazite	China Nangang, Guangdong Monazite	Brazil E. coast Monazite	Malaysia Lahat, Perak Xenotime	China southeast Guangdong Xenotime	China Xunwu, Jiangxi Province RE in clay	China Longnan, Jiangxi Province RE in clay
Lanthanum	33.20	23.00	23.89	21.50	26.00	17.50	23.00	24.00	1.24	1.20	43.37	1.82
Cerium	49.10	50.00	46.02	45.80	51.00	43.70	42.70	47.00	3.13	3.00	2.38	0.37
Praseodymium	4.34	6.20	5.04	5.30	4.00	5.00	4.10	4.50	0.49	0.60	9.02	0.74
Neodymium	12.00	18.50	17.38	18.60	15.00	17.50	17.00	18.50	1.59	3.50	31.65	3.00
Samarium	0.79	0.80	2.53	3.10	1.80	4.90	3.00	3.00	1.14	2.20	3.90	2.82
Europium	0.12	0.20	0.05	0.80	0.40	0.16	0.10	0.06	0.01	0.20	0.50	0.12
Gadolinium	0.17	0.70	1.49	1.80	1.00	6.60	2.00	1.00	3.47	5.00	3.00	6.85
Terbium	0.02	0.10	0.04	0.29	0.10	0.26	0.70	0.10	0.91	1.20	trace	1.29
Dysprosium	0.03	0.10	0.69	0.64	0.20	0.90	0.80	0.35	8.32	9.10	trace	6.67
Holmium	0.01	trace	0.05	0.12	0.10	0.11	1.20	0.04	1.98	2.60	trace	1.64
Erbium	0.00	trace	0.21	0.18	0.20	trace	0.30	0.07	6.43	5.60	trace	4.85
Thulium	0.00	trace	0.02	0.03	trace	trace	trace	0.01	1.12	1.30	trace	0.70
Ytterbium	0.00	trace	0.12	0.11	0.10	0.21	2.40	0.02	6.77	6.00	0.26	2.46
Lutetium	0.00	trace	0.04	0.01	trace	trace	0.14	ND	0.99	1.80	0.10	0.36
Yttrium	0.09	0.50	2.41	2.50	trace	3.20	2.40	1.40	61.00	59.30	8.00	65.00

Percent of total rare-earth content

Source: various and USBM

COMPOSITION OF RARE-EARTH ORES (% REO)

	Bastnasite	Monazite	Xenotime
Cerium	49.20	46.00	3.18
Dysposium	-	-	8.44
Erbium	-	-	6.52
Gadolinium	-	2.00	3.52
Holmium	-	-	2.01
Lanthanum	33.27	24.00	1.26
Neodymium	12.02	17.00	1.61
Praseodymium	4.31	5.00	0.00
Samarium	0.80	3.00	1.16
Thulium	-	-	1.14
Ytterbium	-	-	6.87
Yttrium	-	2.00	61.89
Other	0.40	1.00	2.40
Total	100.00	100.00	100.00

Certain alloys of Sm, La, Ce, Pr, and/or Nd have high coercivity and energy density even at extreme temperatures and thus produce strong permanent magnets [electric motors, alternators, and generators; line printers; computer disc drives; various clasps & closing devices; microphones & speakers]. Sm-based magnets are generally either 35% Sm/65% Co or 24% Sm/20% zirconium plus iron, copper, and cobalt. Nd-based magnets are generally either 35% Nd/64% iron/1% boron or 28% Nd/7% Dy/40% iron/20% aluminum and boron. The Nd-based magnets are less expensive and have better magnetic properties than Sm-based products, but are inferior in terms of temperature and corrosion susceptibility. Gd compounds are used in magnetic refrigeration or cryogenics whereby the solid heats up in a strong magnetic field and cools when removed.

As catalysts, Ce, La, Nd, Pr and/or mischmetal provide structural and thermal stability, high catalytic activity, and processing selectivity [petroleum fluid cracking catalysts (FCC); ammonia synthesis; hydrocarbon oxygenation reactions like self-cleaning ovens; recovery of chlorine from HCl]. The catalyst is composed of a porous zeolite with up to 5% RE lining the cavities (see Zeolites) which is designed to create a strong electrostatic field inducing surface acidity to protect the zeolite against the high temperatures involved in the regeneration by burning off accumulated carbon. The catalytic converter designed to convert the hydrocarbons, carbon monoxide, and nitrous oxides in engine exhausts to water, carbon dioxide, and nitrogen is generally composed of alumina and small amounts of precious metals which are activated by about 5% cerium. The cerium provides oxidation resistance at high exhaust temperatures, to stabilize palladium and rhodium dispersions, to minimize the interaction of rhodium with the alumina, and to boost the oxidizing ability of the system.

Rare earths are used to color and decolor optical glass — colorizing includes pink with Er_2O_3 [photochromic glass, crystalware], light pink-blue-violet with Nd_2O_3 [decorative glass], red with Eu_2O_3, and green with Pr_6O_{11} [special filter glasses, + Nd in welding glasses]. $CeO_2 + TiO_2$ → attractive yellow glass [tableware], $CeO_2 + Nd_2O_3$ → clear glass [medical and TV glass], + Mn → pink-tinted glass that absorbs UV and stabilizes glass against radiation such as X-rays [eye-glass lenses & CRTs]. Cerium added to glass tends to accelerate the melting, oxidize the iron and therefore decolorize and absorb ultraviolet light and so prevent browning. Lanthanum is added to lens glass since it contributes to high refractive index and low dispersion. Rare earths enable glass fibers to transmit data over long distances without booster stations. The glass fiber, made up of fluorides or lanthanum, zircon, barium aluminum, sodium, and hafnium, is formed by chemical-vapor deposition in order to minimize impurities. Color for TVs and CRTs is generated by three phosphors — europium-ytrrium compound for red, a terbium-fluoride-zinc-sulfide for green, and a cerium-strontium-sulfide for blue — which when activated by photons emit luminescence. Typically, a 19" (48 cm)

MAJOR USES OF RARE-EARTH ELEMENTS

	Mixed REE	La	Ce	Pr	Nd	Pm	Sm	Eu	Gd	Tb	Dy	Ho	Er	Tm	Yb	Lu	Y
Metallurgy, ferrous	✔	✔	✔														✔
Metallurgy, nonferrous	✔	✔	✔	✔	✔			✔									✔
Magnets	✔	✔	✔	✔	✔		✔		✔								✔
Ceramics	✔	✔	✔	✔									✔				✔
Electronics	✔	✔	✔	✔	✔		✔	✔	✔	✔	✔	✔	✔	✔	✔		✔
Metallurgical catalysts	✔	✔	✔		✔		✔		✔		✔				✔		✔
Catalysts	✔	✔	✔		✔		✔		✔						✔		
Optical (incl. glasses)	✔	✔	✔	✔	✔	✔	✔	✔	✔	✔		✔	✔	✔			✔
Medical							✔	✔	✔	✔				✔			✔
Pharmaceuticals		✔	✔		✔				✔					✔			
Nuclear fuel			✔														
Nuclear control & shielding			✔				✔	✔	✔		✔	✔					✔
Hydrgen storage		✔	✔	✔	✔												
Cryogenics			✔														
Batteries		✔			✔												✔

Source: adapted from Pincock, Allen, and Holt, Inc., 1988.

TV screen contains 0.5 g of Eu_2O_3 and the TV faceplate glass contains Nd_2O_3 which blocks ambient light from interfering with the picture. Eu_2O_3 is also used to improve fluorescent light emission. The hardness and abrasive qualities of CeO_2 are stable at high speeds and pressures and leave no scratches making it the most efficient glass polishing agent [fine-grain polishing of lenses, TV face plates, mirrors, and gemstones].

In ceramics CeO_2, Y_2O_3, and other rare-earth oxides are used as sintering aids due to their ability to eliminate weakening voids [Si_3N_4, dielectric ceramics]; Pr_6O_{11} in a zircon matrix produces a yellow stain [enamels]; Ho_2O_3 and yttrium stabilized zirconia yield specialty refractories with exceptional high-temperature, high-strength, and high-thermal shock resistance [barrier coating in jet engines].

Rare earths are used in electronic devices that convert energy from one form to another; in some cases input and output may be electricity, but the output variance is determined by another energy type such as thermal or radiation. The rare earths are added to synthetic garnet crystals as dopants which include yttrium-iron garnets (YIG) and gadolinium-iron garnets (GIG) [microwaves]; yttrium-aluminum-garnets (YAG) [simulated diamonds, host crystals for lasers]; neodymium doped YAG [short-wave-length laser beams for scribing semiconductors]; gadolinium-gallium-garnets (GGG) [thin-film magnetic bubble memory system and substrates in computers]. Window glass containing lead lanthanum zirconate titanate (PLZT) can be switched electronically from transparent to opaque.

The use of rare earths in medicine includes cerium oxalate and is used to counter seasickness and morning sickness and neodymium compounds are used in the treatment of thrombosis.

Thorium oxide (thoria) melts at 3,300°C, the highest melting point of any metal oxide [specialty refractories, high-strength high-temperature ceramics, investment molds, and crucibles]. Thorium emits electrons at low temperatures [magnetron tubes, special light bulbs, fuel cell elements] and the nitrate is incandescent [lamp mantles], and thorium-magnesium alloys are strong but lightweight [aerospace].

Consumption of thorium (monazite) in the United States
(tonnes)

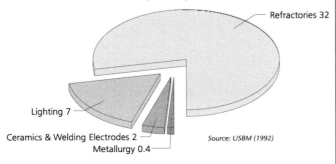

Refractories 32
Lighting 7
Ceramics & Welding Electrodes 2
Metallurgy 0.4

Source: USBM (1992)

Consumption of rare earths
(tonnes REO)

North America

Glass 2,210
Metallurgical 1,140
Magnets 450
Ceramics 330
Phosphors 170
Others 90
Catalysts 3,945

Europe

Glass 2,175
Metallurgical 685
Magnets 210
Ceramics 455
Phosphors 325
Others 95
Catalysts 3,235

Japan

Metallurgical 215
Magnets 1,065
Ceramics 865
Phosphors 350
Others 65
Glass 2,900
Catalysts 510

China

Metallurgical 3,615
Magnets 315
Ceramics 125
Phosphors 300
Others 965
Glass 810
Catalysts 2,120

Others

Metallurgical 4,795
Magnets 110
Ceramics 75
Phosphors 155
Others 35
Glass 2,355
Catalysts 1,040

Source: Kingsnorth, D.J., 1993; data for 1992

RARE-EARTH PRODUCT SPECIFICATIONS FROM INDIA

	Samarium oxide	Mixed rare-earth concentrate Type I	Type II
Sm_2O_3	96% Min.	50.00	42.00
Gd_2O_3		21.00	20.00
Nd_2O_3		17.90	12.00
CeO_2		2.00	2.00
Pr_6O_{11}		2.02	1.10
Eu_2O_3		0.30	0.30
Y_2O_3		0.70	12.00
Other rare earths	4.00% max.	balance	balance
Non-RE impurites	1.00% max.		
LOI	1.00% max.		
Total REO	98-99%		

Source: Indian Rare Earths, Ltd.

MONAZITE FROM WESTERN AUSTRALIA (%)

	Guaranteed	Typical
REO	min. 55	56.0-58.0
ThO_2	min. 6	6.5-7.0
REO + ThO_2	min. 61	62.5-65.0
Acid insolubles	max. 10	7.0-8.5
TiO_2	-	0.3-0.6

TYPICAL REO DISTRIBUTION (%)

Sc_2O_3	<0.005
Y_2O_3	1.36
La_2O_3	13.5
CeO_2	26.0
Pr_6O_{11}	2.85
Nd_2O_3	9.82
Sm_2O_3	1.43
Eu_2O_3	0.03

QUALITY & SPECIFICATIONS: Ore and product grade are variable and measured in rare-earth oxide (REO) and/or Y_2O_3 content.

Bastnasite:- REO contents of 60% (unleached), 70% (leached), and 90% (leached & calcined).

Monazite:- 55%, 60%, or 66% REO concentrates.

Xenotime:- min. 25% Y_2O_3 concentrate may be upgraded to yttrium concentrate with min. 60% Y_2O_3.

Products include mixed rare earth chlorides (min. 45% REO), mixed rare earth fluoride (min. 78% REO), mixed rare earth oxide (min. 96% REO). From these concentrates the individual rare-earths are separated to form compounds such as the acetate, carbonate, nitrate, oxalate, and sulfate; alloys like mischmetal, rare-earth silicide, ferrocerium; and metals up to a purity of 99.999%. Cerium oxide polishing compounds are available in grades from 92 to 99% REO and 50 ppm Fe_2O_3, 30 ppm MnO_2.

WORLD CAPACITY: 70,000 t REO.   **CAPACITY UTILIZATION:** 65%.

MARKET CONDITIONS: Increasing.

MARKETING FACTORS: The development of electronic applications encouraged by R&D. The state of the world economy and the rate of development in developing countries which increase the market for consumer items such as TVs and computers.

HEALTH & SAFETY: Rare earths are regarded as slightly toxic. Humans exposed to airborne lanthanides reported itching, insensitivity to heat, and a sharpening of the senses of taste and smell. Chronic exposure to lanthanide dust can lead to *rare-earth pneumoconiosis*. Certain finely divided rare-earth metals, alloys, and metal powders may oxidize rapidly and explode. Toxicity from rare earths may occur from radioactive lanthanides. Nd, Sm, Gd, and Lu have naturally occurring radioactive isotopes — alpha emitting isotopes are Nd^{144}, Sm^{147}, Sm^{148}, Sm^{149}, Gd^{152}; and Lu^{176} is a negative beta emitting isotope.

RECYCLING: Virtually none except the recycling of TV face plate glass which appears to have considerable potential due to the relatively high price of raw materials.

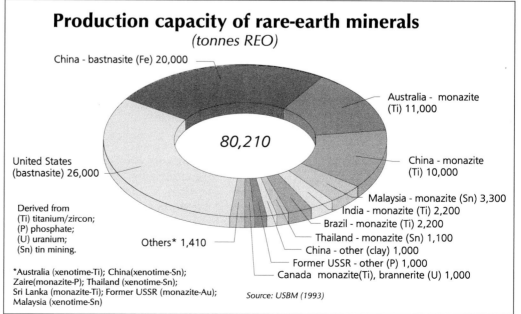

Production capacity of rare-earth minerals
(tonnes REO)

80,210

China - bastnasite (Fe) 20,000
Australia - monazite (Ti) 11,000
China - monazite (Ti) 10,000
United States (bastnasite) 26,000
China - monazite (Ti) 10,000
Malaysia - monazite (Sn) 3,300
India - monazite (Ti) 2,200
Brazil - monazite (Ti) 2,200
Thailand - monazite (Sn) 1,100
China - other (clay) 1,000
Former USSR - other (P) 1,000
Canada monazite(Ti), brannerite (U) 1,000
Others* 1,410

Derived from
(Ti) titanium/zircon;
(P) phosphate;
(U) uranium;
(Sn) tin mining.

*Australia (xenotime-Ti); China(xenotime-Sn);
Zaire(monazite-P); Thailand (xenotime-Sn);
Sri Lanka (monazite-Ti); Former USSR (monazite-Au);
Malaysia (xenotime-Sn)

Source: USBM (1993)

PRODUCERS & WORLD TRADE: Dominated by the United States, China, and the Former USSR, the number of rare-earth mineral producers is limited and declining as smaller suppliers close (Malaysia). In most cases, producing countries convert the ore into concentrates or rare-earth compounds for domestic consumption and export. Importers are confined to developed countries.

PRICES: Bastnasite conc. $2.30/kg REO (70% leached). Monazite A$650-700/t (min. 55% REO, FOB Australia). Yttrium conc. $15-20/kg (60% Y_2O_3, FOB Malaysia). Cerium (99.5%) $25.75/kg. Dysprosium (95%) $132/kg. Erbium (96%) $190/kg. Gadolinium (99.99%) $136.5/kg. Holmium (99.9%) $510/kg. Lanthanum (99.99%) 23/kg. Lutetium (99.99%) $7,000/kg. Neodymium (95%) 20/kg. Praseodymium (96%) 38.85/kg. Samarium (96%) $175/kg. Terbium (99.9%) $880/kg. Thulium (99.9%) $3,600/kg. Ytterbium (99%) $230/kg. Yttrium (99.99%) $115.50/kg. Cerium carbonate (99%) $11.22/kg; cerium fluoride (tech grade) $6.60/kg; cerium nitrate (96%) $5.17/kg.

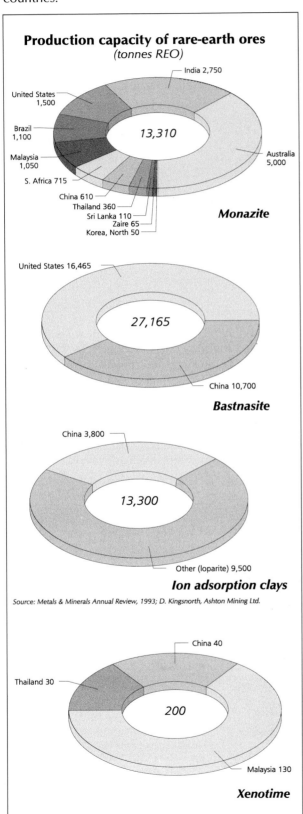

Production capacity of rare-earth ores
(tonnes REO)

Monazite — 13,310

- India 2,750
- United States 1,500
- Brazil 1,100
- Malaysia 1,050
- S. Africa 715
- China 610
- Thailand 360
- Sri Lanka 110
- Zaire 65
- Korea, North 50
- Australia 5,000

Monazite

Bastnasite — 27,165

- United States 16,465
- China 10,700

Bastnasite

Ion adsorption clays — 13,300

- China 3,800
- Other (loparite) 9,500

Ion adsorption clays

Source: Metals & Minerals Annual Review, 1993; D. Kingsnorth, Ashton Mining Ltd.

Xenotime — 200

- China 40
- Thailand 30
- Malaysia 130

Xenotime

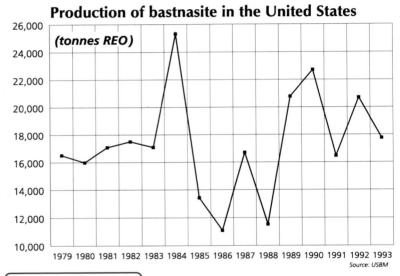

Production of bastnasite in the United States

(tonnes REO)

Source: USBM

RARE-EARTH LEADERS

Producers	Importers	Exporters
Monazite conc.	**RE ores & conc.**	**RE ores & conc.**
Australia	United States	China
India	Malaysia	United States
United States	Brazil	Australia
Brazil	**RE cpds & metals**	Brazil
Malaysia	Japan	India
S. Africa	United States	Malaysia
China	Germany	Thailand
Thailand	Netherlands	**RE cpds & metals**
Sri Lanka	France	China
Zaire	Austria	United States
North Korea	Canada	USSR
Bastnasite conc.	United Kingdom	Austria
United States	Korea	United Kingdom
China	Brazil	Japan
Xenotime conc.	Taiwan	Brazil
Malaysia	Saudi Arabia	Germany
China	Belgium	France
Thailand	Spain	Italy
Ion adsorption clays	Hong Kong	
China	Italy	

Data derived from British Geological Survey (1991)

Lanthanide chloride (46%) $2.20/kg; lanthanum carbonate (99.9%) $12.98/kg; lanthanum-lanthanide chloride (46%) $2.09/kg; lanthanum-lanthanide carbonate (60%) $5.39/kg; lanthanum-lanthanide nitrate (39%) $3.85/kg. Neodymium carbonate (96%) 9.90/kg.

HTS codes: 2612.20.0000 (thorium ores & conc. (monazite); 2805.30.0000 (rare-earth metals, scandium and yttrium, whether or not intermixed or alloyed); 2846.10.0000 (rare-earth oxides except cerium oxide); 2846.90.2010 (rare-earth oxides except cerium oxide); 2846.90.2050 (other compounds of rare-earth metals, yttrium, scandium, or mixtures); 2846.90.5000 (other mixtures of rare-earth oxides or other rare-earth chloride); 3606.90.3000 (ferrocerium and other pyrophoric alloys); 9902.26.2200 (yttrium-bearing materials and compounds).

SUBSTITUTES & ALTERNATIVES: None for the main uses. **Catalysts:-** palladium and ultrastable zeolite (FCC).

ETYMOLOGY: Bastnasite for Bastnäs, Vastmanland, Sweden. **Cerium** for *Ceris*, an asteroid discovered in 1803. **Dysprosium** from the Greek *dysprositos = hard to get at* in reference to the difficulty of separation. **Europium** for the continent of Europe itself named for *Europa*, daughter of a king of Phoenicia. **Gadolinium** for Johan Gadolin (1760-1852), Finnish chemist and discoverer of yttrium. **Holmium** from the Latin *Holmia = ancient name for Stockholm*. **Lanthanum** from the Greek *lanthanein = to be unseen, unnoticed*, or *concealed*. **Lutetium** for Lutetia, the ancient name for Paris. **Monazite** from the Greek *monazein = to be alone* alluding to its rarity. **Neodymium** from the Greek *neos = new* and *didymos = twin*. **Praeseodymium** from the Greek *prasios = green* and *didymos = twin*. **Promethium** for *Prometheus*, a Titan in Greek mythology, who made a man of clay from fire stolen from heaven. **Rare earths** named by Johann Gadolin as a literal description of a group of elements. **Samarium** for Vasilii Erafovich Samarski-Bykhovets (1803-1870), of the Russian Corps of Mining Engineers. **Terbium** from oxide erbia named by C.G. Mosander who discovered it in 1843. **Thorium** for *Thor*, Scandinavian god of thunder and lightening in reference to its use in energy. **Thulite/thulium** for *Thule*, the ancient name of Scandinavia. **Xenotime** from the Greek *xenos = foreign, a stranger* and *time = to honor* alluding to the fact that crystals are small and rare, and were long unnoticed; originally mispelled kenotime, Greek for *vain* and *to honor*. **Yttrium** and **Ytterbium** for Ytterby, Sweden.

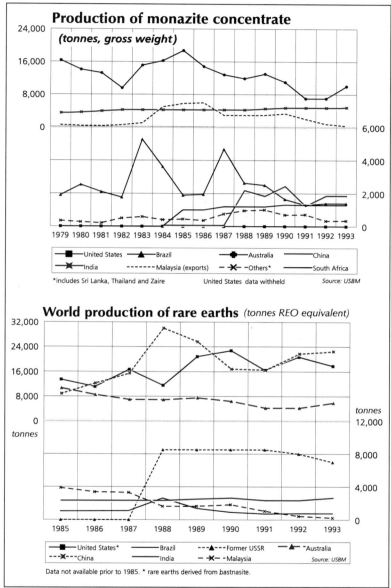

Production of monazite concentrate (tonnes, gross weight)

United States — Brazil — Australia — China — India — Malaysia (exports) — Others* — South Africa
*includes Sri Lanka, Thailand and Zaire   United States data withheld   Source: USBM

World production of rare earths (tonnes REO equivalent)

United States* — Brazil — Former USSR — Australia — China — India — Malaysia   Source: USBM
Data not available prior to 1985. * rare earths derived from bastnasite.

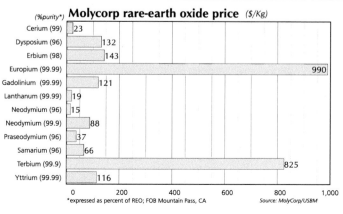

Molycorp rare-earth oxide price ($/Kg)   (%purity*)

Element	$/Kg
Cerium (99)	23
Dysposium (96)	132
Erbium (98)	143
Europium (99.99)	990
Gadolinium (99.99)	121
Lanthanum (99.99)	19
Neodymium (96)	15
Neodymium (99.9)	88
Praseodymium (96)	37
Samarium (96)	66
Terbium (99.9)	825
Yttrium (99.99)	116

*expressed as percent of REO; FOB Mountain Pass, CA   Source: MolyCorp/USBM

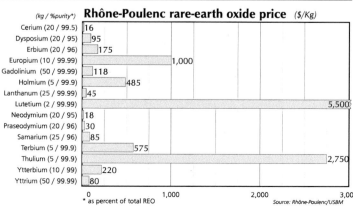

Rhône-Poulenc rare-earth oxide price ($/Kg)   (kg / %purity*)

Element	$/Kg
Cerium (20 / 99.5)	16
Dysposium (20 / 95)	95
Erbium (20 / 96)	175
Europium (10 / 99.99)	1,000
Gadolinium (50 / 99.99)	118
Holmium (5 / 99.9)	485
Lanthanum (25 / 99.99)	45
Lutetium (2 / 99.99)	5,500
Neodymium (20 / 95)	18
Praseodymium (20 / 96)	30
Samarium (25 / 96)	85
Terbium (5 / 99.9)	575
Thulium (5 / 99.9)	2,750
Ytterbium (10 / 99)	220
Yttrium (50 / 99.99)	80

* as percent of total REO   Source: Rhône-Poulenc/USBM

Mineral	Formula	%Na	%Na₂O	%Cl	Color	SG	H
Halite	NaCl	39.34	62.0	60.66	white or gray	2.1-2.6	2.5

The main types of commercial salt are rock salt extracted from (mainly room-and-pillar) underground mines; vacuum pan salt produced by the mechanical evaporation of brines (mainly but not exclusively derived from solution mining) using multiple-effect evaporators connected to vacuum pumps which allow the brine to boil at a lower temperature; brines derived from solution mining and used directly as a feedstock; and solar salt produced by using solar evaporation to concentrate seawater or other brines.

PROPERTIES & USES: Salt is the cheapest and most common source of soda (Na_2O) and chlorine (Cl_2).

Salt has nutritional, preservative, binding, color development, and taste properties [food processing; canning; meat packing; baking; flour processing; animal feedstuffs], medical properties [saline solutions], is a fairly efficient freezing point depressant to about -6°C [de-icing agent], contributes stabilizing effects [soil and pond sealants], acts as a flux [high-purity aluminum alloys], contributes alkalinity [pulp & paper; oilwell drilling fluids], removes oxide scale [steel plate cleaning], aids in solvent extraction [U, Be, & V ore concentration], inhibits microbial activity [tanning and leather treatment], promotes coagulation in emulsified latex derived from chlorinated butadiene [neoprene, white, and buna rubber], and promotes flocculation [oilwell drilling fluids]. In commercial dye manufacture, salt is used as a brine rinse to help separate organic contaminants, promote salting out of dyestuff precipitates, and blend with dyes to standardize concentrated dyes.

Salt is a critical feedstock chemical and the basis for the enormous chloralkali industry encompassing sodium hydroxide, chlorine, and soda ash.

Salt (via electrolysis in diaphragm, mercury, or membrane cell) ➔ caustic soda (NaOH a.k.a. lye) + chlorine (1.75 t of salt yields 1.0 t chlorine + 1.1 t caustic soda). NaOH is an extremely versatile source of Na_2O (77.5%) [pulp & paper; soap & detergents; alumina processing; water treatment; pesticides; petroleum refining; food preparation; textiles & dyes] and a feedstock or intermediate chemical. NaOH + phosphoric acid ➔ sodium orthophosphate ➔ sodium tripolyphosphates (STPP) [detergents; food]. NaOH + S sand ➔ sodium silicate [detergents; catalysts; pigment; adhesives; paper; ore treatment].

Chlorine is a coproduct [pulp & paper; water treatment] ➔ vinyl chloride monomer (VCM)/ethylene dichloride (EDC) ➔ polyvinyl chloride (PVC) [pipes, flooring, siding, sheet, film, coating, wire & cable covering, bottles, & other molded objects].

Chlorine ➔ chloromethanes [chlorinated solvents] ➔ CFCs [aerosol propellants; refrigerants]; ➔ hydrochloric acid [food processing; chemical production; petroleum production; steel manufacture] ➔ hydrochlorides [rubber & plastics manufacturing; pharmaceuticals]. Along with fluorine, iodine, bromine, and astatine, chlorine is part of the halogen family.

Salt + limestone + ammonia in the Solvay process ➔ soda ash, Na_2CO_3 [glass & ceramics; soap & detergents; pulp & paper; water treatment; FGD] plus byproduct calcium chloride. Sodium carbonate (crude from the filtration stage) + steam ➔ sodium bicarbonate, $NaHCO_3$ [chemicals; baking & food; pharmaceuticals; detergents; textiles; food; fire extinguishers; FGD] ➔ sodium benzoate [food preservative; antiseptic; medicine; tobacco; rust/mildew inhibitor]. Light soda ash + sodium bicarbonate ➔ Sodium sesquicarbonate ($Na_2CO_3 \cdot NaHCO_3 \cdot 2H_2O$) [mild alkali in water softening, detergent].

Salt ➔ metallic sodium [lead antiknocks; titanium reduction; catalysts; dyes; pharmaceuticals; perfumes; herbicides]. Salt ➔ sodium hypochlorite, chlorine dioxide, sodium chlorate, sodium perchlorate [bleaching; pulp & paper].

SOURCES OF SODA

		Na₂O
Sodium hydroxide	NaOH	77.5
Salt	NaCl	62.0
Sodium carbonate	Na₂CO₃	58.5
Sodium silicate	Na₂SiO₃	50.8
Sodium sulfate	Na₂SO₄	43.7 ·
Sodium bicarbonate	NaHCO₃	36.9
Washing soda	Na₂CO₃·10H₂O	21.7

CHEMICAL ANALYSIS OF INDUSTRIAL SALT

	China	Mexico	Australia Port Hedland	Australia Dampier	Australia Lake MacCleod	Australia Shark Bay	Australia Port Alma	Australia Thevenard	India	Total Average
Moisture	2.77	2.19	2.32	1.94	1.79	1.99	3.52	2.08	4.71	2.59
NaCl	95.65	97.23	97.15	97.60	97.60	97.45	97.04	97.00	95.76	96.94
Na	37.63	38.24	38.22	38.40	38.40	38.35	37.67	38.16	36.59	37.96
Cl	58.28	59.04	58.99	59.26	59.28	59.21	58.13	58.89	56.92	58.67
SO₄	0.55	0.18	0.13	0.11	0.12	0.15	0.20	0.27	0.78	0.28
Ca	0.17	0.07	0.04	0.04	0.05	0.05	0.07	0.12	0.20	0.09
Mg	0.12	0.02	0.02	0.02	0.02	0.03	0.02	0.01	0.22	0.05
K	0.02	0.02	0.01	0.01	0.01	0.01	0.01	0.01	0.08	0.02
Insolubles	0.33	0.03	0.02	0.01	0.01	0.02	0.01	0.04	0.54	0.11

Source: Analysis of shipments to Japan in 1989.

Salt (via Downs Cell Electrolytic Process) → sodium metal [production of thorium, titanium, zirconium sponge; heat transfer liquid; sodium arc lights] and feedstock → sodium cyanide [gold & silver recovery; electroplating baths; fumigant & insecticide; ore flotation agent; feedstock for metallic cyanides]; → sodium ethylate [reducing agent in organic synthesis]; sodium hydride feedstock; descaling steel; alkylation of amines]; → sodium monoxide [polymerization agent; dehydrating agent; strong base].

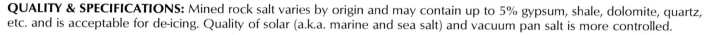

Consumption of salt in the United States
(tonnes)

- Ice Control and/or Stabilization 9,360,000
- Water Treatment 475,000
- General Industrial 1,977,000
- Food Processing 1,394,000
- Distributors 4,641,000
- Other, Not Elsewhere Specified* 2,248,000
- Agriculture 1,608,000
- Alkalies & Chlorine 22,061,000

Source: USBM (1991)

Salt → sodium hypochlorite [bleach; water purification; medicine]; → sodium bifluioride [antiseptic; specimen preservative; etching glass]; → sodium bisulfate [mineral flux; dyeing; soda alum; magnesia cements]; → sodium chlorate [ore processing; herbicide & defoliant; medicine; explosives; leather tanning; textile mordant; feedstock for ammonium perchlorate, sodium perchlorate, sodium iodate, chlorine dioxide]; → sodium sulfide [dyes; rayon; paper pulp; ore flotation; sheep dip; photographic reagent; soap; rubber].

QUALITY & SPECIFICATIONS: Mined rock salt varies by origin and may contain up to 5% gypsum, shale, dolomite, quartz, etc. and is acceptable for de-icing. Quality of solar (a.k.a. marine and sea salt) and vacuum pan salt is more controlled.

Chemical grade:- min. 95.5% NaCl, max. 2.5% moisture, 0.1% Ca, Mg, and K, and 0.5% insolubles.

Food grade:- min. 97.5%, max. 1 ppm As, 4 ppm heavy metals (as Pb), 2% Ca & Mg, 0.0016% Fe, and (for iodized salt) 0.010% - 0.006% iodine. Covered by FCC III Food Chemicals Codex, 3rd Edition administered by Food and Nutrition Board, National Academy of Sciences (United States).

Specialty salt:- (Alberger salt for food processing) min. 99.95% NaCl, 0.02-0.06% $CaSO_4$, max. 0.02% $CaCl_2$, 0.01% Na_2SO_4, 0.4 ppm Cu, 1.5 ppm Fe, 20 ppm insolubles, 0.1% surface moisture.

Other specifications in the United States include highway salt - ASTM-D-632-89 and American Association of State Highway Transportation Officials (AASHTO-M-143-86); medical salt - US Pharmacopoeia XXI, 1985, 21st Revision; packaging salt - ANSI/Z2353.1-19834/; soil stabilization salt - ASTM-D-1411-82; water treatment - General Services Administration (A-A-694) and ANSI/AWWA-B200-88.

APPARENT CONSUMPTION OF SALT (TONNES)

	Apparent Consumption
United States	40,619,449
China	20,099,366
Former USSR	14,200,844
Canada	11,374,291
Germany	10,511,563
India	9,117,033
Japan	8,415,013
United Kingdom	6,275,255
France	5,466,352
Italy	4,941,265
Romania	4,418,500
Spain	4,320,480
Brazil	4,113,827
Poland	3,863,758
Mexico	1,969,776
Turkey	1,904,666
Netherlands	1,254,871
Taiwan	1,017,204
Argentina	1,003,457
Pakistan	950,402
Indonesia	949,042
Sweden	929,198
Egypt	891,350
Belgium	878,839
Portugal	852,385

NOTE: Numbers are approximate and rounded and for 1990 or thereabouts; absence of a country does not necessarily indicate no production or trade; absence of a number does not necessarily mean zero

Source: British Geological Survey and USBM

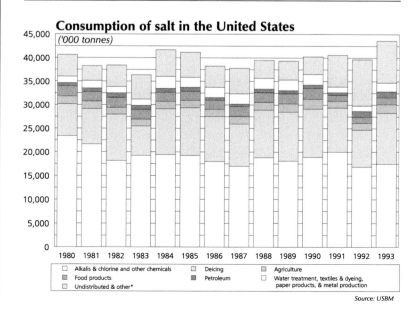

Consumption of salt in the United States
('000 tonnes)

Legend:
- Alkalis & chlorine and other chemicals
- Food products
- Undistributed & other*
- Deicing
- Petroleum
- Agriculture
- Water treatment, textiles & dyeing, paper products, & metal production

Source: USBM

WORLD CAPACITY: 220M. t.

CAPACITY UTILIZATION: 84%.

MARKET CONDITIONS: Stable - declining.

MARKETING FACTORS: Chemical production, particularly chloralkalis, is the major factor driving salt demand. For example, salt demand declined as the US Solvay plants gradually closed. Concern over the adverse environmental effects of chlorine has dampened demand which in turn has influenced salt demand. Weather is another indicator — harsh winters often create local or regional salt shortages.

HEALTH & SAFETY: Salt was identified as a possible cause of hypertension or high blood pressure, although subsequent tests have indicated that it may be a contributing factor in a small segment of the population. Nevertheless, it is generally considered prudent to moderate salt intake.

Capacity for salt
('000 tonnes)

Former USSR 18,688
Germany 16,352
India 12,706
Canada 12,339
United Kingdom 10,773
France 10,387
Australia 7,802
Romania 5,443
Brazil 5,080
Italy 5,107

220,890

China 29,937
Others* 77,567
Mexico 8,709

* more than 100 countries

On a positive note, iodized salt is used as a vehicle to introduce iodine to the human diet. Soils deficient in iodine expose the local population to the risk of iodine deficiency disorders (IDD) which in turn cause health problems ranging from goiter (enlargement of thyroid gland) to severe mental disorders. IDD also impairs reproduction in poultry, sheep, goats, and cattle plus lowers the yield of meat, wool, and/or milk. The effects of IDD can be totally eradicated by the introduction of iodine into the diet through edible salt (and salt licks in the case of animals). The concentration of iodine in the salt — generally added as sodium or potassium iodide/iodate — needs to be sufficient to supply 150-200 micrograms of iodine per capita per day (equivalent to one teaspoon per <u>lifetime</u>). This is generally regarded as 40-100 mg iodine per kilogram of salt (iodized salt contains 0.010% - 0.006% iodine).

SUBSTITUTES & ALTERNATIVES: Deicing:- calcium chloride and calcium magnesium acetate. **Food additive**:- potassium chloride.

RECYCLING: Virtually none. Some salt produced as a byproduct/waste in the production of other materials (such as potash mining) may be marketed.

PRODUCERS & WORLD TRADE: Salt is produced on a significant scale in more than 100 countries and on a more modest scale in many others. Most is consumed domestically, often forming the basis of a large chemical industry, although some low-cost, large-scale producers such as Australia and Mexico export significant quantities considerable distances.

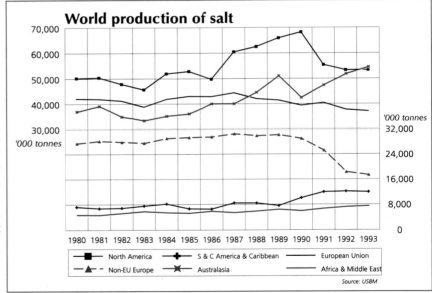

World production of salt

70,000
60,000
50,000
40,000
30,000
'000 tonnes

'000 tonnes
32,000
24,000
16,000
8,000
0

1980 1981 1982 1983 1984 1985 1986 1987 1988 1989 1990 1991 1992 1993

■ North America   ✚ S & C America & Caribbean   — European Union
▲ Non-EU Europe   ✕ Australasia   — Africa & Middle East

Source: USBM

PRODUCTION AND TRADE IN SALT (TONNES)

	Production	Imports	Exports	Apparent Consumption	Net Supplier	Net Consumer
North America	55,242,506	8,072,044	9,351,034	53,963,516	1,278,990	
South America	8,179,318	301,235	1,484,843	6,995,710	1,183,608	
Central America & Carib.	541,847	22,490	198,336	366,001	175,846	
European Union	40,074,817	3,646,184	8,529,630	35,191,371	4,883,446	
Non-EU Europe	27,329,263	3,363,403	1,299,560	29,393,106		(2,063,843)
Australasia	41,949,040	10,470,436	7,376,023	45,043,453		(3,094,413)
Middle East	1,904,951	26,826	29,973	1,901,804	3,147	
Africa	3,427,404	895,167	937,465	3,385,106	42,298	

NOTE: Numbers are approximate and rounded and for 1990 or thereabouts

Source: British Geological Survey and USBM

HTS CODES: 2501.000.000 (salt (including table and denatured salt) and pure sodium chloride, whether or not in aqueous solution, seawater).

PRICES: Salt $4 (evaporated, per 80-lb bag (36 kg), carlots or truckloads, N. USA); $66/t (evaporated, bulk, same basis); $4.30 (chemical grade, per 80-lb bag (36 kg), carlots or truckloads); $2.70 (medium, coarse, per 80lb bag (36kg), carlots or truckloads); $19.80-27.50/t (medium, coarse, bulk, ex-works, N. USA). Sodium chloride $0.64/kg (USP, granular, bagged). Australian solar salt, bulk, FOB $15-19/t. Rock salt, ground, delivered UK $30-45/t.

Chlorine $248-281/t (tanks, single units, FOB works, freight equalized). Sodium bromide $1.54/kg (bags, ex-works). Sodium hydroxide $2.49/kg (USP, pellets, drums, ex-works, freight equalized). Sodium metal ex-works $3.25/kg (12-lb bricks, drums); $3.10/kg (fused, drums); $2.53/kg (fused, tanks).

ETYMOLOGY: Halite from the Greek *hals = the sea*. **Salt** from the Latin *sal* which originated from the Greek for *hals = the sea*.

POSTSCRIPT: Essential to the human body itself, salt has spiced human history, geography, language, and food since ancient times.

SALT LEADERS

Producers	Importers	Exporters
United States	Japan	Australia
China	United States	Mexico
Former USSR	Canada	Germany
Germany	Belgium	Netherlands
Canada	Taiwan	United States
India	Sweden	Canada
Australia	Germany	Chile
Mexico	Finland	Bahamas
United Kingdom	Italy	France
France	Norway	Romania
Romania	Hungary	India
Italy	Nigeria	Togo
Poland	Bangladesh	China
Spain	Indonesia	Poland
Brazil	Netherlands	United Kingdom
Netherlands	Former Yugoslavia	Denmark
Turkey	Bulgaria	Former USSR
Chile	Malaysia	Argentina
Argentina	Brazil	Neth. Antilles
Bahamas	Spain	Italy
Egypt	France	Namibia
Pakistan	United Kingdom	Egypt
Iran	Hong Kong	South Africa
Portugal	South Africa	Senegal
South Africa	Czechoslovakia	Belgium

Historical price of salt in the United States

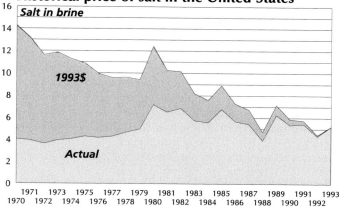

Salt in brine

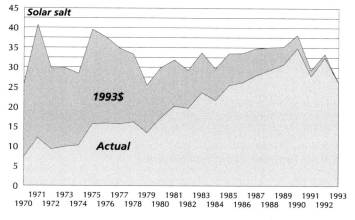

Rock salt

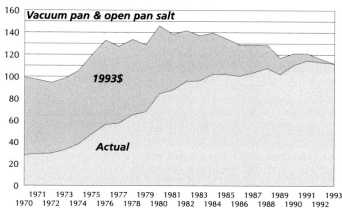

Solar salt

Vacuum pan & open pan salt

✧ Sandstone & silica sand   ✧ Quartz & quartzite   ✧ Quartz crystal   ✧ Tripoli & novaculite

✧ Synthetic silicas & silicon chemicals   ✧ Flint & silex   ✧ Diatomite (covered separately)

PROPERTIES & USES: *Consolidated sandstone* is resilient and may be crushed for aggregate [construction] and if aesthetically attractive, cut and shaped into blocks or slabs for building [dimension stone]. When crushed or ground, pure forms of *sandstone, silica sand, and quartzite* are a source of SiO_2 [glass, ceramics, chemicals] and fluxing agent [iron & steel; welding rods]. Silica is the principal glass-forming oxide making up approximately 60% of the soda-lime-silica glass batch. Silica sand/quartz is heat resistant to approx. 1,470°C and is used as a foundry sand in the manufacture of molds and cores for casting metals [steel; ductile iron; gray iron; aluminum- and copper-based alloys] and a refractory [iron & steel]. Acid-leached silica sand yields high-purity & ultra-high purity quartz ➔ synthetic quartz (see below).

Silica is relatively inexpensive, hard (H7), inert & resilient, with a conchoidal fracture [abrasive; filtration media; engine sand; construction sand & gravel] with certain grades having a round-shaped grain used as a proppant or fracturing sand to prop open fissures and voids in bedrock and so improve permeability [oilwell drilling & production]. These attributes plus whiteness, low oil absorption, and grindability to specific particle sizes allow silica sand and flour to be used as a filler [paint; plastics; rubber; adhesives; putty, caulks, and sealants].

Silica sand + soda ash or caustic soda ➔ sodium silicate (water glass) [detergents; catalysts; pigment; adhesives; paper; ore treatment; zeolite A manufacture]. Sodium silicate + metallic salts ➔ Al silicate [extender for TiO_2; filler in printing inks] and Ca silicate [carrier & flow additive for pesticides; additive in adhesives & rubber]. Sodium silicate + sulfuric acid ➔ various high-brightness (97%) precipitated silicas with particle sizes of 10-60nm and surface area of 25-700 m^2/gm used as a fine-grained filler, agent, & anti-slip agent [rubber, LDPE films, PVC, polyolefins], carriers [pesticides], liquid thickener & clarifier [printing inks; adhesives], free-flow & anti-caking agent [food; pharmaceuticals; chemicals; fertilizers] & silica gels with pores of 20-200 Å and a surface area of 240-800 m^2/gm [desiccant; static drying; flatting agent in paint; anti-caking agent].

Silica sand + potassium carbonate or caustic potash ➔ potassium silicate [welding rods; detergents]; + Bayer alumina ➔ synthetic mullite [refractories].

Quartz crystal may exhibit excellent clarity, color, and crystal shape [natural lenses & prisms; mineral specimens; gemstones] or piezoelectric properties which allow accurate frequency control, timing, & filtration [electronic circuitry]. Less perfect specimens (*lascas*) or upgraded silica sand are a source of SiO_2 ➔ cultured quartz [optical, electronic]; lascas/silica sand/silica tetrachloride ➔ fused silica [optical lenses; mirrors; windows] and vitreous silica (quartz glass) with low thermal expansion, refractoriness, inertness, and may be opaque or transparent [tubing; optical units; semiconductors].

Lump quartz/quartzite ➔ silicon [aluminum; steel; superalloys; chemicals] ➔ silicones used as lubricants, water-repellents, moisture proofing, electrical insulating [paint; rubber; plastics; surfactants; resins; pharmaceuticals; cosmetics; textiles], silanes [intermediate chemicals; surface modification agents], and silicon tetrachloride ➔ super-pure silicon [semiconductors; integrated circuits; solar cells; infrared optical systems], pyrogenic silicas & fumed silicas with particle sizes of 7-20nm are used for

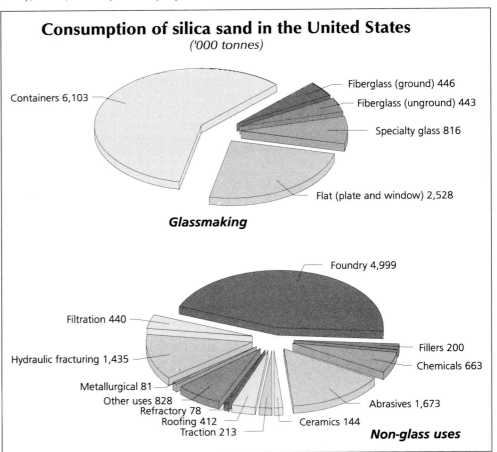

Consumption of silica sand in the United States
('000 tonnes)

Containers 6,103
Fiberglass (ground) 446
Fiberglass (unground) 443
Specialty glass 816
Flat (plate and window) 2,528

Glassmaking

Foundry 4,999
Filtration 440
Hydraulic fracturing 1,435
Metallurgical 81
Other uses 828
Refractory 78
Roofing 412
Traction 213
Ceramics 144
Abrasives 1,673
Chemicals 663
Fillers 200

Non-glass uses

thickening, viscosity control, thixotropy, reinforcement [plastics; rubber; adhesives; printing inks; pharmaceuticals; cosmetics].

Lump quartz/quartzite → ferrosilicon used as a deoxidizing and alloying agent [steel; cast iron; alloys & superalloys]. Byproduct microsilica (94-98% SiO_2 from silicon, 85-90% SiO_2 from ferrosilicon with spherical particles of 0.15 µm, and surface area of 20m^2/gm) is a filler [plastics; cement], superpozzolan [cement & concrete], and refractory [refractory cements, castables, and bricks]. Crushed quartz or silica sand + petroleum coke → green and black silicon carbide (SiC) which is inert, hard (Knoop 2,500), and highly refractory with high thermal conductivity and low thermal expansion [abrasives; bonded refractories; crucibles; hot cyclone liners; metal matrix composites]; + nitric acid → silicon nitride (SiN) [abrasives; specialty ceramics].

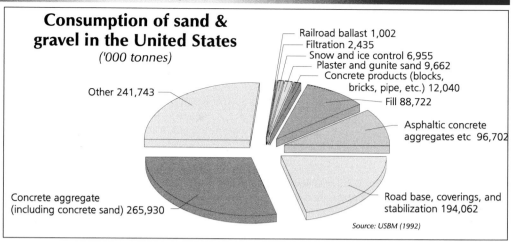

Consumption of sand & gravel in the United States
('000 tonnes)

- Railroad ballast 1,002
- Filtration 2,435
- Snow and ice control 6,955
- Plaster and gunite sand 9,662
- Concrete products (blocks, bricks, pipe, etc.) 12,040
- Fill 88,722
- Asphaltic concrete aggregates etc 96,702
- Road base, coverings, and stabilization 194,062
- Concrete aggregate (including concrete sand) 265,930
- Other 241,743

Source: USBM (1992)

Tripoli (a.k.a. amorphous silica) is an inert, porous, and friable microcrystalline silica with H7, SG 2.65, brightness of 84-91, and ave. particle size of 0.1-0.5 µm. It is white (dry) to gray (wet) with an index of refraction of 1.550 and an oil adsorption (rub-out method) of 17-20% and therefore is used as a filler/pigment [paint; rubber; plastics; adhesives & sealants] and abrasive [scouring powders; polishing compounds; tooth polishes]. Tripoli contributes durability, weatherability, and chemical resistance to floor, marine, highway, and other specialty paints. In adhesives, sealants, plastics, and rubber tripoli contributes whiteness, opacity, and rigidity and its low oil absorption allows a high level of loading (up to 75%) without increasing the viscosity.

Novaculite is a porous white to gray to light brown to black rock comprising closely packed sharp anhedral quartz grains (H7 and SG 2.63-2.64) which make an excellent abrasive [metal sharpening (whetstone, oilstones, hones, files); grinding media], refractory, and light-weight aggregate. *Flint* is compact cryptocrystalline chalcedonic silica [ceramics - bone china, earthenware] that is inert, with H7, SG 2.62, and a conchoidal fracture [grinding mill media; poultry grit]. *Silex* is a fine-grained siliceous rock (>96% SiO_2) with similar properties to flint [metal sharpening (whetstone, oilstones, hones, files); grinding media and ball-mill lining].

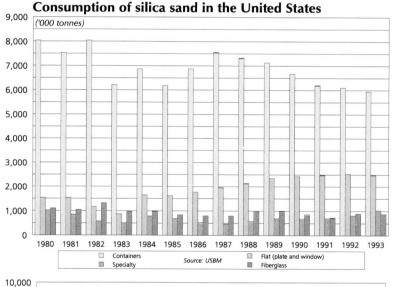

Consumption of silica sand in the United States
('000 tonnes)

- Containers
- Specialty
- Flat (plate and window)
- Fiberglass

Source: USBM

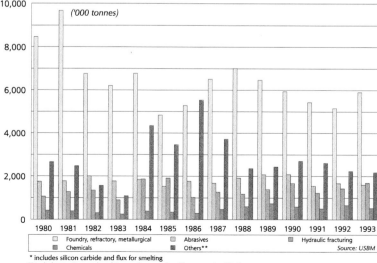

('000 tonnes)

- Foundry, refractory, metallurgical
- Chemicals
- Abrasives
- Others**
- Hydraulic fracturing

Source: USBM

* includes silicon carbide and flux for smelting
** includes traction, coal washing, roofing granules, fillers, ceramics, filtration

Consumption of quartz crystal in the United States
('000 kg)

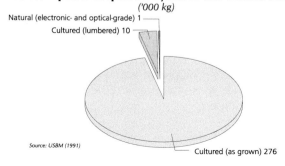

- Natural (electronic- and optical-grade) 1
- Cultured (lumbered) 10
- Cultured (as grown) 276

Source: USBM (1991)

QUALITY & SPECIFICATIONS: *Glass-grade silica sand:-* min. 98.5-99% SiO_2 with Fe_2O_3 of <0.04% (flat glass), 0.03% (flint container), 0.18% (amber container), and 0.3% (fiberglass), 0.2-1.6% Al_2O_3, with limits on alkalis, colorants (Ni, Cu, Co) & refractory minerals (chromite, zircon, rutile). *First grade optical glass:* -min. 99.8% SiO_2, <0.1% Al_2O_3 and 0.02% Fe_2O_3.

Ceramic-grade:- (-200 mesh) >97.5% SiO_2, <0.55% Al_2O_3 & 0.2% Fe_2O_3.

Filtration sand:- relatively pure and free of dust, clay, and micaceous or organic matter. Grain shape should be angular or round but should not be elongated or flat. A uniform size is required with a narrow PSD which is measured by effective size (size of a sieve opening that will just pass 10% by weight of a representative sample) and uniformity coefficient (a ratio of the size of a sieve opening that will just pass 60% of a representative sample of the sand to the size of the sieve opening that will just pass 10% (i.e. the effective size) of the same sample).

Foundry sand:- (-200 & -200 mesh) min. 98% SiO_2 with limits on CaO and MgO in order to reduce the acid demand value (ADV) which is a measure of the binder required. Particle size may be quantified by the American Foundryman's Society or AFS grain fineness number which is approximately the number of openings per inch corresponding to a sieve that would pass a sand sample if its grains were of uniform size, i.e. the average size of grains in the sample.

Frac or proppant sand:- well-rounded sand with only minor amounts of impurities such as clay, feldspar, and calcite (<0.3% solubility in HCl). Common screen sizes are 3.35x1.70mm; 2.36x1.18mm; 1.70x0.850mm; 0.425x0.212mm; and 0.212x0.106mm.

Flux sand:- (iron & steel) lumpy >90% SiO_2. *Refractory sand:-* 95-99% SiO_2.

Ground silica and silica flour:- <0.10% Fe_2O_3, <0.38% Al_2O_3, <0.10% Na_2O, <0.10%K_2O. Flour has an APS of 60 µm and both require a brightness of 89%+.

Sodium silicate feedstock:- >99.4% SiO_2, <0.03% Fe_2O_3.

Tripoli:- 98-99.5% SiO_2, 0.025-1% Fe_2O_3 with particle size 99% -74 µm to 99% -10 µm. *Novaculite* > 60% SiO_2, 20% Al_2O_3, 3% C, & 2% Fe_2O_3; porosity range 0.07 (Arkansas Stone for perfect edges) to 16% (Washita Stone for rapid sharpening).

Flint:- (typical) 97.4% SiO_2, 0.35% Al_2O_3, trace Fe_2O_3, 0.46% CaO, 0.18% MgO, 1.3% LOI; 10 µm APS (ceramics) and 1½-2½", 2½-3". & 3"-4" (grinding pebbles).

Feedstock for: *silicon:-* >98.5-99% SiO_2, <0.1% Fe_2O_3, <0.15% Al_2O_3, no P or As, <0.2% CaO, MgO, and LOI with lumps >2.54cm diameter and a min. softening point of 1,700°C and decrepitation point of 950°C; *ferrosilicon:-* >98% SiO_2, < 0.2% Fe_2O_3, 0.4% Al_2O_3, 0.2% CaO and MgO, & 0.1% P with lumps of 0.32-10.16cm diameter; *SiC:-* >99.7% SiO_2, < 0.05% Fe_2O_3 & Al_2O_3, 0.01% CaO, & 5% moisture; *cultured and synthetic quartz:-* Fe, Al, transition elements, alkali content measured in the <100 and even <10ppm ranges.

Lascas:- ave. 15-20ppm Al, 2-5ppm Fe, 2-25ppm Na, 2-10ppm K, & 1ppm Ca, Mg, Li, Ti and are divided into Grade 1:- 90% clear to the unaided eye and essentially free of crystal faces; Grade 2:- 50-60% clear to the unaided eye, contains minor air and water inclusions but essentially clear of crystal faces; Grade 3:- translucent to light; Grade 4:- opaque quartz of milky white appearance. Cultured quartz may be "as grown" or processed by sawing and grinding to form "lumbered quartz".

WORLD CAPACITY: Silica sand 150M. t; ferrosilicon/silicon 4M. t contained silicon.

MARKET CONDITIONS: Silica sand:- steady; silicon:- increasing; ferrosilicon:- decreasing.

MARKETING FACTORS: Glass & ceramics depend on the construction activity which is driven by the economy. Consumption is affected by increased glass recycling. Due to a combination of negative economic and health & safety factors, consumption of silica in markets such as abrasives, foundry sands, and fillers continues to decline.

HEALTH & SAFETY: In 1987 crystalline silica was classified as a probable carcinogen by the International Agency for Research on Cancer (IARC), a unit of the World Health Organization. This was followed by IARC's Supplement 7 in which crystalline silica was classified in Group 2A, that is probably carcinogenic to humans. Therefore, silica comes under the OSHA Hazard Communication Standards, 29 CFR Section 1900.1200 which require labeling and other forms of warning, material safety data sheets, and employee training for products containing identified carcinogens with concentrations greater than 0.1%.

Some grades of silica sand have been certified for permissible dry outdoor blasting by the State of California Air Resources Board.

RECYCLING: The use of cullet or recycled glass is increasing which in turn is reducing the need for virgin raw materials in the glass batch. The recycling rate is about 33% in the United States and as high as 90% in some European countries like Switzerland. Silica sand used in abrasive blasting is not usually recycled since it is cheap and breaks down rapidly during use.

CHEMICAL COMPOSITION OF SILICA GLASS SANDS (%)

	USA New Jersey	USA Illinois	USA Oklahoma	USA California	France Fontainebleau	UK Loch Aline
SiO_2	99.66	99.81	99.73	92.76	99.65	99.73
Fe_2O_3	0.025	0.017	0.020	0.127	0.02	0.013
Al_2O_3	0.143	0.055	.090	3.779	0.08	0.057
TiO_2	0.027	0.015	0.012	0.034	NA	NA
CaO	0.007	<0.01	<0.01	0.060	NA	NA
MgO	0.004	<0.01	<0.01	0.017	NA	NA
K_2O	-	-	-	2.734	-	-
Na_2O	-	-	-	0.114	-	-
LOI	0.130	0.100	0.140	0.373	0.13	0.04

COMPOSITION OF SiC GRAIN (%)

	Black	Green
SiC	97.5	98.6
Free SiC	0.5	0.15
Free C	0.6	0.36
SiO_2	0.8	0.63
Fe	0.2	0.08
Al	0.2	0.08
Ca	0.05	0.05
Mg	0.5	0.03

TYPICAL FILTRATION SAND (%)

Sizes (mm)	Uniformity coefficient max.	—— Chemical ——	
		SiO_2	99.39
0.40 - 0.50	1.60	Fe_2O_3	0.24
0.50 - 0.60	1.60	Al_2O_3	0.19
0.60 - 0.70	1.60	TiO_2	0.12
0.70 - 0.80	1.60	CaO	0.01
0.80 - 1.00	1.65	MgO	0.004
1.00 - 1.50	1.70	LOI	0.046

MAXIMUM IMPURITY LEVELS FOR VITREOUS SILICA (PPM)

	Translucent	Transparent Type I	Transparent Type II
Al	500	74	68
Sb	na	0.3	0.1
B	9	4	3
Ca	200	16	0.4
Cr	na	0.1	na
Cu	na	1	1
OH	na	60	450
Fe	77	7	1.5
Li	3	7	1
Mg	150	4	na
Mn	na	1	0.2
P	na	0.01	0.005
K	37	6	<1
Na	60	9	5
Ti	120	3	2
Zr	15	3	na

Type I obtained by electric melting of mineral quartz

Type II obtained by flame fusing of quartz

Source: Encyclopoedia of Chemical Technology, John Wley & Sons Inc., 1982

COMPOSITION OF FUSED SILICA (%)

	UK	N'lands	USA
SiO_2	99.7	99.5	99.6
Fe_2O_3	0.02	0.01	0.03
Al_2O_3	0.08	0.20	0.20
TiO_2	0.02	0.05	-
CaO+MgO	0.07	0.02	0.04
Na_2O+K_2O	0.07	0.03	0.01

HIGH-PURITY FLOTATION QUARTZ SAND FOR FUSED QUARTZ (PPM)

	IOTA Standard Mean	IOTA Standard Max.	IOTA-4 Mean	IOTA-4 Max.	IOTA-6 Mean	IOTA-6 Max.
Al	15.2	22.0	7.9	10.0	7.9	9.5
Ca	0.4	1.5	0.6	1.0	0.5	0.7
Fe	0.3	1.5	0.6	1.0	0.2	0.3
Li	0.7	1.5	0.2	1.0	0.2	0.3
Na	0.9	1.5	1.0	1.3	0.1	0.2
K	0.7	1.5	0.4	1.0	0.1	0.2
B	0.08	0.10	0.04	0.05	0.03	0.04

Max. 1% >300μ: Max. 1% <75μ

IOTA Standard - in manufacture of quartz tubing used in halogen and high-intensity discharge lights

IOTA-4 & IOTA-6 - in manufacture of semiconductor quartz glass such as CZ crucibles, diffusion tubes, quartz rods and ingots

Source: Unimin Corp.

COMPOSITION OF TRIPOLI & NOVACULITE (%)

	Illinois Tripoli	Arkansas Novaculite
SiO_2	98.60	99.49
Fe_2O_3	0.05	0.039
Al_2O_3	0.70	0.102
TiO_2	0.05	0.015
CaO	0.04	0.014
MgO	0.04	0.021
Na_2O	0.03	
K_2O	0.05	
LOI	0.44	
APS, μm	1.5-1.9*	7.3-12.9
	2.1-2.5**	8.9-14.9

* micronized; ** airfloated

SUBSTITUTES & ALTERNATIVES: Abrasives:- bauxite & alumina (fused alumina), corundum/emery, diamonds, diatomite, feldspar, garnet, iron oxide (magnetite), nepheline syenite, olivine, perlite, pumice, silica sand, staurolite, tripoli, and silicon carbide, ilmenite. **Anti-blocking agent:-** calcined kaolin, diatomite, talc. **Construction:-** crushed granite, limestone, marble, traprock, etc. **Dimension stone**:- granite, marble, limestone, soapstone, slate, brick. **Filler:-** ATH, barite, calcium carbonate, diatomite, feldspar, kaolin, mica, nepheline syenite, perlite, talc, wollastonite. **Filter media**:- Activated carbon/anthracite, asbestos, cellulose, diatomite, garnet, iron oxide (magnetite), perlite, pumice, ilmenite. **Foundry**:- bauxite & alumina, chromite, clays (kaolin & bauxite), olivine, perlite, pyrophyllite, vermiculite, zircon. **Frac sand:-** alumina-based proppants. **Friction material**:- asbestos, barite, bauxite & alumina, clays (attapulgite, kaolin, sepiolite), garnet, graphite, gypsum, mica, pumice, pyrophyllite, slate, vermiculite, wollastonite, zircon. **Refractories:-** andalusite, bauxite, chromite, kyanite, dolomite, graphite, magnesite, olivine, pyrophyllite, refractory clays, sillimanite, zircon.

PRODUCERS & WORLD TRADE: A very common commodity, silica is produced and consumed in most countries which, combined with the low price of most silica products, minimizes trade. However, silica with the desired specifications is less common and may be shipped to large markets without a local source. Production of silicon and ferrosilicon is more dependent on the availability of low-cost energy than a source of silica.

EXPORTERS: Virtually all the large producers of higher quality silica products are exporters.

IMPORTERS: Largely importing specific grades unavailable domestically.

HTS CODES: 2502.90 (construction sand); 2517.10 (construction gravel); 2505.10 (industrial sand, >95% silica, <0.6% iron oxide); 2506.10.0010 (quartz sand, other than natural); 2506.10.0050 (quartz sand, other); 2506.21.0000 (quartzite); 2804.61.0000 (silicon, >99.99% Si); 2804.69.1000 (silicon, 99.00-99.99% Si); 2804.69.5000 (silicon, other); 2811.22.1000 (synthetic silica gel); 2811.22.5000 (other synthetic silica gel); 2849.20.1000 (carbides of silicon, crude); 2849.20.2000 (carbides of silicon, in grains, or ground, pulverized, or refined); 7202.21.1000 (ferrosilicon, 55-80% Si, >3% Ca); 7202.21.5000 (ferrosilicon, 55-80% Si, other); 7202.21.7500 (ferrosilicon, 80-90% Si); 7202.21.9000 (ferrosilicon, >90% Si); 7202.29.0010 (ferrosilicon, other, >3% Mg); 7202.29.0050 (ferrosilicon, other).

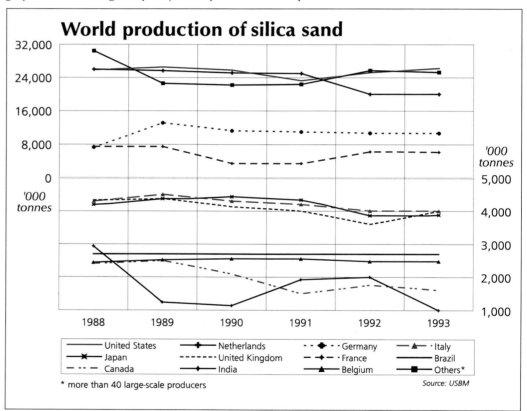

World production of silica sand

Source: USBM

* more than 40 large-scale producers

United States — Netherlands — Germany — Italy — Japan — United Kingdom — France — Brazil — Canada — India — Belgium — Others*

PRICES: Silica sand $8-25/t. Tripoli $200-305/t (micronized); $115-155/t (air-floated). Novaculite $110-185/t. As grown cultured quartz $30/kg; lumbered quartz $140/kg.

Potassium silicate (ex-works) $529/t (solution, 29.8-30.2°Be, 2.5 ratio*, tank cars); $727/t (solution, 29.8-30.2°Be, 2.1 ratio*, drums); $702/t (40-40.5°Be, 2.1 ratio*, tank cars); $898/t (40-40.5°Be, 2.1 ratio*, drums); $732/t (electronics, 20-30.4°Be, 2.1 ratio*); $927/t (electronics, 30-30.4°Be, 2.1-2.2 ratio*, drums); $1,276/t (solid or glass, 2.5 ratio*, drums). Sodium silicate (bulk, ex-works) $496/t (solid or glass, 3.22-3.25 ratio**); $6427/t (solid or glass, 1.95-2.00 ratio**); $198/t (41° solid, 3.22-3.25 ratio**, freight equalized).

SILICA LEADERS (PRODUCTION ONLY)

Silica sand	Ferrosilicon/silicon	Cultured quartz
United States	Former USSR	United States
Netherlands	United States	Japan
Argentina	Norway	Germany
Germany	China	Belgium
Italy	Brazil	Brazil
Japan	France	France
United Kingdom	S. Africa	S. Korea
France	Canada	United Kingdom
Brazil	Italy	**Vitreous silica**
India	Japan	United States
Belgium	Argentina	Germany
Spain	Spain	Japan
Australia	India	United Kingdom
Austria	Iceland	France
Paraguay	Egypt	**Fused silica**
South Africa	Germany	United States
Canada	Sweden	Germany
Mexico	Venezuela	Netherlands
Tripoli & novaculite		United Kingdom
United States		
Flint		
France		
Denmark		
Belgium		

Silicon tetrachloride, technical, ex-works $5.40/kg (drums); 3.20/kg (tanks). Silicon metal $1,125-1,200/t (min. 98%, ex-works, UK); $750-760/t (min. 98.5%, fob main Chinese port). 50% ferrosilicon $1.10/kg; 75% FeSi $1.08/kg (all per kg of contained silicon). SiC (CIF Europe) $1,125-1,200/t (black, 99%, Grade 1)); $1,050-1,125/t (black, 99%, Grade 2); $1,275-1,425/t (green, 99.5%, FEPA 8-220).

* ratio is % by weight SO_3 : K_2O;

** ratio is % by weight SO_3 : Na_2O

ETYMOLOGY: **Agate** for the River Achates, now Drillo in Sicily, where it was originally found. **Aggregate** from the Latin *aggregatus* = *to lead to a flock, add to*. **Chalcedony** from Chalcedon or Calchedon, an ancient maritime city of Bithynia on the Sea of Marmara in modern Turkey. **Chert** origin is unknown. **Cristobalite** for Cerro San Cristóbal near Pachuca, Mexico and Greek *lithos* = *stone*. **Flint** from the Greek *plinthos* = *a brick*. **Jade/jadeite** from the Spanish term *piedra de yjada* = stone of the side since the stone was supposed to cure side pains. **Jasper** from the Latin *iaspis*, which is of oriental origin, equivalent to the Persian *iashm* and *jashp* and the Assyrian *ashpu*. **Novaculite** from the Latin *novacula* = *razor hone* alluding to its use as a sharpening stone. **Quartz** from the Saxon word *querkluftertz* = *cross-vein ore*; first condensed to *quererz*. **Tridymite** from the Greek *tridymos* = *threefold* since the crystals are often trillings. **Tripoli** for the city of Tripoli, Libya, in North Africa where a variety occurs (the rock is actually a diatomaceous earth).

Silicon & ferrosilicon prices

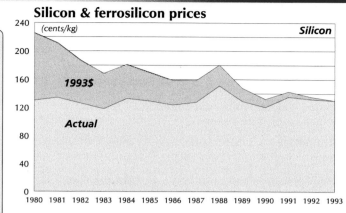

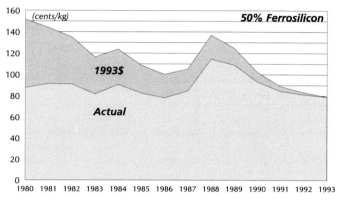

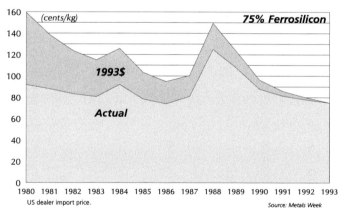

US dealer import price.

Source: Metals Week

Historical price of sand & gravel in the United States

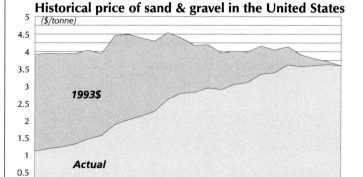

SILLIMANITE MINERALS

Minerals	Formula	Color	SG	H	Temp. of mullitization	Volume change on conversion
Andalusite	Al_2SiO_5	gray to flesh red	3.13-3.16	7.5	$1,380^\circ C$	+ 5%
Kyanite	Al_2SiO_5	light blue to white	3.53-3.65	4-7	$1,350^\circ C$	+ 18%
Sillimanite	Al_2SiO_5	brown-gray-green	3.23-3.27	6-7	$1,550^\circ C$	+ 7%

Related but currently non-commercial minerals are topaz $(9Al_2SiO_4(OH,F)_2)$, dumortierite $(Al_7(BO_3)(SiO_4)_3O_3)$, and pinite (actually a mixture of sericite + chlorite + serpentine).

PROPERTIES & USES: Andalusite, kyanite, and sillimanite are the structural polymorphs of Al_2SiO_5 and form the sillimanite group of minerals. When calcined, all three minerals convert to mullite plus free silica.

$$3(Al_2O_3 \cdot SiO_2) + heat \rightarrow 3Al_2O_3 \cdot 2SiO_2 + SiO_2$$

Andalusite → mullite + free silica

Mullite, which does not occur in commercial quantities in nature, may be formed by the calcination of other aluminosilicate minerals such as refractory clays, and pyrophyllite; other forms include sintered mullite produced by calcining a mixture of kaolin and bauxite at $1,750^\circ C$ and fused mullite derived from the fusing of a combination alumina and silica. In all cases, it is the mullite that is the ultimate commercial product with the minerals merely being a convenient and natural feedstock.

By far the most important use of mullite and therefore the sillimanite minerals is as a refractory. Mullite consists of interlocking crystals that remain stable up to $1,800^\circ C$ which in turn imparts good refractoriness, a high loading capacity, and excellent creep resistance at high temperatures [refractory lining for blast, copper roasting, and glass furnaces, cement kilns, and combustion chambers; ladles, nozzles, kiln furniture]. Additional advantages include resistance to thermal shock due to its low thermal

ANALYSIS OF SILLIMANITE (%)

	India Sillimanite OR grade	China Sillimanite Jixi Mine	China Sillimanite Henan	China Sillimanite Tuguiwula Mine	China Sillimanite Putian Mine
Al_2O_3	60.1	26.48	25.36	21.06	17.77
SiO_2	36.9	59.74	50.79	64.49	78.50
Fe_2O_3	0.5	2.55	13.00	6.02	0.23
FeO		3.21		2.63	0.14
Total Fe	NA				
TiO_2	0.32	1.40	1.40	0.44	0.48
CaO	NA	0.26	0.22	1.00	0.26
MgO	NA	0.75	0.92	0.064	0.11
K_2O		3.50	1.86	0.31	0.19
Na_2O		0.33	0.14	0.02	0.13
Alkalis	NA				
MnO_2		0.08		0.023	
P_2O_5		0.09		0.079	
C					
LOI	NA				

Source: Feng & Wu, 1994 (China)

ANALYSIS OF KYANITE (%)

	USA Raw kyanite	USA* Mullite calcine	Sweden Kyanite
Al_2O_3	54.00-60.06	54.17-60.06	59.8
SiO_2	37.64-43.70	37.84-43.73	35.8
Fe_2O_3	0.16-0.94	0.16-0.94	NA
Total Fe	NA	NA	1.3
TiO_2	0.67	0.67	0.64
CaO	0.03	0.03	0.2
MgO	0.01	0.01	0.2
K_2O			
Na_2O			
Alkalis	0.42	0.42	0.028
C			
LOI	0.21	-	0.43

* from US kyanite

ANALYSIS OF ANDALUSITE (%)

	S. Africa Andalusite Purusite	S. Africa Andalusite Randalusite	S. Africa Andalusite Andrafrax	S. Africa Andalusite Krugerire	France Andalusite KF	France Andalusite KA	France Andalusite KB	China Andalusite Jilin	China Andalusite Shangxi	China Andalusite Henan	China Andalusite Liaoning	China Andalusite Jiangxi
Al_2O_3	59.1	60.0	59.3	57.5	60.0	59.0	53.0	20.27	51.23	19.02	19.83	22.87
SiO_2	38.6	37.9	38.6	40.4	38.4	38.5	44.2	65.38	31.34	61.7	60.28	57.44
Fe_2O_3	0.84	0.7	0.9	0.9	0.5	1.0	1.1	6.16	4.26	7.64	7.92	7.60
Total Fe	NA	NA										
TiO_2	0.14	0.15	0.2	0.3	0.2	0.2	0.3	0.71	2.78	0.79	0.60	1.60
CaO	0.16	0.15	0.1	0.1	0.1	0.1	0.1	0.16	3.28	0.42		1.6
MgO	0.11	0.12	0.1	0.1	0.1	0.1	0.2	0.83	0.71	2.15		1.6
K_2O	0.3	0.21	0.2	0.2	0.2	0.3	0.4	4.96	0.91	2.80	3.65	2.80
Na_2O	0.09	0.07	0.1	0.1	0.1	0.1	0.2	1.28	0.16	1.06	1.73	
Alkalis	0.32	0.19										
C										1.11	1.30	
LOI	0.82	0.7	0.6	0.05	0.6	0.7	0.7		1.18	2.48	2.60	

Source: Feng & Wu, 1994 (China); Dickson, 1994 (S. Africa & France)

APPARENT CONSUMPTION OF SILLIMANITE MINERALS (TONNES)

	Apparent Consumption
Former USSR*	100,000
Germany	88,379
South Africa** & ***	85,425
Czechoslovakia	75,000
Romania	70,000
United States*	58,528
United Kingdom	48,234
Japan	34,175
Italy	21,829
South Korea	17,712
Spain**	15,887
France**	14,032
India * & ***	7,399
Belgium	6,910
Australia*	6,722
Canada	6,358
Netherlands	4,781
Sweden*	4,597
China	2,500
Zimbabwe*	2,463
Norway	2,452
Mexico	2,231
Austria	2,209
Denmark	1,660
Finland	1,091
Brazil*	1,000

*production mainly * kyanite; ** andalusite; *** sillimanite*

NOTE: Numbers are approximate and rounded for 1991 or thereabouts; absence of a country does not necessarily indicate no production or trade; absence of a number does not necessarily mean zero

Source: British Geological Survey

expansion, satisfactory thermal conductivity, resistance to chemical attack and abrasion, and its electric resistivity.

Although similar chemically, each of the sillimanite minerals has a different crystal structure and therefore physical properties. Of the three minerals, kyanite converts to mullite at the lowest temperature, but with the highest volume change (expansion); andalusite converts at a slightly higher temperature but with only a moderate volume change. Sillimanite's volume change is similar to andalusite, although the conversion temperature is 200°C higher. The lower expansion of andalusite eliminates the need for precalcination and therefore reduces energy consumption and improves controlled dimensions. It is also an advantage in monolithic materials and unfired bricks and shapes since it tends to seal the joints and form a monolithic structure. Andalusite in particular has excellent resistance in reducing environments, low porosity, and a low coefficient of expansion [specialty refractories like castables, gunning & ramming mixes; graphitic pitch-bonded; monolithics]. Kyanite is mainly used in monolithics.

Andalusite and kyanite may also be used in ceramics [sanitaryware, whiteware, and spark-plug bodies; acoustic tiles; investment castings; and foundry sand]. The sillimanite minerals have a moderately high SG and H with an uneven and tough fracture [abrasives; non-slip flooring].

QUALITY & SPECIFICATIONS: Sillimanite minerals require min. 54% Al_2O_3 and 42% SiO_2 with max. 1% Fe_2O_3, 2% TiO_2, and 0.1% each CaO & MgO. Lumpy or boulder-size ore is preferred to yield coarse-grained material for high-duty refractories; fine-grained must be blended or used in monolithic refractories. General analysis from commercial examples is as follows:

	Al_2O_3	Fe_2O_3
Andalusite	57-61%	0.6-0.9%
Kyanite	54-61%	0.1-1.0%
Sillimanite	40-58%	0.5%
Fused mullite	72-78%	0.5-0.15%

WORLD CAPACITY: 670,000 t. **CAPACITY UTILIZATION:** NA.

MARKET CONDITIONS: Stable; higher grades of mullite are becoming increasingly popular.

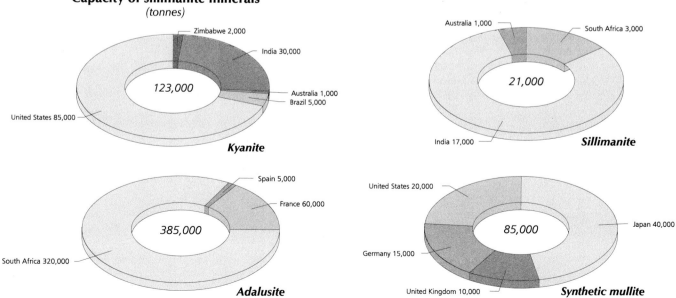

Capacity of sillimanite minerals
(tonnes)

Kyanite — 123,000
- Zimbabwe 2,000
- India 30,000
- Australia 1,000
- Brazil 5,000
- United States 85,000

Sillimanite — 21,000
- Australia 1,000
- South Africa 3,000
- India 17,000

Adalusite — 385,000
- Spain 5,000
- France 60,000
- South Africa 320,000

Synthetic mullite — 85,000
- United States 20,000
- Japan 40,000
- Germany 15,000
- United Kingdom 10,000

Source: USBM 1993

MARKETING FACTORS: Production of iron & steel, cement, and glass which in turn depends on the construction industry and therefore the state of the economy. The trend towards higher quality refractories is boosting demand, although this is countered by greater efficiency in the refractory industry.

HEALTH & SAFETY: Crystalline silica has been classified as a probable carcinogen by the IARC (see silica for further details). Therefore, because of its crystalline silica content, unless processing has the capability to reduce the crystalline silica content to less than 0.1%, sillimanite minerals will come under the OSHA Hazard Communication Standards, 29 CFR Section 1900.1200 which require labeling and other forms of warning, material safety data sheets, and employee training for products containing identified carcinogens with concentrations greater than 0.1%.

RECYCLING: Virtually none.

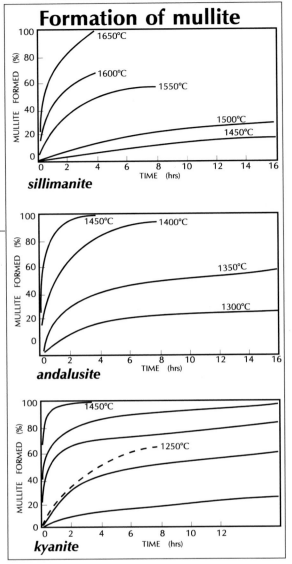

Formation of mullite

sillimanite

andalusite

kyanite

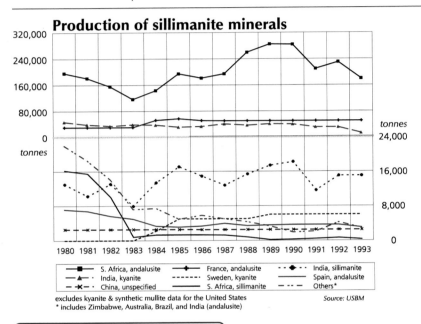

Production of sillimanite minerals

excludes kyanite & synthetic mullite data for the United States
* includes Zimbabwe, Australia, Brazil, and India (andalusite)

Source: USBM

Legend:
- S. Africa, andalusite
- India, kyanite
- China, unspecified
- France, andalusite
- Sweden, kyanite
- S. Africa, sillimanite
- India, sillimanite
- Spain, andalusite
- Others*

FUSED AND SINTERED MULLITE (%)

	UK Keith Ceramic Materials	UK Keith Ceramic Materials	UK Keith Ceramic Materials Zirconia mullite	Germany Huls	Brazil Elfusa	USA Washington Mills	Hungary Hungalu
	Sintered	Dense Fused					
Al₂O₃	73.3	76.3	45.8	75.2	72.3	77.7	76.0
SiO₂	24.7	23.3	17.1	24.5	28.5	21.8	23.0
Fe₂O₃	0.5	max. 0.1	max. 0.2	0.05	0.13	0.12	0.08
FeO							
Total Fe							
TiO₂	max. 0.2	max. 0.02	max. 0.2	0.01		0.05	0.05
CaO				0.04	0.15		0.15
MgO				0.03	0.15		0.01
CaO+MgO	max. 0.2	max. 0.1	max. 0.1				
K₂O	0.82	max. 0.02	max. 0.02	0.01	0.04		
Na₂O	max. 0.3	max. 0.3	max. 0.3	0.20	0.38		
Na₂O+K₂O						0.35	0.25
ZrO₂+HfO₂			36.5				

Source: Dickson, 1994

SILLIMANITE MINERAL LEADERS

Producers	Importers	Exporters
South Africa** & ***	Germany	South Africa
Former USSR*	United Kingdom	India
United States*	Japan	France
Czechoslovakia	Italy	United States
Romania	South Korea	Germany
India * & ***	Spain	Japan
France**	France	United Kingdom
Sweden*	Belgium	Sweden
Spain**	Netherlands	Netherlands
China	Canada	Italy
Brazil*	Australia	Belgium
Australia*	United States	

* kyanite; ** andalusite; *** sillimanite

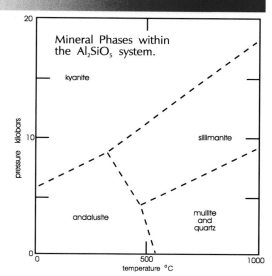

Mineral Phases within the Al_2SiO_5 system.

kyanite

sillimanite

andalusite

mullite and quartz

pressure kilobars

temperature °C

PRODUCERS & WORLD TRADE: Andalusite production is dominated by South Africa, France, and Spain; kyanite by the Former USSR, United States, India, Sweden, Brazil, and Zimbabwe; and sillimanite by India and South Africa. Synthetic mullite is produced where possible close to sources of low-cost energy in the United States, Japan, Germany, United Kingdom, and Italy.

PRICES: Andalusite FOB, Transvaal, South Africa, bulk $160-180/t (57.5% Al_2O_3); 180-200/t (59.5% Al_2O_3). Kyanite USA, 54-60% Al_2O_3, 35-325 Tyler mesh FOB Virginia, USA, bulk $110-140 (raw); $202-232 (calcined). Sillimanite (South African) CIF Europe, bags $285/t (70% Al_2O_3).

HTS CODES: 2508.50 (kyanite, sillimanite, andalusite, and dumortierite); 2508.60 (mullite).

SUBSTITUTES & ALTERNATIVES: Refractory:- fused and sintered mullite (60-76%+); calcined kaolin, flint clay, chamotte (35-45% Al_2O_3); pyrophyllite (28-29% Al_2O_3).

ETYMOLOGY: Andalusite for Andalusia, Spain. **Dumortierite** for Eugène Dumortier (1802-1873), French paleontologist. **Kyanite** from the Greek *kyanos = dark blue* reflecting its color. **Mullite** for the island of Mull, Scotland, Greek *lithos* = stone. **Sillimanite** for Professor Benjamin Silliman (1779-1864), American mineralogist, Yale. **Topaz** from the Greek *Topazion = to seek* and the name of an island in the Red Sea which is difficult to see since it is covered by mist.

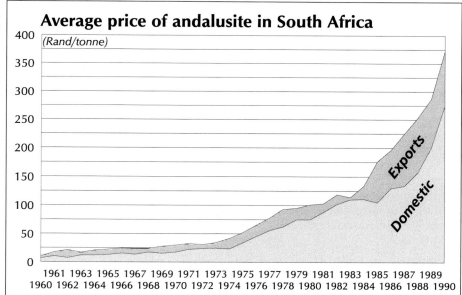

Average price of andalusite in South Africa

(Rand/tonne)

Exports

Domestic

1960 1961 1962 1963 1964 1965 1966 1967 1968 1969 1970 1971 1972 1973 1974 1975 1976 1977 1978 1979 1980 1981 1982 1983 1984 1985 1986 1987 1988 1989 1990

PRODUCTION AND TRADE IN SILLIMANITE MINERALS (TONNES)

	Production	Imports	Exports	Apparent Consumption	Net Supplier	Net Consumer
North America	85,000	14,190	32,073	67,117	17,883	
South America	1,000			1,000		
European Union	53,600	207,662	59,532	201,730		(148,130)
Non-EU Europe	251,000	7,577	2,386	256,191		(5,191)
Australasia	60,799	63,221		124,020		(63,221)
Africa	210,246	2,463	124,821	87,888	122,358	

NOTE: Numbers are approximate and rounded for 1991 or thereabouts

Source: British Geological Survey

Minerals	Formula	% Na_2CO_3	%Na_2O	Color	SG	H
Trona	$Na_2CO_3 \cdot NaHCO_3 \cdot 2H_2O$	70.4	62.0	gray or yellowish white	2.18	2.5-3

Other minerals containing sodium carbonate of less commercial significance include:

		%Na_2CO_3
Nahcolite	Na_2HCO_3	63.1
Northupite	$2Na_2CO_3 \cdot NaCl \cdot MgCO_3$	40.6
Gaylussite	$Na_2CO_3 \cdot CaCO_3 \cdot 5H_2O$	35.8
Shortite	$Na_2CO_3 \cdot 2CaCO_3$	34.6
Burkeite	$Na_2CO_3 \cdot 2Na_2SO_4$	27.2
Hanksite	$2Na_2CO_3 \cdot 9Na_2SO_4 \cdot KCl$	13.6

Commercial soda ash, Na_2CO_3, is extracted from lake brines or the mineral trona, the natural sodium sesquicarbonate (1.8 t trona → 1 t soda ash) or produced synthetically via the ammonia-soda or Solvay process which utilizes 1.7 t of salt, 1.4 t of limestone, 0.6 t coal for the boilers and 0.2 t for the dryers, and an ammonia catalyst to produce 1 t of soda ash plus 1.7 t of waste sodium and calcium chloride [de-icing agent; dust control and roadway base stabilization; industrial processing; additive in oilwell drilling fluids; cement additive; tire ballast]. The main chemical reactions in the Solvay process are as follows:

$$CaCO_3 \text{ (Limestone)} \rightarrow CaO + CO_2$$

$$C + O_2 \text{ (Amorphous)} \rightarrow CO_2$$

$$CaO + H_2O \rightarrow Ca(OH)_2 \text{ (Slaked lime)}$$

$$NH_3 + H_2O \text{ (Ammonia carrier)} \rightarrow NH_4OH$$

$$2NH_4OH + CO_2 \rightarrow (NH_4)_2CO_3 + H_2O(NH_4)_2$$

$$(NH_4)_2CO_3 + CO_2 + H_2O \rightarrow 2NH_4HCO_3$$

$$NaCl \text{ (Salt)} + NH_4HCO_3 \rightarrow NH_4Cl + NaHCO_3$$

$$2NaHCO_3 \rightarrow Na_2CO_3 + CO_2 + H_2O$$

$$NH_4Cl + Ca(OH)_2 \rightarrow NH_3 + CaCl_2 + 2H_2O$$

TYPICAL SODA CONTENT BY GLASS TYPE (% NA_2O BY WEIGHT)	
Container glass - white	13.0
Container glass - green	12.5
Flat glass	13.7
Pressed ware	16.9
Boro-silicate glass	4.2
Lead-crystal glass	1.0
CRT faceplate	7.5
Fiber optics	14.0
Textile fiberglass	
A-Glass (Al_2O_3+Fe_2O_3)	13.0
C-Glass (Al_2O_3+Fe_2O_3)	0.5
D-Glass	1.0
E-Glass	0.8 (+K_2O)
R-Glass	0.4
S-Glass	—
AR-Glass	—

Some 70% of the world's soda ash is produced via the Solvay process with much of balance derived from trona or saline lakes. Other minor or potential sources include nahcolite and the New Asahi (NA) Process.

PROPERTIES & USES: Soda ash is a principal industrial source of soda (Na_2O) which reduces the viscosity and acts as a flux in glass melting [soda-lime glass (flat and container glass), fiberglass, specialty glass (e.g. borosilicate glass)]. The soda ash content per 450 kg of silica sand used in a typical glass batch may be 155 kg for flint container glass and 115 kg for flat glass. Soda contributes alkalinity [pulp & paper; soap & detergents; alumina and other NF metal refining; steel

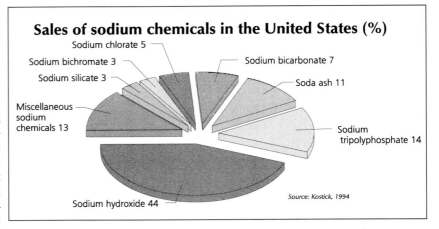

Sales of sodium chemicals in the United States (%)

Sodium chlorate 5
Sodium bichromate 3
Sodium silicate 3
Miscellaneous sodium chemicals 13
Sodium bicarbonate 7
Soda ash 11
Sodium tripolyphosphate 14
Sodium hydroxide 44

Source: Kostick, 1994

desulfurization; flue gas desulfurization or FGD systems; water treatment]. As well as a source of alkalinity, soda ash acts as an agglomerating aid and surfactant carrier in soaps & detergents and is a feedstock for various detergent builders including STPP, sodium silicate, and synthetic zeolites (see below). Soda ash and related products such as sodium bicarbonate and sodium sesquicarbonate are effective dry sorbents used to remove sulfur and nitrogen compounds from stack gases in an FGD process.

$$Na_2CO_3 + SO_2 + \tfrac{1}{2}O_2 \rightarrow Na_2SO_4 + CO_2$$

Coproducts of natural soda ash production in the United States include sodium bicarbonate (Na_2HCO_3), sodium phosphate, sodium cyanide, and sodium hydroxide. Soda ash is used as a chemical feedstock in the manufacture of several important sodium chemicals.

Soda ash + silica sand @ 2,450°C → sodium silicate [soap & detergents; silica-based catalysts; silica gels; pigments; paper adhesives; paper; ore and water treatment; synthetic zeolite manufacture]. Consumption of soda ash per ton of sodium silicate produced depends on the type - sodium orthosilicate requires 0.8 t, sodium metasilicate pentahydrate 0.33 t, and water glass (0.37 t).

Soda ash → non-electrolytic or chemical caustic soda (NaOH) [pulp & paper; soap & detergents; alumina processing; water treatment; pesticides; petroleum refining; food preparation; textiles & dyes; feedstock to produce sodium chemicals including sodium cyanide; synthetic zeolite manufacture]. In the causticization process lime is slaked to $Ca(OH)_2$ and added to 1.3 t of dissolved soda ash to yield 1 t of chemical caustic soda. The calcium carbonate precipitated is calcined to lime and recycled.

$$Ca(OH)_2 + Na_2CO_3 \rightarrow CaCO_3 + 2NaOH$$

Aqueous sodium silicate + sodium aluminate solution @ 77-110°C (hydrogel process) → zeolite NaA.

$$2NaOH + Al_2O_3 \cdot 3H_2O \xrightarrow{\text{moderate temperature}} 2NaAl(OH)_4 \text{ sodium aluminate}$$

$$12NaAl(OH)_4 + 4(Na_2O)\cdot(SiO_2)_3 + 7H_2O \xrightarrow{\text{moderate temperature}} Na_{12}((AlO_2))_{12}\cdot27H_2O + NaOH \text{ zeolite NaA}$$

Or kaolin + aqueous NaOH @ 500-600°C forms an amorphous sodium aluminosilicate → zeolite NaA.

$$2Al_2Si_2O_5(OH)_4 \text{ Kaolin} \rightarrow 2Al_2Si_2O_7 + H_2O \text{ calcined metakaolin}$$

$$12H_2O + 6Al_2Si_2O_7 + 12NaOH \xrightarrow{\text{moderate temperature}} Na_{12}((AlO_2))_{12} \text{ zeolite NaA}$$

Soda ash + phosphoric acid → sodium phosphate monobasic or monosodium phosphate (NaH_2PO_4) [boiler water treatment; dyes; photography; textile processing; industrial cleaner] → sodium acid pyrophosphate ($Na_2H_2P_2O_7$) [acid detergent formulations; deflocculant in drilling muds; electroplating baths; baking additive]; → sodium tripolyphosphates (STPP, $Na_5P_3O_{10}$) [detergent builder; deflocculant in drilling muds; electroplating baths; alkaline cleaning]; → sodium metaphosphate ($NaPO_3$) [dental polishing agent; sequestering agent; water softener]. Sodium phosphate dibasic or disodium phosphate (Na_2HPO_4) [ceramic glazes; dyes; fertilizers; pharmaceuticals; fireproofing; leather tanning; baking powder; processed cheese; water treatment] → aluminum phosphate [ceramics; cosmetics; dental cements; refractory bonding agent]; → monobasic (see above); → sodium phosphate tribasic or trisodium phosphate (Na_3HPO_4) [boiler water treatment; dyes; photographic developers; paint remover; cleaning formulations; sugar purification; water softening; feedstock for calcium and zinc phosphate, tribasic]; → tetrasodium pyrophosphate ($Na_4P_2O_7$) [boiler water treatment; soap & detergent builder; deflocculant in drilling muds; alkaline cleaning formulations; dyes; processed cheese; electroplating baths; synthetic rubber manufacture]. Soda ash requirement per ton

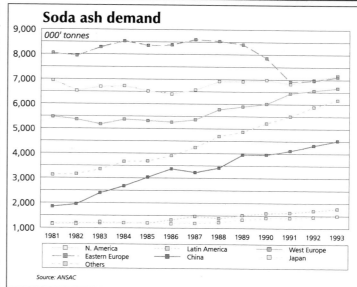

Soda ash demand

000' tonnes

Source: ANSAC

Legend: N. America; Latin America; West Europe; Eastern Europe; China; Japan; Others

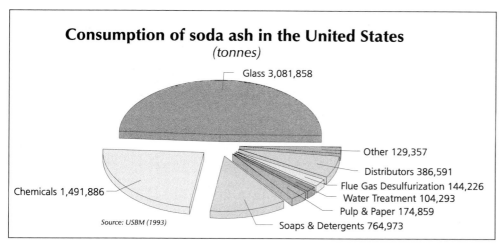

Consumption of soda ash in the United States
(tonnes)

- Glass 3,081,858
- Other 129,357
- Distributors 386,591
- Flue Gas Desulfurization 144,226
- Water Treatment 104,293
- Pulp & Paper 174,859
- Soaps & Detergents 764,973
- Chemicals 1,491,886

Source: USBM (1993)

of sodium tripolyphosphate produced is 0.76 t; monosodium phosphate 0.45 t; disodium phosphate 0.747 t; trisodium phosphate 0.68 t; sodium metaphosphate 0.557 t; sodium acid pyrophosphate 0.478 t; and tetrasodium pyrophosphate $(Na_4P_2O_7)$ 0.84 t.

Soda ash solution plus CO_2 gas → sodium bicarbonate or baking soda [animal feed; chemicals; baking & food; pharmaceuticals; detergents; household consumer products; textiles; FGD]. Approximately 0.68 t of soda ash is required per ton of sodium bicarbonate produced.

↳ Flue Gas Desulfurization

Soda ash + chromite roasted in a rotary kiln → sodium chromate or sodium bichromate [batteries; bleaching waxes and oils; chemical intermediate (chromic acid, chromium oxide, chromic sulfate); copper alloy processing; drilling-mud additive; leather tanning; metal finishing; textile mordant; water treatment; wood preservative]. 1 t of sodium bichromate requires 0.79 t of soda ash for the following chemical reaction:

$$2Cr_2O_3 + Na_2CO_3 + 3O_2 \quad \rightarrow \quad 4Na_2CrO_4 + 4CO_2$$

$$2Na_2CrO_4 + H_2SO_4 \quad \rightarrow \quad Na_2Cr_2O_7 + Na_2SO_4 + H_2O$$

QUALITY & SPECIFICATIONS: Light ash [detergents] has a particle size of 80 to 100 μm and a pouring density of 500kg/m³ (32-39 pounds/ft³) compared with heavy, dense, or granular ash [glass] at 250 to 300 μm and 1050 to 1150kg/m³ (60-66 pounds/ft³).

Natural ash:- min. 99.8% Na_2CO_3, 0.01-0.02% NaCl; *synthetic ash:*- 0.3-0.6% NaCl, <10ppm Fe.

British Standard:- 57.25% Na_2O and < 0.005% Fe_2O_3; *ASTM Standard:*- min. 99.16% Na_2CO_3.

Container glass:- min. 58.0% Na_2O, max. 0.2% Na_2SO_4, 0.03% NaCl; screen max. 1% on US 20, 5% on US 30, 20% through US 100 and 1% through US 200.

WORLD CAPACITY: 27.5M. t (synthetic) & 11M. t (natural).

CAPACITY UTILIZATION: 91%.

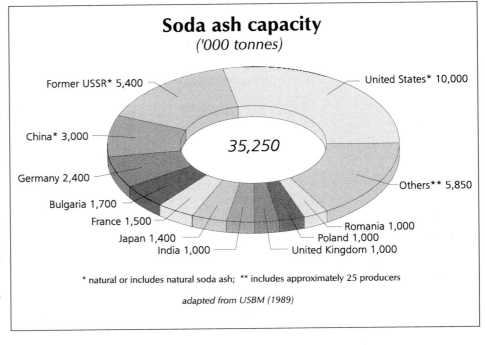

Soda ash capacity
('000 tonnes)

35,250

- Former USSR* 5,400
- China* 3,000
- Germany 2,400
- Bulgaria 1,700
- France 1,500
- Japan 1,400
- India 1,000
- United States* 10,000
- Others** 5,850
- Romania 1,000
- Poland 1,000
- United Kingdom 1,000

* natural or includes natural soda ash; ** includes approximately 25 producers

adapted from USBM (1989)

MARKET CONDITIONS: Steady-increasing particularly with developing economies.

MARKETING FACTORS: Glass & ceramics depend on the construction activity which is driven by the economy. Consumption is affected by increased glass recycling. The reduced use of STPP as a builder in detergents has increased the use of soda ash in some detergent formulations. Increased application in FGD plants could boost soda ash/sodium bicarbonate consumption in certain regions.

↳ Flue Gas

COMPOSITION OF COMMERCIAL SODA ASH (%)

	USA brine lake typical dense	Kenya brine lake typical dense	USA trona specification dense	USA trona typical dense	USA trona specification light	USA trona typical light	UK Solvay plant specification dense
Na_2CO_3	97.1	97.33*	99.2 min.	99.8	99.2 min.	99.8	99.0 min.
Na_2O	57.1	99.64**	58	58.4	58.0 min.	58.3	
$NaHCO_3$	-	0.25					
Na_2SO_4	0.7	0.48	0.2	0.04	0.20 max.	0.04	400ppm max.
NaCl	0.5	0.45	0.2	0.03	0.20 max.	0.03	0.6 max.
$Na_2B_4O_7$	1.3						
NaF		0.9					
Fe_2O_3	-	0.02	20ppm max.	6ppm	0.05 max.	0	50ppm max.

* soda alkalinity as Na_2CO_3; ** sodium oxide equivalent Na_2CO_3.

HEALTH & SAFETY: Although soda ash is not regarded as toxic, contact with the eyes may cause injury and prolonged contact with the skin may cause irritation. Soda ash is corrosive to the stomach lining if ingested. Simultaneous exposure to soda ash and lime should be avoided since this forms caustic soda which is harmful. Care is needed in the disposing of calcium chloride waste from Solvay plants.

RECYCLING: The use of cullet or recycled glass is increasing which in turn is reducing the need for virgin raw materials in the glass batch. The recycling rate is about 33% in the US and as high as 90% in some European countries like Switzerland.

SUBSTITUTES & ALTERNATIVES: Cleansers and detergents:- borates, phosphates, sodium silicate, sodium sulfate, STPP, zeolites. **FGD**:- limestone, lime, magnesia, nahcolite.**Glass**:- feldspar; nepheline syenite, sodium sulfate. **Soda source**:- caustic soda, nahcolite, sodium sulfate.

PRODUCERS & WORLD TRADE: Nearly 40 countries produce soda ash on a commercial scale, all based on the Solvay process except for natural production in the United States, Mexico, Kenya, and China. The United States is a major exporter of soda ash (almost 3M. t/y) with convenient cross-border trade largely in Europe and southern Africa.

HTS CODES: 2836.20 (disodium carbonate).

PRICES: Soda ash, 58% Na_2O, fob works $161/t (dense, bags); $108/t (dense, bulk); $166/t (light, bags); $114/t (light, bulk).

Sodium bicarbonate ex-works, freight equalized $458/t USP, powder (regular grade, bags); 480/t (coarse, bags); $461/t (fine, bags); $475/t (granular, fine, bags). Sodium bichromate $1.32/kg (crystal, bags, ex-works, freight equalized); $1.21/kg (liquid, bulk, fob plant). Sodium cyanide $1.87-2.01/kg (briquettes or granular, 99% min., drums, delivered). Sodium hydroxide $2.49/kg (USP, pellets, drums, ex-works, freight equalized). Sodium metal ex-works $3.25/kg (12-lb bricks, drums); $3.10/kg (fused, drums); $2.53/kg (fused, tanks).

Sodium phosphate (ex-works, freight equalized) $1,578/t (anhydrous, dibasic, technical, bags); $1,678/t (anhydrous, dibasic, food grade, bags); $1,617/t (monobasic, technical, bags); $1,738/t (monobasic, food grade, bags); $1,590/t (tribasic, technical, bags); $1,884/t (tribasic, food grade, bags). Sodium tripolyphosphate (STPP) (USA ex-works, freight equalized) $935/t (technical, bags); $865/t (technical, bulk); $1,144/t (food grade, bags).

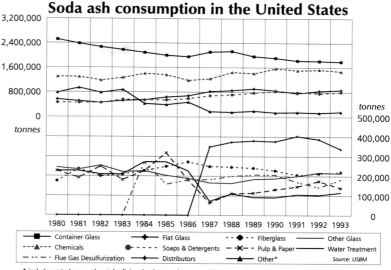

Soda ash consumption in the United States

Source: USBM

* includes petroleum and metal refining, leather tanning, enamels, etc. plus data not available

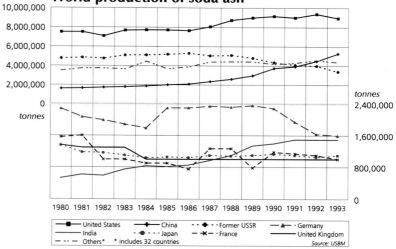

World production of soda ash

Source: USBM

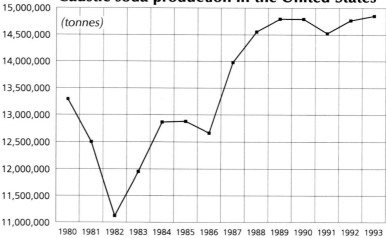

Caustic soda production in the United States

Figures from 1990 onwards includes chemical caustic soda from trona;

Source: USBM

Sodium silicate (bulk, ex-works) $496/t (solid or glass, 3.22-3.25 ratio*); $6427/t (solid or glass, 1.95-2.00 ratio*); $198/t (41° solid, 3.22-3.25 ratio*, freight equalized). Zeolite A (detergent grade) $500-600/t.

* ratio is % by weight $SO_3 : Na_2O$

ETYMOLOGY: Burkeite for William Edmund Burke, American chemical engineer. **Dawsonite** for John William Dawson (1820-1899), Canadian geologist, principal of McGill University, Montreal, Canada. **Gaylussite** for Joseph Louis Gay-Lussac (1778-1850), French chemist, Greek *lithos = stone.* **Hanksite** for Henry Garber Hanks (1826-1907), State Mineralogist of California. **Nahcolite** is an acronym of *Na, H, C, O* plus Greek *lithos = stone.* **Natron** from the Latin *natrium* or Greek *nitron = native soda.* **Northupite** for Charles H. Northup (b. 1861), American grocer and first observer. **Shortite** for Maxwell Naylor Short (1889-1952), American mineralogist, University of Arizona, and Greek *lithos = stone.* **Soda ash** from *soda* and *ash*, originally prepared by evaporating the lixivium of wood ashes in iron pots (see potash). **Trona** from the Arabic name of the native salt.

SODA ASH LEADERS

Producers	Importers	Exporters
United States	Japan	United States
China	S. Korea	Germany
Former USSR	Indonesia	France
Germany	Mexico	Former USSR
India	Venezuela	United Kingdom
Japan	Belgium	Poland
France	Taiwan	Bulgaria
United Kingdom	Canada	Kenya
Poland	Thailand	Botswana
Bulgaria	Argentina	Romania
Romania	Brazil	Italy
Italy	Philippines	Spain
Spain	Netherlands	Netherlands
Netherlands	Colombia	Belgium
Mexico	Spain	Australia

Price of soda ash in the United States

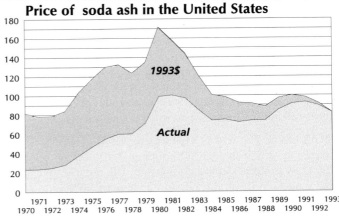

Values are the combined total revenue of California and Wyoming natural soda ash sold at list prices, spot prices, discount, long-term contracts, and for export, divided by the quantity of soda ash sold on a bulk f.o.b basis.

Source: USBM

Historical price of soda ash *($/short ton)*

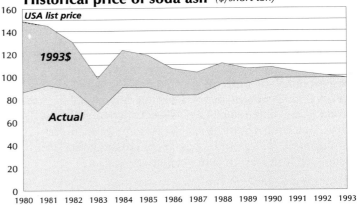

USA list price

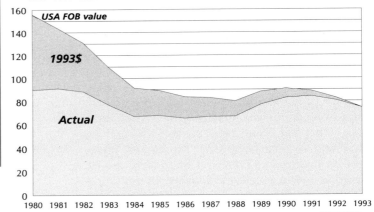

USA FOB value

Source: USBM

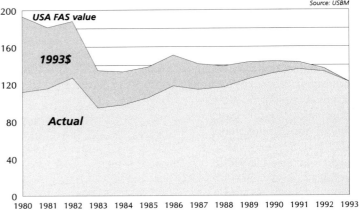

USA FAS value

SODIUM SULFATE

Minerals	Formula	%Na₂SO₄	%Na₂O	Color	SG	H
Thenardite	Na_2SO_4	100	43.6	colorless to white	2.67	2.5-3
Mirabilite (Glauber's salt)	$Na_2SO_4 \cdot 10H_2O$	44.1	34.8	white or yellow	1.48	1.5-2

Other minerals containing sodium sulfate include:

		%Na₂SO₄
Haksite	$2Na_2CO_3 \cdot 9Na_2SO_4 \cdot KCl$	81.7
Sulphohalite	$2Na_2SO_4 \cdot NaCl$	73.9
Glauberite	$Na_2SO_4 \cdot NaSO_4$	51.1
Bloedite	$Na_2SO_4 \cdot MgSO_4 \cdot H_2O$	42.5

Sodium sulfate is also a byproduct of certain manufacturing processes: *Natural nitrate processing in Chile*: as a byproduct in the processing of natural nitrate (caliche) ore. *Rayon*: in rayon spinning, the viscose solution is extruded through a spinneret into a bath containing sulfuric acid, sodium sulfate, zinc sulfate, and minor quantities of surface active agents. Sodium sulfate, formed through the reaction of sodium cellulose xanthate and sulfuric acid, is recovered. *Hydrochloric acid*: in the Mannheim process for the manufacture of hydrochloric acid from salt and sulfuric acid, byproduct sodium bisulfate (niter cake) is recovered and converted to salt cake. *Dichromate*: sodium carbonate, limestone, and chromite are combined to produce sodium chromate which is then treated with sulfuric acid to produce sodium dichromate plus sodium sulfate (chrome cake). *Phenol, resorcinol, and cresylic acids*: in the sulfonation of benzene and toluene to manufacture phenol, resorcinol, and cresylic acids, a yellow sodium sulfate (phenol cake) is produced. *Formic acid*: sodium formate is produced when sodium hydroxide and carbon monoxide are reacted under pressure; this is reacted with sulfuric acid to produce formic acid and sodium sulfate. *Boric acid*: borax or kernite plus sulfuric acid yields boric acid and byproduct sodium sulfate. *Lithium carbonate*: a hot solution of sodium carbonate plus lithium sulfate yields lithium carbonate and byproduct sodium sulfate. *Ascorbic acid*: in the Reichstein and Grissmer synthesis, sulfuric acid and sodium hydroxide are mixed to yield ascorbic acid (vitamin C) and byproduct sodium sulfate. *Others*: the manufacture of methionine and caprolactam, and uranium extraction.

PROPERTIES & USES: Source of soda (Na_2O) and/or sulfur in a number of industries [sulfate chemical pulping of wood; Kraft paper; glass; ceramic glazes; dyeing wool textiles; tanning; spinning baths for viscose rayon; nickel smelting; animal feed supplements; photography; water treatment; sulfonated oils]. In the chemical pulping of wood, the digestion reagents consist of caustic soda (NaOH) plus sodium sulfide (Na_2S) which is obtained by using sodium sulfate as a make-up material. Use in dyes is to provide standardization of strengths in the dyeing process, to separate organic contaminants, and to promote "salting out" of dyestuffs precipitates. Whiteness, relative inertness, and cheapness allow sodium sulfate to be used as a diluent or filler [detergents]. It acts as a flux and scum preventer [glass]. Typically, sodium sulfate constitutes 1% of the batch for container glass, 0.5% for flat glass, and 0.3-0.8% for fiberglass.

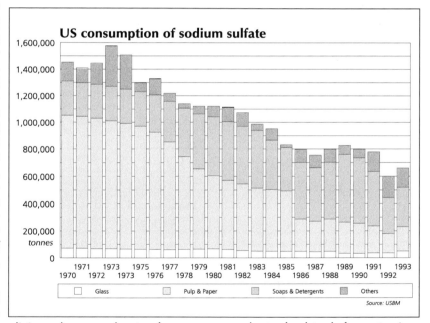

US consumption of sodium sulfate

Source: USBM

Sodium sulfate as a chemical feedstock → lead sulfate [storage batteries; paint pigment]; → potassium sulfate [fertilizer for specialized crops; medicine; glass; accelerator for gypsum products; feedstock for potassium aluminum sulfate, bisulfate, formate, persulfate, and sulfide (see potash)]; → sodium aluminum sulfate; → sodium hyposulfite; → sodium silicate [detergents; catalysts; pigment; adhesives; paper; ore treatment]; → sodium sulfide [leather dipilatory; organic chemicals; dyes; rayon; soap; flotation agent for gold & silver; photography].

QUALITY & SPECIFICATIONS: *Salt cake*:- impure sodium sulfate containing 90-99% Na_2SO_4 [pulp]. *Refined sodium sulfate (anhydrous sodium sulfate)*:- white crystalline powder with BD 77-87 lb/ft³; high purity is 99% [detergents, glass, pharmaceuticals, dyestuffs, ceramic glazes] whereas low purity is often discolored [pulp]. *Glass-grade*:- low iron content. Most natural commercial products are 99.3-99.7% pure. *Detergent grade*:- min. 99.2% Na_2SO_4, whiteness 88-89, BD 80 lb/ft³; *Kraft paper grade*;- min. 96% Na_2SO_4, max. 2% NaCl, 1% Mg as $MgSO_4$, 117% Ca as $CaSO_4$, free flowing. *Food grade*:- min. 99.0% Na_2SO_4 after drying, <3 ppm As, <10 ppm heavy metals (as Pb), selenium <0.003%, loss on drying <1% (anhydrous form) and 51-57% (decahydrate). Available as Fine, Standard, and Coarse grade.

WORLD CAPACITY: Natural 3.6M. t; synthetic 2.5M. t.

CAPACITY UTILIZATION: 55% (natural)/ 100% (synthetic).

MARKET CONDITIONS: Declining rapidly.

MARKETING FACTORS: Consumption is dependent on activity in detergents and to a lesser extent pulp & paper and glass. The increased popularity of compact, ultracompact, and liquid versions of detergents has severely reduced consumption of sodium sulfate. Improved efficiencies and recycling have reduced the consumption of sodium sulfate per unit of pulp produced — from 180 kg of sodium sulfate/ton of pulp in 1950 to 36 kg in 1980 to less than 20 kg today. Less sodium sulfate is being used in the glass batch (to reduce S emissions), and recycled glass (cullet) has reduced the volume of mineral and chemical feedstock. Involuntary (byproduct) production has to be sold or disposed of which has increased the supply. Research is continuing on the conversion of sodium sulfate into sodium carbonate (soda ash) on a commercial scale.

HEALTH & SAFETY: Many of the negative market trends in sodium sulfate are driven by environmental concerns — reduction of packaging waste (compact and liquid detergents); improved efficiencies and recycling (pulp and glass); and reduced S emissions (glass); reduced dumping of byproduct as waste (involuntary production).

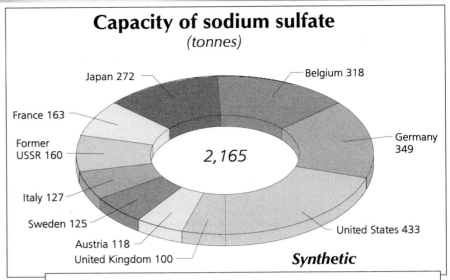

Capacity of sodium sulfate
(tonnes)

Japan 272
Belgium 318
France 163
Former USSR 160
Germany 349
Italy 127
Sweden 125
Austria 118
United Kingdom 100
United States 433

2,165

Synthetic

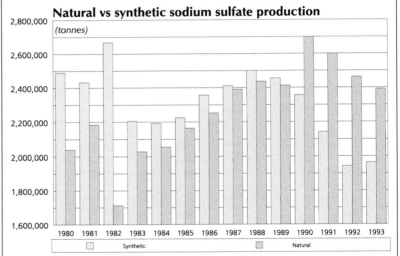

Natural vs synthetic sodium sulfate production

(tonnes)

2,800,000
2,600,000
2,400,000
2,200,000
2,000,000
1,800,000
1,600,000

1980 1981 1982 1983 1984 1985 1986 1987 1988 1989 1990 1991 1992 1993

☐ Synthetic   ☐ Natural

COMPOSITION OF ANHYDROUS SODIUM SULFATE

	Theoretical	Typical	Screen analysis US Standard Sieve	Fine	Standard	Coarse
Na	32.38%		20	0	0.5	0.05
SO$_4$	67.62%		40	0.1	10	17
Na$_2$O	43.64%		60	1	35	50
SO$_3$	56.36%		100	6	65	73
Na$_2$SO$_4$		98.30%	200	45	85	90
NaCl		0.36%				
Na$_2$CO$_3$		0.23%				
B$_2$O$_3$		0.09%				
H$_2$O		0.02%				
Fe		10 ppm				
As$_2$O$_3$		2.0 ppm				
Insoluble		40 ppm				

Bulk density, poured: Fine 80 lb/ft³; Standard 86 lb/ft³; Coarse 86 lb/ft³.

Source: NACC

SUBSTITUTES & ALTERNATIVES: **Detergents**:- nothing. **Glass**:- calcium sulfate and soda ash (glass). **Pulp**:- caustic soda and emulsified sulfur.

RECYCLING: Sodium sulfate forms part of large-scale industrial recycling which converts a waste material into a product sold on the open market.

Sodium sulfate production and exports in Canada

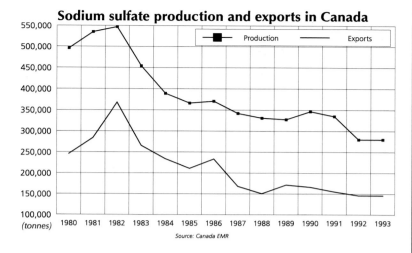

Source: Canada EMR

Price history of sodium sulfate

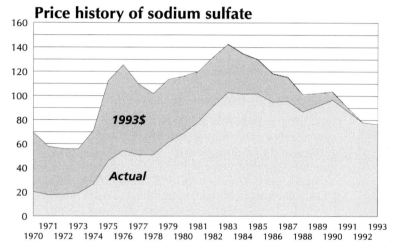

1993$

Actual

Based on the average valuation by producers of their annual total production and reported sales. The values incorporate the price differences changed by producers for the same finished product sold in bulk at the plant.

Source: USBM

Production of sodium sulfate

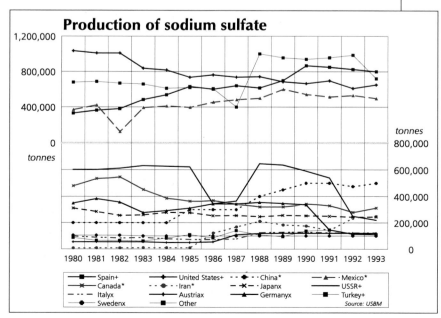

■ Spain+	◆ United States+
✕ Canada*	● Iran*
--- Italyx	▲ Austriax
● Swedenx	■ Other
● China*	▲ Mexico*
✕ Japanx	USSR+
▲ Germanyx	■ Turkey+

Source: USBM

PRODUCERS & WORLD TRADE: World production of sodium sulfate is almost evenly divided between natural and synthetic product. The leading natural producers are Spain, Mexico, Canada, China, and the United States whereas the main synthetic producers are the United States, Former USSR, Japan, and a number of industrialized countries. Several countries produce both. There is some international trade in sodium sulfate, but most is confined to convenient cross-border traffic.

PRICES: Salt cake $79/t (E. USA, bulk, freight equalized, ex-works). Anhydrous sodium sulfate USA, bulk, ex-works, freight equalized $124-126/t (East); $121/t (Gulf Coast); $140/t (West).

Lithium sulfate $79.15/kg (anhydrous, delivered). Potassium sulfate $198/t (agricultural, min. 50% K_2O, standard, bulk, FOB works); $2,200-2.860/t (300-lb drums, granular, purified).

HTS CODES: 2833.11.10 (disodium sulfate, saltcake); 2833.11.50 (disodium sulfate, other).

ETYMOLOGY: Bloedite for Carl August Bloede (1773-1820), German chemist. **Glauberite** for Johann Wilhelm Glauber (1603-1668), German chemist. **Hanksite** for Henry Garber Hanks (1826-1907), State Mineralogist of California. **Mirabilite** Latin *sal mirabilis* = *wonderful salt*, Greek *lithos* = *stone*. **Thenardite** for Louis Jacques Thénard (1777-1857), French chemist, University of Paris.

STAUROLITE

Minerals	Formula	Color	SG	H
Staurolite	$FeAl_4Si_2O_{10}(OH)_2$	red brown-black	3.6-3.65	7-7.5 or $2(Al_2SiO_5)\cdot Fe(OH)_2$

PROPERTIES: High H, medium SG, and bulk density of 2,176 kg/m³ allow fine & medium grades of staurolite concentrate to be utilized as a loose-grain blasting abrasive [metal cleaning; sandblasting buildings] and coarse grades for engraving and polishing [marble monuments and headstones]. Staurolite (Starblast® and Starblast® XL) has several advantages as an abrasive including a relatively low silica content; greater visibility because of low dusting; good flow characteristics (no lumps); nonhygroscopic (less likely to freeze); faster cleaning rates; the ability to recycle; and more uniform blasting patterns.

Staurolite has a low coefficient of expansion (7.8×10^{-6}), high melting point (1,537°C), and uniformly rounded grains required in nonferrous foundry mold sand [aluminum, brass and bronze, magnesium, and ferrous metals such as copper]. The main advantages of staurolite (Biasill®) as a foundry sand are its relatively low silica content (health & safety benefit); low thermal expansion compared with silica sand (eliminates cracking and warpage); high thermal conductivity (finer grained castings and reduction in shell and hot box cure cycles); clean, round grains free of fines (reduces binder demand and gas evolution); and hard durable grains (reduces fractures). The low melting point limits its use to thin sectioned castings. Staurolite may be blended with silica sand and used to produce small iron castings since it reduces binder demand, produces more dense metal structures, and promotes chill and metal solidifications.

Resistance to weathering and chemical attack is the basis for the use of staurolite flour as a filler [paint primers]. Source of Al_2O_3 and Fe_2O_3 to replace clay and iron in portland cement.

QUALITY & SPECIFICATIONS: As a byproduct of heavy mineral production, staurolite is chemically scrubbed, washed, graded, and then magnetically separated from other heavy minerals in order to minimize the content of titanium minerals (max. 4%), kyanite (1%), zircon (2%), and quartz (4%). The typical staurolite content of the main grades are as follows:- Coarse Staurolite Sand 85%; Biasill® 86%; Starblast® 87%; Starblast® XL 90%. The chemical composition varies by grade but is generally min. 45% Al_2O_3, max 18% Fe_2O_3, 5% TiO_2, 3% ZrO_2, and 4% free silica. Starblast® XL typically contains 0.8% free silica. The particle size distribution of three grades is given on the table over the page.

WORLD CAPACITY: Varies with titanium mineral production.

CAPACITY UTILIZATION: 100%.

MARKET CONDITIONS: Small and generally local.

MARKETING FACTORS: Environmental and health & safety laws may encourage the replacement of silica sand as a foundry sand and abrasive. Staurolite is a byproduct of titanium mineral mining in Florida. Price is unrelated to cost of production and is priced to sit between silica sand/slags and garnet in the range of blasting abrasives.

BREAKDOWN FACTORS FOR ABRASIVES

	Breakdown factor* (1 pass)	Breakdown factor* (3 passes)
Aluminum oxide (30 FDT)	0.80	0.61
Garnet RT-60	0.61	0.38
Starblast®	0.77	0.45
Flintshot®	0.68	0.36
Flintbrasive® #3	0.58	0.32

* breakdown factors can range from 1 to 0 with 1 equal to no change after blasting and 0 breaking down completely to dust.

Tests conducted by DuPont Engineering Test Center in 1970. Conditions: 0.64 cm nozzle; 634-655 x 10³ Pa nozzle pressure; 0.64 cm steel plate target..

Ownership trademarks - Starblast® E.I. duPont de Nemours and Co. Ltd.; Flintshot® US Silica Co.

Source: Fulton, 1994

CLEANING RATE AND PROFILE FOR BLAST CLEANING ABRASIVES

	Cleaning rate m²/hr	Abrasive flow rate kg/hr	Profile mm
Aluminum oxide (80/100)	23	245	0.028
Starblast®	22	272	0.028
Biasill®	22	263	0.023
Aluminum oxide (54/70)	21	261	0.033
Garnet RT-80	21	290	0.025
Flint silica	20	331	0.036
Flintshot®	19	318	0.043
Coarse staurolite	19	243	0.038
Garnet RT-60	18	238	0.025
Aluminum oxide (30 FDT)	16	302	0.038
Black Beauty®	15	340	0.038
Rotoblast® G80A (metallic grit)	14	318	0.030
Rotoblast® G40A (metallic grit)	11	340	0.053
Flintbrasive® #3	11	236	0.043

Tests conducted by DuPont Engineering Test Center in 1970. 100% mill scale on new steel plate. All surfaces to Class 1 white metal. Conditions: 0.95 cm nozzle; 634-655 x 10³ Pa nozzle pressure.

Ownership trademarks - Starblast® and Biasill® E.I. duPont de Nemours and Co. Ltd.; Rotoblast® Pangborn Corp.; Black Beauty® H.B. Reed Corp.; Flintshot® US Silica Co.

Source: Fulton, 1994

SPECIFICATIONS OF STAUROLITE

US Standard mesh size % retained	Opening (μm)	Coarse (cement)	Starblast® (abrasive)	Biasil® (foundry)
20	850	1	-	-
30	600	3	<1	-
40	425	23	4	<1
50	300	51	11	5
70	212	13	20	19
100	150	9	45	53
140	106	-	17	19
200	75	-	3	3
270	53	-	<1	<1
Pan	<53	trace	trace	trace
APS (μm)		317	215	188

Source: DuPont

HEALTH & SAFETY: Crystalline silica has been classified as a probable carcinogen by the IARC (see silica for further details). Therefore, because of its crystalline silica content (staurolite can contain up to 5% silica), unless processing has the capability to reduce the crystalline silica content to less than 0.1%, mica will come under the OSHA Hazard Communication Standards, 29 CFR Section 1900.1200 which require labeling and other forms of warning, material safety data sheets, and employee training for products containing identified carcinogens with concentrations greater than 0.1%. Biasill®, Starblast®, Starblast® XL, Coarse Staurolite Sand are all certified for permissible dry outdoor blastibg by the State of California Air Resources Board.

SUBSTITUTES & ALTERNATIVES: Abrasives:- bauxite & alumina (fused alumina), corundum/emery, diamonds, diatomite, feldspar, garnet, iron oxide (magnetite), nepheline syenite, olivine, perlite, pumice, silica sand, staurolite, tripoli, and silicon carbide, ilmenite.

RECYCLING: One of the major strengths of staurolite as an abrasive is the fact that it can be recovered, cleaned, resized, and reused. Higher initial costs compared with rival abrasives may be justified in some cases by an increased life cycle based on recycling.

PRODUCERS & WORLD TRADE: United States & India (99%).

EXPORTERS: Insignificant or none

IMPORTERS: Insignificant or none

PRICES: $65/t (bagged, truckloads, FOB plant); $0.20-0.45/kg (Coarse Staurolite Sand, #60, via distributor); $0.16-0.30/kg (Starblast®, #80, via distributor); $0.18-0.33/kg (Biasill®, #90, via distributor).

ETYMOLOGY: Staurolite from the Greek *stauros = a cross* and *lithos = stone* because of its common cruciform twins.

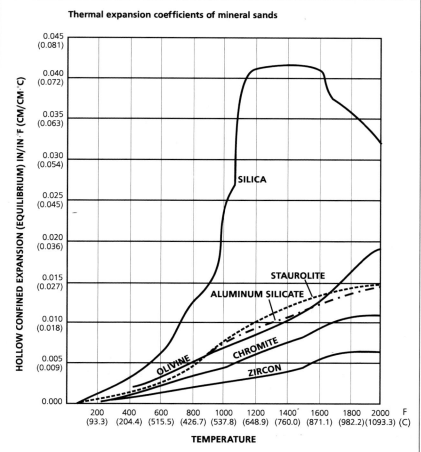

Thermal expansion coefficients of mineral sands

y-axis: HOLLOW CONFINED EXPANSION (EQUILIBRIUM) IN/IN °F (CM/CM °C)

0.045 (0.081)
0.040 (0.072)
0.035 (0.063)
0.030 (0.054)
0.025 (0.045)
0.020 (0.036)
0.015 (0.027)
0.010 (0.018)
0.005 (0.009)
0.000

SILICA
STAUROLITE
ALUMINUM SILICATE
OLIVINE
CHROMITE
ZIRCON

x-axis: 200 (93.3) 400 (204.4) 600 (515.5) 800 (426.7) 1000 (537.8) 1200 (648.9) 1400 (760.0) 1600 (871.1) 1800 (982.2) 2000 (1093.3) F (C)

TEMPERATURE

SULFUR

Minerals	Formula	%S	Color	SG	H
Pyrite	FeS$_2$	53.4	bronze yellow to pale brass yellow	4.8-5.1	6-6.5
Anhydrite	CaSO$_4$	23.5	white to gray	2.93	3.0-3.5

Sulfur is derived from native sulfur deposits by the Frasch or traditional mining methods (Frasch and native sulfur); extracted from petroleum, natural gas, or coal (recovered sulfur); produced by the roasting and smelting on nonferrous sulfide ores such as chalcopyrite (copper), galena (lead), sphalerite (zinc), pyrrhotite and pentlandite (nickel), stibnite (antimony), etc. (byproduct sulfuric acid), pyrite ore, and rarely anhydrite. Overall, production may be divided into voluntary or discretionary sulfur (produced by the mining of sulfur or pyrites) and involuntary or nondiscretionary sulfur (sulfur or sulfuric acid produced as a byproduct where the volume produced is dictated by the demand for the primary product).

PROPERTIES & USES: As a plant nutrient, sulfur may be applied directly or as part of a fertilizer such as ammonium sulfate (23.7% S) where it increases the availability of other nutrients, controls pests, mites, and mildews, and lowers the pH of saline and alkali soils [fertilizer; soil conditioner; insecticide, pesticide, and herbicide]. Sulfur in the elemental form or as sulfur dioxide is an essential feedstock for a variety of chemicals including ammonium hydrosulfide [photography; textiles]; barium sulfate [paint, rubber, inks, photographic paper; barium meal in X-rays; pharmaceuticals]; hydrogen sulfide [vulcanizes synthetic rubber; chemical feedstock]; molybdenum disulfide [solid lubricant]; phosphorus pentasulfide [oil additive; rubber additive; flotation agent; insecticide]; sulfur monochloride [chlorinating agent; organic acid anhydrides; sulfur dichloride; rubber vulcanizing; textiles; catalyst for benzene to chlorobenzene conversion]; sulfur trioxide [feedstock for ammonium sulfamate, chlorosulfonic acid, dioxane sulfotioxide, fluosulfonic acid, oleum, high purity sulfur dioxide, sulfuric acid]; sulfuric acid (H$_2$SO$_4$) [see below].

Sulfur $\rightarrow$ SO$_3$ & sulfurous acid as a cooking liquor in the manufacture of wood pulp via the sulfite process [pulp & paper].

Because of its low cost, availability, and versatility, sulfuric acid is the most important inorganic chemical used in commerce. It is an important sulfur source or, in many cases, it acts as a facilitator and may be regenerated, refined, concentrated, and reused (e.g. phosphoric acid production, oil refining). Sulfuric acid oxidizes metals, converts insoluble oxides, sulfides, carbonates, and silicates to soluble compounds [copper and uranium ore leaching; metallurgy; mineral processing]; oxidizes and removes tars and organic sulfides in petroleum and serves as a catalyst in alkylation [petroleum refining]; pickles steel to remove mill scale, rust, dirt, etc. prior to processing [iron & steel]; has a great avidity for water which makes it a drying and dehydrating agent [explosives; celluloid; acetates; and lacquers]; reacts with aromatic compounds to form sulfonic acids [organic chemicals; rubber; plastics].

Sulfuric acid (+ ore or compound) is a major process chemical or manufacturing reagent $\rightarrow$ aluminum sulfate or alum [antiperspirant; clarifier for fats and oils; deodorizer & decolorizer in petroleum processing; fireproofing; leather tanning; water clarifier in papermaking; water treatment]; $\rightarrow$ ammonium sulfate [fire retardant; fertilizer; viscose rayon; chemical feedstock]; $\rightarrow$ antimony sulfate [explosives]; $\rightarrow$ barium sulfate [pigment in paints]; $\rightarrow$ boric acid [antiseptics; borosilicate glass; catalyst; fiberglass; nuclear applications; pharmaceuticals & cosmetics; photography; porcelain enamels, frits, glazes; liquid SO$_3$ stabilizer; textile treating]; $\rightarrow$ chromic acid [chrome plating; green pigment; ceramic colorant; metallurgy; refractory additive;

SOURCES OF SULFUR

Source	Formula	S Content
Native sulfur	S	Grades average 22 - 33% wt. S
Pyrite	FeS$_2$	53.4% S* with an average 40-50% S
Chalcopyrite	CuFeS$_2$	34.9% S*
Galena	PbS	13.4% S*
Sphalerite	ZnS	32.9% S*
Pyrrhotite	NiFeS$_2$	38% S*
Gypsum	CaSO$_4$·2H$_2$O	18.6% S*
Anhydrite	CaSO$_4$	23.6% S*
Tar sands		Averages 11% bitumen containing 5% S as organic sulfur compounds
Oil shales		Averages 0.3 - 6.2% S
Coal		Variable; averages 1.5% S
Sulfuric acid	H$_2$SO$_4$	32.69% S

theoretical content

SULFURIC ACID

CONVERSION FROM DEGREES BAUMÉ

°Bé	% H$_2$SO$_4$
50.3	63
53.0	67
55.0	70
60.5	79
65.1	90
65.5	92

RELATIVE DENSITIES @ 20°C

	kg/l
63%	1.531
67%	1.576
70%	1.611
79%	1.716
90%	1.814
92%	1.824
100%	1.831

chemical feedstock]; ➔ lead sulfate [ceramics; pigment; vinyl plastics stabilizer]; ➔ lithium sulfate [pharmaceuticals]; ➔ magnesium sulfate (Epsom Salts) [pharmaceuticals; chemicals; dyes; paper sizing; explosives; fertilizers]; ➔ nickel sulfate [catalyst; nickel plating; textiles]; ➔ sodium sulfate [sulfate chemical pulping of wood; Kraft paper; glass; ceramic glazes; dyeing wool textiles; tanning; spinning baths for viscose rayon; nickel smelting; animal feed supplements; photography; water treatment; sulfonated oils; chemical feedstock]; ➔ zinc sulfate [mordant; aniline black; ceramic coloring].

Sulfuric acid + fluorspar ➔ anhydrous hydrogen fluoride or hydrofluoric acid (70% HF) [acidizing oilwells; brick & stone cleaning; electronic etching; electroplating; enamel stripping; glass etching and polishing; master alloy salts; petroleum alkylation; brass, copper, stainless steel pickling; fluorine chemical feedstock].

Sulfuric acid + manganese ore (reduced) ➔ manganese sulfate [animal feed additive; fertilizer (citrus trees); food supplement; fungicide; paint additive; textile dye; intermediate manganese chemical].

Sulfuric acid + phosphate rock ➔ normal superphosphate (0-18-0 to 0-20-0) [fertilizer] or merchant grade, wet-process phosphoric acid, H_3PO_4 (0-52-0 to 0-54-0) ➔ superphosphoric acid (0-68-0 to 0-72-0) [deep-sea traded phosphates; liquid mixed fertilizers; high-analysis superphosphate (54% P_2O_5)]. Fertilizer production is by far the largest consumer of sulfuric acid. Sulfuric acid + KCl ➔ potassium sulfate [fertilizer for specialized crops; medicine; glass; accelerator for gypsum products; chemical feedstock].

Sulfuric acid + titanium minerals ➔ sulfate-route titanium dioxide pigment [paper; paint; plastics; rubber].

QUALITY & SPECIFICATIONS: Crude sulfur or brimstone is elemental sulfur as either a liquid (a.k.a. molten) or solid with a min. sulfur content of 99.55%. Formed sulfur in the shape of prills (pellets produced by cooling molten sulfur in air or water) or slates (slate-like lumps formed by allowing molten sulfur to solidify on a moving belt) are used for trading to avoid dusting problems. The only significant impurity is carbon present as hydrocarbons dispersed throughout the

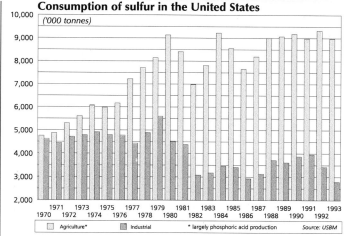

Consumption of sulfur in the United States
('000 tonnes)

☐ Agriculture*   ▨ Industrial   * largely phosphoric acid production   Source: USBM

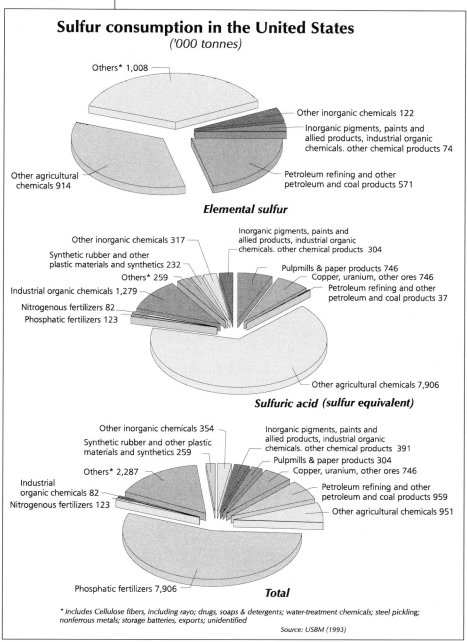

Sulfur consumption in the United States
('000 tonnes)

Others* 1,008
Other inorganic chemicals 122
Inorganic pigments, paints and allied products, industrial organic chemicals. other chemical products 74
Petroleum refining and other petroleum and coal products 571
Other agricultural chemicals 914

Elemental sulfur

Other inorganic chemicals 317
Synthetic rubber and other plastic materials and synthetics 232
Others* 259
Industrial organic chemicals 1,279
Nitrogenous fertilizers 82
Phosphatic fertilizers 123
Inorganic pigments, paints and allied products, industrial organic chemicals. other chemical products 304
Pulpmills & paper products 746
Copper, uranium, other ores 746
Petroleum refining and other petroleum and coal products 37
Other agricultural chemicals 7,906

Sulfuric acid (sulfur equivalent)

Other inorganic chemicals 354
Synthetic rubber and other plastic materials and synthetics 259
Others* 2,287
Industrial organic chemicals 82
Nitrogenous fertilizers 123
Inorganic pigments, paints and allied products, industrial organic chemicals. other chemical products 391
Pulpmills & paper products 304
Copper, uranium, other ores 746
Petroleum refining and other petroleum and coal products 959
Other agricultural chemicals 951
Phosphatic fertilizers 7,906

Total

* includes Cellulose fibers, including rayo; drugs, soaps & detergents; water-treatment chemicals; steel pickling; nonferrous metals; storage batteries, exports; unidentified

Source: USBM (1993)

APPARENT CONSUMPTION OF SULFUR (TONNES)

	Apparent Consumption
United States	12,545,356
Former USSR	7,509,400
Japan	2,340,504
Morocco	2,228,027
Canada	1,758,677
France	1,458,647
Saudi Arabia	1,450,000
Germany	1,318,753
Brazil	1,305,739
Poland	1,233,531
India	1,208,270
Tunisia	1,154,746
Mexico	1,126,863
China	995,804
Belgium	720,125
United Kingdom	637,509
Australia	630,459
South Korea	559,984
Iran	550,100
South Africa	519,236
Italy	472,115
Iraq	430,000
Greece	387,271
Taiwan	351,373
Indonesia	346,705
Chile	335,343
Netherlands	285,362
Jordan	281,154
Senegal	269,000
Romania	268,000
Finland	265,561
Czechoslovakia	259,628

NOTE: Numbers are approximate and rounded for 1990 or thereabouts; absence of a country does not necessarily indicate no production or trade; absence of a number does not necessarily mean zero

Source; British Geological Survet and USBM

sulfur (dark sulfur may contain up to 0.3% carbon).

Sulfuric acid is marketed on a 100% basis (32.69% S content) but shipped at 66° Baumé (93% H_2SO_4), as 98% acid, or as sulfur trioxide dissolved in sulfuric acid known as 20% to 22% fuming oleum. Grades include *commercial 66° Bé* (typical 93.5% H_2SO_4), *electrolytic 1.835* (93.5% H_2SO_4), *commercial 98/99%* (98.5% H_2SO_4), *oleum 20%* (20.0% free SO_3), *oleum 25%* (25.0% free SO_3), and *oleum 30%* (30.0% free SO_3); Fe <30ppm, nitrate <3ppm, mercury <0.5ppm, and arsenic <0.5ppm.

WORLD CAPACITY: Sulfur content, all forms 70M. t. (approx. 33% recovered, 20% Frasch, 20% pyrite, 13% metallurgy, 5% native).

CAPACITY UTILIZATION: 74%.

MARKET CONDITIONS: Steady - increasing in certain regions where manufacturing output is expanding such as Latin America and Australasia.

MARKETING FACTORS: Consumption depends on the level of manufacturing activity which in turn depends on the general state of the economy, the level of industrial development, and the population. An increasing proportion of sulfur is produced involuntarily and therefore it is difficult to control the supply side of the supply-demand equation.

APPARENT CONSUMPTION OF PYRITE (TONNES)

	Apparent Consumption
China	4,556,612
Former USSR	1,526,000
Spain	572,315
Japan	375,293
South Africa	292,693
Italy	254,233
North Korea	210,000
Former Yugoslavia	208,743
Sweden	167,760
Philippines	150,000
Bulgaria	147,000
Turkey	97,604
Norway	83,461
Belgium	78,459
Brazil	64,000
Czechoslovakia	50,000
Sweden	42,600
India	41,000
Romania	36,000
Greece	35,333
Zambia	33,285
Zimbabwe	29,337
Cyprus	25,944
Hungary	21,000

NOTE: Numbers are approximate and rounded for 1991 or thereabouts; absence of a country does not necessarily indicate no production or trade; absence of a number does not necessarily mean zero

Source: British Geological Survey

Capacity of sulfur all forms
('000 tonnes sulfur content)

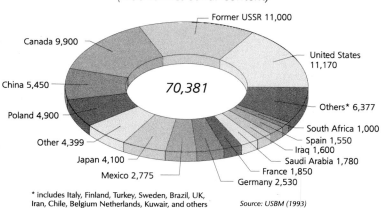

70,381

Former USSR 11,000
Canada 9,900
China 5,450
Poland 4,900
Other 4,399
Japan 4,100
Mexico 2,775
Germany 2,530
France 1,850
Saudi Arabia 1,780
Iraq 1,600
Spain 1,550
South Africa 1,000
Others* 6,377
United States 11,170

* includes Italy, Finland, Turkey, Sweden, Brazil, UK, Iran, Chile, Belgium Netherlands, Kuwair, and others

Source: USBM (1993)

HEALTH & SAFETY: Sulfur is at the center of many health & safety/environmental questions. It is regarded as a major pollutant and the Clean Air Act and similar legislation around the world are designed to reduce the levels of sulfur dioxide emissions from industrial plants such as power plants, oil refineries, smelters. At the same time, this increased recovery generates large tonnages of sulfur which in many cases far exceeds the market. At the same time, environmental legislation restricting the production of certain chemicals such as fluorocarbons and sulfate-route titanium dioxide is reducing the demand for sulfur thus vexing the oversupply situation.

RECYCLING: Sulfur is the ultimate recycled mineral since material produced by industry is either re-used internally or sold on the merchant market. For example, the sulfuric acid produced by the stack gas scrubbers of a copper smelter may be utilized to acid leach the copper that feeds the smelter.

SUBSTITUTES & ALTERNATIVES: None except for certain other mineral acids in particular hydrochloric.

PRODUCERS & WORLD TRADE: The largest sulfur (excluding pyrite) producers are concentrated in North America and eastern Europe — the United States, Canada, Former USSR, Poland, Japan, and Mexico. The United States is also the world's largest importer; Morocco, the second largest importer, requires sulfur for its phosphoric acid production facilities based on domestic phosphate rock. Canada and Poland are the largest exporters. The leading producer of pyrite is China which accounts for the bulk of its production. Other leaders are the Former USSR, Spain, South Africa, and Finland. The largest importer is Japan.

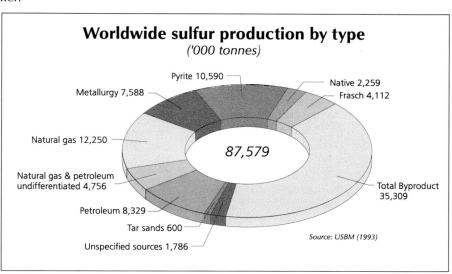

Worldwide sulfur production by type
('000 tonnes)

Pyrite 10,590
Native 2,259
Frasch 4,112
Metallurgy 7,588
Natural gas 12,250
87,579
Natural gas & petroleum undifferentiated 4,756
Total Byproduct 35,309
Petroleum 8,329
Tar sands 600
Unspecified sources 1,786

Source: USBM (1993)

PRODUCTION AND TRADE IN SULFUR* (TONNES)

	Production	Imports	Exports	Apparent Consumption	Net Supplier	Net Consumer
North America	19,952,414	3,409,918	7,931,436	15,430,896	4,521,518	
South America	798,550	1,263,839	6,928	2,055,461		(1,256,911)
C. America & Carib.	34,513	158,702	25,513	167,702		(133,189)
European Union	4,503,364	2,241,970	1,322,277	5,423,057		(919,693)
Non-EU Europe	11,560,108	1,806,545	2,945,743	10,420,910	1,139,198	
Australasia	4,857,819	2,510,497	399,249	6,969,067		(2,111,248)
Middle East	2,976,000	537,866	189,806	3,324,060		(348,060)
Africa	474,653	4,150,289	15,861	4,609,081		(4,134,428)

* excludes pyrite

NOTE: Numbers are approximate and rounded for 1991 or thereabouts

Source: British Geological Survey

PRODUCTION AND TRADE IN PYRITE* (TONNES)

	Production	Imports	Exports	Apparent Consumption	Net Supplier	Net Consumer
North America	4,000	8,756	3	12,753		(8,753)
South America	64,000			64,000		
European Union	833,332	135,302	13,081	955,553		(122,221)
Non-EU Europe	2,621,324	278,988	575,528	2,324,784	296,540	
Australasia	5,207,000	321,293	195,388	5,332,905		(125,905)
Africa	418,721	154	84,097	334,778	83,943	

* excludes sulfur in other forms

NOTE: Numbers are approximate and rounded for 1991 or thereabouts

Source: British Geological Survey

HTS CODES: 2503.10.0000 (sulfur in ores, crude or unrefined); 2503.10.0090 (other sulfur); 2802.00.0000 (sulfur, sublimed, precipitated, colloidal); 3204.19.1100 (sulfur black); 2811.23.0000 (sulfur dioxide); 2806.20.0000 (chlorosulfuric acid); 2807.00.0000 (sulfuric acid; oleum).

PRICES: Crude sulfur $48-58/long ton (recovered, del. Houston); $5-10/long ton (recovered, Alberta, Canada, for US del., tanks); $29-33/t (recovered, FOB Vancouver); $60-70/long ton (Frasch, dark, ex-Tampa, FL); $58-69/long ton (Frasch, del. New Orleans, LA); $300/t (99.5% min. purity, commercial flour and lump, bags, mine basis). Refined sulfur $385/t (99.5% min. purity, rolls, bags, mines basis); $440/t (99.5% min. purity, flour, light, bags, mines basis); $572/t (resublimed, N.F., 99.85% min. purity, bags, mines basis); 300/t (rubbermakers, 99.5% min. purity, bags, mines basis); $321/t (rubbermakers, 99.5% min. purity, 98% min. 325 mesh, bags, mines basis).

Sulfur dichloride $0.50/kg (tanks, freight equalized). Sulfur dioxide 254/t (liquid, bulk, FOB work). Sulfur monochloride, ex-works $0.64-0.68/kg (drums); $0.42/kg (tanks, freight equalized). Sulfuric acid, virgin, 100% basis, ex-works $83/t (East and Gulf Coast, USA); $95/t (midwest US); $81/t (southeast US); 94/t (west US). Sulfuric acid, smelter, 100% tanks, ex-works $53-57/t (Gulf Coast US); $70/t (southeast US); $83/t (93%, northwest US).

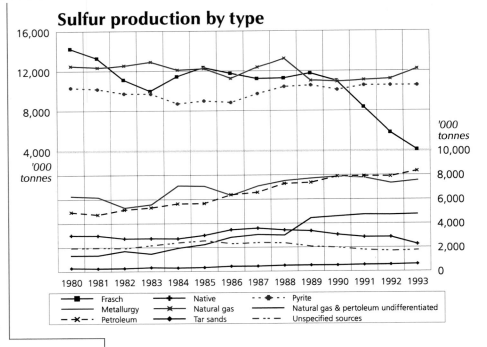

Sulfur production by type

Legend:
- Frasch
- Native
- Pyrite
- Metallurgy
- Natural gas
- Natural gas & petroleum undifferentiated
- Petroleum
- Tar sands
- Unspecified sources

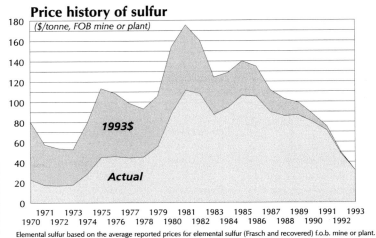

Price history of sulfur
($/tonne, FOB mine or plant)

1993$

Actual

Elemental sulfur based on the average reported prices for elemental sulfur (Frasch and recovered) f.o.b. mine or plant.

Source: USBM

PYRITE LEADERS

Producers	Importers	Exporters
China	Japan	Finland
Former USSR	Sweden	China
Spain	Belgium	Former USSR
South Africa	Bulgaria	Namibia
Finland	Italy	Norway
Italy	Hungary	Spain
North Korea	Former Yugoslavia	Italy
Former Yugoslavia	United Kingdom	Belgium
Norway	Canada	Sweden
Philippines	Turkey	
Turkey	United States	
Bulgaria	France	
Brazil	Austria	
Namibia	Switzerland	
Japan	South Africa	

SULFUR LEADERS

Producers	Importers	Exporters
United States	United States	Canada
Canada	Morocco	Poland
Former USSR	Tunisia	Mexico
Poland	Former USSR	United States
Japan	India	Germany
Mexico	Brazil	France
Germany	France	Japan
Saudi Arabia	South Korea	Iran
France	United Kingdom	Netherlands
China	Belgium	Spain
Iran	Mexico	Bahrain
Australia	Indonesia	Italy
Iraq	Jordan	Singapore
South Africa	Senegal	Sweden
Italy	Taiwan	Switzerland
Belgium	Germany	Netherlands Antilles

Production of byproduct sulfur

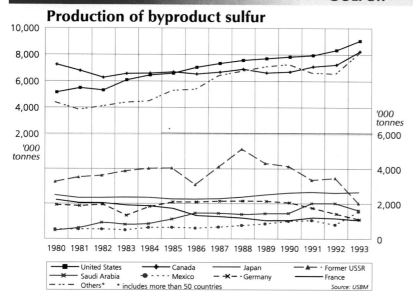

Legend:
- United States
- Canada
- Japan
- Former USSR
- Saudi Arabia
- Mexico
- Germany
- France
- Others*   * includes more than 50 countries

Source: USBM

Production of frasch & native sulfur

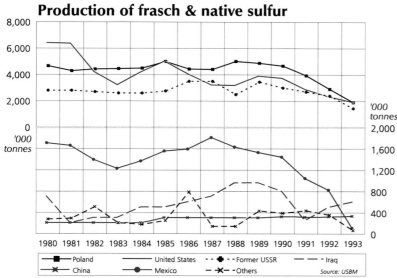

Legend:
- Poland
- United States
- Former USSR
- Iraq
- China
- Mexico
- Others

Source: USBM

Production of sulfur from pyrites

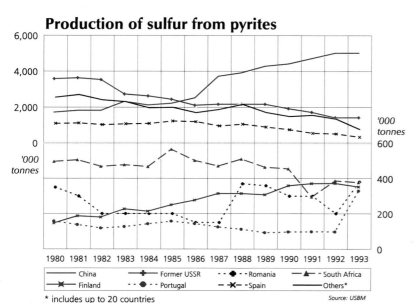

Legend:
- China
- Former USSR
- Romania
- South Africa
- Finland
- Portugal
- Spain
- Others*

* includes up to 20 countries

Source: USBM

Alum, $165/t (technical); $290/t (iron-free). Aluminum sulfate $270 (commercial grade, 17% Al_2O_3, E. and Gulf Coasts); $358-380/t (iron-free, 17% Al_2O_3, dry, bags). Ammonium sulfate $94-116/t (granular, bulk, ex-works); $42-50/t (standard, commercial, FOB works); $146/t (technical, bags, ex-works). Ammonium sulfide $507/t (liquid, 40-44%, tanks, 100% basis, freight equalized). Ammonium thiosulfate $286/t (photographic, 60% tanks, FOB works). Barium sulfate $1.54-1.76/kg (USP, X-ray diagnosis grade, powder). Barium sulfide (black ash) $706/t (drums, ex-works). Blanc fixe $0.45/kg. Lithium sulfate $79.15/kg (anhydrous, delivered). Magnesium sulfate (Epsom salts) ex-works $0.37-0.4/kg (10% Mg, technical, bags); $0.35/kg (bulk); $0.40-0.42/kg (USP, crystal, bags); 0.6/kg (USP, crystal, bags). Manganese sulfate $524/t (29.5% Mn, powder and mini granular, FOB Mobile, AL, bags); $595/t (32% Mn, granular, ex-works, bags). Potassium sulfate $198/t (agricultural, min. 50% K_2O, standard, bulk, FOB works); $2,200-2.860/t (300-lb drums, granular, purified). Sodium sulfide (flake, E. USA, ex-works, freight equalized) $800/t (drums); $711/t (bags).

ETYMOLOGY: Anhydrite from the Greek *anhydros = dry* or *without water*. **Chalcopyrite** from the Latin *chalcos = copper* and its similarity with pyrite. **Galena** from the Latin *galena = lead ore* or dross remaining after melting lead. **Gypsum** from the Latin *gypsum*, Greek *gypsos = plaster* or *chalk*. **Pentlandite** for Joseph Barclay Pentland (1797-1873), Irish natural scientist and traveler. **Pyrite** from the Greek *pyrites = flint* or *millstone from pyros = a fire* since it gives off sparks when struck. **Pyrrhotite** Greek for *redness* alluding to the liveliness of its color. **Sphalerite** from the Greek for *treacherous* or *slippery* since it was often mistaken for galena but yielded no lead. **Stibnite** from the Greek *stimmi* and Latin *stibium = old names for antimony*. **Sulfur** from the Latin *sulfur*, an old name; akin to Sanskrit *sulvere*.

TALC

Minerals	Formula	Color	SG	H
Talc	$Mg_3Si_4O_{10}(OH)_2$	White to green	2.7-2.8	1
Serpentine	$Mg_6Si_4O_{10}(OH)_8$	green-black-red	2.5-2.6	3.4
Chlorite	$(Mg, Fe)_5Al(AlSi_3)O_{10}(OH)_8$	green	2.65-2.94	1.5-2.5

PROPERTIES & USES: Talc is a soft, nonabrasive, inert mineral that can be ground easily (flaky habit) to form a white and bright (>78 GE) fine to micronized powder that acts as a functional filler [paint; plastics (polypropylene and polyethylene); paper; rubber; adhesives; joint compounds; stucco; pharmaceuticals]. Additional advantages include its high oil and grease absorption capabilities (organophilic/hydrophobic) [paint; cosmetics and pharmaceuticals; pitch-control in pulp; paper filler and coater; dusting and mold release agent; bitumen filler; food, feedstuff, and fertilizer anti-caking agent; insecticide carrier] and its flaky habit provides structural strength, pigmentation, opacity, rheology, viscosity, and corrosion and weathering resistance [paint; specialty plastics; various rubber compounds].

In paint talc has a reinforcing effect, controls viscosity, prevents sagging of paint films, improves suspension characteristics, and because of its large surface area (>12m²/g) dictates gloss. In plastics talc has a strong reinforcing effect (in polypropylene, a 20% loading increases stiffness by 80% and a 40% loading by 150%), increases heat resistance, reduces mold shrinkage, improves melt rheology, and reduces mold cycle time [appliance panels & housings, automotive parts, packaging, plastic furniture]. Talc is also used as an anti-blocking agent to roughen the surface of tacky film in order to prevent cold welding. In paper filler-grade talc improves ink receptivity, opacity, and brightness with a minimal negative effect on sheet strength. The unique property of preferentially wetting oily substances in the presence of water plus its large surface area (>12m²/g) allows talc to remove pitch and other oleoresinous components of pulp {pitch-control agent}. Ultrafine talc (<5 μm) is used to pigment latex, starch, or alpha protein coating colors in paper.

MINERAL COMPOSITION OF SOME US TALCS (%)

	California	Montana	New York	North Carolina	Vermont
Talc	85 - 90	90 - 95	35 - 60	80 - 92	80 - 92
Tremolite	0 - 12	0	30 - 55	0	0
Anthophyllite	0	0	3 - 10	0 - 5	0
Serpentine	0	0	2- 5	0	0
Quartz	<1	<1	1 - 3	1 - 3	<1
Chlorite	0	2 - 4	0	5 - 7	2 - 4
Dolomite	0 - 3	1 - 3	0 - 2	2 - 4	1 - 3
Calcite	0	0	1 - 2	0	0
Magnesite	0	0 - 5	1 - 3	0	0 - 5

Source: Grexa, Cyprus Industrial Minerals Co.

In pharmaceuticals and cosmetics talc's greasy feel [lubricant or glident], fragrance retention [talcum powder, antiperspirant sticks, soaps, and creams and lotions] and hiding power [cosmetics] are useful characteristics. Talc's lubricity and ease of dispersion are also utilized in lubricants and greases required to function over a wide range of temperatures.

In roofing products talc acts as a stabilizer for the melted asphalt thus increasing resistance to fire and weathering [tar paper; asphalt shingles; roll roofing]. Talc also prevents the shingles or roll roofing from sticking together during manufacture and installation.

CHEMICAL COMPOSITION OF COMMERCIAL TALC (%)

	USA Montana Filler	USA Montana USP	USA Montana Pitch-control	Canada Cosmetic	France Ceramics	Italy	China Cosmetic	USA New York Ceramics	Austria talc/dolomite
SiO_2	61.5-63.1	60.7	61.3	61.5	46.3	61.8	62	57.3	18.5
MgO	31.0-32.9	31.9	31.1	31.3	32.0	31.65	31.9	30.7	29.8
CaO	0.19-3.90	0.1	0.15	0.4	0.7	0.2	0.21	6.17	3.1
Al_2O_3	0.93-2.37	0.47	1.5	0.1	9.5	0.6	0.29	0.38	3.4
Fe_2O_3	1.0-1.3	0.6	0.9	1.3	1.9	0.59	0.15	0.16	3.8
TiO_2	0.05-0.13				0.2				
K_2O	0.01-0.41								
LOI	5.5-6.2	4.9	5.6	5	8.8	5.16	5.21	5.04	13.8
Acid insol		<2.0	max. 2.5						
Water sol.		<0.1	max. 0.2						
Pb			<5ppm			<2ppm			
As			<1ppm			<3ppm			
Brightness	70-84	92.5	88	88				98 (fired)	
Oil absorption		30-48	50						

Source: company literature

In ceramics, talc's high fusion point (heat-stable up to 900°C), fluxing action (due to MgO), and predictable thermal expansion allow lower firing temperatures and shorter firing cycles to be achieved [wall tiles (which may contain 50-70% talc), sanitaryware, vitreous china, catalytic converter substrate]; its high thermal conductivity, high dielectric strength, and low electrical conductivity are required for specialty ceramics [electrical porcelain]; and its low shrinkage prevents crazing and cracking [glazes]. As the talc dissociates on firing (800-1,050°C) products include enstatite (yielding high thermal expansion bodies which are in compression thereby minimizing glaze crazing) as well as cordierite and mullite (which have low thermal expansion). The fluxing action reduces the amount of feldspar required to produce the required strength.

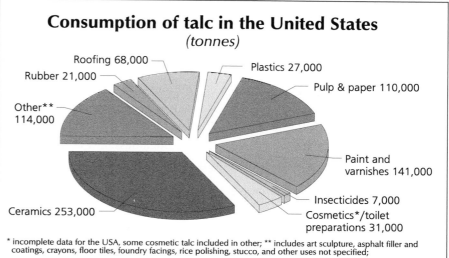

Consumption of talc in the United States
(tonnes)

Roofing 68,000
Rubber 21,000
Other** 114,000
Ceramics 253,000
Plastics 27,000
Pulp & paper 110,000
Paint and varnishes 141,000
Insecticides 7,000
Cosmetics*/toilet preparations 31,000

* incomplete data for the USA, some cosmetic talc included in other; ** includes art sculpture, asphalt filler and coatings, crayons, floor tiles, foundry facings, rice polishing, stucco, and other uses not specified;

Source: USBM (USA) EMR (Canada)

APPARENT CONSUMPTION OF TALC (TONNES)

	Apparent Consumption
China	1,676,745
United States	1,048,121
Former USSR	502,900
Brazil	448,402
Germany	212,853
France	192,268
Finland	167,890
Canada	158,859
North Korea	158,000
Italy	155,121
South Korea	148,545
Mexico	106,536
Spain	97,175
United Kingdom	81,639
Norway	65,892
Romania	55,000
Netherlands	54,536
Indonesia	43,770
Venezuela	33,671
Belgium	32,648
Australia	31,073
Pakistan	30,960
Sweden	30,116
Argentina	26,778
Former Yugoslavia	24,429
Austria	24,378
Iran	23,000
Poland	22,905
Malaysia	22,715
Portugal	20,114

NOTE: Numbers are approximate and rounded for 1990 or thereabouts; absence of a country does not necessarily indicate no production or trade; absence of a number does not necessarily mean zero

Source: British Geological Survey

Steatite is a massive, cryptocrystalline form of talc which can be machined easily, has uniform low shrinkage in all directions, and high electrical resistivity when fired [electronic insulators].

Chlorite has similar properties to talc, but lacks whiteness.

Soapstone is a massive green to gray to black mixture of talc and magnesite that is aesthetically pleasing and can be cut with a knife or machined [hand carving and sculpturing], resists weathering and acid and alkali attack, is nontoxic and non-absorbent [specialized sinks & countertops; brine tanks], retains heat, and has a melting point of 1,630°C [refractories; fireplaces], and can be polished [dimension stone; flooring; countertops; window sills].

QUALITY & SPECIFICATIONS: Mineral composition of talc deposits influences potential end uses (see table).

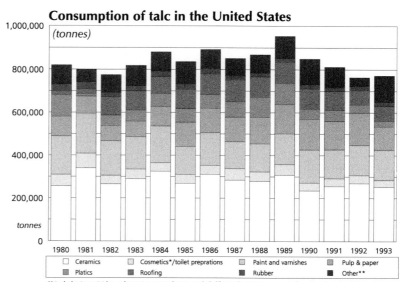

Consumption of talc in the United States
(tonnes)

Legend: Ceramics, Cosmetics*/toilet preprations, Paint and varnishes, Pulp & paper, Platics, Roofing, Rubber, Other**

** includes insecticides, refractories, art sculpture, asphalt filler and coatings, crayons, floor tiles, foundry facings, rice polishing, stucco, and other uses not specified
* incomplete data for the USA, some cosmetic talc included in other

Source: USBM

Ceramic-grade:- min. 30% MgO and 60% SiO_2, max. 1% CaO, 4% Al_2O_3, 1.5% Fe_2O_3, 0.4% alkali (talc containing tremolite is particularly well suited); 95% -325 mesh. Uniform chemical composition, PSD, with constant color and shrinkage rate on firing.

Cosmetic grade:- max. 0.1% water-soluble substances, 6% acid-soluble substances, 6% LOI @ 1,000°C, 0.1-1.0% quartz, 0.1% tremolite, 3ppm As, 20ppm Pb, 40ppm heavy metals, neutral pH, no fibrous materials, grit, or bacteria; odor, slip or lubricity, fragrance retention, and whiteness according to customer preference; , -200 mesh with APS 7 μm.

Paint grade:- min. 88% Mg & Ca silicate, max. CaO, 1% water-soluble matter, 1% moisture and other volatiles, 7% LOI, -325 mesh; good oil absorption (ASTM D 281-84 which measures the number of parts of acid-refined linseed oil required to produce a coherent paste with 100 parts of talc pigment), brightness (>90%), and consistency are required.

Pitch control:- $12m^2/g$ min. surface area, >78 GE brightness; low abrasion; APS of 2 - 5 μm.

Paper grade:- >78 GE brightness; controlled top size (50 μm max.), APS of 8 - 12 μm.

Roofing grade:- low grade with particle size of -80 mesh.

Rubber grade:- <2 μm median with controlled top size.

Sculpturing-grade soapstone requires attractive coloring, freedom from cracks, and consistency.

COSMETIC TALC STANDARD

CHARACTERISTIC	COMMENT	METHOD
Macroscopic appearance	A powder free from visible extraneous matter.	TPF Method 5(b)
Microscopic appearance	Cosmetic talc is composed predominantly of translucent, lamninar, irregular but substantially isodiametric particles not normally exceeding 60 um in the maximum dimension.	TPF Method 60
Color	White or "off-white". Shade criteria to be agreed between buyer and supplier.	See acid-soluble matter
Odor	Virtually odorless	BP
Texture and slip	Free from gritty particles by palpation.	TPF Methods 77 and 79.
Screen test	100% passes through BX	TPF Method 78 or other method of equivalent accuracy and sensitivity.
Apparent density	100 mesh sieve and 98% minimum through a BS 200 mesh sieve. Finer grades to be as specified by the buyer.	
Loss on drying	Must meet buyer's requirements.	
Acid-soluble matter	Losses not more than 0.6% when dried at 105°C to constant mass.	
Iron	6% maximum. There must be no odor of H_2S.	
Sulphides	Must meet buyer's requirements.	
Water-soluble matter	Absent.	
Identification	Boil 5.0 g with 25 ml water for thirty minutes under a reflux condenser; filter, evaporate the filtrate to dryness and dry at 105°C. The residue weighs not more than 10 mg.	
Amphibole minerals	By X-Ray Diffractometry or Infra-Red Spectroscopy. Not detected by the instrument and technique described.	

Toilet Preparations Federation (TPF)

WORLD CAPACITY: (talc) 9M. t.

CAPACITY UTILIZATION: 89%.

MARKET CONDITIONS: Steady - growing.

MARKETING FACTORS: Development of certain plastics in large-scale use such as automobile parts; the market of various types of ceramics many of which (e.g. wall tiles, semivitreous bodies) are dependent on construction activity. Regional factors are important in that very little talc is used as a filler in the North American paper industry (but large quantities are used for pitch control), whereas in Europe talc is an important paper filler and even coater.

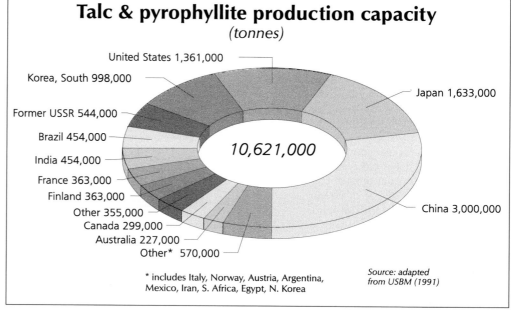

Talc & pyrophyllite production capacity
(tonnes)

United States 1,361,000
Korea, South 998,000
Former USSR 544,000
Brazil 454,000
India 454,000
France 363,000
Finland 363,000
Other 355,000
Canada 299,000
Australia 227,000
Other* 570,000
Japan 1,633,000
China 3,000,000

10,621,000

* includes Italy, Norway, Austria, Argentina, Mexico, Iran, S. Africa, Egypt, N. Korea

Source: adapted from USBM (1991)

HEALTH & SAFETY: Crystalline silica has been classified as a probable carcinogen by the IARC (see silica for further details). Therefore, because of its crystalline silica content, unless processing has the capability to reduce the crystalline silica content to less than 0.1%, talc will come under the OSHA Hazard Communication Standards, 29 CFR Section 1900.1200 which require labeling and other forms of warning, material safety data sheets, and employee training for products containing identified carcinogens with concentrations greater than 0.1%.

Certain talcs have been targeted for environmental concern over the content of fibrous minerals, notably anthophyllite, tremolite, and actinolite. In June 1992 the US Occupational Safety and Health Administration (OSHA) issued a final rule which removed the nonasbestiform varieties of anthophyllite $(Mg,Fe)_7[(OH)Si_4O_{11}]_2$, tremolite $Ca_2(Mg, Fe)_5[(OH)Si_4O_{11}]_2$, and actinolite $Ca_2(Mg, Fe)_5[(OH)Si_4O_{11}]_2$ from the scope of its asbestos standard. The nonasbestiform varieties will be regulated according to limits set for "particulates not otherwise regulated." This is important for the tremolite-bearing forms of talc used in ceramics.

RECYCLING: The increased recycling of paper reduces the consumption of raw pulp which in turn reduces the need for pitch control and therefore talc. Large-scale post-consumer recycling of ceramics has been limited to date; the recycling of demolition material including sanitaryware is increasing.

TALC LEADERS

Producers	Importers	Exporters
China	Japan	China
United States	Germany	United States
Former USSR	Mexico	Australia
Brazil	Belgium	France
France	United Kingdom	Austria
Finland	Netherlands	Finland
Australia	United States	Belgium
South Korea	Taiwan	Norway
North Korea	Hong Kong	Italy
Canada	Italy	Hong Kong
Italy	Canada	Canada
Austria	Indonesia	South Korea
Norway	Thailand	Netherlands
Spain	Spain	India
Japan	France	Sweden

PRODUCTION AND TRADE IN TALC (TONNES)

	Production	Imports	Exports	Apparent Consumption	Net Supplier	Net Consumer
North America	1,352,919	200,992	240,395	1,313,516	39,403	
South America	531,638	17,275	1,598	547,315		(15,677)
Central America & Carib.		4,616		4,616		(4,616)
European Union	571,242	577,477	287,879	860,840		(289,598)
Non-EU Europe	1,105,486	96,972	286,421	916,037	189,449	
Australiasia	3,242,415	905,614		4,148,029		(905,614)
Middle East	23,000	8,868	1,178	30,690		(7,690)
Africa	19,466	17,632	528	36,570		(17,104)

NOTE: Numbers are approximate and rounded for 1990 or thereabouts

Source: British Geological Survey

Talc production

Chart: Talc production, 1980–1993. Left axis (tonnes): 800,000 / 1,600,000 / 2,400,000 / 3,200,000. Right axis (tonnes): 0 / 100,000 / 200,000 / 300,000 / 400,000 / 500,000 / 600,000. Legend: China, United States, Finland, USSR, France, Brazil, Australia, Others*

* includes more than 30 countries and may include some steatite and pyrophyllite

Source: USBM

Steatite production

Chart: Steatite production, 1980–1993. Upper axis (tonnes): 0 / 100,000 / 200,000 / 300,000 / 400,000 / 500,000. Lower axis (tonnes): 0 / 4,000 / 8,000 / 12,000 / 16,000 / 20,000. Legend: Argentina, Austria, India, Spain, Others*

* Argentina, Burma, Greece (some steatite production may be combined in talc figures)

Source: USBM

PRODUCERS & WORLD TRADE:
Statistics on talc production and trade are complicated by the inclusion of pyrophyllite and steatite. An attempt to split these commodities out has been made in the accompanying tables (see pyrophyllite chapter). China and the United States dominate in high-purity talc together with numerous smaller producers. Some are noted for particular grades, for example France, Italy, and Australia produce significant quantities of cosmetic talc. There is active deep-sea trade in high-quality grades of talc.

PRICES: Montana/Canada $205-220/t (Hegman No. 6, micronized). New York, USA, ex-works nonfibrous, bags $110/t (paint, -200 mesh); $198/t (paint, -400 mesh); $92/t (ceramics, -200 mesh); $101/t (ceramics, -325 mesh). Chinese, ex-store UK $285-322/t (-200 mesh); $300-330/t (-350 mesh). French $180-285/t (fine ground). Finnish $210-450/ (micronized). Italian $262/t (cosmetic, CIF N. Europe). Norwegian, ex-store UK $188-243/t (ground); $285-375/t (micronized). South African $420/t (cosmetic, FOB Durban).

HTS CODES: 2526.10 (crude, not ground); 2526.20 (ground, washed, powdered); 6815.99 (cut or sawed).

SUBSTITUTES & ALTERNATIVES:
Animal feed and supplement:- clays (bentonite, sepiolite), dolomite, gypsum, iodine, iron oxide, limestone, magnesite, manganese, perlite, phosphates, salt, sulfur, vermiculite, zeolites. **Anti-blocking agent:**- calcined kaolin, diatomite, precipitated silica. **Cosmetics & pharmaceuticals:**- calcium carbonate, kaolin, magnesia, starch, zeolites. **Carrier:**- attapulgite/sepiolite, bentonite, diatomite, kaolin, pumice, pyrophyllite, vermiculite, zeolites. **Filler:**- ATH, barite, calcium carbonate, diatomite, feldspar, kaolin, mica, nepheline syenite, perlite, microcrystalline silica, ground silica flour and synthetic silica, wollastonite. **Lubricant:**- graphite, lithium, mica, molybdenum disulfide (MoS_2).

ETYMOLOGY: Anthophyllite from the neo-Latin *anthophyllum = clove* for its brown color, Greek *lithos = stone*. **Chlorite** from the Greek *chloros = light green* in reference to its color. **Serpentine** from the Latin *serpens = snake* because of the similar surface patterns. **Steatite** from the Greek *steatos = suet*. **Talc** from the Arabic *talq*. **Tremolite** for the Tremola Valley, near St. Gotthard, Switzerland, and Greek *lithos = stone*.

TITANIUM MINERALS

Minerals	Formula	% TiO₂	Color	SG	H
Rutile	TiO_2	100	red-brown to black	4.2	6-6.5
Anatase	TiO_2	100	brown-blue-black	3.82-3.95	5.5-6
Ilmenite	$FeO \cdot TiO_2$	52.7	iron black	4.5-5	5-6
Leucoxene	$FeO \cdot TiO_2$	variable	whitish		

PROPERTIES & USES: Ilmenite, rutile, anatase, and leucoxene concentrates are mainly used as a feedstock for titanium dioxide pigment (TiO_2) production [paper; paint; plastics; rubber; printing inks; cosmetics; soap and pharmaceuticals].

The need for higher titanium feedstocks has encouraged upgrading ilmenite to titaniferous slag or synthetic rutile. Ilmenite conc. (min. 44% TiO_2) + coal in electric furnace ➔ titanium slag (75-85% TiO_2) float and byproduct pig iron sinks [ductile iron castings; gray iron; allotted cast iron; carbon steels; alloy steels].

$$FeO \cdot TiO_2 \; + \; CaO \; + \; C \quad \rightarrow \quad TiO_2 \; slag \quad + \quad Fe \; + \; Ca \; slag \; + \; CO_2$$
ilmenite   *lime*   *coal*   *smelted @1,500-1,700°C*   *pig iron*

Ilmenite conc. (min. 58% TiO_2) + subbituminous coal ➔ synthetic rutile or SR (92-95% TiO_2) as:

$$FeO \cdot TiO_2 \; + \; C \quad \rightarrow \quad (Fe + TiO_2) \; + \; CO_2$$
ilmenite   *coal*   *reduced @1,200°C*

$$(Fe + TiO_2) \; + \; O_2 \quad \rightarrow \quad FeO \; + \; TiO_2$$
metallic iron   *aeration*   *synthetic rutile*

Titanium dioxide manufacture is via the sulfate or chloride route, each with different feedstock requirements. Natural rutile (94-98% TiO_2), SR (92-95% TiO_2), anatase (90-95% TiO_2), leucoxene (68%+ TiO_2) conc., or titanium slag from beach sands (80-85% TiO_2) in a chlorination fluid bed reactor ➔ (via chloride route) TiO_2 thus:

$$TiO_2 + 2C + 2Cl_2 \quad \rightarrow \quad 2CO + TiCl_4$$
    coke   *@925-1,010°C*

$$TiCl_4 \quad \rightarrow \quad TiO_2$$
titanium tetrachloride   *oxidized @985°C*

Ilmenite conc. (min. 44% TiO_2) or titanium slag from hard-rock ilmenite (75-80% TiO_2) ➔ (via sulfate route) ➔ TiO_2 thus:

$$FeTiO_3 + 5H_2O + 2H_2SO_4 \quad \rightarrow \quad TiOSO_4 + FeSO_4 \cdot 7H_2O$$
ilmenite   *@150-180°C*   *ferrous sulfate (copperas)*

$$TiOSO_4 + 2H_2O \quad \rightarrow \quad TiO(OH)_2 + H_2SO_4$$
titanyl sulfate   *hydrolysis @90°C*   ↓ *ppt. TiO₂*

Titanium dioxide is the premier white pigment with a high refractive index of 2.55-2.7 (provides good opacity) and reflectivity (brightness and whiteness), inertness (color retention), tinting strength, non-toxicity, and thermal stability over a wide range of temperatures [paper; paint; plastics; rubber; ceramics; textiles; cosmetics]. Two main grades are available — rutile (more abrasive with a higher refractive index (2.7), SG, and chemical stability [outdoor paints; plastics; printing inks; cosmetics] and anatase which is less abrasive and has a bluer tone [indoor paint; paper; textiles; latex rubber; soap and pharmaceuticals].

TiO_2 has non-pigment uses [ceramics & electroceramics; enamels & glazes; glass & fiberglass; and welding rods]. TiO_2 ➔ titanium carbide [cutting tools].

Rutile, synthetic rutile, or high-titania slag (Kroll process) ➔ $TiCl_4$ (reduced by molten magnesium) ➔ Ti sponge ➔ Ti metal ingots [Ti metal and alloys]. 1 t of metal requires 4.37 t of $TiCl_4$ and 1.41 t of magnesium.

$$TiO_2 + 2C + 2Cl_2 \quad \rightarrow \quad TiCl_4 \; + \; 2CO$$
      titanium tetrachloride

$$TiCl_4 \; + 2Mg \quad \rightarrow \quad MgCl_2 \; + \; Ti$$
   molten   *reduced @1,100°C*   *sponge*

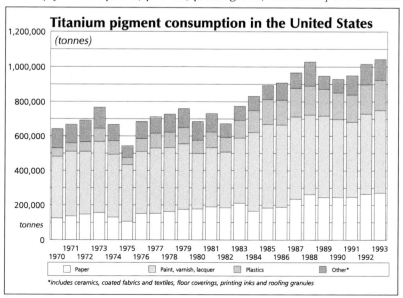

Titanium pigment consumption in the United States

(tonnes)

Chart showing consumption from 1970 to 1993, y-axis in tonnes from 0 to 1,200,000.

Legend: ☐ Paper | Paint, varnish, lacquer | Plastics | Other*

includes ceramics, coated fabrics and textiles, floor coverings, printing inks and roofing granules

APPARENT CONSUMPTION OF TITANIUM MINERALS & DIOXIDE (TONNES)

TITANIUM DIOXIDE		TITANIUM MINERALS	
United States	1,230,614	Canada*	1,291,204
Japan	296,493	South Africa*	1,191,000
Germany	263,011	United States	1,127,361
United Kingdom	174,950	Germany	659,626
Italy	125,026	Japan	576,003
Former USSR	110,600	Australia	526,038
Australia	106,506	Former USSR	415,400
Canada	94,315	United Kingdom	354,482
Netherlands	90,397	Malaysia	331,119
France	82,097	France	254,074
Spain	80,174	Norway	237,734
Brazil	76,005	China	185,000
Taiwan	74,991	Brazil	172,846
Mexico	73,528	Mexico	123,461
Saudi Arabia	57,977	Spain	114,204
South Korea	57,374	Belgium	87,233
India	42,476	India	66,850
Finland	40,834	Italy	65,936
China	37,370	Finland	52,400
Poland	36,000		
South Africa	35,729		
Singapore	32,131		
Former Yugoslavia	28,934		
Thailand	24,759		
Sweden	23,926		
Turkey	23,752		
Indonesia	22,499		
Malaysia	19,172		

* much of the consumption is accounted for by the production of titanium slag

NOTE: Numbers are approximate and rounded for 1991 or thereabouts; absence of a country does not necessarily indicate no production or trade; absence of a number does not necessarily mean zero

Source: British Geological Survey

Worldwide titanium dioxide demand
('000 tonnes)

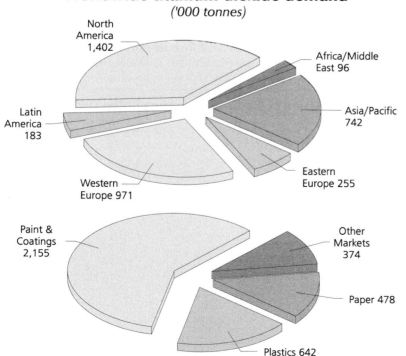

North America 1,402
Africa/Middle East 96
Asia/Pacific 742
Latin America 183
Eastern Europe 255
Western Europe 971

Paint & Coatings 2,155
Other Markets 374
Paper 478
Plastics 642

Source: Paint & Coatings Industry, May 1994/Freedonia Group Inc.

Titanium metal is nontoxic with an excellent strength-to-weight ratio, high melting point, good resistance to corrosion, low coefficient of expansion, and high electrical resistivity [aerospace; casting jet engines, chemical and desalination plants; prosthetic and medical devices; sports & fashion wear; marine applications]. Titanium metal → ferrotitanium [deoxidizer; stabilizer in stainless steel manufacture]; → superconductive alloys (Ti-Nb) [power generation; magnet-levitated train; super computers; cryoelectronics]; → shape-memory alloys (Ti-Ni) [air-conditioning; automobile parts; recording & measurement equipment]; → hydrogen storage alloys (Ti-Fe, T-Mn) [hydrogen storage and transportation; catalyst; fuel-cell electrode; specialty steel]; → abrasion-resistant alloys ((Ti-Ni) [pumps in nuclear & chemical plants].

$TiCl_4$ → various alkyl & butyl titanates have catalytic and water repellent properties [polymerization; surface-treatment]; strontium titanate [synthetic gemstone; optical applications]; metatitanic acid [absorbents; titania sol].

Rutile or synthetic rutile is used as a welding rod coating to stabilize the electric arc, reduce the viscosity of the slag, and decrease the surface tension of the metal droplets on the electrodes [metallurgy]. Ilmenite's inertness and high SG & H are utilized as a weighting agent [drilling muds; high-weight concrete], abrasive [sand blasting media], and filtration media [water and industrial waste filtration].

QUALITY & SPECIFICATIONS: Ilmenite conc. for slag processing may be as low as 44% TiO_2. Feedstock for sulfate pigment use must be sulfatable (rutile or synthetic rutile cannot be used) and requires low Fe (minimizes waste), Cr, V, & Nb (colors pigment), Ca & P (inhibits crystal growth), and U, Th, & radioactive elements (concentrates in waste and process streams). Chloride route feedstock requires low CaO (<0.2%), MgO (<1%), & Cr (form liquid chlorides which clog reactor bed), Fe (minimize iron chloride disposal), Cr & V (toxic in waste stream), Sn & As (accumulate with $TiCl_4$), SiO_2 (<2%) (coats grains and prevents reaction), and minimal U & Th (<500 ppm combined) (concentrates in waste and process streams). Chloride feedstock requires sufficient grain size and bulk density to avoid blow-over in the chlorination fluidized bed reactor.

TiO_2 pigment particle size (ave. 0.2-0.4 µm) must be optimum for light scattering in the particular application.

COMPOSITION OF TITANIUM MINERALS

ILMENITE

	E. Australia ISK Minerals Pty Ltd.	E. Australia RGC Mineral Sands Ltd.	W. Australia Tiwest	W. Australia Cable Sands (WA) Pty Ltd.	Sri Lanka Ceylon Mineral Sands - HiTi	India Indian Rare Earths Q grade	USA Du Pont
TiO_2	60	55.5	61.0	54.6	61.95	60	64
Fe_2O_3	30	28.9	32.5	16.8	-	25.5	28.48
FeO	6	20.7	3.6	23.2	-	-	1.33
Al_2O_3	0.8	1.3	1.2	na	1.57	1.1	1.23
Cr_2O_3	0.05	0.03	0.1	0.0	0.47	-	-
V_2O_5					0.38	-	-
SiO_2	0.4	0.85	0.9	0.7	0.57	0.9	0.28
P_2O_5	0.014	0.03	0.1	0.035			
U+Th (ppm)	210	<70	140	<85			

SYNTHETIC RUTILE

	E. Australia RGC Premium SR	E. Australia Tiwest	W. Australia Westralian Sands Ltd.	India Dhranghadhra C.W.	India Indian Rare Earths Ltd.	Malaysia Malaysian Titanium Corp.	Japan Ishihara	USA Kerr-McGee
TiO_2	92.5	93.5	92.5-93.5	95	91.8	95	96.1	94.15
Fe_2O_3		3.1	2.0-3.0	2	4.6	<1.50	1.3	2.6
FeO							-	9
Total iron	2.7							
Al_2O_3	1.1	0.9	1.4-1.6	na	0.4	<.55	0.46	0.48
SiO_2	1.4						0.5	1.3
Cr_2O_3	0.18	0.23	0.08	na	0.06	<.05	0.15	0.16
V_2O_5	0.26	0.37	0.25	na	0.2	<0.14	0.2	0.16
Nb_2O_5	0.25							
P_2O_5	0.03						0.17	-
MnO	0.9						0.03	0.04
S	0.5						-	-
ZrO_2	0.1	0.06	na	na	0.24	<0.11	0.15	-

RUTILE

	Australia Mineral Deposits Ltd.	Australia Consolidated Rutile Ltd.	Australia Tiwest	Australia RGC Mineral Sands Ltd. (Eneabba)	Australia Westralian Sands Ltd.	Australia RZM Pty Ltd.	Australia Currumbin Minerals Pty Ltd.
TiO_2	95.2	95.5	95.8	95.5	91-92	96.2	95.0
ZrO_2	0.5-0.95	0.69	0.80	0.95	1.5-2.5	0.75	1.0
SiO_2	0.7-1.0	0.72	0.80	0.80	1.1-1.5	0.70	na
Fe_2O_3	0.5-0.9	0.53	0.94	0.90	1.5-3.5	0.35	1.0
Cr_2O_3	0.18-0.28	0.16	0.15	0.15	0.07-0.15	0.20	na
V_2O_5	0.58-0.65	0.75	0.43	0.68	0.02-0.05	0.70	na

TITANIUM SLAG

	Canada QIT Sorelslag	South Africa RBM Ti slag	Norway Tinfos Tinfos slag
TiO_2	77.5	85.8	75
Fe_2O_3	-	-	
FeO	10.9	10.8	7.6
Al_2O_3	3.5	1.3	1.2
CaO	0.6	0.15	
MgO	5.3	1.1	7.9
SiO_2	3	2.1	5.3
Cr_2O_3	0.17	0.17	0.09
V_2O_5	0.57	*0.6	
P_2O_5	-	-	
MnO	0.25	*2.5	
S	0.06	-	
ZrO_2	-	-	
U+Th (ppm)	1.9	15-30	na

LEUCOXENE

	Australia Cable Sands (WA) Pty Ltd.	Australia Tiwest	Australia RGC Mineral Sands Ltd.
TiO_2	90	85	89.5
Fe_2O_3	2.3	10	4.9
P_2O_5	0.09	na	0.07
ZrO_2	2.35	0.2-0.5	0.9
S	0.015	0.02-0.03	0.02
Al_2O_3	na	0.5-1.2	1.6
Cr_2O_3	na	0.13-0.15	0.16

TITANIUM MINERALS

WORLD CAPACITY: Ore (TiO$_2$ content) ilmenite 2.7M. t; rutile 560,000 t; synthetic rutile 6300,000 t. Metal (gross wt) sponge 117,000 t. TiO$_2$ pigment (ave. 95% TiO$_2$) 1.6M. t (sulfate); 1.9M. t (chloride).   **CAPACITY UTILIZATION:** >95%.

MARKET CONDITIONS: Increasing although demand is notoriously cyclic.

MARKETING FACTORS: Demand for paint and plastics depends on construction activity which in turn depends on the state of the economy. Consumption in paper also depends on the economy (mainly influenced through advertising) and on the rate of industrial development. Titanium metal production is largely dependent on aerospace.

HEALTH & SAFETY: The content of radioactive elements (mainly U + Th) has become a concern since they can become concentrated through processing and are known to be carcinogenic (also see zirconium minerals). Radionuclide content of titanium minerals is regulated by federal and regional governments. Another area of concern is in the production of titanium dioxide, in particular the disposal of waste material, particularly ferrous sulfate in the sulfate process.

TITANIUM MINERAL LEADERS

Producers	Importers	Exporters
Canada	United States	Australia
South Africa	Germany	Canada
Australia	Japan	South Africa
Norway	UK	Norway
Former USSR	France	South Korea
Malaysia	Mexico	India
United States	Spain	Norway
Sierra Leone	South Korea	Netherlands
China	Belgium	United States
India	Italy	Sierra Leone
Brazil	Netherlands	Thailand
Norway	Finland	Germany
Sri Lanka	Brazil	France
Thailand	Canada	Brazil
	Malaysia	Sri Lanka
	Taiwan	

TITANIUM DIOXIDE LEADERS

Producers	Importers	Exporters
United States	United States	Germany
Germany	Germany	United States
Japan	Italy	UK
UK	France	France
France	Taiwan	Belgium
Canada	Japan	Japan
Australia	Belgium	Canada
Former USSR	UK	Finland
Mexico	Netherlands	Italy
Finland	South Korea	Mexico
Italy	Spain	Singapore
Belgium	Canada	Norway
Spain	Sweden	Spain
Brazil	China	China
Saudi Arabia	Thailand	Hong Kong
Netherlands	Turkey	South Korea
Poland	Indonesia	Czechoslovakia
Singapore	Brazil	Taiwan
South Africa	Malaysia	Sweden
India	Hong Kong	Netherlands

Source: British Geological Survey

Capacity of titanium products
(tonnes, grosss weight)

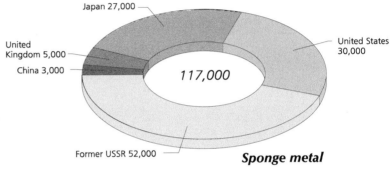

Japan 27,000
United Kingdom 5,000
China 3,000
United States 30,000
117,000
Former USSR 52,000

Sponge metal

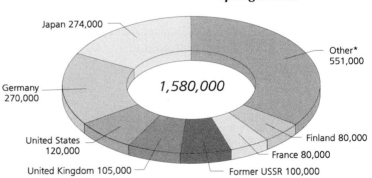

Japan 274,000
Germany 270,000
United States 120,000
United Kingdom 105,000
Other* 551,000
Finland 80,000
France 80,000
Former USSR 100,000
1,580,000

Sulfate pigment

*includes Italy, Canada, Belgium, Spain, Brazil, Australia, South Africa, Former Yugoslavia, Norway, China, Czechoslovakia, South Korea, India, Taiwan

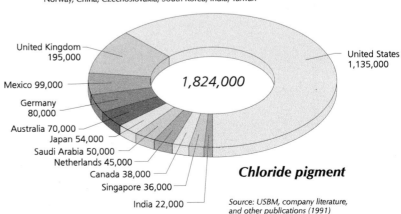

United Kingdom 195,000
Mexico 99,000
Germany 80,000
Australia 70,000
Japan 54,000
Saudi Arabia 50,000
Netherlands 45,000
Canada 38,000
Singapore 36,000
India 22,000
United States 1,135,000
1,824,000

Chloride pigment

Source: USBM, company literature, and other publications (1991)

PRODUCERS & WORLD TRADE: Australia, Canada, and South Africa dominate the titanium feedstock industry both in terms of production and exports. Rutile production is much more restricted than ilmenite, and is dominated by Australia, South Africa, and Sierra Leone. Titanium slag is produced in Canada, South Africa, and Norway. Overall, titanium mineral production is fairly restricted, and therefore large quantities enter deep-sea trade. Titanium dioxide plants are generally located close to consuming markets rather than to raw material supply. Importers are usually developed countries.

World production of ilmenite

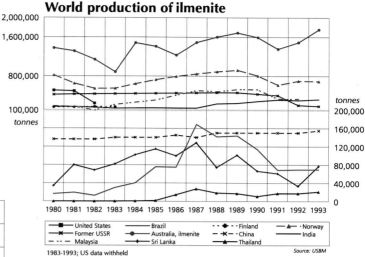

Source: USBM

1983-1993; US data withheld

World production of rutile

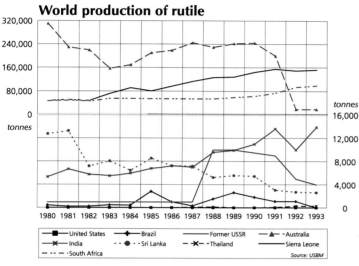

Source: USBM

World production of titanium slag

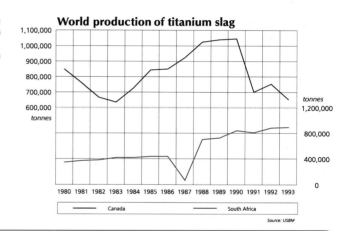

Source: USBM

PRODUCTION AND TRADE IN TITANIUM MINERALS (TONNES)

	Production	Imports	Exports	Apparent Consumption	Net Supplier	Net Consumer
North America	2,267,000	1,056,086	781,060	2,542,026		(275,026)
South America	2,389,000	1,108,561	781,657	2,715,904		(326,904)
European Union	40	468,686		468,726		(468,686)
Non-EU Europe	521,000	6,400	85,000	442,400	78,600	
Australasia	82,983	29,087	14,329	97,741		(14,758)
Africa	2,017,154	29,087	556,719	1,489,522	527,632	

NOTE: Numbers are approximate and rounded for 1990 or thereabouts; absence of a country does not necessarily indicate no production or trade; absence of a number does not necessarily mean zero

Source: British Geological Survey

PRODUCTION AND TRADE IN TITANIUM DIOXIDE (TONNES)

	Production	Imports	Exports	Apparent Consumption	Net Supplier	Net Consumer
North America	1,466,000	196,532	264,075	1,398,457	67,543	
South America	55,000	46,559		101,559		(46,559)
European Union	365,000	92,382	188,778	268,604	96,396	
Non-EU Europe	128,000	35,286		163,286		(35,286)
Australasia	46,000	106,735	20,854	131,881		(85,881)
Africa	35,000	5,853		40,853		(5,853)

NOTE: Numbers are approximate and rounded for 1990 or thereabouts; absence of a country does not necessarily indicate no production or trade; absence of a number does not necessarily mean zero

Source: British Geological Survey

Titanium mineral prices (US$/tonne)

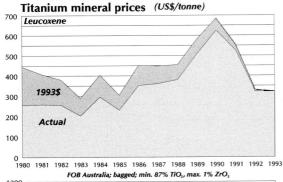

Leucoxene

1993$

Actual

FOB Australia; bagged; min. 87% TiO₂, max. 1% ZrO₂

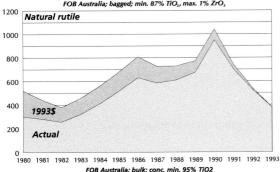

Natural rutile

1993$

Actual

FOB Australia; bulk; conc. min. 95% TiO2

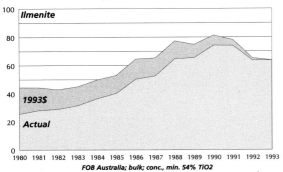

Ilmenite

1993$

Actual

FOB Australia; bulk; conc., min. 54% TiO2

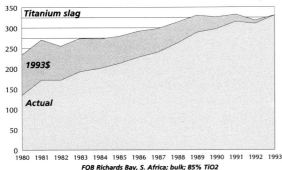

Titanium slag

1993$

Actual

FOB Richards Bay, S. Africa; bulk; 85% TiO2

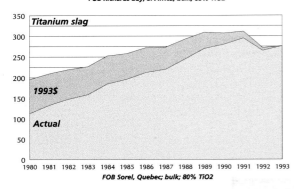

Titanium slag

1993$

Actual

FOB Sorel, Quebec; bulk; 80% TiO2

PRICES: Ilmenite conc., FOB Australia, min. 54% TiO$_2$, A$93-97/t; FOB Neendakara, India, Q grade, 59/60% TiO$_2$, $75-80/t. Leucoxene, FOB W. Australia, min. 91% TiO$_2$, max. 1% ZrO$_2$, A$315-335/t (bulk); A$345-370/t (bags). Rutile, FOB Australia, min 95% TiO$_2$, A$410-430/t (bulk, large volume for pigments); A$450-480/t (bags, small parcels for welding rods). Titanium slag, 80% TiO$_2$, FOB Sorel, Quebec, $279/t; 85% TiO$_2$, FOB Richards Bay, S. Africa $329/t. Titanium dioxide, freight equalized $2.01-2.11/kg (anatase, bags); $2.01-2.09/k (anatase, slurry, dry basis); $2.02-2.07/kg (rutile, regular); $2.24/kg (rutile, slurry, dry basis). Titanium hydride $56.10-57.20/kg (powder, electronics grade, drums). Titanium tetrachloride, FOB works, technical-grade, $0.66-0.75/kg (bulk); $1.10/kg (200-gallon cylinders). Ferrotitanium $3.01-3.12/kg Ti content (70% with max. 4.5% Al). Titanium sponge metal $9.90/kg.

HTS CODES: 2614.00.6020 (ilmenite); 2620.90.5000 (titanium slag); 2614.00.6040 (rutile conc.); 2614.00.3000 (synthetic rutile); 3206.10.00 (titanium dioxide pigments); 2823.00.0000 (titanium oxides); 8108.10.1000 (waste and scrap titanium metal); 8108.10.50 (unwrought metal); 8108.90.60 (wrought metal).

SUBSTITUTES & ALTERNATIVES: Pigment:- ATH, barite, calcium carbonate, diatomite, feldspar, kaolin, lead oxide, mica, nepheline syenite, perlite, talc, microcrystalline silica, ground silica flour and synthetic silica, wollastonite. **Metals and alloys:-** aluminum, magnesium, stainless steel, and various superalloys.

RECYCLING: Although recycling of paper and plastic is designed to reduce raw material consumption, the resulting raw material generally requires a boost in brightness by the addition of titanium dioxide pigment. Paint is rare if ever recycled. Titanium metal and titanium alloys are recycled, although the long life span limits the impact on the marketplace.

ETYMOLOGY: Anatase from the Greek *anatasis = extension* because of the greater length of the common pyramid as compared with other tetragonal minerals. **Brookite** for Henry James Brooke (1771-1857), English mineralogist. **Ilmenite** for the Ilmen Mountains, former USSR, where it was first located. **Leucoxene** from the Greek *leukos = white* and *xenos = stranger* alluding to its color and secondary nature. **Rutile** for the French for shining derived from Latin *rutilus = red* alluding to its color. **Titanium** from the Latin *Titani* and Greek *Titanes = a Titan*, in Greek mythology any one of twelve children of Uranus (Heaven) and Gaea (Earth); denotes strength.

Prices of titanium dioxide pigment

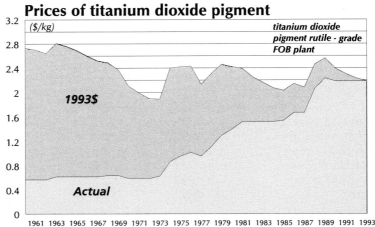

($/kg)

titanium dioxide
pigment rutile - grade
FOB plant

1993$

Actual

VERMICULITE

Minerals	Formula		Color	SG	H
Vermiculite	hydrated sheet mica with Fe, Mg, Al, & K		bronze-brown-black	2.5	2.1-2.8

PROPERTIES & USES: Vermiculite splits easily into thin flexible inelastic flakes. Unexfoliated vermiculite concentrate is used in fire rated wallboard, to reduce slag build up in coal-fired boiler tubes, in drilling muds, and intumescent gasket applications.

On rapid heating to about 870°C the contained water changes to steam and exfoliates the vermiculite which results in an 8- to 12-fold expansion and a decrease in density from 640-960 kg/m^3 to 56-192kg/m^3. Vermiculite may be transported in its raw state and exfoliated at an exfoliation plant close to the point of consumption. Exfoliated vermiculite is generally gold, golden brown, or bronze in color with a metallic luster. Thermally exfoliated vermiculite has similarities with perlite (see below), although is considered less dusty. Consisting of 90% trapped air, expanded vermiculite is lightweight, has good thermal (thermal conductivity of 0.062 - 0.065 W/m°C) and acoustic insulation, is chemically inert, and relatively refractory (therefore fire resistant), rot proof, odorless, and nonirritating, all properties desirable in certain building products [lightweight aggregate; lightweight wallboard; loose-fill insulation; fire-proof coatings including structural steel; sodium silicate-based ceiling tiles; urea-formaldehyde laminated boards] and friction materials [asbestos replacement in brakes, clutches, etc.]. Loosely packed lightweight aggregates have a unit weight of 1,281-1,602 kg/m^3 compared with over 2,000 kg/m^3 or more for crushed rock. Vermiculite mixed with various binders such as portland, high-alumina, or silica cements is used to insulate steam pipes, boilers, and furnaces; vermiculite (or perlite) treated with asphalt emulsion or a silicone for water resistance is utilized as a cavity fill for thermal insulation [cement block and other masonry structures].

Ground chemically exfoliated vermiculite in aqueous dispersions is utilized in coating and film forming applications [glass cloth; flexible films; plastic fillers].

The excellent refractory properties (a sintering temperature of 1,260°C and melting point of 1,315°C) are also utilized in metallurgy [hot-topping compounds] and refractories [insulation bricks, boards, and shapes].

Vermiculite absorbs moisture and remains free-flowing and is used in agriculture and horticulture [fertilizer, herbicide, and insecticide carrier; anticaking agent; packing material for nursery stock; seed encapsulator; soil conditioning agent; plant-growing medium]. A mixture of vermiculite, peat, and plant nutrients forms a soilless hydroponic plant medium [horticulture].

CHEMICAL ANALYSIS OF COMMERCIAL VERMICULITE (WT%)

	United States Enoree, SC W.R. Grace	United States Louisa, VA Virginia Vermiculite Co.	S. Africa Palabora Palabora Mining Co.	Brazil Piaui Eucatex Mineral Ltda.
Li$_2$O		0.01	0.03	
Na$_2$O		1.72	0.80	0.10
K$_2$O	4.42	6.63	2.46	0.50
MgO	20.04	16.38	23.37	23.60
CaO	0.75	1.12	1.46	3.80
BaO	0.12			0.20
MnO	0.07	0.14	0.30	
FeO			1.17	
Al$_2$O$_3$	17.36	12.85	12.08	10.20
Cr$_2$O$_3$	0.50	0.23		
Fe$_2$O$_3$	8.45	8.80	5.45	5.80
SiO$_2$	38.66	38.34	39.37	45.10
TiO$_2$		1.66	1.25	0.70
H$_2$O (total)	8.71	10.66	11.20	10.20

Source: Company litereature

MINERALOGICAL COMPARISON OF PERLITE AND VERMICULITE

	Perlite	Vermiculite
Description	Glassy volcanic rock	Hydrated Mg-Al-Fe-sheet silicate of variable composition
	Metastable amorphous Al-silicate	
Mineral structure	Macro-micro concentric "onion-like" structures formed by shrinkage	Biotite sheet structure but separated by a double layer of water molecules
Color	Light gray to black	Bronze to yellow brown
Mohs hardness	5.5-7.0	2.1-2.8
Expansion characteristics	When contained water vaporizes the heat-softened grains swell into light, fluffy cellular particles.	When contained water vaporizes individual layers are forced apart at right angles to the plane of cleavage. This gives a "concertina" effect.
Expansion temp.	760-1,100°C	870-1,100°C
Expansion ratio	10-20	12-20(volume)

Source: Industrial Minerals

QUALITY & SPECIFICATIONS: Depend on the final end use but generally include vermiculite content (90-99% in concentrates), particle size, exfoliation efficiency, and density after exfoliation. In the United States, approximate top and bottom screen sizes are Grade 1 (Coarse) - 4-8 mesh Tyler (4.75-2.36 mm); Grade 2 (Medium) - 8-14 mesh Tyler (2.35-1.18 mm); Grade 3 (Fine) - 14-28 mesh Tyler (1.18-0.60 mm), etc. Important specifications are covered in ASTM C-332 (vermiculite aggregate for concrete), C-35 (vermiculite aggregate for plaster), and C-516 (vermiculite loosefill insulation).

WORLD CAPACITY: 520,000 t.

CAPACITY UTILIZATION: 94%.

MARKET CONDITIONS: Steady.

MARKETING FACTORS: Construction activity and therefore the economy; new uses and products such as chemically exfoliated vermiculite and use as a catalyst.

HEALTH & SAFETY: Crystalline silica has been classified as a probable carcinogen by the IARC (see silica for further details). Therefore, because of its crystalline silica content, unless processing has the capability to reduce the crystalline silica content to less than 0.1%, vermiculite will come under the OSHA Hazard Communication Standards, 29 CFR Section 1900.1200 which require labeling and other forms of warning, material safety data sheets, and employee training for products containing identified carcinogens with concentrations greater than 0.1%. In general, silica content in vermiculite is low. Contamination by asbestos is extremely deleterious for vermiculite.

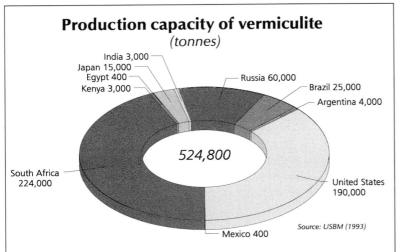

Production capacity of vermiculite
(tonnes)

India 3,000
Japan 15,000
Egypt 400
Kenya 3,000
Russia 60,000
Brazil 25,000
Argentina 4,000
524,800
South Africa 224,000
United States 190,000
Mexico 400

Source: USBM (1993)

SIZE AND DENSITY OF RAW VERMICULITE

Grade	Size range. μm	Density range, km/m³
1	6,680 - 1,700	800 - 1,040
2	2,360 - 1,180	800 - 1,040
3	1,700 - 425	800 - 1,040
4	600 - 212	720 - 1,040
5	-425	640 - 800

Source: The Vermiculite Institute

GRADING AND DENSITY OF EXFOLIATED VERMICULITE

Grade Sieve size	1	2	3	4	5
			Cumulative % retained		
9.5 mm	0 - 10				
4.75 mm	30 - 60	0 - 5			
2.36 mm	65 - 95	20 - 80	0 - 10		
1.18 mm	85 - 100	75 - 99	20 - 60	0 - 5	
600 μm		90 - 100	65 - 95	15 - 65	0 - 10
300 μm			75 - 98	60 - 98	10 - 50
150 μm			90 - 100	90 -100	55 - 85
Density kg/m³	64 - 112	64 - 128	80 - 128	96 - 160	128 - 176

COMMERCIAL GRADES OF VERMICULITE

UNITED STATES

Grade	Density lb./ft³	US sieve size (Tyler mesh)	Approx. max. mm.
1	4-7	3-10	6.7
2	4-8	8-14	2.4
3	5-9	10-35	1.6
4	6-10	28-65	0.6
5	8-11	35+	0.4
		Micron	0.180

SOUTH AFRICA

Grade	Middle Sizes (mm)	Range (mm)
Premium	5.66	2.80-16.0
Large	2.80	1.40—8.0
Medium	1.40	0.71-4.0
Fine	0.71	0.355-2.0
Superfine	0.355	0.18-1.00
	0.09-0.5	

S. African vermiculite is divided into premium (16 mm max. size), large (8 mm), medium (4 mm), fine (2 mm), superfine (1 mm), and micron (0.5 mm) grades.

Source: PMC

SUBSTITUTES & ALTERNATIVES:

Animal feed supplement:- clays (bentonite, sepiolite), perlite, talc, zeolites. **Carrier/absorbent**:- attapulgite, bentonite, diatomite, kaolin, peat, pumice, pyrophyllite, sepiolite, talc, zeolites. **Fire retardant**:- ATH, antimony oxide, asbestos, borates, bromine, chromite, diatomite, magnesite & magnesia, perlite, phosphates, pumic.e. **Friction material**:- asbestos, barite, bauxite & alumina, clays (attapulgite, kaolin, sepiolite), garnet, graphite, gypsum, mica, pumice, pyrophyllite, silica, slate, wollastonite, zircon. **Foundry**:- bauxite & alumina, chromite, clays (kaolin & bauxite), olivine, perlite, pyrophyllite, silica sand, zircon. **Insulation**:- asbestos, diatomite, foamed glass, metals, or cement, perlite, pumice, wollastonite, zeolites. **Lightweight aggregate**:- clay (expanded), perlite, pumice, shale (expanded). **Soil Amendment**:- bentonite/kaolin, diatomite, gypsum, peat, perlite, zeolites. **Thermal and sound insulators**:- brick clays, diatomite, mineral wool, expanded perlite.

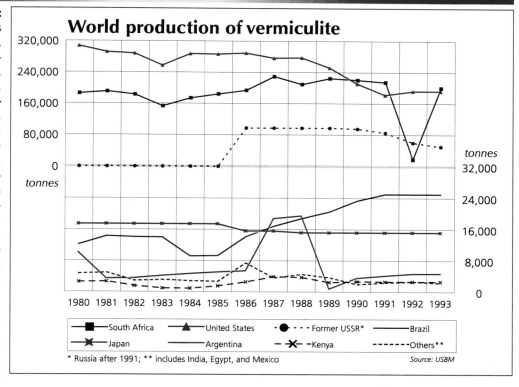

World production of vermiculite

Legend: South Africa, United States, Former USSR*, Brazil, Japan, Argentina, Kenya, Others**

* Russia after 1991; ** includes India, Egypt, and Mexico

Source: USBM

RECYCLING: Virtually none.

PRODUCERS & WORLD TRADE: The United States and South Africa dominate world production and exports.

PRICES: United States $115-175/t (FOB barge, US Gulf Coast); imported $160-175/t; Grade 1 (Coarse) $225-250/t; Grade 2 (Medium) $150-170/t; Grade 3 (Fine) $120-130/t; Grade 4 (Superfine) $75-85/t. Europe $153-230/t (South African, bulk, FOB Rotterdam).

HTS CODES: 2530.10.0000 (vermiculite, perlite and chlorites, unexpanded); 6806.20 (exfoliated vermiculite as mixtures and articles of heat-insulating, sound-insulating, or sound-absorbing materials).

ETYMOLOGY: Vermiculite from the Latin *vermiculare = to breed worms* alluding to its appearance after exfoliation and Greek *lithos = stone*.

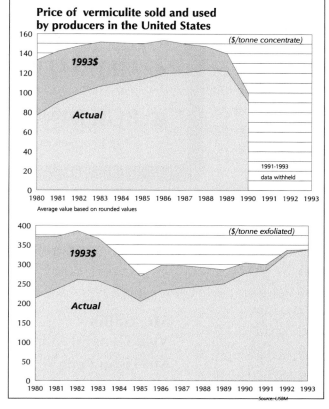

Price of vermiculite sold and used by producers in the United States

($/tonne concentrate)

1993$

Actual

1991-1993 data withheld

Average value based on rounded values

($/tonne exfoliated)

1993$

Actual

Source:-USBM

VERMICULITE LEADERS

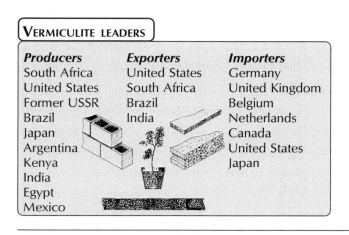

Producers	Exporters	Importers
South Africa	United States	Germany
United States	South Africa	United Kingdom
Former USSR	Brazil	Belgium
Brazil	India	Netherlands
Japan		Canada
Argentina		United States
Kenya		Japan
India		
Egypt		
Mexico		

JILIN PROV. LISHU WOLLASTONITE I/E CO.

DALIAN DEVELOPMENT ZONE BRANCH

▲ **Unfamiliar with Chinese Wollastonite?**

▲ **Do you need high aspect ratio wollastonite powder ?**

LWIEC can help YOU ....

.... LWIEC, the largest and only professional I/E Co. of Wollastonite owns Lishu, Faku and Panshi mines. It is of the first position in capacity and producing all kinds of wollastonite in China, especially in producing and specialising in high aspect ratio wollastonite powder.

▲ **CERAMIC AND GLAZE GRADE**
(200 - 325 mesh)

▲ **FILLER GRADE**
(100 - 2500 mesh)

▲ **METALLURGICAL GRADE**
(100 - 200 mesh)

▲ **BUILDING MATERIAL GRADE**
(H & G series of high aspect ratio wollastonite powder, L/D 20:1 ~ 30:1)

**Mr. Zhang Meng Xian -
General Manager**

CONTACT:

**Mr. Xu Bin -
Vice General Manager**

**Mr. Lishu Peng -
I/E Dept. Manager**

HEAD OFFICE:
Dadingshan, Lishu County,
Jilin Province, China
Tel: 86-4445-710275
Fax: 86-4445-710888

DALIAN BRANCH:
No.3 Bldg., Commercial Mansion,
Dalian Devt. Zone, Dalian, China
Tel: 86-411-7613181
Fax: 86-411-7613182

WOLLASTONITE

Minerals	Formula	CaO	SiO$_2$	Color	SG	H
Wollastonite	CaSiO$_3$	48.3	51.7	white to yellowish brown	2.8-2.9	4.5-5.0

PROPERTIES & USES: Wollastonite is a natural calcium silicate that breaks down into acicular or needle-like cleavage fragments. Commercial uses depend on chemical and/or physical properties, particularly acicularity which is quantified by the ratio of length to width of the fragments (the aspect ratio). High-aspect ratio or HAR grades may have an aspect ratio of 15:1 or even 20:1 [asbestos substitute; functional filler] whereas low-aspect ratio (LAR) or powdered or milled (10-75 µm) grades have an aspect ratio of 3:1 to 5:1 [ceramics; glass; metallurgy]. The aspect ratio of the commercial products depends on the feed material and the method of grinding. HAR and LAR grades have quite different markets.

With a theoretical composition of 48.3% CaO and 51.7% SiO$_2$, wollastonite is used as a pure and white source of SiO$_2$ and CaO [ceramics; glass]. It has minimal gas evolution (LOI <1% @ 1,000°C) and therefore low bubbling, an absence of alkalis which enhances electrical insulation, a low sintering temperature (991-1,196°C) which encourages fast firing, and a low straight-line thermal expansion coefficient (6.5x10^{6}mm/°C) which reduces shrinkage, cracking, and crazing [ceramic-bonded abrasives; ceramic electrical insulators; dinnerware; frits & glazes; investment castings; ovenware; sanitaryware; semivitreous bodies; spark plugs; structural clay products; terra cotta; wall tiles]. Although less important than the chemistry, the acicular shape opens clay bodies to release water vapor during drying and in the early firing cycle, imparts high-impact strength and dimensional stability, and promotes good acoustical properties to tile surfaces. In glazes wollastonite contributes lime to alkaline glaze formulation, improves bonding to a body, generates a smooth surface and diminishes pinholing, and minimizes cracking and crazing. Wollastonite allows frits to be produced with matte finishes and helps stabilize colors or tints. Wollastonite acts as a natural frit in porcelain enamel manufacture and replaces prefritting with limestone and silica.

Wollastonite can replace limestone and silica sand in the glass batch where it reduces the melting temperature and inhibits scum and seed formation [specialty glass; fiberglass].

Acicularity, high brightness (90-93%), chemical inertness, a pH of 9.9, thermal stability and high melting point (1,540°C), good electrical insulation, and low moisture and oil absorption facilitate the use of wollastonite as a functional filler [coatings and related products; plastics; rubber; boards & panels].

In coatings, the acicular particles (3-8 µm) act as a good flattening agent and allow paint to settle out after application to produce a dry film of uniform thickness, and the interlocking particles improve toughness and durability of the coat with excellent tint retention, scrub, and weather resistance. High brightness (84-93%) and whiteness reduce pigment load, and the very low oil absorption value of 26% reduces volume of binder required and contributes to reduced pigment costs. A pH of 9.9 is advantageous in polyvinyl acetate (PVA) paints where it helps to neutralize acidity shift. PVA can decompose into vinyl alcohol

CHEMICAL COMPOSITION OF COMMERCIAL NATURAL WOLLASTONITE (%)

	USA NYCO	USA R.T.V.	Finland Partek (Filler)	Finland Partek (Ceramics)	Russia	Turkey	India Wolkem	China Jilin	China Anhul
CaO	47.5	44.04	47.7	43.5	40.64	47.5	47.04	43	46.1
SiO$_2$	51.0	50.5	52.5	53.0	37.93	47.95	49.52	50	50.59
Fe$_2$O$_3$	0.4	0.26	<0.2	<0.25	1.56	0.58	0.43	0.08	0.38
MgO	0.1	1.48	<0.5	<0.8	1.7	0.78	0.20	0.04	1.03
Al$_2$O$_3$	0.2	1.75	<0.8	<1.0	3.66	2.37	0.6	0.05	0.33
TiO$_2$	0.02	NA	NA	NA	NA	NA	traces	NA	NA
LOI	NA	2.18	<1.2	6.16	13.82	0.52	1.68	2.0	1.3

Source: company literature

PHYSICAL PROPERTIES OF COMMERCIAL NATURAL WOLLASTONITE

	USA NYCO NYAD G	USA NYCO NYAD FP	USA NYCO NYAD 400	USA R.T.V. Vansil	Finland Partek WICROLL	Finland Partek FW	India Wolkem Kemolit
G.E. Brightness	85	70	94	87			
ISO Brightness					88-90	84-86	96-98
Bulk density							
Loose	25	85	40				24-35
Tapped	50	90	60				29-51
Aspect ratio	15:1	5:1			6:1-8:1	3:1	8:1-20:1
Particle size	-200	-10	-400	-200/-325			

Source: company literature

and acetic acid, but wollastonite maintains the alkaline nature of the paint and so combats corrosion [architectural, powder, and industrial coatings including textured paint; putty, caulks, and sealants; roof coatings; stucco and block fillers].

In the compounding of plastics, wollastonite's low plasticizer absorption and high brightness and opaqueness decrease polymer and pigment demand and low viscosity at high loadings reduces mold cycle time. In the filler adds flexural, compressive, and impact strength, enhances electrical insulating properties, increases heat distortion temperature, adds fire resistance, improves machinability of molded parts and dimensional stability [mineral-reinforced nylon; thermosetting plastics such as phenolic molding compounds, friction products, epoxies, polyurethane, polyurea, and BMC polyester; thermoplastics such as polyamide, polyester, and engineering resins]. Wollastonite's natural compatibility with organic polymers is enhanced with surface or chemical treatment (silane coupling agents, organosilicon chemicals, zircoaluminate and titanate wetting agents) which further improves mineral dispersion and wetting, mineral-polymer bonding, electrical properties, and certain mechanical properties. In rubber, wollastonite adds whiteness, low moisture absorption, and resistance to abrasion [specialty elastomers].

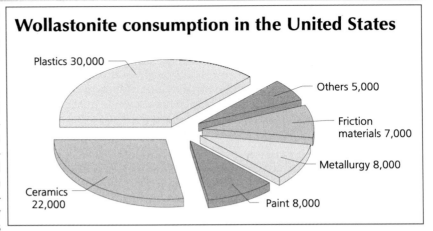

Wollastonite consumption in the United States

Plastics 30,000
Others 5,000
Friction materials 7,000
Metallurgy 8,000
Ceramics 22,000
Paint 8,000

The combination of flexural and impact strength, low thermal conductivity (0.87 Btu/hr ft^2/°F/in), thermal stability, and good sound deadening properties allow wollastonite to substitute for asbestos in fireproof products [interior & exterior construction boards; roof tiles; shaped insulation products; sheets and panels; siding]. Other possible substitutes include various man-made fibers, fiberglass, mica, perlite, and vermiculite.

Since wollastonite is insoluble in water, has low LOI, is readily fusible, and has a low P & S content it may be used as a low-temperature flux [welding powder, casting powder, hot-top for steel ingots].

Synthetic wollastonite, made from pure CaO materials such as calcium carbonate, calcium hydrate, or quicklime, and silica, lacks acicularity but is used for its chemistry in ceramics [white glazes or glaze frits; sintering aid in vitrified bodies] and in metallurgy [arc-welding powders; casting powders in steelmaking; steel refining]. Related synthetic minerals are diopside (CaO·MgO·2SiO$_2$) made from dolomite and silica [sintering aid in vitrified ceramics; welding and casting powders and in hot-metal desulfurization] and mayenite (12CaO·7Al$_2$O$_3$) made from CaO-bearing products and alumina [hot-metal desulfurization; alumina refining; inclusion modification of low-silicon steel].

QUALITY & SPECIFICATIONS: Typical chemical composition of commercial grade wollastonite is given in the table. In ceramics, critical characteristics are whiteness and high chemical purity (low Fe, Ti, Mn, LOI), and PS of -200 and -325 mesh. As a filler, acicularity (aspect ratio of 15:1 to 20:1), grain size (-200 to -1250 mesh), and brightness (>90%) are critical. Surface-modified grades are used in some filler applications. Synthetic wollastonite for ceramics has low-iron grades (max. 0.12% or 0.3% Fe$_2$O$_3$) and a metallurgical grade with low S (max. 0.009%) & P (max. 0.008%).

CHEMICAL COMPOSITION OF COMMERCIAL SYNTHETIC WOLLASTONITE, DIOPSIDE, & MAYENITE (%)

	Wollastonite SW v.low-Fe	Wollastonite SM low-Fe	Wollastonite SE low P/S	Wollastonite SG low P/S	Diopside S	Mayenite low-MgO	Mayenite MgO-enriched
CaO	45.31	45.7	45.44	45.66	25.72	51.15	45.90
SiO$_2$	53.59	52.6	52.36	52.58	55.68	2.90	2.70
MgO	0.47	0.6	0.61	0.55	16.37	0.75	4.60
Al$_2$O$_3$	0.20	0.5	0.38	0.47	0.44	44.6	46.30
Fe$_2$O$_3$	0.075	0.2	0.19	0.22	0.29	0.40	0.40
TiO$_2$	-	-	-	-	-	-0.01	-0.01
S	-	-	0.0034	0.008	-	-0.04	-0.04
P	-	-	0.0038	0.008	-	-0.04	-0.04
C	-	-	-	-	-	-0.01	-0.01
LOI*	0.34	0.4	0.035	0.08	0.24	traces	traces

*110-1,000°C

Source: Rheinische Kalksteinwerke, Germany

WORLD CAPACITY: 400,000 t (natural only).   **CAPACITY UTILIZATION:** 85%.

MARKET CONDITIONS: Increasing from a small base.

MARKETING FACTORS: Development of certain plastics in large-scale use such as automobile parts; the market of various types of ceramics many of which (e.g. wall tiles, semivitreous bodies) are dependent on construction activity. Wollastonite has numerous competitors in virtually all of its markets.

SUBSTITUTES & ALTERNATIVES: Ceramics:- calcium carbonate, dolomite, silica, kaolin, talc, feldspar. **Filler:-** ATH, barite, calcium carbonate, feldspar, kaolin, mica, nepheline syenite, perlite, pumice, pyrophyllite, talc, microcrystalline silica, ground silica flour and synthetic silica. **Friction Material:-** asbestos, barite, bauxite & alumina, clays (attapulgite, kaolin, sepiolite), garnet, graphite, gypsum, mica, pumice, pyrophyllite, silica, slate, vermiculite, zircon. **Insulation:-** asbestos, diatomite, foamed glass, metals, or cement, perlite, pumice, vermiculite, zeolites.

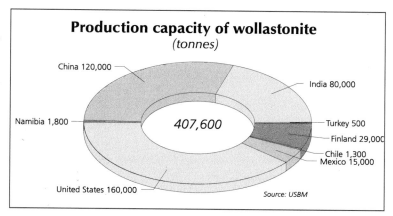

Production capacity of wollastonite
(tonnes)

China 120,000
India 80,000
Namibia 1,800
Turkey 500
Finland 29,000
Chile 1,300
Mexico 15,000
United States 160,000

407,600

Source: USBM

HEALTH & SAFETY: Wollastonite has received some negative health and safety publicity because of its acicular nature and role as an asbestos substitute. Its use is banned in Switzerland and in Sweden the allowable content of wollastonite in the air is less than that of silica. However, research has shown that wollastonite is "structurally, chemically, and crystalographically different from asbestos", and so the mineral has been given a Group 3 classification by the International Agency for Research on Cancer (IARC). Producers have formed the Wollastonite Information Center (WIC) to coordinate the distribution of scientifically sound information on the health and safety aspects of wollastonite.

Crystalline silica has been classified as a probable carcinogen by the IARC (see silica for further details). Therefore, because of its crystalline silica content, unless processing has the capability to reduce the crystalline silica content to less than 0.1%, wollastonite will come under the OSHA Hazard Communication Standards, 29 CFR Section 1900.1200 which require labeling and other forms of warning, material safety data sheets, and employee training for products containing identified carcinogens with concentrations greater than 0.1%.

RECYCLING: Virtually none.

PRODUCERS & WORLD TRADE: Production is dominated by the US, China, India, and Finland. International trade is active.

PRICES: United States (FOB plant, bulk) $166/t (-200 mesh); $210/t (-325 mesh); (acicular, ex-works) $195/t (-200 mesh); $240/t (-325 mesh); $268/t(-400 mesh); $327/t (acicular, 15:1 - 20:1 aspect ratio); $670/t (ground 10μ). United Kingdom $412/t (Finnish, 325 mesh, ex-store).

ETYMOLOGY: Diopside from the Greek *diopsis = to view through* since it is usually transparent. **Mayenite** for a locality near Mayen, Eifel district Rhineland-Palatinate, Germany. **Wollastonite** for William Hyde Wollaston (1766-1828), English chemist and mineralogist.

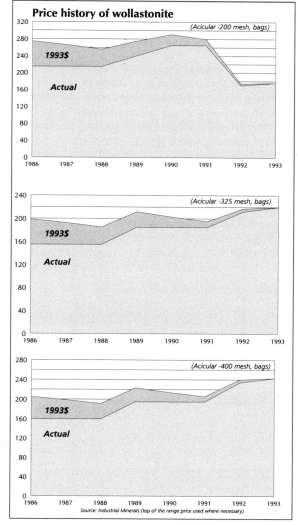

Price history of wollastonite

(Acicular -200 mesh, bags)
1993$
Actual

(Acicular -325 mesh, bags)
1993$
Actual

(Acicular -400 mesh, bags)
1993$
Actual

Source: Industrial Minerals (top of the range price used where necessary)

WOLLASTASTONITE LEADERS

Producers	Importers	Exporters
United States	Germany	China
China	Italy	Finland
Finland	Japan	India
India	Korea	United States
Mexico	Netherlands	
Former USSR	Portugal	
	Spain	
	Taiwan	

Zeolite	Typical Unit-Cell Content	Void volume (%)	SG	Ion-exchange meq./gm
Group 1: Single 4-ring (S4R)				
Analcime	$Na_{16}[(AlO_2)_{16}(SiO_2)_{32} \cdot 16H_2O$	18	2.24-2.29	4.54
Phillipsite	$(K,Na)_{10}[(AlO_2)(SiO_2)_{22}] \cdot 20H_2O$	31	2.15-2.20	3.87
Laumontite	$Ca_4[AlO_2)_8(SiO_2)_{46}] \cdot 16H_2O$	34	2.20-2.30	4.25
Group 2: Single 6-ring (S6R)				
Erionite	$(Ca,Mg,K_2Na_2)_{4.5}[(AlO_2)_9(SiO_2)_{27}] \cdot 27H_2O$	35	2.02-2.08	3.12
Group 3: Double 4-ring (D4R)				
Zeolite A (Linde)	$Na_{12}[(AlO_2)_{12}] \cdot 27H_2O$	47	1.99	5.48
Group 4: Double 6-ring (D6R)				
Faujasite	$Na_2, K_2, Ca, Mg)_{29.5}[(AlO_2)_{59}(SiO_2)_{133}] \cdot 235H_2O$	47		
Zeolite X	$Na_{12}[(AlO_2)_{12}] \cdot 27H_2O$	47		
Zeolite Y	$Na_{86}[(AlO_2)_{86}(SiO_2)_{106}] \cdot 264H_2O$	50	1.93	4.73
Zeolite L	$K_9[(AlO_2)_9(SiO_2)_{27}] \cdot 22H_2O$			
Chabazite	$Na_{56}[(AlO_2)_{56}(SiO_2)_{136}] \cdot 250H_2O$	48	2.05-2.10	3.81
Group 5: Complex 4-1, T_5O_{10} unit (T_5O_{10})				
Natrolite	$Na_{16}[(AlO_2)_{16}(SiO_2)_{24}] \cdot 16H_2O$	23	2.20-2.26	5.26
Group 6: Complex 5-1, T_8O_{16} unit (T_8O_{16})				
Mordenite	$Na_8[(AlO_2)_8(SiO_2)_{40}] \cdot 24H_2O$	28	2.12-2.15	2.29
Group 7: Complex 4-4-1, $T_{10}O_{20}$ unit ($T_{10}O_{20}$)				
Clinoptilolite	$Na_6[(AlO_2)_6(SiO_2)_{30}] \cdot 24H_2O$	34	2.16	2.54

Classification by Breck, 1974

Zeolites are crystalline microporous hydrated aluminosilicates containing cavities (pores) and channels with molecular dimensions of 3 to 10Å. They comprise silicon, oxygen, and aluminum in a three-dimensional framework structure with cavities containing water molecules capable of undergoing desorption and cations

BROAD BASED CATEGORIES OF ZEOLITES

Pore size	No. tetrahedra	Max. free diameter	Commercial examples
Large	12	7.5Å	X, Y, mordenite
Medium	10	6.3Å	ZSM-5, L, ferrierite
Small	6, 8	4.3Å	A, clinoptilolite, chabazite

that are capable of undergoing cation exchange. Chemically, zeolites have an empirical formula of: $M^+_2, M^{++})Al_2O_3 \cdot gSiO_2 \cdot zH_2O$ where M^+ is usually Na or K and M^{++} is Mg, Ca, or Fe. Rarely Li, Sr, or Ba may substitute for M^+ or M^{++}.

Natural zeolites occur in a variety of geological settings and synthetic zeolites are manufactured in large-scale chemical plants. Theoretically, the possibilities for framework topologies are infinite — around 40 are known in nature and more than 150 synthetic zeolites have been manufactured. The most important commercially is zeolite A, which has two main commercial methods of manufacture. In the hydrogel process a mixture of aqueous sodium silicate and a sodium aluminate solution is heated to 77-110°C and zeolite NaA crystallizes out after 1 to 8 hours.

$2NaOH + Al_2O_3 \cdot 3H_2O$ $\xrightarrow[\text{moderate temperature}]{}$ $2NaAl(OH)_4$ sodium aluminate

$12NaAl(OH)_4 + 4(Na_2O) \cdot (SiO_2)_3 + 7H_2O$ $\xrightarrow[\text{moderate temperature}]{}$ $Na_{12}((AlO_2))_{12} \cdot 27H_2O + NaOH$ zeolite NaA

In a second process, kaolin is calcined at about 500-600°C to convert it to the more reactive metakaolin. This is digested in aqueous NaOH to form an amorphous sodium aluminosilicate from which zeolite NaA crystallizes out in a few hours at 90-110°C.

$2Al_2Si_2O_5(OH)_4$ kaolin $\xrightarrow{}$ $2Al_2Si_2O_7 + H_2O$ calcined metakaolin

$12H_2O + 6Al_2Si_2O_7 + 12NaOH$ $\xrightarrow[\text{moderate temperature}]{}$ $Na_{12}((AlO_2))_{12}$ zeolite NaA

PROPERTIES & USES: Within the zeolite field, species may be divided into three broad categories based on pore size which in turn dictates the zeolite's properties and commercial utilization (see table above for summary).

Synthetic faujasites (a.k.a. zeolite X and zeolite Y) and natural mordenite are examples of large-pore zeolites. The large surface pores and interior cavities are the basis for use as a catalyst or a catalyst carrier [petroleum cracking (fluid cracking catalyst or FCC); NO_x control; isomerization; hydrogenation and dehydrogenation; methanation; dehydration]. An FCC catalyst, typically comprising 10 to 40 weight % zeolite Y dispersed in an amorphous matrix such as clay or silica-alumina, is designed to convert heavier petroleum fractions into lighter boiling products such as gasoline, fuel oil, liquefied petroleum gas (LPG), kerosene, and toluene.

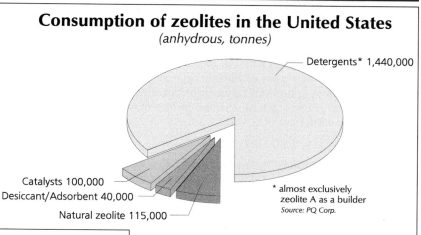

Consumption of zeolites in the United States
(anhydrous, tonnes)

Detergents* 1,440,000

Catalysts 100,000
Desiccant/Adsorbent 40,000
Natural zeolite 115,000

* almost exclusively zeolite A as a builder
Source: PQ Corp.

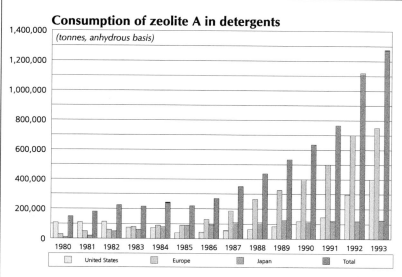

Consumption of zeolite A in detergents
(tonnes, anhydrous basis)

1980 1981 1982 1983 1984 1985 1986 1987 1988 1989 1990 1991 1992 1993

☐ United States　☐ Europe　☐ Japan　☐ Total

Zeolites' affinity for water allows it to adsorb and de-adsorb water and is used for purification, bulk separation, and drying [pet litter; desiccant; carriers for herbicides, fungicides, and pesticides; odor control]. Because of the uniformity of the micropores, zeolites exhibit a sharp sorption cut off with increasing molecular size thus allowing size-selective molecular sieving. The main commercial examples of these molecular sieves are zeolite X and Y [separation of fructose-glucose mixtures; desiccant in double-glazing; air-braking systems in trucks; drying natural gas; air and water treatment] and mordenite [drying acid gas; removing hydrogen sulfide from air; nuclear and municipal waste management; per litter]

Medium pore sized zeolites include ZSM-5 [catalytic dewaxing; olefin drying; benzene alkylation; and xylene isomerization] and zeolite L [reforming]. Catalytic dewaxing is the process of removal of long-chain linear and slightly-branched paraffins which have high melting points and therefore reduce the flowability of oil; reforming is a process whereby low-octane paraffins and naphthenes are converted to higher octane isoparaffins and aromatics. Small amounts of ZSM-5 may also be added to FCC catalysts in order to obtain higher octanes and are used as a selective adsorbent [extracts volatile organic compounds from air].

Ion-exchange properties (measured in millequivalents per gram) depend on the fact that certain loosely bonded ions in zeolites can be exchanged for other ions relatively easily. In particular zeolites can remove ammoniacal nitrogen and possibly heavy metals [aquaculture; pet litter; sewage and agricultural waste]; SO_2, CO_2, H_2S, NH_3 [animal waste; stack gas; contaminated and sour natural gas]; Sr^{90} and Cs^{137} and certain other isotopes [radioactive waste]; magnesium and calcium ions [detergent builder]; fertilizer and soil amendment; animal feed supplement]. The important small pore sized zeolite is zeolite A [builder in detergents; hydrocarbon, oxygen, and nitrogen separation]. The main commercial natural zeolites, chabazite and clinoptilolite, are small-pore varieties [radioactive waste treatment; municipal water waste treatment (mainly clinoptilolite); pet litter; odor control].

TYPICAL HEAVY DUTY POWDERED DETERGENT FORMULATIONS

	High Phosphate	Low Phosphate	Non-Phosphate
Zeolite A	–	20	25-30
Sodium tripolyphosphate (STPP)	30	5	–
Soda ash	15	25	15
Silicates	17	7	10
Salt cake	31	36	22
Linear Alkylate Sulfonate (LAS) & other actives	7	7	10
Carboxymethylcellulose (CMC)	–	–	1

Source: PQ Corp.

Natural zeolite (mainly clinoptilolite and mordenite) added to animal feed increases feed efficiency, reduces health problems, and yields drier and less odiferous excrement (1-3% of total broiler chicken feed).

Zeolites are inert and white or near white and can be used as a filler [paper]; mildly abrasive [toothpaste]; lightweight, durable, and can be carved [dimension stone]; have pozzolanic properties [cement ingredient]; and can be "popped" and expanded when calcined to 1,200 to 1,400°C [lightweight aggregate];

QUALITY & SPECIFICATIONS: An important difference between natural and synthetic zeolites is that natural zeolites may contain impurities and be nonuniform whereas synthetic zeolites are high-purity specialty chemicals manufactured to exact specifications on a consistent basis. Sophisticated uses like molecular sieves and catalysts are served by synthetic zeolites whereas natural zeolites are best suited to less demanding uses such as adsorption and ion-exchange in aquaculture, liquid carriers, and pet litter.

WORLD CAPACITY: 1,700,000 t (anhydrous)   **CAPACITY UTILIZATION:** NA.

MARKET CONDITIONS: The market for certain synthetic zeolites has been growing steadily since the 1950s and received a considerable boost when zeolite A began to replace STPP as a builder in detergents. Natural zeolites, the full potential of which has yet to be fulfilled, are in the unusual position of being a challenger to their synthetic counterparts which can be mass produced to exact specifications.

MARKETING FACTORS: The spread of anti-phosphate legislation will expand the market for zeolite A (see phosphates). Continued R&D is finding new uses for these extremely versatile minerals.

HEALTH & SAFETY: Under section 5(a)[2] of the Toxic Substances Control Act (TSCA), the US Environmental Protection Agency (EPA) issued a final rule in 1991 that persons who intended to manufacture, import, or process erionite fiber for any new use must notify EPA at least 90 days before beginning that activity. The EPA classified fibrous erionite as a Category B1 or probable human carcinogen. Mordenite is also a fibrous mineral, but to date has no record of carcinogenic problems.

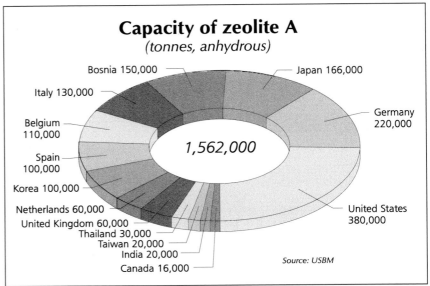

Capacity of zeolite A
(tonnes, anhydrous)

1,562,000

Bosnia 150,000
Japan 166,000
Italy 130,000
Germany 220,000
Belgium 110,000
Spain 100,000
Korea 100,000
Netherlands 60,000
United Kingdom 60,000
Thailand 30,000
Taiwan 20,000
India 20,000
Canada 16,000
United States 380,000

Source: USBM

CHEMICAL COMPOSITION OF COMMERCIAL ZEOLITES (%)

	Ash Meadows, CA clinoptilolite natural	Mud Hills, CA PDZ-140 natural	Mud Hills, CA PDZ-150 natural	Zeolite Na-A Valfor® 100 synthetic
Clinoptilolite	90±5			
SiO_2	69.1	66.03	69.54	33
Al_2O_3	11.9	10.47	9.86	28
CaO	0.7	1.55	0.88	
MgO	0.4	0.58	0.17	
TiO_2		0.13	0.32	
Na_2O	3.5	3.25	1.16	17
K_2O	3.8	1.81	4.65	
Fe_2O_3	0.7	1.12	1.92	
MnO	0.2	0.027	0.034	
H_2O				22
Pore size (Å)	4.0	4.0	4.0	4.2
Pore volume (%)	15	15	15	
Specific surface area (m^2/g)	40	40	40	
pH stability	0-13	3-10	3-10	10-11
Cation exchange capacity (m equiv/g)	1.85	1.65	1.55	5.6 (hydrated) 7.0 (anhydrous)

Crystalline silica has been classified as a probable carcinogen by the IARC (see silica for further details). Therefore, because of its crystalline silica content, unless processing has the capability to reduce the crystalline silica content to less than 0.1%, zeolites will come under the OSHA Hazard Communication Standards, 29 CFR Section 1900.1200 which require labeling and other forms of warning, material safety data sheets, and employee training for products containing identified carcinogens with concentrations greater than 0.1%.

SUBSTITUTES & ALTERNATIVES: Animal feed and supplement:- clays (bentonite, sepiolite), dolomite, gypsum, iodine, iron oxide, limestone, magnesite, manganese, perlite, phosphates, salt, sulfur, talc, vermiculite. **Carrier**:- attapulgite/sepiolite, bentonite, diatomite, kaolin, pumice, pyrophyllite, talc, vermiculite. **Detergent builder**:- sodium tripolyphosphate, sodium silicate, citrates. **Lightweight aggregate**:- clay (expanded), perlite, pumice, shale (expanded), vermiculite. **Molecular sieves**:- activated carbon, activated clays, alumina powder, attapulgite/sepiolite, bentonite, silica gel. **Pet litter**:- diatomite, various clays including attapulgite/sepiolite, bentonite, and kaolin.

RECYCLING: In many cases, zeolites can be cleaned and reused.

PRODUCERS & WORLD TRADE: Production and consumption of synthetic zeolites are concentrated in the United States, Japan, Korea, and Taiwan, and Europe. There is a substantial trade in synthetic zeolites, although imports are generally confined to industrialized countries. Consumption is dominated by companies manufacturing detergents and catalysts. The production of natural zeolites is more widespread, and eastern Europe and Asia have traditionally been major consumers. International trade is somewhat limited.

PRICES: Natural zeolites:- $50-100/t; Synthetic zeolites:- zeolite A (detergent grade) $500-600/t; others range up to $45/kg for specialty catalyst-grades.

ETYMOLOGY: Analcime from the Greek *analkis = without strength* due to its weak electrical properties when heated or rubbed. **Chabazite** from the Greek *chabazios* or *chalazios,* an ancient name of a stone celebrated in a poem ascribed to Orpheus. **Clinoptilolite** from the Greek *klinein = to bend* or *slope,* mono*clinic* Greek for *wing* or *down* alluding to its light nature, and *lithos = stone.* **Erionite** from the Greek *erion = wool* alluding to its white wool-like appearance. **Faujasite** for Barthélemy Faujas de Saint Fond (1741-1819), French geologist. **Ferrierite** for Walter Frederick Ferrier (1865-1950), Canadian geologist and mining engineer. **Heulandite** for John Henry Heuland (1778-1856), English mineral collector. **Laumontite** for François Pierre Nicolas Giller de Laumont (1747-1834), French discoverer. **Mordenite** for Morden, King's County, Nova Scotia, Canada. **Natrolite** from the Latin *natrium* or Greek *natron = native soda* plus *lithos = stone.* **Offretite** for Albert Jules Joseph Offret (1857-?), professor, Lyons, France. **Phillipsite** for William Phillips (1775-1829), British mineralogist, founder of the Geological Society of London. **Zeolites** from the Greek *zein = to boil* and *lithos = stone* (i.e. boiling stones). **Zoisite** for Siegmund Zois, Baron von Edelstein (1747-1819), Austrian scholar.

ZEOLITE LEADERS

Producers Synthetic	Producers Natural	Importers Synthetic/Natural	Exporters Synthetic/Natural
United States	Former USSR	Canada	United States
Germany	Japan	Switzerland	Germany
Japan	Cuba	Sweden	Japan
Italy	United States	Taiwan	Belgium
Belgium	China	Japan	Korea
Spain	Germany	Italy	Netherlands
Korea	Bulgaria	United Kingdom	Bulgaria
Netherlands	Hungary	France	Hungary
United Kingdom	S. Africa		
Thailand	Argentina		
Taiwan	Australia		
India			
Canada			

Minerals	Formula	%ZrO₂	%SiO₂	Color	SG	H
Zircon	$ZrSiO_4$	67.2	32.8	gray-yellow-red-brown	4.7	7.5
Baddeleyite	ZrO_2	100	-	brown	5.4-5.7	6.5

PROPERTIES & USES: The overwhelming source of zirconium products is zircon with baddeleyite making a modest contribution. Zircon is extremely refractory (melting point >2,430°C) with a low and regular coefficient of thermal expansion, low wettability by molten metal, excellent thermal diffusivity, and is chemically stable [refractories for ladle linings, continuous steel casting nozzles, refractory bricks for glass-melting furnaces, ramming mixes, refractory cement]. These properties plus high thermal conductivity and density, superior dimensional and thermal stability at elevated temperatures, the clean rounded shape of its particles which readily accept binders, and its neutral or slightly acid pH also make zircon useful as a foundry sand [steel] and foundry flour [mold paint; investment castings; superalloy and titanium casting]. The fineness of grind improves the surface finish and reduces "burning on".

Fine-ground zircon flour has a very high index of refraction and is used as an opacifier in ceramics and glazes [porcelain glazes; sanitaryware; wall tile; dinnerware; glazed brick & industrial tile] and its good dielectric strength is useful in specialized ceramics [electrical porcelain]. During welding, zircon sand forms a slag with other mineral ingredients to shield the weld pool [welding rod coating].

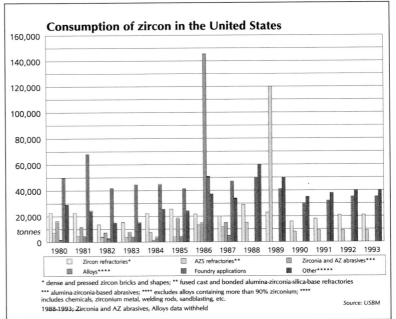

Consumption of zircon in the United States

Legend: ☐ Zircon refractories* ☐ AZS refractories** ☐ Zirconia and AZ abrasives*** ■ Alloys**** ■ Foundry applications ■ Other*****

* dense and pressed zircon bricks and shapes; ** fused cast and bonded alumina-zirconia-silica-base refractories
*** alumina-zirconia-based abrasives; **** excludes alloys containing more than 90% zirconium; ***** includes chemicals, zirconium metal, welding rods, sandblasting, etc.
1988-1993: Zirconia and AZ abrasives, Alloys data withheld

Source: USBM

Zircon → zirconia (ZrO_2) with a melting point of >2,700°C, high purity, exceptional hardness, and inertness [electronics and electronic catalysts; cubic zirconia gemstones (cubic zirconia); optical, ophthalmic, TV picture tube, and CRT glass]. Zirconia may be manufactured into fiber products with great refractoriness, low thermal conductivity, and chemical inertness and formed into cloths and felts, boards and cylinders, lagging ropes and webbing [NiH_2 battery separators; filtration and protection membranes; thermal insulators in crystal-growing furnaces; primary hot face insulation up to 1,750°C].

Zirconia → alumina-zirconia-silica (AZS) [refractories]; alumina-zirconia [AZ abrasives]. Zirconia and zirconia stabilized with MgO or Y_2O_3 yield engineering ceramics that are hard, tough, and inert, and have resistance to thermal shock and low thermal conductivity [extrusion dyes, engine parts, oxygen sensors, piezoelectric devices]. Other "toughened" zirconia ceramics include zirconia toughened alumina (ZTA), partially stabilized zirconia (PSZ), tetragonal stabilized polycrystals (TZP). Zirconia is formulated to produce zircon-iron pinks, zircon-vanadium blues, zircon-praseodymium yellow, and zirconia yellows and oranges [ceramic pigments].

Zircon + Cl_2 → zirconium tetrachloride [refining Al & Mg] → zirconium sponge → zircon metal (99.99% pure) which has a low neutron capture cross section, thermal stability, and resists corrosion [cladding and structural material for nuclear reactors (Hf-free); photography; specialty steel & alloys]; → zircalloys [noncorrosive applications].

$$ZrO_2{\cdot}SiO_2 + C + 4Cl_2 \xrightarrow[@2,000°C]{} ZrCl_4 + SiCl_4 + 4CO$$

zircon   carbon   zirconium tetrachloride

APPARENT CONSUMPTION OF ZIRCON (TONNES)	
	Apparent Consumption
Japan	148,343
United States	106,338
South Africa	100,900
Italy	80,371
Former USSR	67,300
Germany	57,016
France	45,351
Spain	39,133
United Kingdom	35,031
Netherlands	31,157
Sri Lanka	26,123
South Korea	21,445
Brazil	19,766
India	18,200
China	16,500
Taiwan	16,301
Canada	7,102
Turkey	5,719
Mexico	5,644

NOTE: Numbers are approximate and rounded for 1991 or thereabouts; absence of a country does not necessarily indicate no production or trade; absence of a number does not necessarily mean zero

Source: British Geological Survey

Zircon/baddeleyite + appropriate acid or alkali → zirconium acetate [paints; water repellents; cement & drilling mud; metal treatment; foundry binder; photography], zirconium carbonate [paints; catalyst; poison ivy ointment], zirconium fluoride [ceramic colors; glass; gemstones; metal treatment; textiles], zirconium oxychloride [special ceramics; pigment & filler coating; foundry binder; adhesives], zirconium sulfate [pigment stabilizer; adhesives; photography; paper opacifier; catalyst; leather tanning]. Zircon/baddeleyite + C → zirconium carbide [abrasive]; + alumina → AZ abrasives.

QUALITY & SPECIFICATIONS: Zirconium and hafnium are always associated, and chemical analysis is often based on zirconia (ZrO_2) + hafnia (HfO_2). The three main commercial grades of zircon - premium, intermediate, and standard, are outlined in the table. Baddeleyite is generally 97-99% ZrO_2+HfO_2. Zirconium oxides are available in many combinations of chemical and physical properties.

TYPICAL COMPOSITION OF BADDELEYITE (%)

BC Grade	96 Abrasive	99E3 Refractory	99E6 Refractory	99E8 Pigment	99P Pigment	99S Pigment	99SEF Plasma spay
ZrO_2+HfO_2	+96	+98	+98	+98	+98	+99	+99
SiO_2	1.5	0.6	0.6	1.0	0.6	0.5	0.5
TiO_2	1.0	0.3	0.3	0.3	0.3	0.3	0.3
Fe_2O_3	1.0	0.3	0.3	0.3	0.3	0.1	0.1
P_2O_5	0.2	0.02	0.02	0.02	0.02	0.01	0.01
CuO	0.6	0.05	0.05	0.05	0.05	0.01	0.01
ThO_2	0.03	0.03	0.03	0.03	0.03	0.03	0.03
U_3O_8	0.07	0.07	0.07	0.07	0.07	0.07	0.07

PARTICLE SIZE DISTRIBUTION OF COMMERCIAL ZIRCON SANDS

Wt % retained US sieve	Opening μm	Western Australia	Queensland, Australia	Florida Starke	Florida Green Cove Sp.	S. Africa
50	300	trace	-	1	-	-
70	212	14	1	1	trace	trace
100	150	46	6	13	1	8
140	106	30	47	48	25	42
200	75	9	44	36	63	46
270	53	1	2	2	10	4
PAN	53	-	1	trace	1	trace
APS (μm)	165	110	120	100	110	N/A

Source: T.E. Garnar Jr.

SPECIFICATIONS OF COMMERCIAL ZIRCON CONCENTRATES

	E. Australia			W. Australia		United States	
	CRL Premium	CRL Standard	MDL Ceramic	Cable Premium	Standard	RGC Ceramic	Standard
ZrO_2	66.30	66.10	66.35	65.80	65.50	66.40	66.40
TiO_2	0.12	0.24	0.08	0.13	0.20	0.13	0.12
Fe_2O_3	0.052	0.15	0.29	0.09	0.2	0.04	0.04
Al_2O_3	0.29	na	0.40	0.80	1	0.35	0.46
SiO_2	33.00	32.70	32.65	32.14	32.8	32.60	32.40
U+Th (ppm)	na	na	450	450	450	350	350

	Thailand Sakorn Minerals	India Indian Rare Earths Ltd.			S. Africa Richards Bay Minerals		
		OR	MK	Q	Prime	Standard	Refractory
ZrO_2	66.25	65.00	65.30	65.10	65.00	65.00	65.00
TiO_2	0.15	0.30	0.30	0.30	0.15	0.30	0.50
Fe_2O_3	0.075	0.40	0.09	0.10	0.10	0.25	0.15
Al_2O_3	na	na	1.20	1.40	na	na	na
SiO_2	31.23	31.50	32.50	32.40	na	na	na

COMPOSITION OF COMMERCIAL ZIRCONIUM OXIDES

Grade	Ceramic pigment	Special ceramics	Engineering ceramics	Glass/ gemstone	Electronics	Mixed metal oxide
ZrO_2+HfO_2	99	99	92.3	99	98	91
SiO_2	0.20	0.05	0.15	0.20	0.07	0.15
TiO_2	0.15	0.15	0.15	0.15	0.12	0.15
Fe_2O_3	0.02	0.01	0.02	0.006	0.01	0.02
SO_3	0.3	0.02	-	0.25	0.10	0.1
Y_2O_3	-	-	5.3	-	-	8
LOI (1,400°C)	0.30	0.10	2.0	0.30	1.20	0.3
Tamped BD	2.4	1.5	1.5	2.4	1.2	2.80
APS (µm)	14	3.5	<0.5	14	2.5	25
SSA, m^2/g	2-4	1-2	20	2-4	15-20	2.0

Zircon sand is 75-200 µm (foundry & refractory use), flour 45-75 µm (foundry & ceramics use), and ultrafine <20 µm (opacifier). Foundry and refractory sand uses standard grade zircon, opacifier grades use premium or intermediate zircon (low iron & titanium for whiteness). Zirconia generally analyzes 99.5-99.7% ZrO_2+HfO_2. For electronics and catalysts an APS <1µm and surface area of 25-100 m^2/g is standard. There is increased concern over the U+Th content (radioactive) of zircon.

WORLD CAPACITY: 990,000 t zircon; 20,000 t baddeleyite; 500 t caldesite

CAPACITY UTILIZATION: 99%.

MARKET CONDITIONS: Steady-increasing.

MARKETING FACTORS: Iron & steel, economy, Ti mineral production.

Capacity of zircon
(tonnes)

993,000

South Africa 190,000
Australia 550,000
United States 130,000
China 35,000
Former USSR 30,000
Brazil 22,000
India 16,000
Malaysia 12,000
Sri Lanka 6,000
Thailand 2,000

Source: USBM (1993)

HEALTH & SAFETY: Zircon is generally regarded as nontoxic, although finely divided zirconium is classified as flammable and is sold and transported accordingly. The content of radioactive elements (mainly U + Th) has become a concern since they can become concentrated through processing and are known to be carcinogenic (see titanium minerals for details). Crystalline silica has been classified as a probable carcinogen by the IARC (see silica for further details). Therefore, because of its crystalline silica content, unless processing has the capability to reduce the crystalline silica content to less than 0.1%, zircon will come under the OSHA Hazard Communication Standards, 29 CFR Section 1900.1200 which require labeling and other forms of warning, material safety data sheets, and employee training for products containing identified carcinogens with concentrations greater than 0.1%. Nevertheless, Zirclean® is certified for permissible dry outdoor blasting by the State of California Air Resources Board.

RECYCLING: Zircon used as a foundry sand and blasting abrasive is recycled, and in fact this ability is an important selling point.

PRODUCERS & WORLD TRADE: Production and exports are dominated by Australia, South Africa (including baddeleyite), and the United States. Importers are confined to developed countries in Europe, North America, and Asia.

HTS CODES: 2615.10.0000 (zirconium ores & conc.); 2825.60.0000 (germanium oxides and ZrO_2); 7202.99.1000 (ferrozirconium); 8109.10.3000 (waste & scrap); 8109.10.6000 (other (unwrought, powders)); 8109.90.0000 (other (wrought, alloys)).

ZIRCON LEADERS

Producers	Importers	Exporters
Australia	Japan	Australia
South Africa	Italy	South Africa
United States	Germany	United States
Former USSR	Netherlands	Netherlands
Sri Lanka	France	Italy
Brazil	Spain	Malaysia
India	United Kingdom	Brazil
China	United States	Spain
Malaysia	South Korea	Germany
Thailand	Taiwan	United Kingdom

SUBSTITUTES & ALTERNATIVES: Abrasives:- fused alumina, corundum/emery, diamonds, diatomite, feldspar, garnet, magnetite, nepheline syenite, olivine, perlite, pumice, silica sand, staurolite, tripoli, and silicon carbide, ilmenite. **Foundry**:- bauxite & alumina, chromite, clays (kaolin & bauxite), olivine, perlite, pyrophyllite, silica sand, vermiculite. **Friction material**:- asbestos, barite, bauxite & alumina, glays (attapulgite, kaolin, sepiolite), garnet, graphite, gypsum, mica, pumice, pyrophyllite, silica, slate, vermiculite, wollastonite. **Refractories**:- andalusite, bauxite, chromite, kyanite, dolomite, graphite, magnesite, olivine, pyrophyllite, refractory clays, silica, sillimanite.

PRICES: Zircon, FOB Australia A$280-310/t (ceramic); A$270-300 (refractory); A$270-300 (foundry sand). Zircon, FOB USA $210-220/t (ceramic); $210-220/t (refractory); $190-210/t (foundry sand). Zirconium oxide $6.60-14.52/kg (commercial, powder, drums); $7.70-17.60/kg (electronic, drums); $7.37-8.80/kg (insulating, stabilized 350°F); $7.37-8.80/kg (insulating, unstablized, 350°F); $6.60/kg (dense, stabilized 300°F). Zirconium acetate $2.14 (solution, drums, 25% ZrO_2); 1.70/kg (solution, drums, 22% ZrO_2). Zirconium oxychloride $2-2.28/kg (liquid, cartons, 5-ton lots).

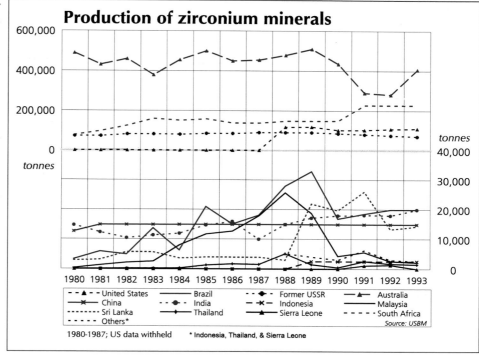

Production of zirconium minerals

Legend: United States, Brazil, Former USSR, Australia, China, India, Indonesia, Malaysia, Sri Lanka, Thailand, Sierra Leone, South Africa, Others*

1980-1987; US data withheld   * Indonesia, Thailand, & Sierra Leone

Source: USBM

Baddeleyite $1.85-2.30/kg (cif USA, 96-98% ZrO_2, -100 mesh); $2.55-$2.86/kg (cif USA, 99%+ ZrO_2, -325 mesh). Hafnium sponge $165-300/kg.

ETYMOLOGY: Baddeleyite for Joseph Baddeley who brought the original specimens from Sri Lanka. **Zircon** from the Arabic *zarqun*, derived from the Persian *zar = gold* and *gun = color*.

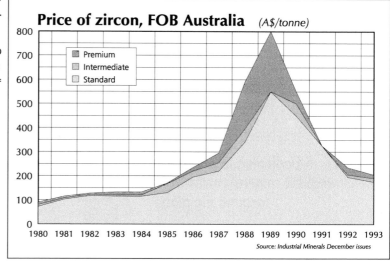

Price of zircon, FOB Australia (A$/tonne)

Legend: Premium, Intermediate, Standard

Source: Industrial Minerals December issues

ZIRCON GRADES

	Premium	Intermediate	Standard
$ZrO_2 + HfO_2$	66.0	65.5	65.0
TiO_2	0.10	0.03	0.25
Fe_2O_3	0.05	0.10	0.12

PRODUCTION AND TRADE IN ZIRCON (TONNES)

	Production	Imports	Exports	Apparent Consumption	Net Supplier	Net Consumer
North America	103,140	47,434	31,490	119,084		(15,944)
South America	20,000	8,262		28,262		(8,262)
European Union		323,042	32,157	290,885		(290,885)
Non-EU Europe	65,000	11,983		76,983		(11,983)
Australasia	356,975	190,579	328,698	218,856	138,119	
Africa	240,000		139,100	100,900	139,100	

NOTE: Numbers are approximate and rounded for 1991 or thereabouts; absence of a country does not necessarily indicate no production or trade; absence of a number does not necessarily mean zero

Source: British Geological Survey

Part II

Industrial Minerals

Silica

Sulphur

Iron Oxide

Nitrogen Compounds

Potash

Diatomite

Feldspar

Tables

Sodium Sulfate

Soda Ash

Zeolites

Carbonate Rocks

Nepheline Syenite

Phosphate Rock

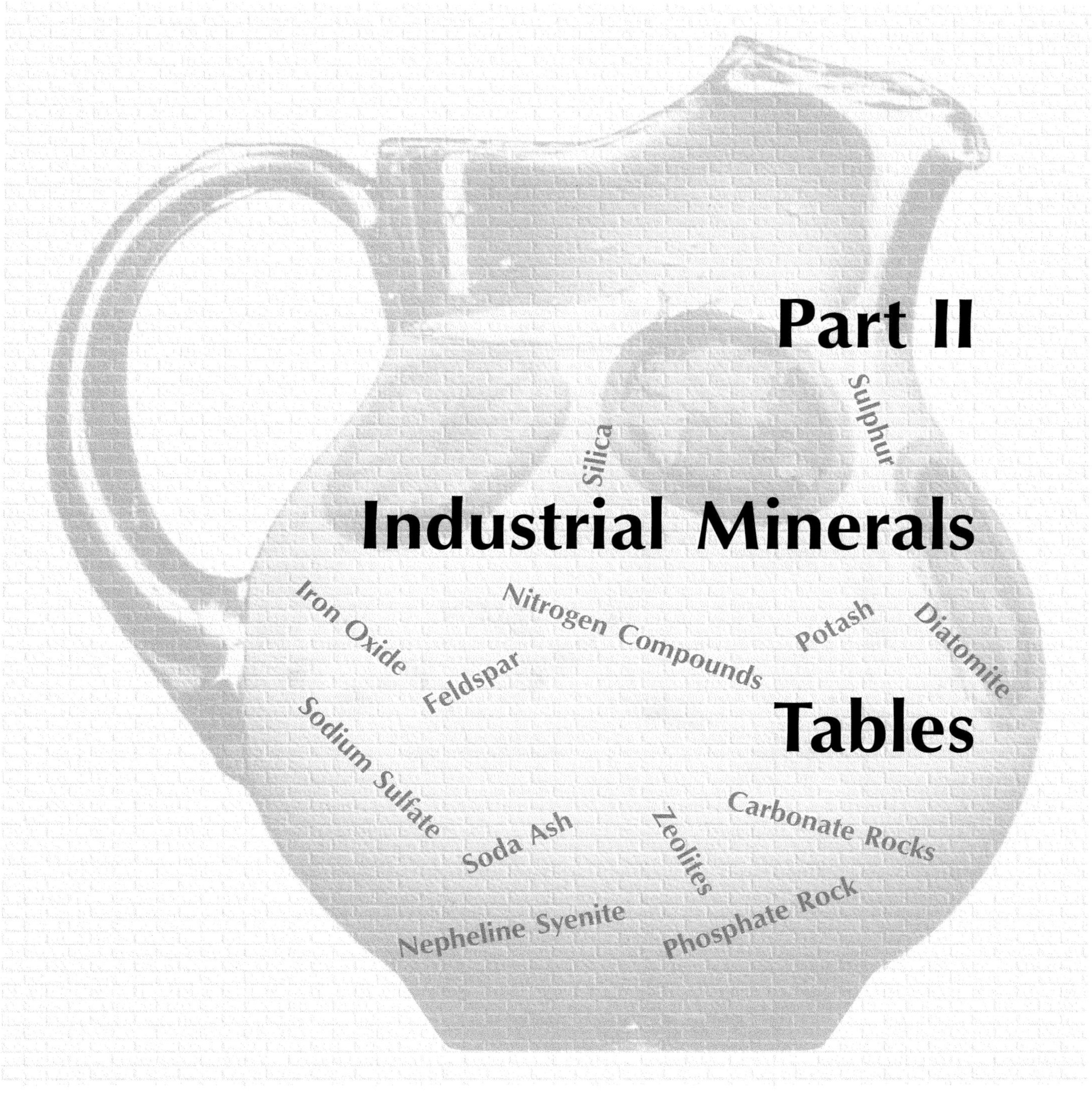

	Production (tonnes)	Percent world production	Percent world production cumulative		Production (tonnes)	Percent world production	Percent world production cumulative
ANTIMONY	**73,738**						
China	50,000	68%	68%	Australia	1,700	2%	91%
USSR	7,600	10%	78%	Mexico	1,469	2%	93%
Bolivia	4,500	6%	84%	Others	4,969	7%	100%
South Africa*	3,500	5%	89%				
ASBESTOS	**2,775,695**						
Former USSR	1,400,000	50%	50%	Zimbabwe	150,000	5%	92%
Canada	515,341	19%	69%	South Africa	100,000	4%	95%
China	240,000	9%	78%	Others	133,354	5%	100%
Brazil	237,000	9%	86%				
ATTAPULGITE/SEPIOLITE	**3,082,421**						
United States (a & s)	2,453,821	80%	80%	Pakistan (a)	19,000	0.6%	99.1%
Senegal (a)	112,000	4%	83%	Australia (a)	20,000	0.6%	99.8%
Spain (a)	20,000	1%	84%	South Africa (a)	7,600	0.2%	100%
Spain (s)	450,000	15%	98%				
BARITE	**4,890,050**						
China	1,900,000	39%	39%	Iran	200,000	4%	75%
India	400,000	8%	47%	Mexico	193,000	4%	79%
Morocco	325,000	7%	54%	Germany	155,000	3%	82%
United States	315,000	6%	60%	Romania	115,000	2%	85%
Turkey	300,000	6%	66%	Others	757,050	15%	100%
Former USSR*	230,000	5%	71%				
BAUXITE	**105,557,000**						
Australia	41,900,000	40%	40%	Surinam	3,400,000	3%	85%
Guinea	14,100,000	13%	53%	Venezuela	2,914,000	3%	88%
Jamaica	11,307,000	11%	64%	China	2,900,000	3%	91%
Brazil	9,357,000	9%	73%	Guyana	2,126,000	2%	93%
India	5,232,000	5%	78%	Others	7,822,000	7%	100%
Former USSR	4,500,000	4%	82%				
BENTONITE	**7,948,965**						
United States	3,092,956	39%	39%	Spain	150,000	2%	86%
Former USSR	1,600,000	20%	59%	Brazil	130,000	2%	88%
Greece	600,000	8%	67%	Mexico	127,289	2%	89%
Germany	575,000	7%	74%	Turkey	125,000	2%	91%
Japan	518,700	7%	80%	Romania	120,000	2%	92%
Italy	300,000	4%	84%	Others*	610,020	8%	100%
BERYL & BERTRANDITE	**6,656**						
United States	4,939	74%	74%	Argentina	35	0.5%	99.5%
Brazil	850	13%	87%	Zimbabwe	23	0.3%	99.9%
Former USSR	800	12%	99%	Others	9	0.1%	100%
BORON MINERALS	**2,178,000**						
United States	1,055,000	48%	48%	Chile	100,000	5%	89%
Turkey	650,000	30%	78%	Former USSR	90,000	4%	94%
Argentina	143,000	7%	85%	Others	140,000	6%	100%
BROMINE	**392,650**						
United States	177,000	45%	45%	Japan	15,000	4%	95.3%
Israel	135,000	34%	79%	China	13,000	3%	98.6%
United Kingdom	28,000	7%	87%	Others	5,650	1%	100%
Former USSR	19,000	5%	91%				
CEMENT ('000 T)	**1,246,351**						
China	303,905	24%	24%	Taiwan	20,684	2%	69%
Japan	90,700	7%	32%	Ukraine	19,958	2%	70%
United States	71,426	6%	37%	Iran	18,144	1%	72%
Russia	68,039	5%	43%	Thailand	18,144	1%	73%
India	49,999	4%	47%	Indonesia	17,280	1%	75%
South Korea	42,637	3%	50%	North Korea	17,236	1%	76%

	Production (tonnes)	Percent world production	Percent world production cumulative		Production (tonnes)	Percent world production	Percent world production cumulative
Italy	41,347	3%	54%	Egypt	16,057	1%	77%
Germany	37,503	3%	57%	Saudi Arabia	15,422	1%	79%
Turkey	28,607	2%	59%	Greece	13,063	1%	80%
Brazil	28,100	2%	61%	Poland	11,975	1%	81%
Mexico	26,853	2%	63%	United Kingdom	10,723	1%	81%
Spain	26,308	2%	65%	Others	230,643	19%	100%
France	21,600	2%	67%				
CHROMITE	**9,182,100**						
Former USSR	3,020,000	33%	33%	Brazil	430,000	5%	91%
South Africa	2,840,000	31%	64%	Zimbabwe	400,000	4%	95%
India	1,070,000	12%	75%	Philippines	105,000	1%	96%
Finland	500,000	5%	81%	Others	327,100	4%	100%
Turkey	490,000	5%	86%				
DIAMOND, INDUSTRIAL	**50,390,000** *CARATS*						
Australia	23,200,000	46%	46%	South Africa	6,050,000	12%	85%
Zaire	5,500,000	11%	57%	Botswana	5,000,000	10%	95%
Russia	8,000,000	16%	73%	Others	2,640,000	5%	100%
DIAMOND, GEM	**57,205,000** *CARATS*						
Australia	19,000,000	33%	33%	South Africa	4,300,000	8%	92%
Botswana	12,000,000	21%	54%	Namibia	1,100,000	2%	94%
Zaire	9,500,000	17%	71%	Angola	470,000	1%	95%
Russia	8,000,000	14%	85%	Others	2,835,000	5%	100%
DIAMOND, SYNTHETIC	**456,000,000** *CARATS*						
Former USSR	120,000,000	26%	26%	Japan	32,000,000	7%	87%
United States	103,000,000	23%	49%	Sweden	25,000,000	5%	92%
South Africa	75,000,000	16%	65%	China	15,500,000	3%	96%
Ireland	66,000,000	14%	80%	Others	19,500,000	4%	100%
DIATOMITE	**1,384,000**						
United States	599,000	43%	43%	Germany	50,000	4%	82%
France	250,000	18%	61%	Mexico	47,000	3%	86%
Former USSR	150,000	11%	72%	Spain	38,000	3%	88%
South Korea	90,000	7%	79%	Others	160,000	12%	100%
EMERY	**37,700**						
Turkey	24,700	66%	66%				
Greece	10,000	27%	92%				
United States	3,000	8%	100%				
FELDSPAR	**6,009,441**						
Italy	1,600,000	27%	27%	Spain	200,000	3%	77%
United States	770,000	13%	39%	Venezuela	175,000	3%	80%
Thailand	600,000	10%	49%	Brazil	140,000	2%	82%
Turkey	500,000	8%	58%	Mexico	112,891	2%	84%
Germany	380,000	6%	64%	Norway	100,000	2%	86%
France	300,000	5%	69%	Others	841,550	14%	100%
South Korea	290,000	5%	74%				
FLUORSPAR	**4,030,852**						
China	2,100,000	52%	52%	France	125,000	3%	80%
Mexico	370,000	9%	61%	Germany	50,000	1.2%	82%
Former USSR	250,000	6%	67%	Thailand	48,000	1.2%	83%
Mongolia	180,000	4%	72%	Others	690,074	17%	100%
South Africa	217,778	5%	77%				
FULLER'S EARTH	**3,079,308**						
United States	1,881,511	61%	61%	UK	210,000	7%	90%
Germany	665,000	22%	83%	Senegal	98,882	3%	93%
GARNET*	**149,700**						
United States	65,000	43%	43%	China	20,000	13%	81%
Norway	8,000	5%	49%	India	28,000	19%	99%

Distribution of world industrial minerals production

	Production (tonnes)	Percent world production	Percent world production cumulative		Production (tonnes)	Percent world production	Percent world production cumulative
Turkey	700	0%	49%	Sri Lanka	100	0.1%	99%
Former USSR	2,000	1%	51%	Others	900	0.6%	100%
Australia	25,000	17%	67%				
GRAPHITE	**741,040**						
China	310,000	42%	42%	Brazil	29,000	4%	84%
South Korea	80,000	11%	53%	Turkey	20,000	3%	87%
India	64,000	9%	61%	Austria	19,500	3%	89%
Mexico	50,440	7%	68%	Canada	18,800	3%	92%
Former USSR	50,000	7%	75%	Madagascar	8,000	1%	93%
North Korea	38,000	5%	80%	Others	53,300	7%	100%
GYPSUM	**97,790,375**						
United States	14,758,911	15%	15%	Japan	5,443,080	6%	66%
China	10,976,878	11%	26%	Spain	4,989,490	5%	71%
Iran	7,983,184	8%	34%	Germany	4,300,033	4%	75%
Canada	7,054,232	7%	42%	Former USSR	3,501,715	4%	79%
Thailand	6,985,286	7%	49%	United Kingdom	2,993,694	3%	82%
France	5,715,234	6%	55%	Others	17,554,840	18%	100%
Mexico	5,533,798	6%	60%				
IODINE	**16,645**						
Japan	7,200	43%	43%	Former USSR	1,400	8%	97%
Chile	5,550	33%	77%	China	500	3%	99.6%
United States	1,935	12%	88%	Indonesia	60	0.4%	100%
NATURAL IRON OXIDE	**286,772**						
India (ocher)	175,000	61%	61%	Austria	9,500	3%	89%
United States	35,842	12%	74%	Chile	8,000	3%	92%
Spain	24,000	8%	82%	Others	22,430	8%	100%
France	12,000	4%	86%				
KAOLIN	**24,428,753**						
United States	8,957,565	37%	37%	Colombia	900,000	4%	73%
United Kingdom	2,600,000	11%	47%	Brazil	750,000	3%	76%
Czech Rep.	2,500,000	10%	58%	Germany	650,000	3%	79%
South Korea	1,900,000	8%	65%	India	650,000	3%	81%
Former USSR	1,000,000	4%	69%	Others	4,521,188	19%	100%
LIME	**106,396,000**						
China	19,500,000	18%	18%	France	3,000,000	3%	67%
United States	16,959,000	16%	34%	Romania	3,000,000	3%	69%
Japan	8,000,000	8%	42%	Poland	2,500,000	2%	72%
Germany	7,500,000	7%	49%	United Kingdom	2,500,000	2%	74%
Mexico	6,500,000	6%	55%	Former USSR	2,000,000	2%	76%
Brazil	5,700,000	5%	60%	Others	25,637,000	24%	100%
Italy	3,600,000	3%	64%				
LITHIUM	**172,720**						
Australia s	40,000	23%	23%	Chile b	10,800	6%	93%
Russia	40,000	23%	46%	Portugal l	10,000	6%	98%
United States s b	20,000	12%	58%	Brazil a l p s	1,600	1%	99%
Canada s m	18,500	11%	69%	Namibia a l p	1,190	1%	99.9%
China	15,500	9%	78%	Argentina b	130	0.1%	100%
Zimbabwe bk l p s	15,000	9%	86%				
MAGNESITE	**10,135,600**			a - amblygonite; bk - bikitaite; b - brine; l - lepidolite; m - montebrasite; p - petalite; s- spodumene			
North Korea	1,600,000	16%	16%	Former USSR	800,000	8%	73%
China	1,500,000	15%	31%	Australia	800,000	8%	81%
Turkey	1,300,000	13%	43%	India	500,000	5%	86%
Czech Rep. & Slovakia	1,200,000	12%	55%	Others	1,435,600	14%	100%
Austria	1,000,000	10%	65%				
MAGNESIA	**2,350,000** MgO CAPACITY						
United States	875,000	37%	37%	Ireland	100,000	4%	84%

	Production (tonnes)	Percent world production	Percent world production cumulative		Production (tonnes)	Percent world production	Percent world production cumulative
Japan	500,000	21%	59%	Netherlands	100,000	4%	88%
United Kingdom	200,000	9%	67%	Former USSR	100,000	4%	92%
Mexico	160,000	7%	74%	Others	185,000	8%	100%
Italy	130,000	6%	79%				
MANGANESE	**21,575,000**						
Former USSR	6,050,000	28%	28%	Gabon	1,460,000	7%	80%
China	5,400,000	25%	53%	India	1,750,000	8%	88%
South Africa	2,507,000	12%	65%	Australia	1,789,000	8%	97%
Brazil	1,900,000	9%	73%	Others	719,000	3%	100%
MICA	**190,314**						
United States	87,931	46%	46%	Mexico	6,159	3%	83%
Former USSR	30,000	16%	62%	Brazil	5,000	3%	85%
Canada (phlogopite)	17,500	9%	71%	India	4,600	2%	88%
France	8,000	4%	75%	Taiwan	1,000	1%	88%
South Korea	7,500	4%	79%	Others	22,624	12%	100%
NEPHELINE SYENITE	**3,410,000**						
Former USSR	2,500,000	73%	73%	Norway	350,000	10%	100%
Canada	560,000	16%	90%				
NITROGEN (AMMONIA)	**91,457,000**						
China	19,000,000	21%	21%	Mexico	1,758,000	2%	71%
United States	12,865,000	14%	35%	Poland	1,500,000	2%	72%
Russia	8,138,000	9%	44%	Trinidad & Tobago	1,462,000	2%	74%
India	7,124,000	8%	52%	Japan	1,447,000	2%	76%
Canada	3,410,000	4%	55%	Pakistan	1,446,000	2%	77%
Ukraine	3,242,000	4%	59%	Uzbekistan	1,105,000	1%	78%
Indonesia	2,888,000	3%	62%	Romania	1,100,000	1%	80%
Netherlands	2,500,000	3%	65%	Saudi Arabia	1,097,000	1%	81%
Germany	2,000,000	2%	67%	Others	17,575,000	19%	100%
France	1,800,000	2%	69%				
PEAT	**147,950**						
Former USSR	128,820	87%	87%	Sweden	1,624	1%	98%
Ireland	6,495	4%	91%	Canada	857	1%	99%
Finland	5,458	4%	95%	United States	599	0%	99%
Germany	3,112	2%	97%	Others	986	1%	100%
PERLITE	**1,584,722**						
United States	568,600	36%	36%	Hungary	90,000	6%	89%
Turkey	300,000	19%	55%	Italy	65,000	4%	93%
Greece	250,000	16%	71%	Czechoslovakia	50,000	3%	96%
Japan	200,000	13%	83%	Others	61,122	4%	100%
PHOSPHATE ROCK*	**38,220,318** P_2O_5						
United States	10,816,000	28%	28%	Jordan	1,300,000	3%	83%
China	7,000,000	18%	47%	Israel	1,151,599	3%	86%
Morocco	5,919,000	15%	62%	South Africa	942,314	2%	89%
Former USSR	5,178,000	14%	76%	Others	4,305,712	11%	100%
Tunisia	1,607,692	4%	80%				
POTASH	**21,230,000** K_2O						
Canada	6,840,000	32%	32%	United Kingdom	550,000	3%	62%
United States	1,500,000	7%	39%	Former USSR	5,580,000	26%	89%
France	900,000	4%	44%	Israel	1,295,000	6%	95%
Germany	2,800,000	13%	57%	Jordan	820,000	4%	99%
Spain	670,000	3%	60%	Others	275,000	1%	100%
PUMICE	**4,780,310**						
Italy	700,000	15%	15%	Iran	350,000	7%	81%
Spain	700,000	15%	29%	Guadeloupe	210,000	4%	86%
Turkey	700,000	15%	44%	Martinique	130,000	3%	89%
Germany	575,000	12%	56%	Dominica	100,000	2%	91%

	Production (tonnes)	Percent world production	Percent world production cumulative		Production (tonnes)	Percent world production	Percent world production cumulative
United States	469,030	10%	66%	Others	446,280	9%	100%
Greece	400,000	8%	74%				
POZZOLAN	**5,955,000**						
Italy	4,500,000	76%	76%	France	400,000	7%	97%
Greece	500,000	8%	84%	Cameroon	130,000	2%	99.6%
Chile	400,000	7%	91%	Cape Verde Is.	25,000	0.4%	100%
PYROPHYLLITE	**2,083,800**						
Japan	1,038,800	50%	50%	Pakistan	56,000	3%	96%
South Korea	600,000	29%	79%	Thailand	35,000	2%	98%
Brazil	150,000	7%	86%	Canada	30,000	1%	98.9%
India	82,000	4%	90%	Others	22,000	1%	100%
United States	70,000	3%	93%				
RARE-EARTH MINERALS	**55,382** *REO*						
United States	20,699	37%	37%	South Africa	715	1%	98.3%
China	17,000	31%	68.1%	Malaysia	435	1%	99.0%
Former USSR	8,000	14%	82.5%	Thailand	360	1%	99.7%
Australia	3,850	7%	89.5%	Sri Lanka	110	0.2%	99.9%
India	2,750	5%	94.4%	Zaire	60	0.1%	99.99%
Brazil	1,400	3%	97.0%	Madagascar	3	0.01%	100.0%
SALT	**181,103,000**						
United States	35,000,000	19%	19%	United Kingdom	6,200,000	3%	75%
China	29,530,000	16%	36%	France	6,100,000	3%	79%
Germany	12,607,000	7%	43%	Poland	4,000,000	2%	81%
Canada	11,169,000	6%	49%	Italy	3,700,000	2%	83%
India	9,502,000	5%	54%	Spain	3,700,000	2%	85%
Australia	9,000,000	5%	59%	Netherlands	3,500,000	2%	87%
Brazil	8,200,000	5%	64%	Romania	2,400,000	1%	88%
Former USSR	7,890,000	4%	68%	Others	21,365,000	12%	100%
Mexico	7,240,000	4%	72%				
SILICA SAND	**106,267,972**						
United States	24,463,923	23%	23%	Belgium	2,474,787	2%	79.6%
Netherlands	19,999,690	19%	41.8%	Spain	2,177,232	2%	81.6%
Argentina	8,500,277	8%	49.8%	Australia	2,004,868	2%	83.5%
Germany	7,983,184	8%	57.4%	Austria	2,000,332	2%	85.4%
Italy	4,000,664	4%	61.1%	Paraguay	1,995,796	2%	87.3%
Japan	3,860,051	4%	64.7%	South Africa	1,749,950	2%	88.9%
United Kingdom	3,601,505	3%	68.1%	Canada	1,489,590	1.4%	90.3%
France	3,501,715	3%	71.4%	Mexico	1,188,406	1.1%	91.5%
Brazil	3,499,900	3%	74.7%	Others	9,072,707	9%	100.0%
India	2,703,396	3%	77.3%				
SILLIMANITE MINERALS	**271,331**						
S. Africa, andalusite	180,000	66%	66.3%	Spain, andalusite	3,000	1%	98.0%
France, andalusite	50,000	18%	84.8%	China, unspecified	2,500	1%	99.0%
India, sillimanite	15,000	6%	90.3%	S. Africa, sillimanite	300	0.1%	99.1%
India, kyanite	12,000	4%	94.7%	Others	2,831	1%	100.1%
Sweden, kyanite	6,000	2%	96.9%				
SODA ASH	**28,226,000**						
United States	8,959,000	32%	32%	Japan	1,100,000	4%	77%
China	5,270,000	19%	50%	France	1,000,000	4%	81%
Former USSR	3,400,000	12%	62%	United Kingdom	1,000,000	4%	84%
Germany	1,600,000	6%	68%	Others	4,397,000	16%	100%
India	1,500,000	5%	73%				
SODIUM SULFATE	**4,767,000**						
Spain	800,000	17%	17%	Former USSR	220,000	5%	73%
United States	651,000	14%	30%	Italy	125,000	3%	76%
China	500,000	10%	41%	Austria	120,000	3%	78%
Mexico	500,000	10%	51%	Germany	110,000	2%	80%

	Production (tonnes)	Percent world production	Percent world production cumulative		Production (tonnes)	Percent world production	Percent world production cumulative
Canada	315,000	7%	58%	Turkey	110,000	2%	83%
Iran	250,000	5%	63%	Sweden	100,000	2%	85%
Japan	245,000	5%	68%	Others	721,000	15%	100%
STRONTIUM MINERALS	**145,828**						
Mexico	69,528	48%	48%	Algeria	5,400	4%	97%
Turkey	35,000	24%	72%	United Kingdom	1,000	1%	98%
Iran	20,000	14%	85%	Others	2,900	2%	100%
Spain	12,000	8%	94%				
SULFUR	**52,474,000**						
United States	10,663,000	20%	20%	Germany	1,415,000	3%	80%
Former USSR	7,250,000	14%	34%	France	1,155,000	2%	82%
Canada	7,246,000	14%	48%	Spain	920,000	2%	84%
China	5,970,000	11%	59%	Iran	750,000	1%	85%
Poland	3,060,000	6%	65%	Finland	635,000	1%	86%
Japan	2,635,000	5%	70%	South Africa	604,000	1%	87%
Saudi Arabia	2,000,000	4%	74%	Iraq	570,000	1%	89%
Mexico	1,600,000	3%	77%	Others	6,001,000	11%	100%
TALC	**6,080,585**						
China	2,700,000	44%	44%	Brazil	290,000	5%	82%
United States	967,880	16%	60%	Australia	210,000	3%	85%
Finland	370,000	6%	66%	Others	892,705	15%	100%
Former USSR	350,000	6%	72%				
France	300,000	5%	77%				
TITANIUM MINERALS							
ILMENITE	**3,580,854**						
Australia	1,518,000	42%	42%	Brazil	70,000	2%	96%
Norway	718,000	20%	62%	Sri Lanka	60,000	2%	98%
Former USSR	350,000	10%	72%	Sierra Leone	60,000	2%	99.5%
Malaysia	337,744	9%	82%	Thailand	17,080	0.5%	99.999%
India	300,000	8%	90%	Portugal	30	0.001%	100%
China	150,000	4%	94%	United States	W		
RUTILE	**442,370**						
Australia	200,000	45%	45%	Sri Lanka	3,200	1%	99.7%
Sierra Leone	145,000	33%	78%	Brazil	1,100	0.25%	99.98%
South Africa	75,000	17%	95%	Thailand	70	0.02%	100%
India	10,000	2%	97%	United States	W		
Former USSR	8,000	2%	99%				
TITANIUM SLAG	**1,637,000**						
South Africa	884,000	54%	54%	Canada	753,000	46%	100%
VERMICULITE	**489,334**						
South Africa	200,000	41%	41%	Japan	15,000	3%	98%
United States	190,000	39%	80%	Argentina	4,500	1%	99%
Former USSR	50,000	10%	90%	Kenya	2,600	1%	99.5%
Brazil	25,000	5%	95%	Others	2,234	0.5%	100%
WOLLASTONITE	**311,000**						
United States	120,000	39%	39%	Finland	28,000	9%	91%
China	80,000	26%	64%	Mexico	13,000	4%	95%
India	55,000	18%	82%	Others	15,000	5%	100%
ZIRCONIUM MINERALS	**851,964**						
Australia	300,000	35%	35%	Thailand	25,000	3%	93%
South Africa	230,000	27%	62%	Brazil	19,000	2%	96%
United States	108,156	13%	75%	India	18,000	2%	98%
Former USSR	78,000	9%	84%	China	15,000	2%	99.6%
Sri Lanka	30,000	4%	88%	Malaysia	2,608	0.3%	99.9%
Indonesia	25,000	3%	91%	Sierra Leone	1,200	0.1%	100%

* capacity

NORTH AMERICA ————————————— SOUTH AMERICA —————

	Canada	Mexico	United States	Total	% world production	Argentina	Bolivia	Brazil	Chile	Colombia
Antimony		1,469		1,469	2%		4,500			
Asbestos	515,341			515,341	19%			237,000		
Att. & Sep.			2,453,821	2,453,821	80%					
Barite		193,000	315,000	508,000	10%					
Bauxite								9,357,000		
Bentonite		127,289	3,092,956	3,220,245	41%			130,000		
Beryl			4,939	4,939	74%	35		850		
Borates			1,055,000	1,055,000	48%	143,000			100,000	
Bromine			177,000	177,000	45%					
Cement '000 t		26,853	71,426	98,278	8%			28,100		
Chromite								430,000		
Emery			3,000	3,000	8%					
Diamond, gem*										
Diamond, industrial*										
Diamond, synthetic*			103,000	103,000	0%					
Diatomite		47,000	599,000	646,000	47%					
Feldspar		112,891	770,000	882,891	15%			140,000		
Fluorspar		370,000		370,000	9%					
Garnet			65,000	65,000	43%					
Graphite	18,800	50,440		69,240	9%			29,000		
Gypsum	7,054,232	5,533,798	14,758,911	27,346,941	28%					
Iodine			1,935	1,935	12%				5,550	
Iron oxide			35,842	35,842	12%				8,000	
Kaolin			8,957,565	8,957,565	37%			750,000		900,000
Lime		6,500,000	16,959,000	23,459,000	22%			5,700,000		
Lithium	18,500		20,000	38,500	22%	130		1,600	10,800	
Magnesite										
Magnesia (MgO)		160,000	875,000	1,035,000	44%					
Manganese								1,900,000		
Mica	17,500	6,159	87,931	111,590	59%			5,000		
Nepheline syenite										
Nitrogen (ammonia)	3,410,000	1,758,000	12,865,000	18,033,000	20%					
Peat	857		599	1,456	1%					
Perlite			568,600	568,600	36%					
Phosphate rock			10,816,000	10,816,000	28%					
Potash	6,840,000		1,500,000	8,340,000	39%					
Pumice			469,030	469,030	10%					
Pozzolan									400,000	
Pyrophyllite										
Rare earths (REO)			20,699	20,699	37%			1,400		
Salt	11,169,000	7,240,000	35,000,000	53,409,000	29%			8,200,000	1,400,000	
Silica	1,489,590	1,188,406	24,463,923	27,141,918	26%	8,500,277		3,499,900		
Silliminite minerals										
Soda ash			8,959,000	8,959,000	32%					
Sodium sulfate	315,000	500,000	651,000	1,466,000	31%					
Strontium minerals		69,528		69,528	48%					
Sulfur	7,246,000	1,600,000	10,663,000	19,509,000	37%					
Talc			967,880	967,880	16%			290,000		
Ilmenite			W					70,000		
Rutile			W					1,100		
Titanium slag	753,000			753,000	46%					
Vermiculite			190,000	190,000	39%	4,500		25,000		
Wollastonite		13,000	120,000	133,000	43%					
Zircon			108,156	108,156	13%			19,000		

* '000 carats

SOUTH AMERICA ———————————————————————————— **CENTRAL AMERICA & CARIBBEAN**

	Guyana	Paraguay	Peru	Surinam	Uruguay	Venezuela	Total	% world production	Dominican Republic	Guadeloupe
Antimony							4,500	6%		
Asbestos							237,000	9%		
Att. & Sep.										
Barite										
Bauxite	2,126,000		3,400,000			2,914,000	17,797,000	17%		
Bentonite							130,000	2%		
Beryl							885	13%		
Borates							243,000	11%		
Bromine										
Cement '000 t							28,100	2%		
Chromite							430,000	5%		
Emery										
Diamond, gem*										
Diamond, industrial*										
Diamond, synthetic*										
Diatomite										
Feldspar						175,000	315,000	5%		
Fluorspar										
Garnet										
Graphite							29,000	4%		
Gypsum										
Iodine							5,550	33%		
Iron oxide							8,000	3%		
Kaolin							1,650,000	7%		
Lime							5,700,000	5%		
Lithium							12,530	7%		
Magnesite										
Magnesia (MgO)										
Manganese							1,900,000	9%		
Mica							5,000	3%		
Nepheline syenite										
Nitrogen (ammonia)										
Peat										
Perlite										
Phosphate rock										
Potash										
Pumice									100,000	
Pozzolan							400,000	7%		210,000
Pyrophyllite										
Rare earths (REO)							1,400	3%		
Salt							9,600,000	5%		
Silica		1,995,796					13,995,973	13%		
Silliminite minerals										
Soda ash										
Sodium sulfate										
Strontium minerals										
Sulfur										
Talc							290,000	5%		
Ilmenite							70,000	2%		
Rutile							1,100			
Titanium slag										
Vermiculite							29,500	6%		
Wollastonite										
Zircon										

* '000 carats

CENTRAL AMERICA & CARIBBEAN —————————————— EUROPEAN UNION ——————

	Jamaica	Martinique	Trindad & Tobago	Total	% world production	Belgium	Denmark	France	Germany
Antimony									
Asbestos									
Att. & Sep.									
Barite									155,000
Bauxite	11,307,000			11,307,000	11%				
Bentonite									575,000
Beryl									
Borates									
Bromine									
Cement '000 t								21,600	37,503
Chromite									
Emery									
Diamond, gem*									
Diamond, industrial*									
Diamond, synthetic*									
Diatomite								250,000	50,000
Feldspar								300,000	380,000
Fluorspar								125,000	50,000
Garnet									
Graphite									
Gypsum								5,715,234	4,300,033
Iodine									
Iron oxide								12,000	
Kaolin									650,000
Lime								3,000,000	7,500,000
Lithium									
Magnesite									
Magnesia (MgO)									
Manganese									
Mica								8,000	
Nepheline syenite									
Nitrogen (ammonia)		1,462,000		1,462,000	2%			1,800,000	2,000,000
Peat									3,112
Perlite									
Phosphate rock									
Potash								900,000	2,800,000
Pumice		130,000		230,000	5%				575,000
Pozzolan				210,000	4%			400,000	
Pyrophyllite									
Rare earths (REO)									
Salt								6,100,000	12,607,000
Silica						2,474,787		3,501,715	7,983,184
Silliminite minerals								50,000	
Soda ash								1,000,000	1,600,000
Sodium sulfate									110,000
Strontium minerals									
Sulfur								1,155,000	1,415,000
Talc								300,000	
Ilmenite									
Rutile									
Titanium slag									
Vermiculite									
Wollastonite									
Zircon									

* '000 carats

EUROPEAN UNION — NON-EU EUROPE

	Greece	Ireland	Italy	Netherlands	Portugal	Spain	United Kingdom	Total	% world production	Austria
Antimony										
Asbestos										
Att. & Sep.						470,000		470,000	15%	
Barite								155,000	3%	
Bauxite										
Bentonite	600,000		300,000			150,000		1,625,000	20%	
Beryl										
Borates										
Bromine							28,000	28,000	7%	
Cement '000 t	13,063		41,347			26,308	10,723	150,544	12%	
Chromite										
Emery	10,000							10,000	27%	
Diamond, gem*										
Diamond, industrial*										
Diamond, synthetic*		66,000						66,000		
Diatomite						38,000		338,000	24%	
Feldspar			1,600,000			200,000		2,480,000	41%	
Fluorspar								175,000	4%	
Garnet										
Graphite										19,500
Gypsum						4,989,490	2,993,694	17,998,451	18%	
Iodine										
Iron oxide						24,000		36,000	13%	9,500
Kaolin							2,600,000	3,250,000	13%	
Lime			3,600,000				2,500,000	16,600,000	16%	
Lithium					10,000			10,000	6%	
Magnesite										1,000,000
Magnesia (MgO)		100,000	130,000	100,000			200,000	530,000	23%	
Manganese										
Mica								8,000	4%	
Nepheline syenite										
Nitrogen (ammonia)				2,500,000				6,300,000	7%	
Peat		6,495						9,607	6%	
Perlite	250,000		65,000					315,000	20%	
Phosphate rock										
Potash						670,000	550,000	4,920,000	23%	
Pumice	400,000		700,000			700,000		2,375,000	50%	
Pozzolan	500,000		4,500,000					5,400,000	91%	
Pyrophyllite										
Rare earths (REO)										
Salt			3,700,000	3,500,000		3,700,000	6,200,000	35,807,000	20%	
Silica			4,000,664	19,999,690		2,177,232	3,601,505	43,738,777	41%	2,000,332
Silliminite minerals						3,000		53,000	20%	
Soda ash							1,000,000	3,600,000	13%	
Sodium sulfate			125,000			800,000		1,035,000	22%	120,000
Strontium minerals						12,000	1,000	13,000	9%	
Sulfur						920,000		3,490,000	7%	
Talc								300,000	5%	
Ilmenite					30			30		
Rutile										
Titanium slag										
Vermiculite										
Wollastonite										
Zircon										

* '000 carats

	Czech	Finland	Hungary	Norway	Poland	Romania	Sweden	Turkey	Former USSR	Total
Antimony									7,600	7,600
Asbestos									1,400,000	1,400,000
Att. & Sep.										
Barite					115,000			300,000	230,000	645,000
Bauxite									4,500,000	4,500,000
Bentonite					120,000			125,000	1,600,000	1,845,000
Beryl									800	800
Borates								650,000	90,000	740,000
Bromine									19,000	19,000
Cement '000 t					11,975			28,607	87,996	128,578
Chromite		500,000						490,000	3,020,000	4,010,000
Emery								24,700		24,700
Diamond, gem*									8,000	8,000
Diamond, industrial*									128,000	128,000
Diamond, synthetic*							25,000		150,000	175,000
Diatomite										
Feldspar				100,000				500,000		600,000
Fluorspar									250,000	250,000
Garnet				8,000				700	2,000	10,700
Graphite								20,000	50,000	89,500
Gypsum									3,501,715	3,501,715
Iodine									1,400	1,400
Iron oxide										9,500
Kaolin	2,500,000								1,000,000	3,500,000
Lime					2,500,000	3,000,000			2,000,000	7,500,000
Lithium									40,000	40,000
Magnesite	1,200,000							1,300,000	800,000	4,300,000
Magnesia (MgO)									100,000	100,000
Manganese									6,050,000	6,050,000
Mica									30,000	30,000
Nepheline syenite										
Nitrogen (ammonia)					1,500,000	1,100,000			12,485,000	15,085,000
Peat		5,458					1,624			7,081
Perlite	50,000		90,000					300,000		440,000
Phosphate rock										
Potash										
Pumice										
Pozzolan										
Pyrophyllite										
Rare earths (REO)										
Salt					4,000,000	2,400,000				6,400,000
Silica										2,000,332
Silliminite minerals							6,000			6,000
Soda ash										
Sodium sulfate							100,000	110,000		330,000
Strontium minerals								35,000		35,000
Sulfur		635,000			3,060,000					3,695,000
Talc		370,000								370,000
Ilmenite				718,000						718,000
Rutile										
Titanium slag										
Vermiculite										
Wollastonite		28,000								28,000
Zircon										

* '000 carats

	NON-EU EUROPE	AUSTRALASIA								
	% world production	Australia	Bangladesh	China	India	Indonesia	Japan	North Korea	South Korea	Malaysia
Antimony	10%	1,700		50,000						
Asbestos	50%			240,000						
Att. & Sep.		20,000								
Barite	13%			1,900,000	400,000					
Bauxite	4%	41,900,000		2,900,000	5,232,000					
Bentonite	23%						518,700			
Beryl	12%									
Borates	34%									
Bromine	5%			13,000			15,000			
Cement '000 t	10%			303,905	49,999	17,280	90,700	17,236	42,637	
Chromite	44%				1,070,000					
Emery	66%									
Diamond, gem*		19,000								
Diamond, industrial*		23,200								
Diamond, synthetic*				15,500			32,000			
Diatomite									90,000	
Feldspar	10%								290,000	
Fluorspar	6%			2,100,000						
Garnet	7%	25,000		20,000	28,000					
Graphite	12%			310,000	64,000			38,000	80,000	
Gypsum	4%			10,976,878			5,443,080			
Iodine	8%			500		60	7,200			
Iron oxide	3%				175,000					
Kaolin	14%				650,000				1,900,000	
Lime	7%			19,500,000			8,000,000			
Lithium	23%	40,000		15,500						
Magnesite	42%	800,000		1,500,000	500,000			1,600,000		
Magnesia (MgO)	4%						500,000			
Manganese	28%	1,789,000		5,400,000	1,750,000					
Mica	16%				4,600				7,500	
Nepheline syenite										
Nitrogen (ammonia)	16%			19,000,000	7,124,000	2,888,000	1,447,000			
Peat	5%									
Perlite	28%						200,000			
Phosphate rock				7,000,000						
Potash										
Pumice										
Pozzolan										
Pyrophyllite										
Rare earths (REO)		3,850		17,000	2,750					435
Salt	4%	9,000,000		29,530,000	9,502,000					
Silica	2%	2,004,868			2,703,396		3,860,051			
Silliminite minerals	2%			2,500	27,000					
Soda ash				5,270,000	1,500,000		1,100,000			
Sodium sulfate	7%			500,000			245,000			
Strontium minerals	24%									
Sulfur	7%			5,970,000			2,635,000			
Talc	6%	210,000		2,700,000						
Ilmenite	20%	1,518,000		150,000	300,000					337,744
Rutile		200,000			10,000					
Titanium slag										
Vermiculite							15,000			
Wollastonite	9%			80,000	55,000					
Zircon		300,000		15,000	18,000	25,000				2,608

* '000 carats

	Mongolia	Pakistan	Philippines	Sri Lanka	Taiwan	Thailand	Total	% world production	Iran	Iraq
Antimony							51,700	70%		
Asbestos							240,000	9%		
Att. & Sep.		19,000					39,000	1%		
Barite							2,300,000	47%		200,000
Bauxite							50,032,000	47%		
Bentonite							518,700	7%		
Beryl										
Borates										
Bromine							28,000	7%		
Cement '000 t					20,684	18,144	560,586	45%	18,144	
Chromite			105,000				1,175,000	13%		
Emery										
Diamond, gem*							19,000			
Diamond, industrial*							23,200			
Diamond, synthetic*							47,500			
Diatomite							90,000	7%		
Feldspar						600,000	890,000	15%		
Fluorspar	180,000					48,000	2,328,000	58%		
Garnet				100			73,100	49%		
Graphite							492,000	66%		
Gypsum						6,985,286	23,405,244	24%	7,983,184	
Iodine							7,760	47%		
Iron oxide							175,000	61%		
Kaolin							2,550,000	10%		
Lime							27,500,000	26%		
Lithium							55,500	32%		
Magnesite							4,400,000	43%		
Magnesia (MgO)							500,000	21%		
Manganese							8,939,000	41%		
Mica				1,000			13,100	7%		
Nepheline syenite										
Nitrogen (ammonia)		1,446,000					31,905,000	35%		
Peat										
Perlite							200,000	13%		
Phosphate rock							7,000,000	18%		
Potash										
Pumice									350,000	
Pozzolan										
Pyrophyllite										
Rare earths (REO)				110		360	24,505	44%		
Salt							48,032,000	27%		
Silica							8,568,315	8%		
Silliminite minerals							29,500	11%		
Soda ash							7,870,000	28%		
Sodium sulfate							745,000	16%	250,000	
Strontium minerals									20,000	
Sulfur							8,605,000	16%	750,000	570,000
Talc							2,910,000	48%		
Ilmenite				60,000		17,080	2,382,824	67%		
Rutile				3,200		70	213,270	48%		
Titanium slag										
Vermiculite							15,000	3%		
Wollastonite							135,000	43%		
Zircon				30,000		25,000	415,608	49%		

* '000 carats

MIDDLE EAST — AFRICA —

	Israel	Jordan	Saudi Arabia	Total	% world production	Angola	Botswana	Cameroon	Cape Verde Is.	Egypt
Antimony										
Asbestos										
Att. & Sep.										
Barite				200,000	4%					
Bauxite										
Bentonite										
Beryl										
Borates										
Bromine	135,000			135,000	34%					
Cement '000 t			15,422	33,566	3%					16,057
Chromite										
Emery										
Diamond, gem*						470	12,000			
Diamond, industrial*							5,000			
Diamond, synthetic*										
Diatomite										
Feldspar										
Fluorspar										
Garnet										
Graphite										
Gypsum				7,983,184	8%					
Iodine										
Iron oxide										
Kaolin										
Lime										
Lithium										
Magnesite										
Magnesia (MgO)										
Manganese										
Mica										
Nepheline syenite										
Nitrogen (ammonia)			1,097,000	1,097,000	1%					
Peat										
Perlite										
Phosphate rock	1151599.4	1300000		2451599.4	6%					
Potash	1,295,000	820,000		2,115,000	10%					
Pumice				350,000	7%					
Pozzolan								130,000	25,000	
Pyrophyllite										
Rare earths (REO)										
Salt										
Silica										
Silliminite minerals										
Soda ash										
Sodium sulfate				250000	5%					
Strontium minerals				20,000	14%					
Sulfur			2,000,000	3,320,000	6%					
Talc										
Ilmenite										
Rutile										
Titanium slag										
Vermiculite										
Wollastonite										
Zircon										

* '000 carats

	Gabon	Guinea	Kenya	Madagascar	Morocco	Mozambique	Namibia	Senegal	Sierra Leone	South Africa
Antimony										3,500
Asbestos										100,000
Att. & Sep.								112,000		7,600
Barite					325,000					
Bauxite		14,100,000								
Bentonite										
Beryl										
Borates										
Bromine										
Cement '000 t										
Chromite										2,840,000
Emery										
Diamond, gem*							1,100			4,300
Diamond, industrial*										6,050
Diamond, synthetic*										75,000
Diatomite										
Feldspar										
Fluorspar										217,778
Garnet										
Graphite				8,000						
Gypsum										
Iodine										
Iron oxide										
Kaolin										
Lime										
Lithium							1,190			
Magnesite										
Magnesia (MgO)										
Manganese	1,460,000									2,507,000
Mica										
Nepheline syenite										
Nitrogen (ammonia)										
Peat										
Perlite										
Phosphate rock					5,919,000					942,314
Potash										
Pumice										
Pozzolan										
Pyrophyllite										
Rare earths (REO)				3						715
Salt										
Silica										1,749,950
Silliminite minerals										180,300
Soda ash										
Sodium sulfate										
Strontium minerals										
Sulfur										604,000
Talc										
Ilmenite									60,000	75,000
Rutile									145,000	100,000
Titanium slag										
Vermiculite				2,600						200,000
Wollastonite										
Zircon									1,200	230,000

* '000 carats

AFRICA

	Tunisia	Zaire	Zimbabwe	Total	% world production
Antimony				3,500	5%
Asbestos			150,000	250,000	9%
Att. & Sep.				119,600	4%
Barite				325,000	7%
Bauxite				14,100,000	13%
Bentonite					
Beryl			23	23	
Borates					
Bromine					
Cement '000 t				16,057	1%
Chromite			400,000	3,240,000	35%
Emery					
Diamond, gem*		9,500		27,370	
Diamond, industrial*		5,500		16,550	
Diamond, synthetic*				75,000	
Diatomite					
Feldspar					
Fluorspar				217,778	5%
Garnet					
Graphite				8,000	1%
Gypsum					
Iodine					
Iron oxide					
Kaolin					
Lime					
Lithium			15,000	16,190	9%
Magnesite					
Magnesia (MgO)					
Manganese				3,967,000	18%
Mica					
Nepheline syenite					
Nitrogen (ammonia)					
Peat					
Perlite					
Phosphate rock	1,607,692			8,469,006	22%
Potash					
Pumice					
Pozzolan				155,000	3%
Pyrophyllite					
Rare earths (REO)		60		778	1%
Salt					
Silica				1,749,950	2%
Silliminite minerals				180,300	66%
Soda ash					
Sodium sulfate					
Strontium minerals					
Sulfur				604,000	1%
Talc					
Ilmenite				135,000	4%
Rutile				245,000	55%
Titanium slag					
Vermiculite				202,600	41%
Wollastonite					
Zircon				231,200	27%

* '000 carats

WORLD TOTAL

Mineral	tonnes
Antimony	73,738
Asbestos	2,775,695
Att. & Sep.	3,082,421
Barite	4,890,050
Bauxite	105,557,000
Bentonite	7,948,965
Beryl	6,656
Borates	2,178,000
Bromine	392,650
Cement '000 t	1,246,351
Chromite	9,182,100
Emery	37,700
Diamond, gem	50,390,000
Diamond, industrial	57,205,000
Diamond, synthetic	456,000,000
Diatomite	1,384,000
Feldspar	6,009,441
Fluorspar	4,030,852
Garnet	149,700
Graphite	741,040
Gypsum	97,790,375
Iodine	16,645
Iron oxide	286,772
Kaolin	24,428,753
Lime	106,396,000
Lithium	172,720
Magnesite	10,135,600
Magnesia (MgO)	2,350,000
Manganese	21,575,000
Mica	190,314
Nepheline syenite	3,410,000
Nitrogen (ammonia)	91,457,000
Peat	147,950
Perlite	1,584,722
Phosphate rock	38,220,318
Potash	21,230,000
Pumice	4,780,310
Pozzolan	5,955,000
Pyrophyllite	2,083,800
Rare earths (REO)	55,382
Salt	181,103,000
Silica	106,267,972
Silliminite minerals	271,331
Soda ash	28,226,000
Sodium sulfate	4,767,000
Strontium minerals	145,828
Sulfur	52,474,000
Talc	6,080,585
Ilmenite	3,580,854
Rutile	442,370
Titanium slag	1,637,000
Vermiculite	489,334
Wollastonite	311,000
Zircon	851,964

CHARACTERISTICS OF ABRASIVES

Abrasive	Hardness (Mohs)	Grain shape	Specific gravity	Color	Free silica	Free iron	Durability
Corn cobs	2	cubical	1.3	tan	none	none	good
Walnut shells	3	cubical	1.3	lt. brown	none	none	good
Novaculite	4	angular	2.5	white	90%	none	poor
Glass beads	4.5	spherical	3	crystal	none	none	good
Sand	5	rounded	1.75	tan	90-100%	<1%	fair
Pumice	6	cubical	2.35	white	70-80%	none	fair
Mineral shot	6-7	angular	3.16	black	none	<1%	good
Steel shot/grit	6-7	spherical angular	4.8	steel grey	none	99%	excellent
Flint shot	6-7	spherical	1.75	white	90-100%	<1%	good
Tripoli	7	spherical	2.65	white	90-100%	<1%	fair
Garnet	7	spherical	4	red/pink	none	<2%	good
Quartz	7	spherical	2.65	white	100%	<2%	fair
Zircon	7.5	cubical	4.56	tan	<5%	<1%	good
Staurolite	7-8	spherical	3.75	brown-black	<1%	18%	good
Emery	8	angular	4	red/brown	<1%	<3%	good
Aluminum oxide	9	cubical	3.8	brown	<1%	<1%	very good
Silicon carbide	9	cubical	3.13	black	<1%	<1%	good
Diamond	10	cubical	3.5	white/yellow	<1%	<1%	excellent

APPLICATION OF ABRASIVES

	Loose	Coated	Grinding	Polishing	Finishing	Cutting
Pumice	X			X		
Emery	X	X	X			
Tripoli	X			X	X	
Staurolite	X				X	
Garnet	X	X	X		X	
Silica	X			X	X	
Silicon carbide	X	X	X	X	X	X
Aluminum oxide	X	X	X	X		X
Diamond	X		X	X	X	X

RELATIVE HARDNESS OF ABRASIVE MATERIALS ON THE KNOOP SCALE

	Knoop hardness (K100)
Quartz	820
Spinel	1,270
Garnet	1,360
Topaz	1,340
Alumina/25% Zirconia	1,450
Alumina/ 40% Zirconia	1,600
65% Alumina/30% Zirconia/5% Titania	1,700
Sintered bauxite	1,900
Corundum (parallel to C axids)	1,950
Al_2O_3 + 3% TiO_2	1,950
Corundum	2,050
Heat-treated fused aluminum oxide	2,090
Corundum (perp. to C axis)	2,150
Al_2O_3 + 0.3% Cr_2O_3	2,150
Silicon carbide	2,480
Boron carbide	2760
Cubic boron nitride	7,800
Diamond	8,000

Knoop numbers indicate the depth to which a special point can scratch a material.

BREAKDOWN FACTORS FOR ABRASIVES

	Number of uses	Breakdown factor*
Aluminum oxide (30 FDT)	1	0.80
	3	0.61
Garnet RT-60	1	0.61
	3	0.38
Starblast®	1	0.77
	3	0.45
Flintshot®	1	0.68
	3	0.36
Flintbrasive® #3	1	0.58
	3	0.32

* breakdown factors can range from 1 to 0 with 1 equal to no change after blasting and 0 breaking down completely to dust.

Tests conducted by DuPont Engineering Test Center in 1970. Conditions: 0.64 cm nozzle; 634-655 x 10^3 Pa nozzle pressure; 0.64 cm steel plate target.

Ownership trademarks - Starblast® E.I. duPont de Nemours and Co. Ltd.; Flintshot® US Silica Co.

Source: Fulton, 1994

CLEANING RATE AND PROFILE FOR BLAST CLEANING ABRASIVES

	Cleaning rate m²/hr	Abrasive flow rate kg/hr	Profile mm
Starblast®	22	272	0.028
Biasill®	22	263	0.023
Coarse staurolite	19	243	0.038
Rotoblast® G80A (metallic grit)	14	318	0.030
Rotoblast® G40A (metallic grit)	11	340	0.053
Garnet RT-80	21	290	0.025
Garnet RT-60	18	238	0.025
Aluminum oxide (30 FDT)	16	302	0.038
Aluminum oxide (54/70)	21	261	0.033
Aluminum oxide (80/100)	23	245	0.028
Black Beauty®	15	340	0.038
Flintbrasive® #3	11	236	0.043
Flintshot®	19	318	0.043
Flint silica	20	331	0.036

Tests conducted by DuPont Engineering Test Center in 1970. 100% mill scale on new steel plate. All surfaces to Class 1 white metal. Conditions: 0.95 cm nozzle; 634-655 x 10³ Pa nozzle pressure.

Ownership trademarks - Starblast® and Biasill® E.I. duPont de Nemours and Co. Ltd.; Rotoblast® Pangborn Corp.; Black Beauty® H.B. Reed Corp.; Flintshot® US Silica Co. Source: Fulton, 1994

CERAMICS

PROPORTION OF BALL CLAY IN CERAMICS (%)

Semi-vitreous whiteware	25-40
Wall tiles	25-40
Artware	25-40
Engobes	5-40
Vitreous sanitaryware	25-38
Electrical porcelain	15-35
Abrasives (vitreous bond)	15-30
Glazes	5-30
Saggers	15-25
Chinaware	6-25
Refractories	5-25
Floor tiles	0-25
Porcelain enamels	4-10

TYPICAL WHITEWARE COMPOSITIONS

Whiteware type	Kaolin	Ball Clay	Silica	Flux	Talc	Bone Ash
Earthenware*	25	25	35	15	-	-
Porcelain	60	10	15	15	-	-
Bone china	25	-	-	25	-	50
Vitreous china	20-30	20-30	30-40	15-25	0-3	-
Stoneware	50**	20	10	20	-	-
Electrical porcelain	20	30	20	30	-	-

* includes hollow-ware, wall tiles, and sanitary earthenware; ** Plastic clays, includes kaolins

Semivitreous ware	Kaolin	Ball clay	Flint	Feldspar	Tremolitic talc	Pyroph-yllite	Calcium carbonate
Wall tile (1)	18	18	10	-	12	40	2
Wall tile (2)	-	24	17	-	35	16	8
Wall tile (3)	-	28	-	3	61	7	1
Floor tile	25	7	-	52	-	16	-
Electrical porcelain	30	16	-	35	-	19	-

CONVERSION CHARTS

CONVERT → INTO — MULTIPLY BY

CONVERT	Coal tonne	Natural gas 000m³	Natural gas 000ft³	Hydro/ nuclear 000kWh	Oil tonne	Oil Barrel
Coal (tonne)	1.0	0.778	27.503	8.140	0.667	4.667
Natural (000m³)	1.286	1.0	35.315	10.465	0.857	6.000
Gas (000ft³)	0.036	0.028	1.0	0.296	0.024	0.170
Hydro/Nuclear (000kWh)	0.123	0.095	3.379	1.0	0.082	0.573
Oil (tonne)	1.500	1.167	41.254	12.209	1.0	7.000
Oil (barrel)	0.214	0.167	5.893	1.744	0.143	1.0

	tonne/y	m³/year	ft³/day	000kWh/y	tonne	barrel/day
Coal (tonne)	1.0	2.131	75.350	8.140	0.667	0.013
Natural (m³/day)	0.469	1.0	35.315	3.820	0.313	0.006
Gas (ft³/day)	0.013	0.028	1.0	0.108	0.009	0.0002
Hydro/Nuclear (000kWh/y)	0.123	0.262	9.257	1.0	0.082	0.002
Oil (tonne/y)	1.500	3.196	113.025	12.209	1.0	0.019
Oil (barrel/y)	78.214	166.667	5893.434	636.628	52.143	1.0

Calorific values	7000 kCal/kg	9000 kCal/m³	1010 BTU/ft³	860 kCal/kWh	10500 kCal/kg	1.5 million kCal/barrel

PRODUCT — HEAT VALUE

PRODUCT	HEAT VALUE
1 ton bituminous coal	25 Mcf natural gas; 189 US gallons gasoline; 4.17 barrels crude oil
1 Mcf natural gas	0.04 ton (80 pounds) coal; 7.58 US gallon gasoline; 0.17 barrel (7 US gallons) crude oil
1 US gallon gasoline	0.005 ton (10.56 pounds) coal; 0.132 Mcf natural gas; 0.022 barrel (0.917 US gallon) oil
1 barrel oil	0.24 ton (480 pounds) coal; 6 Mcf natural gas; 45.5 US gallons gasoline
1 pound U_3O_8 concentrate	8.9 tons coal; 37.1 barrel crude oil

WORLD PRODUCTION OF ENERGY ('000 BARRELS OF OIL EQUIVALENT/DAY)

COAL		OIL		NATURAL GAS		HEP		NUCLEAR	
China	11,,441	Former USSR	9,042	Former USSR	14,212	Canada	1,688	United States	3,512
United States	11,282	USA	8,850	USA	9,272	United States	1,452	France	1,819
Former USSR	5,245	Saudi Arabia	8,405	Canada	2,293	Brazil	1,245	Japan	1,192
Australia	2,519	Iran	3,461	Netherlands	1,531	Norway	594	Former Soviet Union	933
India	2,330	Mexico	3,117	Algeria	1,029	Sweden	398	Germany	850
South Africa	2,200	China	2,843	United Kingdom	1,027	France	389	Canada	432
Germany	1,939	Venezuela	2,343	Indonesia	997	Italy	262	United Kingdom	416
Poland	1,758	Norway	2,200	Saudi Arabia	627	Venezuela	189	Sweden	342
United Kingdom	1,072	Canada	2,066	Norway	521	Austria	188	South Korea	303
Canada	696	Nigeria	1,961	Mexico	483	Switzerland	182	Spain	299
North Korea	671	United Kingdom	1,927	Iran	461	Colombia	176	Belgium	231
Czechoslovakia	634	Abu Dhabi	1,895	Venezuela	438	Paraguay	175	Taiwan	181
Colombia	355	Indonesia	1,520	Malaysia	416	Mexico	148	Czechoslovakia	130
Others	4,327	Libya	1,519	Romania	408	Turkey	143	Switzerland	126
Total	**46,469**	Algeria	1,233	Australia	406	Other	1,185	Finland	103
		Opec NGLs	1,180	Other	4,731	**Total**	**8,414**	Others	346
		Kuwait	1,048	**Total**	**38,852**			**Total**	**11,215**
		Others	10,444						
		Total	**65,054**						

Source: World Energy Yearbook 1994, Petroleum Economist and Ernst & Young

PRIMARY NUTRIENTS

	N	P₂O₅	K₂O	Ca	Mg	S	Cl	Cu	Mn	Zn	B

NITROGEN

	N	P₂O₅	K₂O	Ca	Mg	S	Cl	Cu	Mn	Zn	B
Ammonia, anhydrous	82	-	-	-	-	-	-	-	-	-	-
Ammonia, aqua	16-25	-	-	-	-	-	-	-	-	-	-
Ammonium nitrate	33.5	-	-	-	-	-	-	-	-	0.1	-
Ammonium nitrate-limestone mixture	20.5	-	-	7.3	4.4	0.4	0.4	-	-	-	-
Ammonium sulfate	21	-	-	0.3	-	23.7	0.5	0.3	-	0.1	-
Ammonium sulfate-nitrate	26	-	-	-	-	15.1	-	-	-	-	-
Calcium cyanamide	21	-	-	38.5	0.06	0.3	0.2	0.02	0.04		-
Calcium nitrate	15	-	-	19.4	1.5	0.02	0.2	-	-	-	-
Nitrogen solutions	21-49	-	-	-	-	-	-	-	-	-	-
Sodium nitrate	16	-	0.2	0.1	0.05	0.07	0.4	0.07	-	-	0.01
Urea	46	-	-	-	-	-	-	-	-	-	-
Urea-form	38	-	-	-	-	-	-	-	-	-	-

PHOSPHATE

	N	P₂O₅	K₂O	Ca	Mg	S	Cl	Cu	Mn	Zn	B
Basic slag	-	8-12	-	29	3.4	0.3	-	-	2.2	-	-
Bone meal	2-4.5	22-28	0.2	20-25	0.4	0.1	0.2	-	-	0.02	-
Phosphoric acid	-	52-60	-	-	-	-	-	-	-	-	-
Rock phosphate	-	30-36	-	33.2	0.2	0.3	0.1	-	0.03	-	-
Superphosphate, normal	-	18-20	0.2	20.4	0.2	11.9	0.3	-	-	0.1	-
Superphosphate, conc.	-	42-50	0.4	13.6	0.3	1.4	-	0.01	0.01	-	0.01
Superphosphoric acid	-	69-76	-	-	-	-	-	-	-	-	-

POTASH

	N	P₂O₅	K₂O	Ca	Mg	S	Cl	Cu	Mn	Zn	B
Potassium chloride (MOP)	-	-	60-62	0.1	0.1	-	47.0	-	-	-	0.03
Potassium magnesium sulfate	-	-	22	-	11.2	22.7	1.5	-	-	-	-
Potassium sulfate	-	-	50	0.7	1.2	17.6	2.1	0.001	-	-	0.002

MULTIPLE NUTRIENTS

	N	P₂O₅	K₂O	Ca	Mg	S	Cl	Cu	Mn	Zn	B
Ammoniated superphosphate	3-6	18-20	-	17.2	-	12	-	-	-	-	-
Ammonium phosphate nitrate	27	15	-	-	-	-	-	-	-	-	-
Ammonium phosphate sulfate	13-16	20-39	0.2	0.3	0.1	15.4	0.1	0.02	0.2	0.02	0.03
Diammonium phosphate (DAP)	16-21	48-53	-	-	-	-	-	-	-	-	-
Monoammonium phosphate (MAP)	11	48	0.2	1.1	0.3	2.2	0.1	0.02	0.03	0.03	0.02
Nitric phosphates	14-22	10-22	-	8-10	0.1	0.2-3.6	1-12	0.02	0.2	0.02	0.03
Nitrate of soda-potash	15	-	14	-	-	-	0.5	-	-	-	0.13
Potassium nitrate	13	-	44	0.6	0.4	0.2	1.1	-	-	-	0.10
Wood ashes	-	1.8	5.5	23.3	2.2	0.4	0.2	0.12	0.76	0.20	0.16
Blast furnace slag	-	1.7	0.6	29.3	3.8	1.4	-	-	1.02	0.001	0.01
Dolomite	-	-	-	21.5	11.4	0.3	-	0.001	0.11	-	0.01
Gypsum	-	-	0.5	22.5	0.4	16.8	0.3	-	-	-	-
Kieserite	-	-	-	1.6	18.2	-	-	-	-	-	-
Limestone	-	-	0.3	31.7	3.4	0.1	-	0.004	0.48	0.05	0.003
Lime-sulfur solution	-	-	-	6.7	-	23.8	-	-	-	-	-
Magnesium sulfate (Epsom salt)	-	-	-	2.2	10.5	14.0	0.4	-	-	-	-
Sulfur	-	-	-	-	-	30-99.6	-	-	-	-	-

SECONDARY & MICRONUTRIENTS

CALCIUM

Soil amendment		% Ca	Fertilizers		% Ca
Calcitic limestone	$CaCO_3$	32	Calcium nitrate	$Ca(NO_3)_2$	19
Dolomitic limestone	$CaCO_3+MgCO_3$	22	Normal superphosphate	$Ca(H_2PO_4)_2 \ CaSO_4$	20
Hydrated lime	$Ca(OH)_2$	46	Triple superphosphate	$Ca(H_2PO_4)_2$	14
Precipitated lime	CaO	60	Synthetic chelates	CaEDTA	3.5
Gypsum	$CaSO_4 \cdot 2H_2O$	23	Natural organic complexes		4-12
Blast furnace slag	$CaSiO_3$	29			

MAGNESIUM

		% Mg			% Mg
Dolomitic limestone	$CaCO_3+MgCO_3$	11	Magnesium oxide	MgO	55
Basic slag	$MgSiO_3$	4	Potassium magnesium sulfate	$K_2SO_4 \cdot 2MgSO_4$	11
Mag sulfate (Epsom salts)	$MgSO_4 \cdot 7H_2O$	10	Synthetic chelates	MgEDTA	2-4
Kieserite, calcined	$MgSO_4 \cdot H_2O$	18	Natural organic complexes		4-9

SULFUR

		%S			%S
Elemental sulfur	S	30-100	Magnesium sulfate (Epsom salts)	$MgSO_4 \cdot 7H_2O$	11-14
Ammonium polysulfide	NH_4S_x	40-45	Potassium magnesium sulfate	$K_2SO_4 \cdot 2MgSO_4$	20-23
Ammonium bisulfite	NH_4HSO_3	17-32	Potassium sulfate	K_2SO_4	16-18
Ammonium thiosulfate	$(NH_4)_2S_2O_3$	26-43	Copper sulfate	$CuSO_4 \cdot 5H_2O$	12-14
Ammonium sulfate	$(NH_4)_2SO_4$	10-25	Ferrous sulfate	$FeSO_4 \cdot 7H_2O$	10-14
Gypsum	$CaSO_4 \cdot 2H_2O$	15-18	Manganese sulfate	$MnSO_4 \cdot 4H_2O$	12-16
Normal superphosphate	$Ca(H_2PO_4)_2 \cdot CaSO_4$	10-14	Zinc sulfate	$ZnSO_4 \cdot H_2O$	12-18
Ammonium phosphate sulfate	MAP, DAP, + $(NH_4)_2SO_4$	14-16			

BORON

		% B			% B
Borax	$Na_2B_4O_7 \cdot 10H_2O$	11	Sodium perborate	$Na_2B_{10}O_{18} \cdot 10H_2O$	18
Boric acid	H_3BO_3	17	Solubor	$Na_2B_{10}O_{16} \cdot 10H_2O$	20
Sodium tetraborate			Boron frits	fritted glass	10-17
Fertilizer borate - 46	$Na_2B_4O_7 \cdot 5H_2O$	14			
Fertilizer borate - 65	$Na_2B_4O_7$	20			

COPPER

		% Cu			% Cu
Copper sulfate monohydrate	$CuSO_4 \cdot H_2O$	35	Copper frits	fritted glass	10-50
pentahydrate	$CuSO_4 \cdot 5H_2O$	35	Synthetic chelates	CuEDTA	8-13
Cupric oxide	CuO	75		CuHEDTA	9
Cuprous oxide	Cu_2O	89	Natural organic complexes		5-6
Copper chloride	$CuCl_2$	17			

IRON

		% Fe			% Fe
Ferrous sulfate	$FeSO_4 \cdot 7H_2O$	20	Synthetic chelates	FeHEDTA	5-12
Ferric sulfate	$Fe_2(SO_4)_3 \cdot 9H_2O$	20		FeDTPA	10
Ferrous ammonium sulfate	$Fe_2(SO_4)_3 \cdot 9H_2O \ (NH_4)_2SO_4$	14		FeEDDHA	6
Ferrous carbonate	$FeCO_3 \cdot H_2O$	42	Natural organic complexes		4-11
Iron frits	fritted glass	10-40			

MANGANESE

		% Mn			% Mn
Manganese sulfate	$MnSO_4 \cdot 4H_2O$	23-28	Synthetic chelates	MnEDTA	5-12
Manganous oxide	MnO	41-68	Natural organic complexes		5-9
Manganese frits	fritted glass	10-35			

MOLYBDENUM

		% Mo			% Mo
Ammonium molybdate	$(NH_4)_6Mo_7O_{24} \cdot 2H_2O$	54	Molybdenum trioxide	MoO_3	66
Sodium molybdate	$Na_2MoO_4 \cdot 2H_2O$	39	Molybdenum frits	fritted glass	1-30

ZINC

		% Zn			% Zn
Zinc sulfate	$ZnSO_4 \cdot H_2O$	36	Zinc frits	fritted glass	10-30
Zinc oxide	ZnO	50-80	Synthetic chelates	ZnEDTA	6-14
Zinc carbonate	$ZnCO_3$	52-56		ZnHEDTA	3-12
Zinc chloride	$ZnCl_2$	50	Natural organic complexes		3-12

Source: The Fertilizer Institute

	Mohs hardness	Shape	SG	% Bright	Refractive index	Oil absorption	Stability	Cost
Aplite	6	EQ	2.62	80-85	1.53	10-30	IN	L
Aragonite	3.5	EL	2.95	75-90	1.68	15-40	AS	L
Asbestos	2.5-4.0	EL	2.5-2.6	-	1.51-1.55	40-90	IN	L-M
Attapulgite	4.0	EL	2.2-2.6	50-70	1.50	30-50	IN	L-M
Barite	2.5-3.5	EQ	4.3-4.6	80-97	1.64	6-10	IN	L-M
Bentonite	1.5	PL	2.3-2.6	50-90	1.55-1.56	20-60	AS, BS	L-M
Blanc fixe	3.0	EQ	4.35	98	1.64		IN	M
Calcium carbonate								
Natural-ground	3.0	EQ	2.7	80-97	1.56	18-21	AS	L-M
Precipitated	3.0	EQ	2.7-3.0	90-98	1.56	25-50	AS	L-M
Diatomite, natural	4.5-5.0	PL	1.95-2.05	59-75	1.42-1.49	140-180	IN	L-M
Diatomite, processed	5-6	PL	2.30-2.36	85-95	1.42-1.49	100-250	IN	L-M
Dolomite	3.5-4.0	EQ	2.85	80-90	1.68	10-30	AS	L
Feldspar	6.0	EQ	2.57	-	1.52	10-30	IN	L-M
Gypsum	1.5-2.0	EQ	2.3	75-95	1.52	20-25	AS	L-M
Iron oxide, natural								
Hematite	3.8-5.1	EQ	4.5-5.1	red	2.94-3.22	10-35	IN	M
Micaceous iron oxide		PL	4.8-5.0	gray	-	18-30	IN	M
Kaolin								
Air-classified, coarse	2.0	PL	2.58	74-84	1.56	28-32	IN	L
Air-classified, fine	2.0	PL	2.58	74-80	1.56	34-40	IN	L
Water class., coarse	2.0	PL	2.58	79-85	1.56	28-32	IN	L-M
Water class., medium	2.0	PL	2.58	85-87	1.56	32-40	IN	L-M
Water class, fine	2.0	PL	2.58	87-90	1.56	40-48	IN	L-M
Beneficiated, coarse	2.0	PL	2.58	85-86	1.56	50-60	IN	L-M
Beneficiated, medium	2.0	PL	2.58	86-88	1.56	45-55	IN	L-M
Beneficiated, fine	2.0	PL	2.58	89-91	1.56	40-50	IN	L-M
Calcined, partial	4-6	PL	2.50	89-91	1.62	45-60	IN	M-H
Calcined, fully	6-8	PL	2.63	89-91	1.62	45-90	IN	M-H
Surface modified Silane	2-8	PL	2.58	89-91	1.56-1.62	28-60	IN	H
Resin	2.0	PL	2.58	89-91	1.56	28-31	IN	H
Cationic	2.0	PL	2.58	89-91	1.56	24-33	IN	H
Mica	2-3	PL	2.7-3.2	70-80	1.59	25-50	IN	L-M
Nepheline syenite	5.5-6	EQ	2.6-2.65	70-85	1.54	10-30	IN	L-M
Perlite	5.0	EQ	2.5-2.6	70-85	1.48-1.49	10-30	IN	L-M
Phlogopite	2.5-3	PL	2.9	70-80	1.598	NA	IN	L-M
Pumicite	5-6	EQ	2.2-2.63	60-80	1.49-1.50	30-40	IN	L
Pyrophyllite	1-2	PL	2.8-2.9	75-85	1.57-1.59	40-70	IN	L-M
Sepiolite	4.0	EL	2.5	60-75	1.49	30-50	IN	L-M
Silica								
Ground crystalline	7	EQ	2.65	78-91	1.46		IN	M
Microcrystalline	7	EQ	2.65	84-91	1.54-1.55	27-31	IN	M
Precipitated	7	EQ	2.05	97	1.46		IN	M
Gel	7	EQ	2.0	-	1.46		IN	M
Fumed	7	EQ	2.2	-	1.46		IN	M
Slate	4-6	PL	2.7-2.8	-	-	20-25	IN	L
Talc	1-1.5	PL	2.6-3	85-96	1.57-1.59	20-50	IN	L-M
Titanium dioxide								
Rutile	6-7	EQ	4.2	97-98	2.76	16-45	IN	H
Anatase	5-6	EQ	3.9	98.5-99	2.55	18-30	IN	H
Vermiculite	1.5	PL	2.2-2.7	-	1.56	25-60	IN	M
Wollastonite	4.5	EL	2.9	85-95	1.63	25-30	IN	L-M
Zeolite	3.5-4.0	EQ	2.1-2.2	75-90	1.48	30-100	AS	L-M
Zinc pigments								
Lithopone		EQ	4.3	98	1.84		IN	M
Zinc sulfide		EQ	4.0	98	2.37		IN	H
Zinc oxide		EQ	5.6	98	2.01		IN	H

EQ - equidimensional; El - elongate; PL - platy. IN - chemically inert, pH 4-9; AS - acid soluble; BS - base soluble.

L - low cost (<5¢/lb); M - medium cost (5-20¢/lb); H - high cost >20¢/lb. Adapted from Murray.

TYPICAL CHEMISTRY OF DIFFERENT GLASS TYPES (% BY WEIGHT)

	Container glass-white	Container glass-green	Flat glass	Pressed ware	Borosilicate glass	CRT faceplate	Lead-crystal glass	Glass ceramics	Fiber optics
SiO_2	73.0	72.0	72.8	72.2	80.2	64.0	60.0	67.4	61.0
Al_2O_3	1.5	2.6	—	0.3	2.4	3.5	0.02	20.9	3.0
Na_2O	13.0	12.5	13.7	16.9	4.2	7.5	1.0	—	14.0
K_2O	1.0	1.5	0.2	—	—	10.5	14.9	—	—
CaO	11.3	11.4	8.2	6.2	0.1	3.5	0.2	2.7	—
MgO	0.1	0.1	4.0	4.4	—	1.5	—	—	—
B_2O_3	—	—	—	—	12.9	—	0.025	—	22.0
Fe_2O_3	0.04	0.5	0.1	—	—	—	—	—	—
PbO	—	—	—	—	—	—	31.4	—	—
Li_2O	—	—	—	—	—	—	—	3.9	—
Cr_2O_3	—	0.2	—	—	—	—	—	—	—
TiO_2	—	—	—	—	—	—	—	1.8	—
ZrO_2	—	—	—	—	—	—	—	2.0	—
SO_3	—	—	—	—	—	—	—	—	—
BaO	—	—	—	—	—	8.0	—	—	—
ZnO	—	—	—	—	—	—	—	1.3	—

TYPICAL CHEMISTRY OF FIBERGLASS TYPES (% BY WEIGHT)

	A-Glass	C-Glass	D-Glass	E-Glass	R-Glass	S-Glass	AR-Glass
SiO_2	72.5	65.0	74.0	54.5	60.0	65.0	71.0
Al_2O_3	{ 1.5	{ 4.0	—	14.5	25.0	25.0	1.0
Fe_2O_3			0.2	0.5	0.3	—	—
B_2O_3	—	5.0	22.5	7.5	—	—	—
CaO	9.0	14.0	0.5	17.0	9.0	—	—
MgO	3.5	3.0	0.2	4.5	6.0	10.0	—
Na_2O	13.0	0.5	1.0	{ 0.8	0.4	—	—
K_2O	—	8.0	1.5		0.1	—	—
BaO	NA	1.0	NA	NA	NA	NA	NA
Li_2O	NA	NA	NA	NA	NA	NA	1.0
TiO_2	NA	NA	NA	0.1	0.2	NA	NA
ZrO_2	NA	NA	NA	NA	NA	NA	16.0

Source: Adapted from various including Bourne, 1994

SUMMARY OF CHEMICAL SPECIFICATIONS FOR GLASS RAW MATERIALS (% AND PPM)

	Flat glass Silica sand	Soda ash	Feldspathics	Limestone	Dolomite	Container glass Silica sand	Soda ash	Feldspathics	Limestone	Dolomite
SiO_2	>99.5		±0.5			>99.5		±0.5	±0.5	±0.5
Fe_2O_3	<0.04	<20 ppm	<0.01	<0.075	<0.1	<0.03	<20 ppm	<0.01	<0.25	<0.1
Al_2O_3	<0.3		±0.5	<0.35	±0.5	±0.01		±0.5	<0.4	±0.5
TiO_2	<0.1					<0.1				
Cr_2O_3	<2 ppm		<10 ppm		<10 ppm	<0.03		<10 ppm		<10 ppm
Co_3O_4	<2 ppm					<10 ppm				
MnO_2	<20 ppm									
$CaO-MgO$						±0.1				
ZrO_2						<0.01				
Na_2O-K_2O			±0.5			±0.1		±0.5		
Moisture						<0.1				
Na_2CO_3		>99.2					>99.2			
Na_2O		>58					>58			
Na_2SO_4		<0.2					<0.2			
$NaCl$		<0.2					<0.2			
CaO			±0.5	>54.8	>29.5			±0.5	>54.8	±0.3
MgO				<0.8	<21.4				<0.8	±0.3

Source: Various including Bourne, 1994

INFLUENCE OF FILLERS ON THERMOPLASTICS

	Asbestos	Mica	Wollastonite	Silica	Talc	Kaolin	Glass spheres
Tensile strength	+1		+1	0			+1
Compressive strength			+1		+1		
Modulus of elasticity +2	+2	+2	+1	+1		+1	
Impact strength	-1	-1	-1/+1	-1	-1	-1	-1
Reduced thermal expansion	+1		+1	+1	+1	+1	
Reduced shrinkage +1	+1	+1	+1	+1	+1	+1	
Increased thermal condition	+1	+1		+1	+1		
Increased heat deflection temp.	+1	+1	+1	+1			+1
Electrical resistance	+1	+2	+1	+1	+2		
Thermal stability		+1	+1	+1	+1	+1	
Chemical resistance +1	+1	+1		0	+1	+1	

+2 considerable influence; +1 some influence; 0 no influence; -1 negative influence.

Source: Gächler, R. and Müller, H. (eds.), Plastics Additives Handbook, Hanser, Munich, 1983.

MINERAL FILLERS IN PLASTICS

Mineral	Major Resin	Function
Aluminum hydrate	Polyester	Flame retardation
Aluminum hydrate	Cable, PVC, EPDM	Flame retardation, processing properties
Calcium carbonate, ground	PVC	Cost reduction
Calcium carbonate, ppt.	PVC	Impact strength
Calcium carbonate*	PVC pipe	Higher loadings
Kaolin, air floated	Polyester	Thixotropy
Kaolin, calcined	PVC	Electrical resistance
Kaolin*	Tire, EPDM, cable	Electrical properties
Kaolin**	Nylon	Dimensional stability
Mica	Polypropylene	Flexural strength
Mica*	Polyolefins	Physical properties
Microspheres*	Nylon	Physical properties
Organophilic clays	Coatings	Rheological properties
Silica, ground	Epoxy	Dimensional stability
Silica, ground*	Epoxy molding cpds.	Electrical properties
Silica, fumed*	Silicone rubber	Processing
Talc	Polypropylene	Stiffness
Talc*	Industrial rubber	Physical properties
Wollastonite	Nylon	Dimensional stability
Wollastonite*	Nylon	Physical properties, glass replacement

* chemically modified; ** surface treated

Source: Kline & Co.

POLYMER ALPHABET

ABS	acrylonitrile-butadiene-styrene
BMC	bulk molding compound
CAB	cellulose acetate butyrate
CTFE	chlorotrifluorethylene
DAP	diallyl phthalate
ETFE	ethylene trifluorethylene
EPM,EPDM	ethylene propylene diene monomer
HDPE	high-density polyethylene
LDPE	low-density polyethylene
LLDPE	linear low-density polyethylene
LIM	liquid injection molding
OPP	oriented polypropylene
PC	polycarbonate
PE	polyethylene
PEEK	polyetheretherketone
PES	polyethersulfone
PET	polyethylene terephthalate
PP	polypropylene
PEU	polyethylene unsaturated
PMMA	polymethyl methacrylate
PP	polypropylene
PPO	polyphenylene oxides
PPS	polyphenylene sulfides
PS	polystyrene
PTFE	polytetrafluoroethylene
PUR	polyurethane
PVC	polyvinyl chloride
RIM	reaction injection molding
RRIM	reinforced reaction injection molding
SAN	styrene acrylonitrile
SEBS	styrene-ethylene-butylene-styrene
SMC	sheet molding compound
SRIM	structural reaction injection molding
TFE	tetrafluoroethylene
TPE	thermoplastic elastomers

RESIN CONSUMPTION IN THE UNITED STATES ('000 TONNES)

	Appliances	Construction	Electrical & electronic	Transportation	Furniture	Toys	Housewares	Packaging
ABS	106	63	50	149	3	16		3
Acrylic	5	96		32				
Cellulosics	1	2	1			1	1	2
Epoxy	4	21	23					17
EVA							103	37
HDPE			67			91	209	2,240
LDPE			177			83		2,430
Nylon			41	67				
PET								684
Phenolics	13	1,002	42	10	43		16	5
Polyacetal	6		2	16				
Polycarbonate	24	55	17	27				10
Polyester	44	163	48	25	3			
Polyurethane					283			
PP	85	13	15	13	53	31	134	770
PS	123	186	215		37	93	117	782
PVC	64	2,646	223	10	39	18	88	250
SAN	5	14	2				10	6
Urea/melamine		638	24					1
Others	128	891	35	774	26	48	38	265

Source: USBM (1992)

REFRACTORIES

PYROMETRIC CONE EQUIVALENT

The quality and properties of refractory (and ceramic) clays are expressed as pyrometric cone equivalents or PCE which measures the combined effect of temperature and time.

The clay is cut into the size and shape of a standard pyrometric cone and heated at a rate of 2.5°C per minute with a range of standard cones (in accordance with the Standard Method of Test for Pyrometric Cone Equivalent (PCE) of refractory materials (ASTM C 24)). The PCE is the number of the standard cone whose tip touches the supporting plaque simultaneously with the cone of the material being investigated. The end points and the equivalent temperatures are given in the table.

END POINTS OF SMALL ORTON PYROMETRIC CONES

Cone No.	End Point °C	Cone No.	End Point °C	Cone No.	End Point °C
07	1,008	8	1,300	26	1,621
06	1,023	9	1,317	27	1,640
05	1,062	10	1,330	28	1,646
04	1,098	11	1,336	29	1,659
03	1,131	12	1,355	30	1,665
02	1,148	13	1,349	31	1,683
01	1,178	14	1,398	31½	1,699
1	1,179	15	1,430	32	1,717
2	1,179	16	1,491	32½	1,724
3	1,196	17	1,512	33	1,743
4	1,209	18	1,522	34	1,763
5	1,221	19	1,541	35	1,785
6	1,255	20	1,564	36	1,804
7	1,264	23	1,605		

MELTING AND DECOMPOSITION TEMPERATURES OF REFRACTORY CONSTITUENTS

Material	Formula	Melting Point °C
Cristobalite	SiO_2	1,723
Corundum	Al_2O_3	2,050
Chromium (III) oxide	Cr_2O_3	2,435
Periclase	MgO	2,825
Calcium oxide	CaO	2,572
Zirconium oxide	ZrO_2	2,390
Rutile	TiO_2	1,830
Silicon carbide*	SiC	2,760
Silicon nitride*	Si_3N_4	1,900
Mullite	$3Al_2O_3 \cdot 2SiO_2$	1,850
Kyanite**	$3Al_2O_3 \cdot 2SiO_2$	1,325
Andalusite**	$3Al_2O_3 \cdot 2SiO_2$	1,350
Sillimanite**	$3Al_2O_3 \cdot 2SiO_2$	1,530
Wollastonite	$CaO \cdot SiO_2$	1,540
Fosterite	$2MgO \cdot SiO_2$	1,890
Chromite	$FeO \cdot Cr_2O_3$	2,180
Picrochromite	$MgO \cdot Cr_2O_3$	2,330
Spinel	$MgO \cdot Al_2O_3$	2,135

* decomposition temperature

** decomposition to mullite and cristobalite

Source: Büchner, et al, 1989

CLASSIFICATION OF REFRACTORY PRODUCTS

Category	Main ingredient % by weight	Formula	Other major ingredient
Silica products	>93	SiO_2	-
Fireclay products			
Acidic	67 - 76	SiO_2	Al_2O_3
Half acidic	22 - 30	Al_2O_3	SiO_2
Basic	30 - 45	Al_2O_3	SiO_2
Alumina-rich products			
Alumina-enriched products	50 - 55	Al_2O_3	SiO_2
Kyanite bricks	55 -65	Al_2O_3	SiO_2
Sillimanite bricks	60 - 70	Al_2O_3	SiO_2
Mullite bricks	72 -75	Al_2O_3	SiO_2
Bauxite bricks	75 -85	Al_2O_3	SiO_2
Corundum bricks	60 - 99.5	Al_2O_3	SiO_2
Neutral products			
Zirconium silicate bricks	<67	ZrO_2	SiO_2
Chromium ore bricks	<50	Cr_2O_3	MgO, FeO, Al_2O_3
Basic products			
Magnesia bricks	>80	MgO	-
Magnesia-chrome bricks	55 - 80	MgO	Cr_2O_3
Chrome-magnesia bricks	25 - 55	MgO	Cr_2O_3
Forsterite bricks	<55	MgO	SiO_2, FeO

Source: Büchner, et al, 1989

WORLD PRODUCTION OF STEEL

Canada	13,924	Belgium	10,276	Albania	5	Australia	6,322	Iran	2,937
Mexico	8,435	Denmark	591	Austria	3,946	Bangladesh	44	Iraq	100
United States	84,322	France	17,961	Azerbaijan	300	China	80,000	Israel	160
North America	**106,681**	Germany	39,768	Belarus	700	Hong Kong	350	Jordan	200
Argentina	2,600	Greece	923	Bosnia & Herzegovina	250	India	18,000	Kazakhstan	5,000
Brazil	24,000	Ireland	257	Bulgaria	1,500	Indonesia	3,100	Qatar	580
Chile	850	Italy	24,904	Croatia	100	Japan	98,131	Saudi Arabia	1,900
Colombia	670	Luxembourg	3,068	Czechoslovakia	11,140	Korea, North	8,100	Syria	70
Ecuador	19	Netherlands	5,438	Finland	3,077	Korea, South	28,054	Uzbekistan	800
Paraguay	60	Portugal	749	Georgia	700	Malaysia	1,250	**Middle East**	**11,747**
Peru	400	Spain	12,295	Hungary	1,559	New Zealand	600	Algeria	1,400
Uruguay	40	United Kingdom	16,050	Latvia	246	Pakistan	1,000	Angola	10
Venezuela	3,200	**European Union**	**132,280**	Macedonia	150	Philippines	250	Benin	8
South America	**31,839**			Moldavia	619	Singapore	500	Egypt	2,500
Cuba	162			Norway	446	Taiwan	11,000	Libya	822
Dominican Republic	35			Poland	9,800	Thailand	750	Morocco	7
El Salvador	11			Romania	5,372	Vietnam	120	Nigeria	140
Guatemala	18			Russia	67,000	**Australasia**	**257,571**	South Africa	9,061
Honduras	7			Serbia & Montenegro	700			Tunisia	200
Jamaica	37			Slovenia	400			Zimbabwe	580
Trinidad and Tobago	440			Sweden	4,356			**Africa**	**14,728**
C. America & Caribbean	**710**			Switzerland	1,050				
				Turkey	10,343				
				Ukraine	42,000				
Source: USBM (1993)				**Non-EU Europe**	**165,759**				

1-1.99

Mirabilite	1.48	Borax (tincal)	1.7	Sylvite	1.98
Carnallite	1.6	Gaylussite	1.94	Diatomite	1.9-2.3
Ulexite	1.65	Kernite	1.95		

2-2.99

Sepiolite (Meerschaum)	2	Bauxite	2.6	Talc	2.7-2.8
Sulfur	2	Bertrandite	2.6	Vermiculite	2.7
Halloysite	2.0-2.2	Chert	2.6	Muscovite	2.76-3.0
Zeolites	2-2.5	Beryl	2.6-2.9	Phlogopite	2.78-2.85
Bentonite	2.1	Kaolinite	2.6	Dolomite	2.8-2.9
Halite	2.1-2.6	Kieserite	2.6	Lepidolite	2.8-3.3
Kainite	2.1	Chlorite	2.65-2.75	Pyrophyllite	2.8-2.9
Trona	2.13	Novaculite	2.65	Wollastonite	2.8-2.9
Chrysotile	2.2	Quartz	2.65-2.66	Anhydrite	2.93
Graphite	2.2	Silica	2.65	Anthophyllite	2.85-3.1
Gibbsite	2.3-2.4	Tripoli	2.65	Aragonite	2.9
Gypsum	2.38	Thenardite	2.68	Tremolite	2.9-3.2
Brucite	2.39	Alunite	2.7	Cryolite	2.97
Colemanite	2.4	Calcite	2.7		
Feldspar	2.57	Marble	2.7		

3-3.99

Fluorspar	3.0-3.3	Crocidolite	3.2-3.3	Diamond	3.5
Amosite	3.1-3.25	Garnet	3.2-4.3	Kyanite	3.6-3.7
Magnesite	3.1	Olivine	3.2-4.3	Anatase	3.82-3.95
Spodumene	3.1-3.2	Phosphate rock	3.2	Celestite	3.9-4.0
Apatite	3.17-3.23	Sillimanite	3.23	Corundum	3.9-4.1
Andalusite	3.2	Diaspore	3.3-3.5		

4-4.99

Emery	4-4.5	Barite	4.3-4.6	Xenotime	4.5
Rutile	4.2	Chromite	4.3-4.6	Pyrite	4.8-5.1
Zircon	4.2-4.7	Ilmenite	4.5-5.0	Pyrolusite	4.8

> 5

Bastnaesite	5	Monazite	5.27	Baddeleyite	5.4-5.7

INDUSTRIAL MINERALS BY PRICE

$1 - $10/t

Aggregates	Anhydrite	Gypsum	Salt	Sand & gravel

$10 - $100/t

Aplite	Cement	Ilmenite	Olivine	Salt
Aragonite	Celestite	Kaolin	Phosphates	Salt cake
Barite	Chromite	Lime	Potash	Soda ash
Bentonite	Dolomite	Magnesite	Pumice	Zeolites
Calcium carbonate	Feldspar	Nepheline syenite	Pyrophyllite	

$100 - $1,000/t

Alumina	Calcium carbonate	Kaolin	Petalite	Vermiculite
Anatase	Chromite	Kyanite	Rare earth oxides	Wollastonite
Andalusite	Diatomite	Magnesite	Rutile	Xenotime
Asbestos	Emery	Manganese	Sepiolite	Zeolites
Attapulgite	Flint clay	Mica	Silica	Zircon
Barite	Fluorspar	Monazite	Sillimanite	
Bauxite	Garnet	Nepheline syenite	Spodumene	
Bentonite	Graphite	Nitrates	Sulfur	
Borax	Iron oxide	Perlite	Talc	

$1,000 - $10,000/t

Antimony oxide	Bastnaesite	Graphite	Rutile	Silicon carbide
Asbestos	Bromine	Rare earth oxides		

Over $10,000/tonne

Diamonds	Iodine	Rare earth oxides

INDUSTRIAL MINERALS BY SPECIFIC GRAVITY

1.0-1.99

Bauxite	1.0-3.0	Pyrophyllite	1.0-2.0	Mirabilite	1.5-2.0
Bentonite	1	Ulexite	1	Vermiculite	1.5
Graphite	1.0-2.0	Talc	1.0-1.5	Chrysotile	1.7
Halloysite	1.0-2.0	Chlorite	1.5-2		
Pyrolusite	1.0-2.5	Gypsum	1.5-2.0		

2.0-2.99

Borax (tincal)	2.0-2.5	Sulfur	2	Halite	2.5
Gibbsite	2.0-3.5	Sylvite	2	Phlogopite	2.5-3
Gaylussite	3-Feb	Barite	2.5-3.5	Thenardite	2.5
Kaolinite	2.0-2.5	Brucite	2.5	Kainite	2.8
Sepiolite	2-2.5	Carnallite	2.5		
Muscovite	2-2.5	Cryolite	2.5		

3.0-3.99

Calcite	3	Lepidolite	3	Dolomite	3.5-4.0
Celestite	3.0-3.5	Marble	3	Zeolites	3.5-5.5
Anhydrite	3-3.5	Kieserite	3.3	Alunite	3.8
Kernite	3	Aragonite	3.5-4.0		

4.0-4.99

Colemanite	4.0-4.5	Kyanite	7-Apr	Wollastonite	4.5-5.0
Crocidolite	4	Apatite	4.5-5.0	Xenotime	4.5
Fluorspar	4	Bastnaesite	4.5		
Magnesite	4.0-4.5	Diatomite	2		

5.0-5.99

Anthophyllite	6-May	Phosphate rock	5	Amosite	5.5-6.0
Ilmenite	5.0-6.0	Tremolite	6-May	Anatase	5.5-6.0
Monazite	5.0-5.5	Chromite	5.5		

6.0-6.99

Bertrandite	6	Sillimanite	7-Jun	Olivine	6.5-7.0
Feldspar	6	Baddeleyite	6.5	Spodumene	6.5-7.0
Pyrite	6.0-6.5	Diaspore	6.5-7.0		
Rutile	6.0-6.5	Garnet	6.5-7.5		

>7.0

Chert	7	Tripoli	7	Zircon	7.5
Novaculite	7	Emery	7.25	Corundum	9
Quartz	7	Andalusite	7.5	Diamond	10
Silica	7	Beryl	7.5-8.0		

Carbonate Rocks
Diatomite
Feldspar
Iron Oxide
Nepheline Syenite
Nitrogen Compounds
Phosphate Rock
Potash
Silica
Soda Ash
Sodium Sulfate
Sulphur
Zeolites

abt.	about	f.	fresh	m.v.	motor vessel
a/c	account	f.a.c.	forwarding agents commission	n.o.e.	not otherwise enumerated
ad val.	ad valorem			n.o.r.	notice of readiness
A.H.R.	Antwerp-Hamburg range	f.a.c.	fast as can	n.o.s.	not otherwise specified
a.p.	all purposes	f.a.c.c.o.p.	fast as can, custom of the port	n.r.t.	net registered tonnage
a.p.	additional premium			o.b.o.	ore/bulk/oil carrier
a.p.s.	arrival pilot station	f.a.f.	fuel adjustment factor	o/o	ore/oil carrier
a.p.t.	after peak tank	f.a.k.	freight all kinds	o/t	overtime
a.s.	alongside	f.a.s.	free alongside	p.f.t.	per freight ton
a.t.d.n.	any time day or night	f. & c.c.	full & complete cargo	p.l.t.c.	port liner term charges
b.	bale	f.c.l.	full container load	p.p.	posted price
b.a.f.	bunker adjustment factor	f.d.	free dispatch	ro-ro	roll-on roll-off
b.b.	below bridges	f.d.	free discharge	s.	summer
bdl.	bundle	f.d.& d.	freight, demurrage & defence	s.c.q.	special commodity quotation
b.h.p.	brake horse power	f.h.e.x.	Fridays & holidays excepted		
b/l	bill of lading	f.i.l.o.	free in liner out	secs.	seconds
blt.	built	f.i.l.t.d.	free in liner terms discharge	s.g.	specific gravity
b/n	booking note	f.i.o.	free in & out	s.h.e.x.	Sunday & holidays excepted
b/s	bunker surcharge	f.i.o.l.s. & d.	free in & out, lashed, secured & dunnaged		
bs/l	bills of lading			s.h.i.n.c.	Sunday & holidays included
c.a.b.a.f.	currency & bunker adjustment factor	f.i.o.s.	free in & out & stowed	s. & p.	sale & purchase
		f.i.o.t.	free in & out & trimmed	s.p.d.	steamer pays dues
c.a.d.	cash against documents	f.o.	free out	s.s.h.e.x.	Saturdays, Sundays & holidays excepted
c.a.f.	currency adjustment factor	f.o.b.	free on board		
c.b.r.	commodity box rate	f.o.q.	free on quay	s.s.h.i.n.c.	Saturdays, Sundays & holidays included
c&f	cost & freight	f.o.r.	free on rail		
c.f.s.	container freight station	f.o.s.	fuel oil surcharge	s.t.c.	said to contain
c.i.f.	cost, insurance, & freight	f.o.t.	free on truck	s.w.l.	safe working load
c.i.f.c.	cost, insurance, freight & commission	g.a.	general average	t.	metric ton
		G.M.T.	Greenwich Mean Time	T.A. round	trans-Atlantic round voyage
c.i.f.f.o.	cost, insurance & freight, free out	g.o.	gas oil	t.b.n.	to be nominated (a ship)
		g.p.	general purpose	t.d.w.	total deadweight
c.i.p.	calling in point	gr.	grain	t.i.r.	transport international routir
c.k.d.	completely knocked down	g.r.i.	general rate increase		
c.o.p.	custom of the port	g.r.t.	gross registered tonnage	t.l.o.	total loss only
c.o.w.	crude oil washing	h.f.o.	heavy fuel oil	t.p.c.	tonnes per centimeter
c/p	charter party	h.p.	horse power	t.p.d.	tonnes per day
c.p.d.	charterer pays dues	h.s.s	heavy grain, sorghum, & soya	t.p.i.	tons per inch
c.p.p.	clean petroleum products	h.w.	high water	t.t.	telegraphic transfer
cr.	credit	i.a.f.	inflation adjustment factor	u.l.c.c.	ultra large crude carrier
c.s.d.	closed shelter deck ship	i.c.d.	inland container depot	U.S.D.	United States Dollar
c.t.	conference terms	i.f.o.	intermediate fuel oil	u.u.	unless used
c.t.l.	constructive total loss	kt.	knot or 1 nautical mile/hour	v.a.t.	value added tax
cu. ft.	cubic feet	l/c	letter of credit	v/c	voyage charter
c.y.	container yard	l.c.l.	less than container load	v.l.c.c.	very large crude carrier
dets.	details	l.i.f.o.	liner in free out	voy.	voyage
dly.	delivery	l.n.g.	liquid or liquified natural gas	w.	weight
d.o.	diesel oil	l.o.a.	length overall	w.	winter
d.o.p.	dropping outward pilot	lo-lo	lift-on lift-off	w.e.f.	with effect from
d.p.p.	dirty petroleum products	l.p.g.	liquid or liquified petroleum gas	w.i.b.o.n.	whether in berth or not
d.t.	deep tank			w.i.f.p.o.n.	whether in free pratique or not
d.w.a.t.	deadweight all told	l.s.&d.	landing, storage & delivery		
d.w.c.c.	deadweight cargo capacity	l.t.	long ton	w.i.p.o.n.	whether in port or not
d.w.t.	deadweight	l.t.	liner terms	w/m	weight or measurement
d½d.	demurrage half dispatch	m.	meter	w.o.g.	without guarantee
e.i.u.	even if used	max.	maximum	w.p.	weather permitting
e.t.a.	estimated time of arrival	m.d.o.	marine diesel oil	w.t.s.	working time saves
e.t.c.	estimated time of completion	min.	minimum	w.w.r.	when where ready
e.t.d.	estimated time of departure	mol.	more or less		
e.t.r.	estimated time of readiness	m/r	mate's receipt		
e.t.s.	estimated time of sailing	m.t.	metric ton		

Multiplication factor	prefix	symbol
$1,000,000,000,000,000,000 = 10^{18}$	exa	E
$1,000,000,000,000,000 = 10^{15}$	peta	P
$1,000,000,000,000 = 10^{12}$	tera	T
$1,000,000,000 = 10^{9}$	giga	G
$1,000,000 = 10^{5}$	mega	M
$1,000 = 10^{3}$	kilo	k
$100 = 10^{2}$	hecto	h
$10 = 10^{1}$	deka	d
$0.1 = 10^{-1}$	deci	d
$0.01 = 10^{-2}$	centi	c
$0.001 = 10^{-3}$	milli	m
$0.000.001 = 10^{-6}$	micro	μ
$0.000.000.001 = 10^{-9}$	nano	n
$0.000.000.000.001 = 10^{-12}$	pico	p
$0.000.000.000.000.001 = 10^{-15}$	femto	f
$0.000.000.000.000.000.001 = 10^{-18}$	atto	a

LENGTH & SPEED

Multiply	by	to calculate	Multiply	by	to calculate
cm	0.393	inches	m/min	3.281	feet/sec
cm	0.01	m	m/min	0.05468	feet/sec
cm	10	mm	m/min	0.06	km/hr
fathom	6	feet	m/min	2.237	miles/hr
			m/min	0.03728	miles/min
feet	30.48	cm	m/sec	196.8	feet/min
feet	12	inches	m/sec	3.281	feet/sec
feet	0.3048	m	m/sec	3.6	km/hr
feet	0.3333	yard	m/sec	0.06	km/min
hectometers	100	m	m/sec	2.237	miles/hr
			m/sec	0.03728	miles/hr
inches	2.540	cm	microns	10^{-6}	m
inches	25.40	mm			
inches	12	feet	mile	1.609×10^{5}	cm
inches	36	yard	mile	5280	feet
km	10^{5}	cm	mile	1.609	km
km	3281	feet	mile	1760	yards
km	10^{3}	m	Multiply	by	to calculate
km	0.6214	miles	mile/hr	44.70	cm/sec
km	1094	yards	mile/hr	88	feet/min
km/hr	27.78	cm/sec	mile/hr	1.467	feet/sec
km/hr	54.68	feet/min	mile/hr	1.609	km/hr
km/hr	0.9113	feet/sec	mile/hr	0.8684	knots
km/hr	0.5396	knots	mile/hr	26.82	m/min
km/hr	16.67	m/min	mile/min	2682	cm/sec
km/hr	0.6214	miles/hr	mile/min	88	feet/sec
			mile/min	1.609	km/min
m	100	cm	mile/min	60	miles/hr
m	3.281	feet			
m	39.37	inches	mm	0.1	cm
m	10^{-3}	km	mm	0.03937	inches
m	10^{3}	mm	yard	91.44	cm
m	1.094	yards	yard	3	feet
			yard	36	inches
m/min	1.667	cm/sec	yard	0.9144	m

AREA

Multiply	by	to calculate	Multiply	by	to calculate
acre	0.404	ha	inch^2	6.452	cm^2
acre	43,560	feet^2	inch^2	6.944 x 10^{-3}	feet^2
acre	4047	m^2	inch^2	645.2	mm^2
acre	1.526 x 10^{-3}	mile^2			
acre	4840	yard^2	km^2	247.1	acres
ares	1076	feet^2	km^2	10.76 x 10^6	feet^2
ares	100	m^2	km^2	10^6	m^2
			km^2	0.3861	mile^2
board feet	144 inch^2 x 1 inch	inches^3	km^2	1.196 x 10^6	yard^2
board feet	1/12	feet^3			
			m^2	2.471 x 10^{-4}	acres
centares (centiares)	1	m^2	m^2	10.76	feet^2
			m^2	3.861 x 10^{-7}	mile^2
cm^2	1.076 x 10^{-3}	feet^2	m^2	1.196	yard^2
cm^2	0.1550	inch^2			
cm^2	10^{-4}	m^2	mile^2	640	acres
cm^2	100	mm^2	mile^2	27.88 x 10^6	feet^2
			mile^2	2.589	km^2
feet^2	2.296 x 10^{-5}	acres	mile^2	3.098 x 10^6	yard^2
feet^2	929.0	cm^2	mm^2	0.01	cm^2
feet^2	144	inch^2	mm^2	1.550 x 10^{-3}	inch^2
feet^2	0.09290	m^2			
feet^2	3.587 x 10^{-8}	miles^2	yard^2	2.066 x 10^{-4}	acres
feet^2	0.11111	yard^2	yard^2	9	feet^2
			yard^2	0.8361	m^2
ha	2.471	acres	yard^2	3.228 x 10^{-7}	mile^2
ha	1.076 x 10^5	feet^2			

CAPACITY & VOLUME

Multiply	by	to calculate	Multiply	by	to calculate
acre-feet	43,560	feet^3	cm^3	10^{-6}	m^3
acre-feet	325,851	gallons	cm^3	1.308 x 10^{-6}	yard^3
acre-feet	1233.49	m^3	cm^3	2.642 x 10^{-4}	gallons
			cm^3	10^{-3}	L
barrels (British dry)	5.780	feet^3	cm^3	2.113 x 10^{-3}	pints (liquid)
barrels (British dry)	0.1637	m^3	cm^3	1.057 x 10^{-3}	quarts (liquid)
barrels (British dry)	36	gallons (Imperial)	deciliters	0.1	L
barrels (US dry)	4.083	feet^3	dekaliters	10	L
barrels (US dry)	0.11562	m^3	feet^3	2.832 x 10^4	cm^3
barrels (US liquid)	4.211	feet^3	feet^3	0.02832	m^3
barrels (US liquid)	0.1192	m^3	feet^3	1728	inch^3
barrels (US liquid)	31.5	gallons (US)	feet^3	0.03704	yard^3
barrels (cement)	376	pounds - cement	feet^3	7.48052	gallons
barrels (cement)	0.17055	metric tons	feet^3	28.32	L
barrels (cement)	170.6	kg	feet^3	59.84	pints (liquid)
barrels (oil)	5.615	feet^3	feet^3	29.92	quarts (liquid)
barrels (oil)	0.1590	m^3			
barrels (oil)	42	gallons (oil)	US gallon	3785.434	cm^3
			US gallon	0.13368	feet^3
bags - cement	94	pounds - cement	US gallon	231	inch^3
			US gallon	3.785 x 10^{-3}	m^3
centiliters	0.01	L	US gallon	128	ounces (US fluid)
cm^3	0.061	inch^3	US gallon	4.951 x 10^{-3}	yard^3
cm^3	3.531 x 10^{-5}	feet^3	US gallon	3.78533	L
			US gallon	0.83267	Imperial gallon

CAPACITY & VOLUME

Multiply	by	to calculate	Multiply	by	to calculate
gallon	8	pints (liquid)	L	2.113	pints
gallon	4	quarts (liquid)	L	1.057	quarts
Imperial gallon	4516.086	cm^3	L/min	5.886 x 10^{-4}	feet^3/sec
Imperial gallon	1.20095	US gallon	L/min	4.403 x 10^{-3}	gallons/sec
Imperial gallon	10	pounds (avdp) water @ 62°F			
			m^3	10^6	cm^3
gallon water	8.3453	pounds water	m^3	35.314	feet^3
gallon/min.	2.228 v 10^{-3}	feet^3/sec.	m^3	61,023	inch^3
gallon/min.	0.06308	L/sec.	m^3	1.308	yards^3
gallon/min.	8.0208	feet^3/hr.	m^3	264.2	gallons
gallon water/min.	6.0086	tons water/24 hrs.	m^3	10^3	L
			m^3	2113	pints (liquid)
g/L	58.417	grains/gallon	m^3	1057	quarts (liquid)
g/L	8.345	pounds 1,000 gallons			
			mg/L	1	ppm
g/L	0.062427	pounds/foot^3			
g/L	1,000	ppm	million gallons/day	1.54723	feet^3/sec
hectoliters	100	L	ounce (fluid)	1.805	inch^3
			ounce (fluid)	0.02957	L
inch^3	16.387	cm^3			
inch^3	5.787 x 10^{-4}	feet^3	pint	0.568	L
inch^3	1.639 x 10^{-5}	m^3	ppm	0.0584	grains/US gallon
inch^3	2.143 x 10^{-5}	yard^3	ppm	0.07016	grains/Imp. gallon
inch^3	4.328 x 10^{-3}	gallons	ppm	8.345	pounds/million gallon
inch^3	1.639 x 10^{-2}	L			
inch^3	0.03463	pints (liquid)			
inch^3	0.01732	quarts (liquid)	quart (dry)	67.20	inch^3
			quart (liquid)	57.75	inch^3
kiloL	10^3	L	quart (liquid)	1.136	L
mL	10^{-3}	L	yard^3	7.646 x 10^5	cm^3
			yard^3	27	feet^3
L	10^3	cm	yard^3	46,656	inch^3
L	0.03531	feet^3	yard^3	0.7646	m^3
L	61.02	inches^3	yard^3	202.0	gallons
L	10^{-3}	cm	yard^3	764.6	L
L	1.308 x 10^{-3}	yards^3	yard^3	1616	pints (liquid)
L	0.2642	gallons	yard^3	807.9	quarts (liquid)

MASS & PRESSURE

Multiply	by	to calculate	Multiply	by	to calculate
atmospheres	76.0	cms. mercury	centals	100	pounds
atmospheres	29.92	inches mercury			
atmospheres	33.90	feet water	decigrams	0.1	g
atmospheres	10,333	kgs/m^2	dekagrams	10	g
atmospheres	14.70	pounds/inch^2			
atmospheres	1.058	tons/feet^2	drams	27.34375	grains
			drams	0.0625	ounces
centigrams	0.01	g	drams	1.771845	grams
cms. mercury	0.01316	atmospheres	feet water	0.02950	atmospheres
cms. mercury	0.4461	feet water	feet water	0.8826	inches mercury
cms. mercury	136.0	kgs/m^2	feet water	304.8	kgs/m^2
cms. mercury	27.85	pounds/foot^2	feet water	62.43	pounds/foot^2
cms. mercury	0.1934	pounds/inch^2	feet water	0.4335	pounds/inch^2
carats (metric)	3.0865	grains	grains (troy)	1	grains (avdp)
carats (metric)	0.2	grams	grains (troy)	0.06480	grams

MASS & PRESSURE

Multiply	by	to calculate
grains (troy)	0.04167	pennyweights (troy)
grains (troy)	2.0833×10^{-3}	ounces (troy)
grains/US gallon	17.118	ppm
grains/US gallon	142.86	pounds million gallon
grains/Imp. gallon	14.286	ppm
g	9980.7	dynes
g	15.43	grains
g	10^{-3}	kg
g	10^3	mg
g	0.03527	ounces (avdp)
g	0.03215	ounces (troy)
g	2.205×10^{-3}	pounds
g/m³	5.6000×10^{-3}	pounds/inch
g/cm³	62.43	pounds/foot³
g/cm³	0.03613	pounds/inch³
inches mercury	0.03342	atmospheres
inches mercury	1.133	feet water
inches mercury	345.3	kgs/m²
inches mercury	70.73	pounds/foot²
inches mercury	0.4912	pounds/inch²
inches water	0.002458	atmospheres
inches water	0.07355	inches mercury
inches water	25.40	kgs/m²
inches water	0.5781	ounces/inch²
inches water	5.202	pounds/foot²
inches water	0.03613	pounds/inch²
kg	980.663	dynes
kg	2.205	pounds (avdp)
kg	0.001102	short tons
kg	10^3	g
kg/m	0.6720	pounds/foot
kg/m²	9.678×10^{-5}	atmospheres
kg/m²	3.281×10^{-3}	feet water
kg/m²	2.896×10^{-3}	inches mercury
kg/m²	0.2048	pounds/foot²
kg/m²	1.422×10^{-3}	pounds/inch²
kg/mm²	10^6	kg/m²
milliers	10^3	kg
mg	10^{-3}	g
ounce (avdp)	16	drams
ounce (avdp)	437.5	grains
ounce (avdp)	0.025	pounds
ounce (avdp)	28.349527	g
ounce (avdp)	0.9115	ounces (troy)
ounce (avdp)	2.790×10^{-5}	long tons
ounce (avdp)	2.835×10^{-5}	metric tonnes
ounce (troy)	480	grains
ounce (troy)	20	pennyweights (troy)
ounce (troy)	0.08333	pounds (troy)
ounce (troy)	31.103481	g
ounce (troy)	1.09714	ounces (avdp)
ounces/inch²	0.0625	pounds/inch²
pennyweight (troy)	24	grains
pennyweight (troy)	1.55517	grams
pennyweight (troy)	0.05	ounces (troy)

Multiply	by	to calculate
pennyweight (troy)	4.1667×10^{-3}	pounds (troy)
pound (avdp)	16	ounces
pound (avdp)	256	drams
pound (avdp)	7000	grains
pound (avdp)	0.0005	short tons
pound (avdp)	453.5924	grams
pound (avdp)	1.21528	pounds (troy)
pound (avdp)	14.5833	ounces (troy)
pound (avdp)	0.453	kg
pound (troy)	5760	grains
pound (troy)	240	pennyweights (troy)
pound (troy)	12	ounces (troy)
pound (troy)	373.24177	grams
pound (troy)	0.822857	pounds (avdp)
pound (troy)	13.1657	ounces (avdp)
pound (troy)	3.6735×10^{-4}	long tons
pound (troy)	4.1143×10^{-4}	short tons
pound (troy)	3.7324×10^{-4}	metric tonne
pounds water	0.01602	feet³
pounds water	27.68	inch³
pounds water	0.1198	gallons
pounds water/min	2.670×10^{-4}	feet³/sec
pound/foot³	0.01602	g/cm³
pound/foot³	16.02	kg/m³
pound/foot³	5.787×10^{-4}	pounds/inch³
pound/inch³	27.68	g/cm³
pound/inch³	2.768×10^4	kg/m³
pound/inch³	1728	pounds/foot³
pound/foot²	0.01602	feet water
pound/foot²	4.883	kg/m²
pound/foot²	6.945×10^{-3}	pounds/inch²
pound/inch²	0.06804	atmospheres
pound/inch²	2.307	feet water
pound/inch²	2.036	inches mercury
pound/inch²	703.1	kg/m²
stones (British)	6.350	kg
stones (British)	14	pounds
assay tons	29.17	g
long ton	1016	kg
long ton	2240	pounds
long ton	1.12000	short ton
long ton	1.016	metric ton
metric tonne	10^3	kg
metric tonne	2205	pounds
metric tonne	0.984	long ton
metric tonne	1.102	short tons
short ton	2000	pounds
short ton	32000	ounces
short ton	907.18486	kg
short ton	2430.56	pounds (troy)
short ton	0.89287	long ton
short ton	29166.66	ounces (troy)
short ton	0.90718	metric tonne

THERMAL & POWER UNITS

Multiply	by	to calculate	Multiply	by	to calculate
BTU	0.2520	kg-calories	kg-calories	3.968	BTU
BTU	777.5	foot-pounds	kg-calories	3086	foot-pound
BTU	3.927×10^{-4}	Horse-power-hrs	kg-calories	$1,558 \times 10^{-3}$	horse-power-hrs
BTU	107.5	kg-m	kg-calories	1.162×10^{-3}	Kw-hrs
BTU	2.928×10^{-4}	Kw-hrs			
			Kw	3415	BTU/min
foot-pound	1.286×10^{-3}	BTU	Kw	4.425×10^{4}	foot-pound/min
foot-pound	5.050×10^{-7}	Horse-power-hrs	Kw	737.6	foot-pound/sec
foot-pound	3.241×10^{-4}	kg-calories	Kw	1.341	horse-power
foot-pound	0.1383	kg-m	Kw	14.34	kg-calories/min
foot-pound	3.766×10^{-7}	Kw-hrs	Kw	10^{3}	watts
			Kw-hrs	3415	BTU
horse-power	42.44	BTU/min.	Kw-hrs	2.655×10^{6}	foot-pound
horse-power	33,000	foot-pound/min.	Kw-hrs	1.341	horse-power-hrs
horse-power	550	foot-pound/sec.	Kw-hrs	860.5	kg-calories
horse-power	1.014	horse-power (metric)	Kw-hrs	3.671×10^{5}	kg-m
horse-power	10.70	kg-calories/min.			
horse-power	0.7457	Kw	watt	0.01434	kg-calories/min
horse-power	745.7	watts	watt	10^{-3}	Kw
horse-power (boiler)	33,479	BTU/hr	watt-hrs	3.415	BTU
horse-power (boiler)	9.803	BTU/hr	watt-hrs	2655	foot-pounds
horse-power-hrs	2,547	BTU	watt-hrs	1.341×10^{-3}	horse-power-hrs
horse-power-hrs	1.98×10^{5}	foot-pound	watt-hrs	0.8605	kg-calories
horse-power-hrs	641.7	kg-calories	watt-hrs	367.1	kg-m
horse-power-hrs	2.737×10^{5}	kg-m	watt-hrs	10^{-3}	Kw-hrs
horse-power-hrs	0.7457	Kw-hrs			

ATOMIC WEIGHTS OF ELEMENTS

	Symbol	Atomic weight		Symbol	Atomic weight		Symbol	Atomic weight
Aluminum	Al	26.9	Holmium	Ho	163.4	Radon	Rn	222.0
Antimony	Sb	121.7	Hydrogen	H	1.0	Rhodium	Rh	102.9
Argon	A	39.9	Indium	In	114.8	Rubidium	Rb	85.4
Arsenic	As	74.9	Iodine	I	126.9	Ruthenium	Ru	101.7
Barium	Ba	137.3	Iridium	Ir	193.1	Samarium	Sa	150.4
Beryllium	Be	9.0	Iron	Ge	55.8	Scandium	Sc	45.1
Bismuth	Bi	209.0	Krypton	Kr	82.9	Selenium	Se	79.2
Boron	B	10.8	Lanthanum	La	138.9	Silicon	Si	28.0
Bromine	Br	79.9	Lead	Pb	206.0	Silver	Ag	107.8
Cadmium	Cd	112.4	Lithium	Li	6.9	Sodium	Na	22.9
Cesium	Cs	132.8	Lutecium	Lu	175.0	Strontium	Sr	87.6
Calcium	Ca	40.0	Magnesium	Mg	24.3	Sulfur	S	32.0
Carbon	C	12.0	Manganese	Mn	54.9	Tantalum	Ta	181.5
Cerium	Ce	140.2	Mercury	Hg	200.6	Tellurium	Te	127.5
Chlorine	Cl	35.4	Molybdenum	Mo	96.0	Terbium	Tb	159.2
Chromium	Cr	52.0	Neodymium	Nd	144.2	Thallium	Tl	204.3
Cobalt	Co	58.9	Neon	Ne	20.2	Thorium	Th	232.1
Columbium - see niobium			Nickel	Ni	58.6	Thulium	Tm	169.4
Copper	Cu	63.5	Niobium	Nb	93.1	Tin	Sn	118.7
Dysprosium	Dy	162.5	Nitrogen	N	14.0	Titanium	Ti	48.1
Erbium	Er	167.7	Osmium	Os	190.8	Tungsten	W	184.0
Europium	Eu	152.0	Oxygen	O	16.0	Uranium	U	238.1
Fluorine	F	19.0	Palladium	Pd	106.7	Vanadium	V	50.9
Gadolinium	Gd	72.6	Phosphorus	P	31.0	Xenon	Xe	130.2
Gallium	Ga	69.7	Platinum	Pt	195.2	Ytterbium	Yb	173.6
Germanium	Ge	72.6	Potassium	K	39.0	Yttrium	Y	88.9
Gold	Au	197.2	Praseodymium	Pr	140.9	Zinc	Zn	65.3
Helium	He	4.0	Radium	Ra	225.9	Zirconium	Zr	91.0

	Basic indicators Area (000' sq. km)	Population growth & projections				Urban Population as % of population	Structure of production					
		1991	2000	2025	Avg 1991-2000		GDP	GDP\capita	GDP Agriculture %	GDP Industry %	GDP Manufacturing %	GDP Services (%)
Algeria	2,382	26	33	53	3	53	32,678	1,257	14	50	10	36
Argentina	2,767	33	36	43	1	87	114,344	3,465	15	40		46
Armenia	30	3	4	5	2	68						
Australia	7,687	17	19	23	1	86	299,800	17,635	3	31	15	65
Austria	84	8	8	8	0	59	163,992	20,499	3	36	25	61
Azerbaijan	87	7	8	11	1	54						
Bangladesh	144	111	131	180	2	17	23,394	211	36	16	9	48
Belarus	208	10	11	11	0	66						
Belgium	31	10	10	10	0	97	196,873	19,687	2	30	22	68
Benin	113	5	6	11	3	38	1,886	377	37	14	9	49
Bhutan	47	1	2	3	2	6	240	240	43	27	10	29
Bolivia	1,099	7	9	14	2	52	5,019	717				
Botswana	582	1	2	3	3	29	3,644	3,644	5	54	4	41
Brazil	8,512	151	172	224	1	76	414,061	2,742	10	39	26	51
Bulgaria	111	9	9	8	(0)	68	7,909	879	13	50		37
Burkina Faso	274	9	12	23	3	9	2,629	292	44	20	12	37
Burundi	28	6	7	14	3	6	1,035	173	55	16	12	29
Cameroon	475	12	16	29	3	42	11,666	972	27	22	12	51
Canada	9,976	27	29	34	1	77	510,835	18,920				
Central African Rep.	623	3	4	7	3	48	1,202	401	41	16		42
Chad	1,284	6	7	14	3	30	1,236	206	43	18	16	39
Chile	757	13	15	19	1	86	31,311	2,409				
China	9,561	1,150	1,290	1,569	1	60	369,651	321	27	42	38	32
Colombia	1,139	33	38	50	2	71	41,692	1,263	17	35	20	48
Congo	342	2	3	6	3	41	2,909	1,455	12	37	8	50
Costa Rica	51	3	4	5	2	48	5,560	1,853	18	25	19	56
Cote d'Ivoire	322	12	17	32	3	41	7,283	607	38	22	21	40
Czechoslovakia	128	16					33,172	2,073	8	56		36
Denmark	43	5	5	5	0	87	112,084	22,417	5	28	19	67
Dominican Rep.	49	7	8	11	2	61	7,172	1,025	18	25	13	57
Ecuador	284	11	13	18	2	57	11,595	1,054	15	35	21	50
Egypt, Arab Rep.	1,001	54	65	92	2	47	30,265	560	18	30		52
El Salvador	21	5	6	9	2	45	5,915	1,183	10	24	19	66
Estonia	45	2	2	2		72						
Ethiopia	1,222	53	67	130	3	13	5,982	113	47	13	9	40
Finland	338	5	5	5	0	60	110,033	22,007	6	34	24	60
France	552	57	59	63	0	74	1,199,286	21,040	3	29	21	68
Gabon	268	1	2	3	3	47	4,863	4,863	9	45	6	46
Georgia	70	5	6	6	0	56						
Germany	357	80	80	75			1,574,316	19,679	2	39	23	59
Ghana	239	15	20	36	3	33	6,413	428	53	17	10	29
Greece	132	10	10	10	0	63	57,900	5,790	17	27	14	56
Guatemala	109	9	12	21	3	40	9,353	1,039	26	20		55
Guinea	246	6	8	14	3	26	2,937	490	29	35	5	36
Guinea-Bissau	36	1	1	2	2	20	211	211	46	12	8	42
Haiti	28	7	8	10	2	29	2,641	377				
Honduras	112	5	7	11	3	45	2,661	532	22	27	16	51
Hong Kong	1	6	6	7	1	94	67,555	11,259		25	17	75
Hungary	93	10	10	10	(0)	62	30,795	3,080	10	34	29	55
India	3,288	866	1,017	1,365	2	27	221,925	256	31	27	18	41
Indonesia	1,905	181	206	265	1	31	116,476	644	19	41	21	39
Iran, Islamic Rep.	1,648	58	78	160	3	57	96,989	1,672	21	21	9	58
Ireland	70	4	4	4	0	57	39,028	9,757	11	9	3	80
Israel	21	5	6	8	3	92	62,687	12,537				
Italy	301	58	58	55	0	69	1,150,516	19,836	3	33	21	64
Jamaica	11	2	2	3	1	53	3,497	1,749	5	40	17	56
Japan	378	124	127	126	0	77	3,362,282	27,115			25	56
Jordan	89	4	5	9	4	69	3,524	881	7	26	13	67
Kazakhstan	2,717	17	18	22	1	57						
Kenya	580	25	34	73	4	24	7,125	285	27	22	12	51
Korea, Rep.	99	43	47	53	1	73	282,970	6,581	8	45	28	47
Kyrgyzstan	199	4	5	7	1	38						
Lao PDR	237	4	6	10	3	19	1,027	257				
Latvia	65	3	3	3	(0)	71			20	48	41	32

HOW BIG IS THE MARKET?

Basic indicators	Area (000' sq. km)	Population growth & projections 1991	2000	2025	Avg 1991-2000	Urban Population as % of population	Structure of production GDP	GDP\capita	GDP Agriculture %	GDP Industry %	GDP Manufacturing %	GDP Services (%)
Lesotho	30	2	2	3	2	21	578	289	14	38	13	48
Lithuania	65	4	4	4	0	68			20	45		35
Madagascar	587	12	15	26	3	25	2,488	207	33	14		53
Malawi	118	9	12	24	3	12	1,986	221	35	20	13	45
Malaysia	330	18	22	31	2	44	46,980	2,610				
Mali	1,240	9	11	24	3	20	2,451	272	44	12	11	43
Mauritania	1,026	2	3	5	3	48	1,030	515	22	31		47
Mauritius	2	1	1	1		41	2,253	2,253	11	33	23	56
Mexico		99	136		2	73	282,526	3,404	9	30	22	61
Moldova	34	4	4	5	0	47						
Morocco	447	26	31	45	2	49	27,652	1,064	19	31	18	50
Mozambique	802	16	21	43	3	28	1,219	76	64	15		21
Namibia	824	1	2	3	3	28	1,961	1,961	10	28	4	62
Nepal	141	19	24	38	3	10	3,063	161	59	14	5	27
Netherlands	37	15	16	16	1	89	290,725	19,382	4	32	20	64
New Zealand	271	3	4	4	1	84	42,861	14,287	9	27	18	65
Nicaragua	130	4	5	8	3	60	6,950	1,738	30	23	19	47
Niger	1,267	8	11	24	4	20	2,284	286	38	19	8	42
Nigeria	924	99	128	217	3	36	34,124	345	37	38		26
Norway	324	4	4	5	0	75	105,929	26,482	3	36	14	62
Oman	212	2	2	5	4	11	10,236	5,118	4	52	4	44
Pakistan	796	116	148	244	3	33	40,244	347	26	26	17	49
Panama	77	2	3	4	2	54	5,544	2,772	10	11		79
Papua New Guinea	463	4	5	7	2	16	3,734	934	26	35	10	38
Paraguay	407	4	6	9	3	48	6,254	1,564	22	24	18	54
Peru	1,285	22	26	36	2	71	48,366	2,198				
Philippines	300	63	74	102	2	43	44,908	713	21	34	26	44
Poland	313	38	39	43	0	62	78,031	2,053	7	50		43
Portugal	92	10	10	10		34	65,103	6,510				
Puerto Rico	9	4	4	5	1	75	32,469	8,117	1	41	39	57
Romania	238	23	23	25	0	53	27,619	1,201	19	49		33
Russian Federation	17,075	149	149	153		74			13	48		39
Rwanda	26	7	9	17	2	8	1,579	226	38	22	20	40
Saudi Arabia	2,150	15	21	41	4	78	108,640	7,243	7	52	7	41
Senegal	197	8	10	18	3	39	5,774	722	20	19	13	62
Sierra Leone	72	4	5	10	3	33	743	186	43	14	3	43
Singapore	1	3	3	4	2	100	39,984	13,328		38	29	62
South Africa	1,221	39	47	69	2	60	91,167	2,338	5	44	25	51
Spain	505	39	39	39	0	79	527,131	13,516				
Sri Lanka	66	17	19	24	1	22	8,195	482	27	25	14	48
Sudan	2,506	26	34	60	3	22						
Sweden	450	9	9	10	1	84	206,411	22,935			22	63
Switzerland	41	7	7	7	1	60	232,000	33,143				
Syrian Arab Rep.	185	13	17	34	3	51	17,236	1,326	30	23		47
Taiwan, China												
Tajikistan	143	5	7	13	3	32						
Tanzania	945	25	33	59	3	34	2,223	89	61	5	4	34
Thailand	513	57	65	82	1	23	93,310	1,637	12	39	27	49
Togo	57	4	5	9	3	26	1,633	408	33	23	10	44
Trinidad and Tobago	5	1	1	2	1	70	4,920	4,920	3	39	9	58
Tunisia	164	8	10	13	2	55	11,594	1,449	18	32	17	50
Turkey	779	57	68	91	2	63	95,763	1,680	18	34	24	49
Turkmenistan	488	4	5	8	3							
Uganda	236	17	23	48	3	11	2,527	149	51	12	4	37
Ukraine	604	52	52	52		67						
United Kingdom	245	58	58	60	0	89	876,758	15,117				
United States	9,373	253	274	319	1	75	5,610,800	22,177				
Uruguay	177	3	3	4	1	86	9,479	3,160	10	32	25	58
Uzbekistan	447	21	26	42	2	41						
Venezuela	912	20	23	32	2	85	53,440	2,672	5	47	17	48
Yemen, Rep.	528	13	17	37	4	30	7,524	579	22	26	9	52
Yugoslavia	256	24					82,317	3,430	12	48		40
Zambia	753	8	11	21	3	51	3,831	479	16	47	36	37
Zimbabwe	391	10	12	18	2	28	5,543	554	20	32	26	49

NATIONAL CURRENCY PER US DOLLAR

Country	Currency	1980	1981	1982	1983	1984	1985	1986	1987
Afghanistan	Afghani	44.129	49.481	50.600	50.600	50.600	50.600	50.600	50.600
Algeria	Dinar	3.838	4.316	4.592	4.789	4.983	5.028	4.702	4.850
Antigua & Barbuba	$E. Carib.	2.700	2.700	2.700	2.700	2.700	2.700	2.700	2.700
Argentina*	Pesos	0.01837	0.04403	0.25923	1.05300	0.00676	0.06018	0.09430	0.21443
Aruba	Aruban Florin							1.7900	1.7900
Australia	$Australian	0.8776	0.8701	0.9829	1.1082	1.1369	1.4269	1.4905	1.4267
Austria	Schilling	12.938	15.927	17.059	17.963	20.009	20.690	15.267	12.643
The Bahamas	$Bahamian	1.000	1.000	1.000	1.000	1.000	1.000	1.000	1.000
Bahrain	Dinar	0.3770	0.3760	0.3760	0.3760	0.3760	0.3760	0.3760	0.3760
Bangladesh	Taka	15.454	17.987	22.118	24.615	25.354	27.995	30.407	30.950
Barbados	$Barbados	2.0113	2.0113	2.0113	2.0113	2.0113	2.0113	2.0113	2.0113
Belgium	Franc	29.242	37.129	45.691	51.132	57.784	59.378	44.672	37.334
Belize	$Belize	2.0000	2.0000	2.0000	2.0000	2.0000	2.0000	2.0000	2.0000
Benin	Franc	211.28	271.73	328.61	381.06	436.96	449.26	346.30	300.54
Bhutan	Ngultrum	7.863	8.659	9.455	10.099	11.363	12.369	12.611	12.962
Bolivia**	Bolivianos	24.5	24.5	64.1	231.6	3135.9	0.4400	1.9220	2.0549
Botswana	Pula	0.7769	0.8330	1.0216	1.0960	1.2839	1.8882	1.8678	1.6778
Brazil***	Cruzados Reals	0.05	0.09	0.18	0.58	1.85	0.01	0.01	0.04
Burkino Faso	Franc	211.28	271.73	328.61	381.06	436.96	449.26	346.30	300.54
Burundi	Franc	90.00	90.00	90.00	92.95	119.71	120.69	114.17	123.56
Cameroon	Franc	211.28	271.73	328.61	381.06	436.96	449.26	346.30	300.54
Canada	$Canadian	1.1692	1.1989	1.2337	1.2324	1.2951	1.3655	1.3895	1.3260
Cape Verde	Escudos	40.175	48.695	58.293	71.686	84.878	91.632	80.145	72.466
Central African Rep	Franc	211.28	271.73	328.61	381.06	436.96	449.26	346.30	300.54
Chad	Franc	211.28	271.73	328.61	381.06	436.96	449.26	346.30	300.54
Chile	Pesos	39.000	39.000	50.909	78.842	98.656	161.081	193.016	219.540
China	Yuan	1.4984	1.7045	1.8925	1.9757	2.3200	2.9367	3.4528	3.7221
Colombia	Pesos	47.28	54.49	64.09	78.85	100.82	142.31	194.26	242.61
Congo	Franc	211.28	271.73	328.61	381.06	436.96	449.26	346.30	300.54
Costa Rica	Colones	8.57	21.76	37.41	41.09	44.53	50.45	55.99	62.78
Côte d'Ivoire	Franc	211.28	271.73	328.61	381.06	436.96	449.26	346.30	300.54
Cyprus	Pound	0.3529	0.4197	0.4746	0.5259	0.5869	0.6095	0.5167	0.4807
Czech Rep.	Koruna	-	-	-	-	-	-	-	-
Czechoslovakia	Koruny	14.27	13.25	13.71	14.16	16.61	17.14	14.99	13.69
Denmark	Krone	5.636	7.123	8.332	9.145	10.357	10.596	8.091	6.840
Djibouti	Francs	177.72	177.72	177.72	177.72	177.72	177.72	177.72	177.72
Dominica	$E. Carib.	2.7000	2.7000	2.7000	2.7000	2.7000	2.7000	2.7000	2.7000
Dominican Rep	Pesos	1.000	1.000	1.000	1.000	1.000	3.113	2.904	3.845
Ecuador	Sucres	25.0	25.0	30.0	44.1	62.5	69.6	122.8	170.5
Egypt	Po0==*und	0.7000	0.7000	0.7000	0.7000	0.7000	0.7000	0.7000	0.7000
El Salvador	Colones	2.500	2.500	2.500	2.500	2.500	2.500	5.000	5.000
Equitorial Guinea	Bipkwele/Francs	211.28	271.73	328.60	381.06	436.95	449.26	346.30	300.54
Ethiopia	Birr	2.0700	2.0700	2.0700	2.0700	2.0700	2.0700	2.0700	2.0700
Fiji	$Fiji	0.8180	0.8546	0.9324	1.0170	1.0826	1.1536	1.1329	1.2439
Finland	Markkaa	3.7301	4.3153	4.8204	5.5701	6.0100	6.1979	5.0695	4.3956
France	Franc	4.2256	5.4346	6.5210	7.6213	8.7391	8.9852	6.9261	6.0107
Gabon	Franc	211.28	271.73	328.61	381.06	436.96	449.26	346.30	300.54
The Gambia	Dalasi	1.721	1.990	2.290	2.639	3.584	3.894	6.938	7.074
Germany	Deutschemark	1.8177	2.2600	2.4266	2.5533	2.8459	2.9440	2.1715	1.7974
Ghana	Cedi	2.75	2.75	2.75	8.83	35.99	54.37	89.20	153.73
Greece	Drachma	42.62	55.41	66.80	88.06	112.72	138.12	139.98	135.43
Grenada#	$E. Carib.	2.700	2.700	2.700	2.700	2.700	2.700	2.700	2.700
Guatamala	Quetzales	1.0000	1.0000	1.0000	1.0000	1.0000	1.0000	1.8750	2.5000
Guyana	$Guyana	2.6	2.8	3.0	3.0	3.8	4.3	4.3	9.8
Haiti#	Gourdes	5.00	5.00	5.00	5.00	5.00	5.00	5.00	5.00
Honduras#	Lempiras	2.0000	2.0000	2.0000	2.0000	2.0000	2.0000	2.0000	2.0000
Honk Kong	HK$						7.818	7.791	7.803	7.798
Hungary	Forint	32.532	34.314	36.631	42.671	48.042	50.119	45.832	46.971
Iceland	Kronur	4.798	7.224	12.352	24.843	31.694	41.508	41.104	36.677

1988	1989	1990	1991	1992	1993	1994	Currency	Country
50.600	50.600	50.600	50.600	50.600	50.600		Afghani	Afghanistan
5.915	7.609	8.958	18.473	21.836	23.345		Dinar	Algeria
2.700	2.700	2.700	2.700	2.700	2.700	2.700	$E. Carib.	Antigua & Barbuba
0.87526	0.04233	0.48759	0.95355	0.99064	0.99895	0.99900	Pesos	Argentina*
1.7900	1.7900	1.7900	1.7900	1.7900	1.7900		Aruban Florin	Aruba
1.2752	1.2618	1.2799	1.2835	1.3600	1.4703	1.3499	$Australian	Australia
12.348	13.231	11.370	11.676	10.989	11.632	10.682	Schilling	Austria
1.000	1.000	1.000	1.000	1.000	1.000		$Bahamian	The Bahamas
0.3760	0.3760	0.3760	0.3760	0.3760	0.3760		Dinar	Bahrain
31.733	32.270	34.569	36.596	38.951	39.567		Taka	Bangladesh
2.0113	2.0113	2.0113	2.0113	2.0113	2.0113		$Barbados	Barbados
36.768	39.404	33.418	34.148	32.150	34.597	30.770	Franc	Belgium
2.0000	2.0000	2.0000	2.0000	2.0000	2.0000		$Belize	Belize
297.85	319.01	272.26	282.11	264.69	283.16		Franc	Benin
13.917	16.226	17.504	22.742	25.918	30.493		Ngultrum	Bhutan
2.3502	2.6917	3.1727	3.5806	3.9005	4.2651		Bolivianos	Bolivia**
1.8159	2.0124	1.8600	2.0170	2.1320	2.4189		Pula	Botswana
0.26	-	0.07	0.41	4.51	88.45	0.84	Cruzados Reals	Brazil***
297.85	319.01	272.26	282.11	264.69	283.16		Franc	Burkino Faso
140.40	158.67	171.26	181.51	208.30	242.78		Franc	Burundi
297.85	319.01	272.26	282.11	264.69	283.16		Franc	Cameroon
1.2307	1.1840	1.1668	1.1457	1.2087	1.2901	1.3557	$Canadian	Canada
72.068	77.978	70031.000	71.408	68.018	80.427		Escudos	Cape Verde
297.85	319.01	272.26	282.11	264.69	283.16		Franc	Central African Rep
297.85	319.01	272.26	282.11	264.69	283.16		Franc	Chad
245.048	267.155	305.062	349.373	362.588	404.350	399.770	Pesos	Chile
3.7221	3.7651	4.7832	5.3234	5.5146	5.7620	8.5113	Yuan	China
299.17	382.57	502.26	633.05	759.28	863.06	837.21	Pesos	Colombia
297.85	319.01	272.26	282.11	264.69	283.16		Franc	Congo
75.80	81.50	91.58	122.43	134.51	142.17		Colones	Costa Rica
297.85	319.01	272.26	282.11	264.69	283.16		Franc	Côte d'Ivoire
0.4663	0.4933	0.4572	0.4615	0.4502	0.4970		Pound	Cyprus
-	-	-	-	-	29.15	27.34	Koruna	Czech Rep.
14.36	15.05	17.95	29.48	28.26	-	-	Koruny	Czechoslovakia
6.732	7.310	6.189	6.396	6.036	6.484	5.856	Krone	Denmark
177.72	177.72	177.72	177.72	177.72	177.72		Francs	Djibouti
2.7000	2.7000	2.7000	2.7000	2.7000	2.7000		$E. Carib.	Dominica
6.113	6.340	8.525	12.692	12.774	12.679		Pesos	Dominican Rep
301.6	526.3	767.8	1,046.2	1,534.0	na	2,265.0	Sucres	Ecuador
0.7000	1.1000	2.0000	3.3000	3.3303	3.3704	3.3881	Pound	Egypt
5.000	5.000	8.030	8.080	9.170	8.670		Colones	El Salvador
297.85	319.01	272.26	282.11	264.69	283.16		Bipkwele/Francs	Equitorial Guinea
2.0700	2.0700	2.0700	2.0700	5.0000	5.0000		Birr	Ethiopia
1.4303	1.4833	1.4809	1.4756	1.5030	1.5418		$Fiji	Fiji
4.1828	4.2912	3.8235	4.0440	4.4794	5.7123	4.6630	Markkaa	Finland
5.9569	6.3801	5.4453	5.6421	5.2938	5.6632	5.1940	Franc	France
297.85	319.01	272.26	282.11	264.69	283.16		Franc	Gabon
6.709	7.585	.6157	1.6595	1.5617	1.6533	1.5180	Deutschemark	Germany
202.35	270.00	326.33	367.83	437.09	641.83		Cedi	Ghana
141.86	162.42	158.51	182.27	190.62	229.25	234.00	Drachma	Greece
2.700	2.700	2.700	2.700	2.700	2.700		$E. Carib.	Grenada#
2.6196	2.8161	4.4858	5.0289	5.1706	5.6354		Quetzales	Guatamala
10.0	27.2	39.5	111.8	125.0	126.7		$Guyana	Guyana
5.00	5.00	5.00	5.00	5.00	na		Gourdes	Haiti#
2.0000	2.0000	2.0000	5.4000	5.8300	7.2600		Lempiras	Honduras#
7.806	7.800	7.789	7.771	7.741	7.736	7.730	HK$	Hong Kong
50.413	59.066	63.206	74.735	78.988	91.933	106.920	Forint	Hungary
43.014	57.042	58.284	58.996	57.546	67.603		Kronur	Iceland
13.917	16.226	17.504	22.742	25.918	30.493	31.330	Rupees	India

NATIONAL CURRENCY PER US DOLLAR

Country	Currency	1980	1981	1982	1983	1984	1985	1986	1987
India	Rupees	7.863	8.659	9.455	10.099	11.363	12.369	12.611	12.962
Indonesia	Rupiah	630.0	631.8	661.4	909.3	1,025.9	1,110.6	1,282.6	1,643.8
Iran	Rial	70.615	78.328	83.602	86.358	90.030	91.052	78.760	71.460
Iraq	Dinar	0.2953	0.2953	0.2984	0.3109	0.3109	0.3109	0.3109	0.3109
Ireland	Punt	0.4859	0.6185	0.7031	0.8012	0.9199	0.9384	0.7454	0.6720
Israel	New Sheqalim	0.0050	0.0114	0.0243	0.0562	0.2932	1.1788	1.4878	1.5946
Italy	Lira	856.4	1,136.8	1,352.5	1,518.8	1,757.0	1,909.4	1,490.8	1,296.1
Jamaica	$Jamaica	1.781	1.781	1.781	1.932	3.943	5.559	5.478	5.487
Japan	Yen	226.74	220.54	249.08	237.51	237.52	238.54	168.52	144.64
Jordan	Dinar	0.2981	0.3301	0.3523	0.3630	0.3841	0.3940	0.3499	0.3387
Kenya	Shilling	7.420	9.048	10.922	13.312	14.414	16.432	16.226	16.454
Korea, South	Won	607.43	681.03	731.08	775.75	805.98	870.02	881.45	822.57
Kuwait	Dinar	0.2703	0.2787	0.2879	0.2915	0.2960	0.3007	0.2919	0.2786
Lebanon	Pound	3.4	4.3	4.7	4.5	6.5	16.4	38.4	224.6
Lesotho	Maloti	0.7780	0.8702	1.0817	1.1122	1.4380	2.1911	2.2686	2.0350
Liberia	$Liberian	1.0000	1.0000	1.0000	1.0000	1.0000	1.0000	1.0000	1.0000
Libya	Dinar	0.2961	0.2961	0.2961	0.2961	0.2961	0.2961	0.3139	0.2706
Luxembourg	Franc	29.242	37.129	45.691	51.132	57.784	59.378	44.672	37.334
Madagascar	Franc	311.3	271.7	349.7	430.4	576.6	662.5	676.3	1,069.2
Malawi	Kwacha	0.8121	0.8953	1.0555	1.1748	1.4134	1.7191	1.8611	2.2087
Malaysia	Ringgit	2.1769	2.3041	2.3354	2.3213	2.3436	2.4830	2.5814	2.5196
Maldives	Rufiyaa	7.550	7.550	7.174	7.050	7.050	7.098	7.151	9.223
Mali	Franc	211.280	271.730	328.610	381.060	436.960	449.260	346.300	
Malta	Lira	0.3453	0.3862	0.4118	0.4322	0.4604	0.4676	0.3924	0.3451
Mauritania	Ouguiyas	45.914	48.296	51.769	54.812	63.803	77.085	74.375	73.878
Mauritius	Rupees	7.684	8.937	10.873	11.706	13.800	15.442	13.466	12.878
Mexico	Pesos			0.1	0.1	0.2	0.3	0.6	1.4
Morocco	Dirham	3.937	5.172	6.023	7.111	8.811	10.063	9.104	8.359
Mozambique	Meticais	36.72	40.07	42.81	45.55	48.11	48.94	45.82	329.53
Myanmar (Burma)	Kyat	12.000	12.336	13.244	14.545	16.459	18.246	21.230	21.819
Netherlands	Guilder	1.9881	2.4952	2.6702	2.8541	3.2087	3.3214	2.4500	2.0257
Netherlands Antilles	Guilder	1.800	1.800	1.800	1.800	1.800	1.800	1.800	1.800
New Zealand	$New Zealand	1.0265	1.1494	1.3300	1.4952	1.7286	2.0064	1.9088	1.6886
Nicaragua****	Gold Cordobas	2.95	2.95	2.95	2.95	2.95	7.77	19.50	20.53
Niger	Franc	211.28	271.73	328.61	381.06	436.96	449.26	346.30	300.54
Nigeria	Naira	0.547	0.618	0.673	0.724	0.767	0.894	1.755	4.016
Norway	Kroner	4.9392	5.7395	6.4554	7.2964	8.1615	8.5972	7.3947	6.7375
Oman#	Rials Omani	0.3454	0.3454	0.3454	0.3454	0.3454	0.3454	0.3845	0.3845
Pakistan	Rupees	9.900	9.900	11.847	13.117	14.046	15.928	16.648	17.399
Panama#	Balboas	1.000	1.000	1.000	1.000	1.000	1.000	1.000	1.000
Papua New Guinea	Kina	0.6704	0.6724	0.7375	0.8341	0.8942	1.0000	0.9713	0.9081
Paraguay	Guaranies	126.0	126.0	126.0	126.0	201.0	306.7	339.2	550.0
Peru*****	New Soles	288.9	422.3	697.6	1,628.6	3,466.9	10,974.9	13,947.5	16,835.8
Philippines	Pesos	7.511	7.900	8.540	11.113	16.699	18.607	20.386	20.568
Poland	Zloty	44	51	85	92	114	147	175	265
Portugal	Escudos	50.06	61.55	79.48	110.78	146.39	170395.00	149.59	140.88
Qatar	Riyal	3.6570	3.6400	3.6400	3.6400	3.6400	3.6400	3.6400	3.6400
Romania	Lei	18.00	15.00	15.00	17.18	21.28	17.14	16.15	14.56
Russia	Ruble	-	-	-	-	-	-	-	-
Rwanda	Francs	92.84	92.84	92.84	94.34	100.17	101.26	87.64	79.67
St. Kitts and Nevis	$E. Carib.	2.7000	2.7000	2.7000	2.7000	2.7000	2.7000	2.7000	2.7000
St. Lucia	$E. Carib.	2.7000	2.7000	2.7000	2.7000	2.7000	2.7000	2.7000	2.7000
St. Vincent & Grans.	$E. Carib.	2.7000	2.7000	2.7000	2.7000	2.7000	2.7000	2.7000	2.7000
Saudi Arabia	Riyal	3.3267	3.3825	3.4282	3.4548	3.5238	3.6221	3.7033	3.7450
Senegal	Franc	211.28	271.73	328.61	381.06	436.96	449.26	346.30	300.54
Seychelles	Rupees	6.3920	6.3149	6.5525	6.7676	7.0589	7.1343	6.1768	5.6000
Sierra Leone	Leone	1.05	1.16	1.24	1.89	2.51	5.09	16.09	34.04
Singapore	$Singapore	2.1412	2.1127	2.1400	2.1131	2.1331	2.2002	2.1774	2.1060
Slovakia rep.	Koruna	-	-	-	-	-	-	-	-
Solomon Islands	$Solomon Is.	0.8298	0.8702	0.9711	1.1486	1.2737	1.4808	1.7415	2.0033

1988	1989	1990	1991	1992	1993	1994	Currency	Country
1,685.7	1,770.1	1,842.8	1,950.3	2,029.9	2,087.1	2,171.0	Rupiah	Indonesia
68.683	72.015	68.096	67.505	65.552	1,267.770		Rial	Iran
0.3109	0.3109	0.3109	0.3109	0.3109	0.3109		Dinar	Iraq
0.6553	0.7047	0.6030	0.6190	0.5864	0.6816	0.6232	Punt	Ireland
1.5989	1.9164	2.0162	2.2791	2.4591	2.8301	3.0320	New Sheqalim	Israel
1,301.6	1,372.1	1,198.1	1,240.6	1,232.4	1,573.7	1,551.0	Lira	Italy
5.489	5.745	7.184	12.116	22.960	22.949		$Jamaica	Jamaica
128.15	137.96	144.79	134.71	126.65	111.20	97.82	Yen	Japan
0.3715	0.5704	0.6636	0.6808	0.6797	0.6928	0.6772	Dinar	Jordan
17.747	20.572	22.915	27.508	32.217	58.001		Shilling	Kenya
731.47	671.46	707.76	733.35	780.65	802.67	797.70	Won	Korea, South
0.2790	0.2937			0.2934	0.3017		Dinar	Kuwait
409.2	496.7	695.1	928.2	1712.8	1741.4	166.1	Pound	Lebanon
2.2609	2.6164	2.5867	2.7563	2.8498	3.2636		Maloti	Lesotho
1.0000	1.0000	1.0000	1.0000	1.0000	1.0000		$Liberian	Liberia
0.2853	0.2921	0.2699	0.2684	0.3013	0.3250		Dinar	Libya
36.768	39.404	33.418	34.148	32.150	34.597		Franc	Luxembourg
1,407.1	1,603.4	1,494.1	1,835.4	1,864.0	1,913.8		Franc	Madagascar
2.5613	2.7595	2.7289	2.8033	3.6033	4.4028		Kwacha	Malawi
2.6188	2.7088	2.7049	2.7501	2.5474	2.5741	2.5560	Ringgit	Malaysia
8.785	9.041	9.552	10.253	10.569	10.957		Rufiyaa	Maldives
					283.160		Franc	Mali
0.3306	0.3483	0.3172	0.3226	0.3178	0.3821		Lira	Malta
75.261	83.051	80.609	81.946	87.027	120.806		Ouguiyas	Mauritania
13.438	15.250	14.863	15.652	15.563	17.648		Rupees	Mauritius
2.3	2.5	2.8	3.0	3.1	3.1	3.431	Pesos	Mexico
8.209	8.488	8.242	8.707	8.538	9.299		Dirham	Morocco
594.67	844.34	1,053.09	1,763.99	2,550.40	3,874.24		Meticais	Mozambique
6.3945	6.7049	6.3386	6.2837	6.1045	6.1570		Kyat	Myanmar (Burma)
23.289	27.189	29.369	37.255	42.718	48.607		Rupees	Nepal
1.9766	2.1207	1.8209	1.8697	1.7585	1.8573	1.6764	Guilder	Netherlands
1.800	1.790	1.790	1.790	1.790	1.790		Guilder	Netherlands Antilles
1.5244	1.6708	1.6750	1.7265	1.8584	1.8494	1.6247	$New Zealand	New Zealand
53.95	3.13	140.92	4.27	na	na		Gold Cordobas	Nicaragua****
297.85	319.01	272.26	282.11	264.69	283.16		Franc	Niger
4.537	7.365	8.038	9.909	17.298	22.065		Naira	Nigeria
6.5170	6.9045	6.2597	6.4829	6.2145	7.0941	6.5275	Kroner	Norway
0.3845	0.3845	0.3845	0.3845	0.3845	0.3845		Rials Omani	Oman#
18.003	20.541	21.707	23.801	25.083	28.107	30.580	Rupees	Pakistan
1.000	1.000	1.000	1.000	1.000	1.000		Balboas	Panama#
0.8667	0.8558	0.9554	0.9520	0.9646	0.9784		Kina	Papua New Guinea
550.0	1,056.2	1,229.8	1,352.2	1,500.3	1,744.3		Guaranies	Paraguay
128.8	2,666.2	187.9	772.5	1,245.8	1,988.3	2.2	New Soles	Peru*****
21.095	21.737	24.311	27.479	25.512	27.120	24.780	Pesos	Philippines
431	1,439	9,500	10,576	13,626	18,115	23,077	Zloty	Poland
143.95	157.46	142.55	144.48	135.00	160.80	153.70	Escudos	Portugal
3.6400	3.6400	3.6400	3.6400	3.6400	3.6400		Riyal	Qatar
14.28	14.92	22.43	76.39	307.95	760.05		Lei	Romania
-	-	-	-	-	1,189	3,085	Ruble	Russia
76.45	79.98	82.60	125.14	133.35	144.25		Francs	Rwanda
2.7000	2.7000	2.7000	2.7000	2.7000	2.7000		$E. Carib.	St. Kitts and Nevis
2.7000	2.7000	2.7000	2.7000	2.7000	2.7000		$E. Carib.	St. Lucia
2.7000	2.7000	2.7000	2.7000	2.7000	2.7000		$E. Carib.	St. Vincent & Grans.
3.7450	3.7450	3.7450	3.7450	3.7450	3.7450	3.7508	Riyal	Saudi Arabia
297.85	319.01	272.26	282.11	264.69	283.16		Franc	Senegal
5.3836	5.6457	5.3369	5.2893	5.1220	5.1815		Rupees	Seychelles
32.51	59.81	151.45	295.34	499.44	567.46		Leone	Sierra Leone
2.0124	1.9503	1.8125	1.7276	1.6290	1.6158	1.4670	$Singapore	Singapore
-	-	-	-	-	-	30.61	Koruna	Slovakia Rep.
2.0825	2.2932	2.5288	2.7148	2.9281	3.1877		$Solomon Is.	Solomon Islands

NATIONAL CURRENCY PER US DOLLAR

Country	Currency	1980	1981	1982	1983	1984	1985	1986	1987
Somalia	Shilling	6.3	6.3	10.8	15.8	20.0	39.5	72.0	105.2
South Africa	Rand	1.2854	1.1491	0.9245	0.8991	0.6954	0.4564	0.4408	0.4914
Spain	Pesetas	71.70	92.32	109.86	143.43	160.76	170.04	140.05	123.48
Sri Lanka	Rupees	16.534	19.246	20.812	23.529	25.438	27.163	28.017	29..445
Sudan	Pound	0.5000	0.5350	0.9380	1.3001	1.3001	2.2883	2.5000	2.8121
Suriname	Guilder	1.7850	1.7850	1.7850	1.7850	1.7850	1.7850	1.7850	1.7850
Swaziland	Lilangeni	0.77795	0.87022	1.08165	1.11224	1.43810	2.19111	2.26850	2.03496
Sweden	Kronor	4.2296	5.0634	6.2826	7.6671	8.2718	8.6039	7.1236	6.3404
Switzerland	Franc	1.6757	1.9642	2.0303	2.0991	2.3497	2.4571	1.7989	1.4912
Syrian Arab Rep	Pound	3.925	3.925	3.925	3.925	3.925	3.925	3.925	3.925
Taiwan	NT$	40.05	37.89	39.96	40.32	39.52	39.90	35.55	28.60
Tanzania	Shilling	8.20	8.28	9.28	11.14	15.29	17.47	32.70	64.26
Thailand	Baht	20.476	21.820	23.000	23.000	23.639	27.159	26.299	25.723
Togo	Franc	211.28	271.73	328.61	381.06	436.96	449.26	346.30	300.54
Tonga	Palanga	0.8782	0.8702	0.9859	1.1100	1.1395	1.4319	1.4960	1.4282
Trinidad & Tobago	$TT	2.4000	2.4000	2.4000	2.4000	2.4000	2.4500	3.6000	3.6000
Tunisia	Dinar	0.4050	0.4938	0.5907	0.6788	0.7768	0.8345	0.7940	0.8287
Turkey	Lira	76.0	111.2	162.6	225.5	366.7	522.0	674.5	857.2
Uganda******	Shilling	74.2	500.5	940.5	1538.6	3597.0	6.7	14.0	42.8
United Arab Emirates	Dirham	3.7074	3.6710	3.6710	3.6710	3.6710	3.6710	3.6710	3.6710
United Kingdom	Pound	0.4299	0.4931	0.5713	0.6592	0.7483	0.7714	0.6817	0.6102
United States	$United States	1.000	1.000	1.000	1.000	1.000	1.000	1.000	1.000
Uruguay	New Pesos	9.10	10.82	13.91	34.54	56.12	101.43	151.99	226.67
Vanuatu	Vatu	68.29	87.83	96.21	99.37	99.23	106.03	106.08	109.85
Venezuela	Bolivares	4.293	4.293	4.293	4.295	7.018	7.500	8.083	14.500
Western Samoa	Tala	0.9195	1.0364	1.2053	1.5394	1.8379	2.2437	2.2351	2.1204
Yemen Arab Rep	Rial	4.5625	4.5625	4.5625	4.5787	5.3533	7.3633	9.6392	10.3417
Yemen, P.D. Rep	Dinar	0.3454	0.3454	0.3454	0.3454	0.3454	0.3454	0.3454	0.3454
Yugoslavia*******	Dinar	2.464	3.497	5.028	9.284	15.282	27.016	37.922	73.700
Zaïre********	New Zaïre	0.933	1.461	1.916	4.296	12.040	16.621	19.871	37.460
Zambia	Kwacha	0.7885	0.8684	0.9282	1.2506	1.7944	2.7137	7.3046	8.8889
Zimbabwe	$Zimbabwe	0.6432	0.6888	0.7573	1.0106	1.2442	1.6119	1.6650	1.6611

Except where stated, exchange rates are the average official or market rates expressed either as unit of currency per US$ or per US$ per unit of currency

Exchange rates in 1994 are for November 1994

* Pesos per million US$ for 1980-1983, per thousand US$ for 1984-1988, and per US$ thereafter

** Bolivianos per million US$ for 1980-1984 and per US$ thereafter

*** Cruzeiros Reais per million US$ for 1980-1984, per thousand US$ for 1985-1988, and per US$ thereafter

**** Gold Cord. per billion US$ through 1987, per million US$ in 1988, per thousand US$in 1989-90, and per US$ thereafter

*****New Soles per billion US$ 1980-87, per million US$ 1988-89, and per thousand US$ thereafter

******Shillings per thousand US$ 1980-1984, per US$ thereafter

*******New Dinars per thousand US$ 1980-1987, per US$ thereafter

********New Zaires per million US$ 1980-1990, per thousand US$ 1991-92, and per US$ thereafter

The currency in Equitorial Guinea changed from a Bipkwele to a Franc in 1985

Source: International Financial Statistics, International Monetary Fund

1988	1989	1990	1991	1992	1993	1994	Currency	Country
170.5	490.7	na	na	na	na		Shilling	Somalia
0.4423	0.3822	0.3866	0.3628	0.3509	0.3064	3.4990	Rand	South Africa
116.49	118.38	101.93	103.91	102.38	127.26	126.40	Pesetas	Spain
31.807	36.047	40.063	41.372	43.830	48.322		Rupees	Sri Lanka
4.5005	4.5005	4.5005	5.4289	69.4444	161.2903		Pound	Sudan
1.7850	1.7850	1.7850	1.7850	1.7850	1.7850		Guilder	Suriname
2.26106	2.61657	2.58632	2.75634	2.84965	3.26360		Lilangeni	Swaziland
6.1272	6.4469	5.9188	6.0475	5.8238	7.7834	7.2635	Kronor	Sweden
1.4633	1.6359	1.3892	1.4340	1.4062	1.4776	1.2680	Franc	Switzerland
11.225	11.225	11.225	11.225	11.225	11.225		Pound	Syrian Arab Rep
28.17	26.17	27.11	25.75	25.40	26.20	26.00	NT$	Taiwan
99.29	143.38	195.06	219.16	297.71	405.27		Shilling	Tanzania
25.294	25.702	25.585	25.517	25.400	25.319	24.930	Baht	Thailand
297.85	319.01	272.26	282.11	264.69	283.16		Franc	Togo
1.2799	1.6370	1.2809	1.2961	1.3471	1.3841		Palanga	Tonga
3.8438	4.2500	4.2500	4.2500	4.2500	5.8141		$TT	Trinidad & Tobago
0.8578	0.9493	0.8783	0.9246	0.8844	1.0037		Dinar	Tunisia
1,422.3	2,121.7	2,608.6	4,171.8	6,872.4	10,984.6	35,817.0	Lira	Turkey
106.1	223.1	428.9	734.0	1133.8	1195.0		Shilling	Uganda******
3.6710	3.6710	3.6710	3.6710	3.6710	3.6710	3.6720	Dirham	United Arab Emirates
0.5614	0.6099	0.5603	0.5652	0.5664	0.6658	0.6135	Pound	United Kingdom
1.000	1.000	1.000	1.000	1.000	1.000	1.000	$United States	United States
359.44	605.51	1171.05	2018.82	3026.95	3.95	5.38	New Pesos	Uruguay
104.43	116.04	116.57	111.68	113.39	121.58		Vatu	Vanuatu
14.500	34.681	46.900	56.816	68.376	90.826	169.570	Bolivares	Venezuela
2.0790	2.2686	2.3095	2.3975	2.4655	2.5680		Tala	Western Samoa
9.7717	9.7600	na	na	na	na		Rial	Yemen Arab Rep
0.3454	0.3454	na	na	na	na		Dinar	Yemen, P.D. Rep
252.259	2.876	11.318	19.638	na	na		Dinar	Yugoslavia*******
62.343	127.121	239.475	5.195	215.136	2.514		New Zaïre	Zaïre********
8.2237	12.9032	28.9855	61.7284	156.2500	434.7826		Kwacha	Zambia
1.8018	2.1133	2.4480	3.4282	5.0942	6.4725		$Zimbabwe	Zimbabwe

ECU EXCHANGE RATE WITH MAJOR CURRENCIES (ANNUAL AVERAGE)

Country	Currency		1980	1981	1982	1983	1984	1985	1986	1987	1988	1989	1990	1991	1992	1993
Belgium	Franc	per ECU	40.598	41.295	44.712	45.4380	45.4420	44.9136	43.7978	43.0392	43.4284	43.3806	42.4252	42.2232	41.6040	40.4660
Denmark	Kroner	per ECU	7.8274	7.9226	8.1569	8.1319	8.1462	8.0188	7.9357	7.8841	7.9515	8.0493	7.8564	7.9085	7.8119	7.5916
France	Franc	per ECU	5.8694	6.0399	6.4312	6.7708	6.8717	6.7951	6.7998	6.9214	7.0328	7.0252	6.9141	6.9733	6.8496	6.6334
Germany	Deutschemark	per ECU	2.0000	2.5147	2.3770	2.2705	2.2380	2.2263	2.1287	2.0715	2.0744	2.0700	2.0519	2.0507	2.0210	1.9368
Greece	Drachma	per ECU	59.24	61.62	65.30	78.09	88.44	105.66	137.41	156.19	167.55	178.88	201.43	225.22	246.60	267.99
Ireland	Punt	per ECU	0.6760	0.6910	0.6896	0.7150	0.7259	0.7152	0.7335	0.7746	0.7753	0.7770	0.7678	0.7678	0.7607	0.7991
Italy	Lira	per ECU	1189.1	1263.1	1323.6	1349.7	1376.0	1430.7	1462.1	1494.7	1537.3	1510.7	1521.9	1533.3	1587.5	1841.6
Luxembourg	Franc	per ECU	40.598	41.295	44.712	45.4380	45.4420	44.9136	43.7978	43.0392	43.4284	43.3806	42.4252	42.2232	41.6040	40.4680
Netherlands	Guilder	per ECU	2.7606	2.7758	2.6153	2.5372	2.5233	2.5111	2.4015	2.3340	2.3343	2.3335	2.3162	2.3127	2.2725	2.1723
Portugal	Escudos	per ECU	69.550	68.500	78.010	98.689	115.680	130.251	147.088	162.581	170.059	173.413	181.108	178.614	174.700	187.800
Spain	Pesetas	per ECU	99.700	102.680	107.560	127.503	126.569	129.164	137.456	142.192	137.601	130.406	129.316	128.486	132.510	?
United Kingdom	Pound	per ECU	0.5985	0.5531	0.5605	0.5870	0.5906	0.5890	0.6715	0.7047	0.6644	0.6733	0.7139	0.7010	0.7376	?
Sweden	Kronor	per ECU	5.8797	5.6327	6.1417	6.8243	6.5113	6.5198	6.9944	7.3096	7.2439	7.1013	7.5200	7.4798	7.5299	9.1146
United States	US Dollar	per ECU	1.3910	1.1176	0.9812	0.8913	0.7890	0.7622	0.9812	1.1543	1.1839	1.1024	1.2730	1.2405	1.2968	1.1723
Japan	Yen	per ECU	315.040	245.380	243.550	211.354	187.089	180.559	164.997	166.602	151.459	151.938	183.678	166.493	164.210	?

The European currency unit or ECU is defined as a basket of currencies composed of specific amounts of the currencies of the member countries of the European Communities.

Each currency's share in the basket is weighed broadly in line with the respective country's gross national product and foreign trade.

Source: International Financial Statistics, International Monetary Fund

REFERENCES

Andrews, R.W., 1970, *Wollastonite*, Monograph, Institute of Geological Services, Her Majesty's Stationery Office, London, 114pp.

Andrews, P.R.A., 1992, Summary Report No. 17: Bentonite, Fuller's Earth and Kaolinitic Clays, CANMET Division Report MSL 92-52 (R), Ottawa, 185 pp.

Andrews, P.R.A., 1993, Summary Report No. 18: Wollastonite, CANMET Division Report MSL 93-10 (R), Ottawa, 31pp.

Badollet, M.S.,1951, "Asbestos, A Mineral of Unparalleled Properties", *Transactions*, Canadian Institute of Mining & Metallurgy, Vol. 54, pp. 134-142.

Bauer, R.R., et al, Bourne, H.L.,1994, "Wollastonite" in *Industrial Minerals and Rocks*, 6th ed., D.D. Carr, Editor, SME, Littleton, CO, pp. 1119-1128.

Bourne, H.L.,1994, "Glass Raw Materials" in *Industrial Minerals and Rocks*, 6th ed., D.D. Carr, Editor, SME, Littleton, CO, pp. 543-550.

Breese, R.O.Y.,1994, "Diatomite" in *Industrial Minerals and Rocks*, 6th ed., D.D. Carr, Editor, SME, Littleton, CO, pp. 397-412.

Breck, D.W., 1974, *Zeolite Molecular Sieves*, Wiley-Interscience, New York, 771 pp.

Brodmann, F.J., 1991, *Synthetic Minerals: Potential Materials from Ontario Resources,* Industrial Minerals Background Paper #15, Ministry of Northern Development and Mines, 45pp.

Cichy, P., 1990, "Fused alumina — pure and alloyed — as an abrasive and refractory material" in *Alumina Chemicals,* L.D. Hart, Ed., The American Ceramics Society, pp.393-426.

Currier, J.W., and Green, R.A., 1986, "The Function of Magnesia in Iron Oxide Agglomerates", *Proceedings*, 45th Iron Making Conference, pp. 23-30.

Fleischer, M, 1975, *Glossary of Mineral Species*; Lyman, K., ed.

Fulton III, R.B.,1994, "Staurolite" in *Industrial Minerals and Rocks*, 6th ed., D.D. Carr, Editor, SME, Littleton, CO, pp. 973-974.

Hand, G.P., 1992, "Applications of high performance, high purity graphites" in *Proceeding of the 10th Inudustrial Minerals Congress*, San Francisco, J.B. Griffiths, ed., Industrial Minerals Div., Metal Bulletin plc, pp. 57-62.

Harben, P.W., 1992, *Industrial Minerals HandyBook: A Guide to Markets, Specifications, & Prices*, Metal Bulletin plc, London, 147pp.

Henning, R.J.,1994, "Olivine and Dunite" in *Industrial Minerals and Rocks*, 6th ed., D.D. Carr, Editor, SME, Littleton, CO, pp. 731-734.

Jackson, W.D., and Christiansen, G., 1993, *International Strategic Minerals Inventory Summary Report — Rare-Earth Oxides*, USGS C 930-N67 pp.

Kenan, W.M., 1993, "Graphite in refractories", *Industrial Minerals*, No. 312, Sept., pp. 73-75.

Kingsnorth, D.J., 1993, "Chinese rare earths: The dragon has entered", *Industrial Minerals*, No. 310, July, pp. 45-49.

Kostick, D.S.,1994, "Soda Ash" in *Industrial Minerals and Rocks*, 6th ed., D.D. Carr, Editor, SME, Littleton, CO, pp. 929-958.

Mitchell, R.S., 1979, *Mineral Names What Do They Mean?*, Van Nostrand Reinhold Co., NY, 204pp.

Odom, I.E., 1992, "Hectorite - deposits, propertites and uses" in *Proceeding of the 10th Inudustrial Minerals Congress*, San Francisco, J.B. Griffiths, ed., Industrial Minerals Div., Metal Bulletin plc, pp. 105-111.

O'Driscoll, M., 1993, "Wollastonite ceramics remains top consumer", *Raw Materials for the Glass & Ceramics Industries*, Consumer Survey, *Industrial Minerals*, London, pp.77-80.

Papp, J.F., 1994, "Chromite" in *Industrial Minerals and Rocks*, 6th ed., D.D. Carr, Editor, SME, Littleton, CO, pp. 209-228.

Pickering, S.M. and Murray, H.H.,1994, "Kaolin" in *Industrial Minerals and Rocks*, 6th ed., D.D. Carr, Editor, SME, Littleton, CO, pp. 255-277.

Podolsky, G., and Keller, D.P.,1994,Pigments, Iron Oxide" in *Industrial Minerals and Rocks*, 6th ed., D.D. Carr, Editor, SME, Littleton, CO, pp. 765-781.

Searls, J.P., 1985, "Potash", *Mineral Facts and Problems*, USBM, Bulletin 675, pp. 617-633.

Spencer, L.J., M.H. Hay, et al, various dates, "Annual lists of new mineral names", *Mineralogical Magazine*.

Trivedi & Hagemeyer, 1994, "Fillers and Coatings" in *Industrial Minerals and Rocks*, 6th ed., D.D. Carr, Editor, SME, Littleton, CO, pp.483-495.

Virta, R.L., 1994, "Asbestos Substitutes" in *Industrial Minerals and Rocks*, 6th ed., D.D. Carr, Editor, SME, Littleton, CO, pp. 429-434.

Virta, R.L. and Mann, E.L.,1994, "Asbestos" in *Industrial Minerals and Rocks*, 6th ed., D.D. Carr, Editor, SME, Littleton, CO, pp. 97-124.

Weiss, S.A., 1977, *Manganese The other uses*, Metal Bulletin Books Ltd., 360 pp.

Williams-Stroud, S.C. Searls, J.P. and Hite, R.J., 1994, Potash Resources in *Industrial Minerals and Rocks*, 6th ed., D.D. Carr, Editor, SME, Littleton, CO, pp. 783-802.

Various authors, *Industrial Minerals* Nos. 1-327, US Bureau of Mines publications including *Minerals Yearbook* and preprints 1975-1993 and *Mineral Facts and Problems* 1985, *Chemical Marketing Reporter*. Prices derived from various sources including those published in *Industrial Minerals, Chemical Marketing Reporter, Mining Engineering*.

Peter W. Harben is an independent consultant and writer specializing in market evaluations of industrial minerals and certain inorganic chemicals. He has made technical visits to more than two dozen countries on four continents and his clients include international mining companies, mineral and chemical consumers, trading firms, financial institutions, transportation companies, state and federal governments, and international organizations such as the United Nations, UNIDO, and the World Bank. He is a former American Editor of *Industrial Minerals*.

Harben has written numerous articles on the subject of industrial minerals and their markets, organized international conferences, and edited special publications on raw materials for glass, ceramics, oilwell drilling, and pulp and paper. Other books published include *Mines and Mining* (1978), *The Universe and the Earth* (1978), and *Mined It! (1992)*, all pre-university, general-interest books; *Geology of the Nonmetallics* (1984) and *Industrial Minerals: Geology and World Deposits* (1990), major text books on the economic geology of industrial minerals; and *The Industrial Minerals HandyBook - A Guide to Markets, Specifications and Prices* (first edition - 1992).

Peter Harben graduated with a joint-honors B.Sc. degree in Geology and Mineral Exploitation from University of Wales, Cardiff, UK, and then gained an M.Sc. in Mineral Exploration from the Royal School of Mines, Imperial College, University of London.

Peter Harben Inc.
P.O. Box 800
Morris, NY 13808, USA
Tel (607) 263 5070
Fax (607) 263 5356

The Industrial Minerals HandyBook, Second edition was composed entirely on PC based computer systems and is comprised of some of the following:

➤ 343 charts

➤ 48 scanned pictures

➤ 87 diagrams/clipart

➤ 264 pages

➤ 269 megabytes of computer data

➤ 6 months of production

INDUSTRIAL MINERALS DIRECTORY

3rd edition

IMIL
INDUSTRIAL MINERALS INFORMATION LTD.

A World Guide to Producers and Processors

**Publication date
November 1995**

- **THE INDUSTRY'S ONLY DIRECTORY OF ITS TYPE**

- **REGARDED BY THE INDUSTRY AS 'THE ULTIMATE MINERALS SOURCE BOOK'**

- **LISTS MINE OWNERS, OPERATORS, PRODUCERS AND PROCESSORS OF OVER 100 NATURALLY OCCURRING AND SYNTHETIC MINERALS**

- **OVER 600 PAGES OF COMPREHENSIVE CONTACT DETAILS**

- **NAMED KEY INDIVIDUALS (where available)**

- **AN INVALUABLE SOURCE OF SUPPLIERS, NEW MATERIAL OPTIONS AND SALES LEADS**

This best-selling directory is an essential reference point for all involved in the production, trading, supply and purchasing of minerals.

For further details and to book your copy contact Sharon Thomas at Industrial Minerals Information Ltd.,
Park House, Park Terrace, Worcester Park, Surrey KT4 7HY, UK
Tel: +44 (0)171 827 9977 Fax: +44 (0)181 337 8943